GATEWAY TO THE GREAT BOOKS

<table>
<tr><td>SYNGE</td><td>CARLYLE</td></tr>
<tr><td>O'NEILL</td><td>EMERSON</td></tr>
<tr><td>~</td><td>HAWTHORNE</td></tr>
<tr><td>VOLUME 5</td><td>WHITMAN</td></tr>
<tr><td>VIRGINIA WOOLF</td><td>VIRGINIA WOOLF</td></tr>
<tr><td>ARNOLD</td><td>XENOPHON</td></tr>
<tr><td>SAINTE-BEUVE</td><td>PRESCOTT</td></tr>
<tr><td>BACON</td><td>LONG</td></tr>
<tr><td>HUME</td><td>PLINY</td></tr>
<tr><td>SCHOPENHAUER</td><td>TACITUS</td></tr>
<tr><td>SCHILLER</td><td>GUIZOT</td></tr>
<tr><td>SHELLEY</td><td>ADAMS</td></tr>
<tr><td>WHITMAN</td><td>BURY</td></tr>
<tr><td>HAZLITT</td><td>LUCIAN</td></tr>
<tr><td>LAMB</td><td>PAINE</td></tr>
<tr><td>JOHNSON</td><td>WASHINGTON</td></tr>
<tr><td>DE QUINCEY</td><td>JEFFERSON</td></tr>
<tr><td>T. S. ELIOT</td><td>FRANKLIN</td></tr>
<tr><td>~</td><td>CRÈVECOEUR</td></tr>
<tr><td>VOLUME 6</td><td>TOCQUEVILLE</td></tr>
<tr><td>J. S. MILL</td><td>THOREAU</td></tr>
<tr><td>TWAIN</td><td>LINCOLN</td></tr>
<tr><td>LA BRUYÈRE</td><td>~</td></tr>
</table>

GATEWAY
TO THE
GREAT BOOKS

Gateway
to the
Great Books

ROBERT M. HUTCHINS, MORTIMER J. ADLER
Editors in Chief

CLIFTON FADIMAN
Associate Editor

8

NATURAL

SCIENCE

Encyclopædia Britannica, Inc.

WILLIAM BENTON
Publisher

Chicago, London, Toronto, Geneva, Sydney

Contents
of Volume 8

Sir Francis Bacon [1]

1561–1626

Francis Bacon was one of the first great enthusiasts of science. Science, in his view, not only could but should benefit the life of man. He explained and extolled scientific method. He pointed the way to the control of nature. He tried to convince his fellow men that they could understand how the world worked, and thereby live "like kings." Men have always wanted to live like kings, and they listened to Bacon.

The Sphinx is a fable. It is not always wise to say much about a fable. It should be read and pondered. There is much to think about in the following selection. Bacon himself draws many conclusions from his own fable. It could be left at that.

But it is worth remarking that Bacon says that "of the Sphinx's riddles there are in all two kinds: one concerning the nature of things, another concerning the nature of man." When these words were written—the early seventeenth century—both kinds of riddles may have seemed equally soluble. But is there not evidence that the one kind is much more difficult than the other?

As to "the nature of things," we cannot help recognizing that much progress has been made in the 350 years since Bacon wrote. His wildest dreams have been realized, and more. Men live now as no king could have imagined living then.

But as to "the nature of man," how much does the modern age know which Bacon did not know? Or has it even forgotten some things that seemed clear and obvious to him? That is another question.

[1] For a biography of Sir Francis Bacon, see Vol. 5, pp. 90–92, in this set. For other works by Bacon in this set, see Vol. 5, pp. 94–98; Vol. 7, pp. 3–27; Vol. 10, pp. 346–360. See also *Great Books of the Western World*, Vol. 30.

The Sphinx

Sphinx, says the story, was a monster combining many shapes in one. She had the face and voice of a virgin, the wings of a bird, the claws of a griffin. She dwelt on the ridge of a mountain near Thebes and infested the roads, lying in ambush for travellers, whom she would suddenly attack and lay hold of; and when she had mastered them, she propounded to them certain dark and perplexing riddles, which she was thought to have obtained from the Muses. And if the wretched captives could not at once solve and interpret the same, as they stood hesitating and confused she cruelly tore them to pieces. Time bringing no abatement of the calamity, the Thebans offered to any man who should expound the Sphinx's riddles (for this was the only way to subdue her) the sovereignty of Thebes as his reward. The greatness of the prize induced Oedipus, a man of wisdom and penetration, but lame from wounds in his feet, to accept the condition and make the trial: who presenting himself full of confidence and alacrity before the Sphinx, and being asked what kind of animal it was which was born four-footed, afterwards became two-footed, then three-footed, and at last four-footed again, answered readily that it was man; who at his birth and during his infancy sprawls on all fours, hardly attempting to creep; in a little while walks upright on two feet; in later years leans on a walking-stick and so goes as it were on three; and at last in extreme age and decrepitude, his sinews all failing, sinks into a quadruped again, and keeps his bed. This was the right answer and gave him the victory; whereupon he slew the Sphinx; whose body was put on the back of an ass and carried about in triumph; while himself was made according to compact king of Thebes.

The fable is an elegant and a wise one, invented apparently in allusion to Science; especially in its application to practical life. Science, being the wonder of the ignorant and unskilful, may be not absurdly called a monster. In figure and aspect it is represented as many-shaped, in allusion to the immense variety of matter with which it deals. It is said to

have the face and voice of a woman, in respect of its beauty and facility of utterance. Wings are added because the sciences and the discoveries of science spread and fly abroad in an instant; the communication of knowledge being like that of one candle with another, which lights up at once. Claws, sharp and hooked, are ascribed to it with great elegance, because the axioms and arguments of science penetrate and hold fast the mind, so that it has no means of evasion or escape; a point which the sacred philosopher also noted: *The words of the wise are as goads, and as nails driven deep in.* Again, all knowledge may be regarded as having its station on the heights of mountains; for it is deservedly esteemed a thing sublime and lofty, which looks down upon ignorance as from an eminence, and has moreover a spacious prospect on every side, such as we find on hill-tops. It is described as infesting the roads, because at every turn in the journey or pilgrimage of human life, matter and occasion for study assails and encounters us. Again Sphinx proposes to men a variety of hard questions and riddles which she received from the Muses. In these, while they remain with the Muses, there is probably no cruelty; for so long as the object of meditation and inquiry is merely to know, the understanding is not oppressed or straitened by it, but is free to wander and expatiate, and finds in the very uncertainty of conclusion and variety of choice a certain pleasure and delight; but when they pass from the Muses to Sphinx, that is from contemplation to practice, whereby there is necessity for present action, choice, and decision, then they begin to be painful and cruel; and unless they be solved and disposed of they strangely torment and worry the mind, pulling it first this way and then that, and fairly tearing it to pieces. Moreover the riddles of the Sphinx have always a twofold condition attached to them; distraction and laceration of mind, if you fail to solve them; if you succeed, a kingdom. For he who understands his subject is master of his end; and every workman is king over his work.

Now of the Sphinx's riddles there are in all two kinds: one concerning the nature of things, another concerning the nature of man; and in like manner there are two kinds of kingdom offered as the reward of solving them: one over nature, and the other over man. For the command over things natural—over bodies, medicines, mechanical powers, and infinite other of the kind—is the one proper and ultimate end of true natural philosophy; however the philosophy of the school, content with what it finds, and swelling with talk, may neglect or spurn the search after realities and works. But the riddle proposed to Oedipus, by the solution of which he became king of Thebes, related to the nature of man; for whoever has a

thorough insight into the nature of man may shape his fortune almost as he will, and is born for empire; as was well declared concerning the arts of the Romans—

> Be thine the art,
> O Rome, with government to rule the nations,
> And to know whom to spare and whom to abate,
> And settle the condition of the world.

And therefore it fell out happily that Augustus Caesar, whether on purpose or by chance, used a Sphinx for his seal. For he certainly excelled in the art of politics if ever man did; and succeeded in the course of his life in solving most happily a great many new riddles concerning the nature of man, which if he had not dexterously and readily answered he would many times have been in imminent danger of destruction. The fable adds very prettily that when the Sphinx was subdued, her body was laid on the back of an ass: for there is nothing so subtle and abstruse, but when it is once thoroughly understood and published to the world, even a dull wit can carry it. Nor is that other point to be passed over, that the Sphinx was subdued by a lame man with club feet; for men generally proceed too fast and in too great a hurry to the solution of the Sphinx's riddles; whence it follows that the Sphinx has the better of them, and instead of obtaining the sovereignty by works and effects, they only distract and worry their minds with disputations.

The foregoing essay is
from Francis Bacon's WISDOM OF THE ANCIENTS.

John Tyndall

1820–1893

John Tyndall was born in Ireland in 1820, and though in his childhood he attended the village school, he was largely self-educated. He became interested in surveying, started out by carrying the chain for a surveying group, and in a few years was in charge of it. He made maps and worked out complicated calculations, in the process practicing his mathematics, for which he had a flair. He then took a job as a railroad builder. After three years of this he went to England, where he found a position as a teacher of science at a provincial college. He had saved four hundred pounds, and now, at the age of twenty-eight, he set out for Marburg University, in Germany. There he exerted himself to the utmost. After a year, he was made assistant to Bunsen, the great chemist, and at the end of the second year, he received his doctorate.

In 1853, after returning to England, Tyndall was appointed professor of physics at the Royal Institution, on the recommendation of Faraday. He held the position for the rest of his life.

Tyndall's most important investigations were probably in the theory of heat. His book, *Heat Considered as a Mode of Motion* (1863), had great influence. It was the first popular exposition of the mechanical theory of heat. He also did work in many other areas of science, particularly in meteorology. Among other experiments was one in which he explained why the sky is blue. But it is likely that he was more distinguished for his exposition of the work of other men than for original researches of his own. His "Belfast Address" (1874), in which he surveyed the entire course of nineteenth-century scientific discovery, was a model of clarity and comprehensibility. He died on December 4, 1893.

Tyndall was extremely close to Faraday, both as colleague and friend. Faraday continued to do active work at the Royal Institution for several years after Tyndall arrived there. Even after his retirement, Faraday would often visit the laboratory and attend the Friday Evening Discourses—a weekly program of popular lectures on science which Faraday had started years before. Faraday died in August, 1867, and four months later, Tyndall gave a memorial discourse on "Faraday as Scientist and Man." This was published in 1868 under the title *Faraday as a Discoverer,* and the following selection consists of its first three chapters.

"It is not my intention," Tyndall says, "to lay before you a *life* of Faraday in the ordinary acceptation of the term. The duty I have to perform is to give you some notion of what he has done in the world." The subject as stated was an immense one. Not only did Faraday rise from the humblest beginnings. Not only was his main research undertaken in an area—electromagnetism—which has proved to be fruitful beyond the wildest expectations. And not only was he so extraordinarily gifted that he produced important and original results in almost every field he entered. But "taking him for all in all," Tyndall concludes, "I think it will be conceded that Michael Faraday was the greatest experimental philosopher the world has ever seen." Hence, Faraday as the subject of even a limited biography would seem to present almost insuperable obstacles.

Tyndall was, however, highly gifted himself, and in exactly the respects that were most necessary for the completion of his task. It goes without saying that he understood Faraday's work. He also had a facility for explaining it, which is evident in the selection that follows. Above all, he knew and loved Faraday. There seems to be no doubt that his knowledge and love were important elements in the success of the book.

Tyndall's *Faraday as a Discoverer* bears comparison in many respects with Eve Curie's *Madame Curie.*[1] Both biographers were presented with similar problems, for few experimentalists can rank with Faraday with as much justice as Marie Curie. And both biographers seem to have made the same decision as to how to proceed. Both

[1] See Vol. 8, pp. 32–42, in this set.

added nothing to the facts; both claimed that nothing except the facts was necessary to make a fascinating story. And both drew analogies from the world of nature itself, in an attempt to explicate their subjects.

"Nature, not education, rendered Faraday strong and refined," Tyndall writes. "A favorite experiment of his own was representative of himself. He loved to show that water in crystallizing excluded all foreign ingredients, however intimately they might be mixed with it. Out of acids, alkalis, or saline solutions, the crystal came sweet and pure. By some such natural process in the formation of this man, beauty and nobleness coalesced, to the exclusion of everything vulgar and low."

Michael Faraday

from *Faraday as a Discoverer*

It has been thought desirable to give you and the world some image of Michael Faraday as a scientific investigator and discoverer. The attempt to respond to this desire has been to me a labour of difficulty, if also a labour of love. For however well acquainted I may be with the researches and discoveries of that great master, however numerous the illustrations which occur to me of the loftiness of Faraday's character and the beauty of his life—still to grasp him and his researches as a whole; to seize upon the ideas which guided him, and connected them; to gain entrance into that strong and active brain, and read from it the riddle of the world—this is a work not easy of performance, and all but impossible amid the distraction of duties of another kind. That I should at one period or another speak to you regarding Faraday and his work is natural, if not inevitable; but I did not expect to be called upon to speak so soon. Still the bare suggestion that this is the fit and proper time for speech sent me immediately to my task; from it I have returned with such results as I could gather, and also with the wish that those results were more worthy than they are of the greatness of my theme.

It is not my intention to lay before you a *life* of Faraday in the ordinary acceptation of the term. The duty I have to perform is to give you some notion of what he has done in the world, dwelling incidentally on the spirit in which his work was executed, and introducing such personal traits as may be necessary to the completion of your picture of the *philosopher*, though by no means adequate to give you a complete idea of the *man*.

The newspapers have already informed you that Michael Faraday was born at Newington Butts, on September 22, 1791, and that he died at Hampton Court, on August 25, 1867. Believing, as I do, in the general truth of the doctrine of hereditary transmission—sharing the opinion of

8

Mr. Carlyle, that "a really able man never proceeded from entirely stupid parents"—I once used the privilege of my intimacy with Mr. Faraday to ask him whether his parents showed any signs of unusual ability. He could remember none. His father, I believe, was a great sufferer during the latter years of his life, and this might have masked whatever intellectual power he possessed. When thirteen years old, that is to say in 1804, Faraday was apprenticed to a bookseller and bookbinder in Blandford Street, Manchester Square; here he spent eight years of his life, after which he worked as a journeyman elsewhere.

You have also heard the account of Faraday's first contact with the Royal Institution; that he was introduced by one of the members to Sir Humphry Davy's last lectures, that he took notes of those lectures, wrote them fairly out, and sent them to Davy, entreating him at the same time to enable him to quit trade, which he detested, and to pursue science, which he loved. Davy was helpful to the young man, and this should never be forgotten; he at once wrote to Faraday, and afterwards, when an opportunity occurred, made him his assistant.[1] Mr. Gassiot has lately favoured me with the following reminiscence of this time:

Clapham Common, Surrey
November 28, 1867

My Dear Tyndall—Sir H. Davy was accustomed to call on the late Mr. Pepys, in the Poultry, on his way to the London Institution, of which Pepys was one of the original managers. The latter told me that on one occasion Sir H. Davy, showing him a letter, said: "Pepys, what am I to do, here is a letter from a young man named Faraday; he has been attending my lectures, and wants me to give him employment at the Royal Institution. What can I do?" "Do?" replied Pepys, "put him to wash bottles; if he is good for anything he will do it directly, if he refuses he is good for nothing." "No, no," replied Davy, "we must try him with something better than that." The result was that Davy engaged him to assist in the Laboratory at *weekly* wages.

1. Here is Davy's recommendation of Faraday, presented to the managers of the Royal Institution, at a meeting on the 18th of March, 1813, Charles Hatchett, Esq., in the chair:

"Sir Humphry Davy has the honour to inform the managers that he has found a person who is desirous to occupy the situation in the Institution lately filled by William Payne. His name is Michael Faraday. He is a youth of twenty-two years of age. As far as Sir H. Davy has been able to observe or ascertain, he appears well fitted for the situation. His habits seem good; his disposition active and cheerful, and his manner intelligent. He is willing to engage himself on the same terms as given to Mr. Payne at the time of quitting the Institution.

"*Resolved*—That Michael Faraday be engaged to fill the situation lately occupied by Mr. Payne, on the same terms."

Davy held the joint office of Professor of Chemistry and Director of the Laboratory; he ultimately gave up the former to the late Professor Brande, but he insisted that Faraday should be appointed Director of the Laboratory, and, as Faraday told me, this enabled him on subsequent occasions to hold a definite position in the Institution, in which he was always supported by Davy. I believe he held that office to the last.

Believe me, my dear Tyndall, yours truly,

J. P. Gassiot

From a letter written by Faraday himself soon after his appointment as Davy's assistant, I extract the following account of his introduction to the Royal Institution:

London, Sept. 13, 1813

As for myself, I am absent (from home) nearly day and night, except occasional calls, and it is likely shall shortly be absent entirely, but this (having nothing more to say, and at the request of my mother) I will explain to you. I was formerly a bookseller and binder, but am now turned philosopher,[2] which happened thus: Whilst an apprentice, I, for amusement, learnt a little chemistry and other parts of philosophy, and felt an eager desire to proceed in that way further. After being a journeyman for six months, under a disagreeable master, I gave up my business, and through the interest of a Sir H. Davy, filled the situation of chemical assistant to the Royal Institution of Great Britain, in which office I now remain; and where I am constantly employed in observing the works of nature, and tracing the manner in which she directs the order and arrangement of the world. I have lately had proposals made to me by Sir Humphry Davy to accompany him in his travels through Europe and Asia, as philosophical assistant. If I go at all I expect it will be in October next—about the end; and my absence from home will perhaps be as long as three years. But as yet all is uncertain.

This account is supplemented by the following letter, written by Faraday to his friend De la Rive,[3] on the occasion of the death of Mrs. Marcet. The letter is dated September 2, 1858:

My Dear Friend—Your subject interested me deeply every way; for Mrs. Marcet was a good friend to me, as she must have been to many of the human race. I entered the shop of a bookseller and bookbinder at the age of thirteen, in the year 1804, remained there eight years, and during the chief part of my time bound books. Now it was in those books, in the hours after work, that I found the beginning of my philosophy. There

2. Faraday loved this word and employed it to the last; he had an intense dislike to the modern term *physicist*.
3. To whom I am indebted for a copy of the original letter.

were two that especially helped me, the *Encyclopædia Britannica,* from which I gained my first notions of electricity, and Mrs. Marcet's *Conversation on Chemistry,* which gave me my foundation in that science.

Do not suppose that I was a very deep thinker, or was marked as a precocious person. I was a very lively imaginative person, and could believe in the *Arabian Nights* as easily as in the *Encyclopædia.* But facts were important to me, and saved me. I could trust a fact, and always cross-examined an assertion. So when I questioned Mrs. Marcet's book by such little experiments as I could find means to perform, and found it true to the facts as I could understand them, I felt that I had got hold of an anchor in chemical knowledge, and clung fast to it. Thence my deep veneration for Mrs. Marcet—first as one who had conferred great personal good and pleasure on me; and then as one able to convey the truth and principle of those boundless fields of knowledge which concern natural things to the young, untaught, and inquiring mind.

You may imagine my delight when I came to know Mrs. Marcet personally; how often I cast my thoughts backward, delighting to connect the past and the present; how often, when sending a paper to her as a thank offering, I thought of my first instructress, and such like thoughts will remain with me.

I have some such thoughts even as regards *your own father;* who was, I may say, the first who personally at Geneva, and afterwards by correspondence, encouraged, and by that sustained me.

Twelve or thirteen years ago Mr. Faraday and myself quitted the Institution one evening together, to pay a visit to our friend Grove in Baker Street. He took my arm at the door, and, pressing it to his side in his warm genial way, said, "Come, Tyndall, I will now show you something that will interest you." We walked northwards, passed the house of Mr. Babbage, which drew forth a reference to the famous evening parties once assembled there. We reached Blandford Street, and after a little looking about he paused before a stationer's shop, and then went in. On entering the shop, his usual animation seemed doubled; he looked rapidly at everything it contained. To the left on entering was a door, through which he looked down into a little room, with a window in front facing Blandford Street. Drawing me towards him, he said eagerly, "Look there, Tyndall, that was my working place. I bound books in that little nook." A respectable-looking woman stood behind the counter: his conversation with me was too low to be heard by her, and he now turned to the counter to buy some cards as an excuse for our being there. He asked the woman her name—her predecessor's name—his predecessor's name. "That won't do," he said, with good-humoured impatience; "who was *his*

predecessor?" "Mr. Riebau," she replied, and immediately added, as if suddenly recollecting herself, "He, sir, was the master of Sir Charles Faraday." "Nonsense!" he responded, "there is no such person." Great was her delight when I told her the name of her visitor; but she assured me that as soon as she saw him running about the shop, she felt—though she did not know why—that it must be "Sir Charles Faraday."

Faraday did, as you know, accompany Davy to Rome; he was re-engaged by the managers of the Royal Institution on May 15, 1815. Here he made rapid progress in chemistry, and after a time was entrusted with easy analyses by Davy. In those days the Royal Institution published *The Quarterly Journal of Science,* the precursor of our own *Proceedings.* Faraday's first contribution to science appeared in that journal in 1816. It was an analysis of some caustic lime from Tuscany, which had been sent to Davy by the Duchess of Montrose. Between this period and 1818 various notes and short papers were published by Faraday. In 1818 he experimented upon "sounding flames." Professor Auguste De la Rive had investigated those sounding flames, and had applied to them an explanation which completely accounted for a class of sounds discovered by himself, but did not account for those known to his predecessors. By a few simple and conclusive experiments, Faraday proved the explanation insufficient. It is an epoch in the life of a young man when he finds himself correcting a person of eminence, and in Faraday's case, where its effect was to develop a modest self-trust, such an event could not fail to act profitably.

From time to time between 1818 and 1820 Faraday published scientific notes and notices of minor weight. At this time he was acquiring, not producing; working hard for his master and storing and strengthening his own mind. He assisted Mr. Brande in his lectures, and so quietly, skilfully, and modestly was his work done, that Mr. Brande's vocation at the time was pronounced "lecturing on velvet." In 1820 Faraday published a chemical paper "on two new compounds of chlorine and carbon, and on a new compound of iodine, carbon, and hydrogen." This paper was read before the Royal Society on December 21, 1820, and it was the first of his that was honoured with a place in the *Philosophical Transactions.*

On June 12, 1821, he married, and obtained leave to bring his young wife into his rooms at the Royal Institution. There for forty-six years they lived together, occupying the suite of apartments which had been previously in the successive occupancy of Young, Davy, and Brande. At the time of her marriage Mrs. Faraday was twenty-one years of age, he being nearly thirty. Regarding this marriage I will at present limit myself to

quoting an entry written in Faraday's own hand in his book of diplomas, which caught my eye while in his company some years ago. It ran thus:

<div align="center">25th January, 1847</div>

Amongst these records and events, I here insert the date of one which, as a source of honour and happiness, far exceeds all the rest. We were *married* on June 12, 1821.

<div align="right">M. Faraday</div>

Then follows the copy of the minutes, dated May 21, 1821, which gave him additional rooms, and thus enabled him to bring his wife to the Royal Institution. A feature of Faraday's character which I have often noticed makes itself apparent in this entry. In his relations to his wife he added *chivalry* to affection.

Oersted, in 1820, discovered the action of a voltaic current on a magnetic needle; and immediately afterwards the splendid intellect of Ampère succeeded in showing that every magnetic phenomenon then known might be reduced to the mutual action of electric currents. The subject occupied all men's thought; and in this country Dr. Wollaston sought to convert the deflection of the needle by the current into a permanent *rotation* of the needle round the current. He also hoped to produce the reciprocal effect of causing a current to rotate round a magnet. In the early part of 1821, Wollaston attempted to realize this idea in the presence of Sir Humphry Davy in the laboratory of the Royal Institution. This was well calculated to attract Faraday's attention to the subject. He read much about it; and in the months of July, August, and September he wrote a *History of the Progress of Electromagnetism*, which he published in Thomson's *Annals of Philosophy*. Soon afterwards he took up the subject of "magnetic rotations," and on the morning of Christmas Day, 1821, he called his wife to witness, for the first time, the revolution of a mag-

Faraday's electromagnetic rotation apparatus, designed in January, 1822. It was made of a piece of glass tubing, with stoppers at each end. The lower stopper carried a magnet and a pool of mercury.
A loose piece of platinum wire, hung by a loop from the top connection, revolved rapidly around the magnet pole when the outside current was connected to the wire terminals of the apparatus.

Hydrate of Chlorine

Liquid Chlorine

Ice

Faraday's apparatus for liquefying the gas chlorine produced the gas
by heating the hydrate. Both chlorine and water vapour were formed,
thus giving pressure within the tube. At the right the tube was cooled with ice.
The combination of pressure with cooling changed the chlorine to a liquid.

netic needle round an electric current. Incidental to the "historic sketch,"
he repeated almost all the experiments there referred to; and these,
added to his own subsequent work, made him practical master of all that
was then known regarding the voltaic current. In 1821, he also touched
upon a subject which subsequently received his closer attention—the
vaporization of mercury at common temperatures; and immediately after-
wards conducted, in company with Mr. Stodart, experiments on the
alloys of steel. He was accustomed in after years to present to his friends
razors formed from one of the alloys then discovered.

During Faraday's hours of liberty from other duties, he took up sub-
jects of inquiry for himself; and in the spring of 1823, thus self-prompted,
he began the examination of a substance which had long been regarded
as the chemical element chlorine, in a solid form, but which Sir Humphry
Davy, in 1810, had proved to be a hydrate of chlorine, that is, a com-
pound of chlorine and water. Faraday first analyzed this hydrate, and
wrote out an account of its composition. This account was looked over
by Davy, who suggested the heating of the hydrate under pressure in a
sealed glass tube. This was done. The hydrate fused at a blood heat, the
tube became filled with a yellow atmosphere, and was afterwards found
to contain two liquid substances. Dr. Paris happened to enter the labora-
tory while Faraday was at work. Seeing the oily liquid in his tube, he
rallied the young chemist for his carelessness in employing soiled vessels.
On filing off the end of the tube, its contents exploded and the oily matter
vanished. Early next morning, Dr. Paris received the following note:

Dear Sir—The *oil* you noticed yesterday turns out to be liquid chlorine.

<div align="right">Yours faithfully,
M. Faraday</div>

The gas had been liquefied by its own pressure. Faraday then tried compression with a syringe, and succeeded thus in liquefying the gas.

To the published account of this experiment Davy added the following note: "In desiring Mr. Faraday to expose the hydrate of chlorine in a closed glass tube, it occurred to me that one of three things would happen: that decomposition of water would occur; . . . or that the chlorine would separate in a fluid state." Davy, moreover, immediately applied the method of self-compressing atmosphere to the liquefaction of muriatic gas. Faraday continued the experiments, and succeeded in reducing a number of gases till then deemed permanent to the liquid condition. In 1844 he returned to the subject, and considerably expanded its limits. These important investigations established the fact that gases are but the vapours of liquids possessing a very low boiling point, and gave a sure basis to our views of molecular aggregation. The account of the first investigation was read before the Royal Society on April 10, 1823, and was published, in Faraday's name, in the *Philosophical Transactions*. The second memoir was sent to the Royal Society on December 19, 1844. I may add that while he was conducting his first experiments on the liquefaction of gases, thirteen pieces of glass were on one occasion driven by an explosion into Faraday's eye.

Some small notices and papers, including the observation that glass readily changes colour in sunlight, follow here. In 1825 and 1826 Faraday published papers in the *Philosophical Transactions* on "new compounds of carbon and hydrogen," and on "sulphonaphthalic acid." In the former of these papers he announced the discovery of benzol,[4] which, in the hands of modern chemists, has become the foundation of our splendid aniline dyes. But he swerved incessantly from chemistry into physics; and in 1826 we find him engaged in investigating the limits of vaporization, and showing, by exceedingly strong and apparently conclusive arguments, that even in the case of mercury such a limit exists; much more he conceived it to be certain that our atmosphere does not contain the vapour of the fixed constituents of the earth's crust. This question, I may say, is likely to remain an open one. Dr. Rankine, for example, has lately

4. *Benzol*. A colourless liquid obtained by the distillation of coal tar; now known chemically as benzene, C_6H_6.

drawn attention to the odour of certain metals; whence comes this odour, if it be not from the vapour of the metal?

In 1825 Faraday became a member of a committee, to which Sir John Herschel and Mr. Dollond also belonged, appointed by the Royal Society to examine, and if possible improve, the manufacture of glass for optical purposes. Their experiments continued till 1829, when the account of them constituted the subject of a "Bakerian Lecture." This lectureship, founded in 1774 by Henry Baker, Esq., of the Strand, London, provides that every year a lecture shall be given before the Royal Society, the sum of four pounds being paid to the lecturer. The Bakerian Lecture, however, has long since passed from the region of pay to that of honour, papers of mark only being chosen for it by the council of the Society. Faraday's first Bakerian Lecture, "On the Manufacture of Glass for Optical Purposes," was delivered at the close of 1829. It is a most elaborate and conscientious description of processes, precautions, and results; the details were so exact and so minute, and the paper consequently so long, that three successive sittings of the Royal Society were taken up by the delivery of the lecture. This glass did not turn out to be of important practical use,[5] but it happened afterwards to be the foundation of two of Faraday's greatest discoveries.

The experiments here referred to were commenced at the Falcon Glass Works, on the premises of Messrs. Green and Pellatt, but Faraday could not conveniently attend to them there. In 1827, therefore, a furnace was erected in the yard of the Royal Institution; and it was at this time, and with a view of assisting him at the furnace, that Faraday engaged Sergeant Anderson, of the Royal Artillery, the respectable, truthful, and altogether trustworthy man whose appearance here is so fresh in our memories. Anderson continued to be the reverential helper of Faraday and the faithful servant of this Institution for nearly forty years.[6]

5. I make the following extract from a letter from Sir John Herschel, written to me from Collingwood, on the 3rd of November, 1867:

 I will take this opportunity to mention that I believe myself to have originated the suggestion of the employment of borate of lead for *optical* purposes. It was somewhere in the year 1822, as well as I can recollect, that I mentioned it to Sir James (then Mr.) South; and, in consequence, the trial was made in his laboratory in Blackman Street, by precipitating and working a large quantity of borate of lead, and fusing it under a muffle in a porcelain evaporating dish. A very limpid (though slightly yellow) glass resulted, the refractive index 1.866! (which you will find set down in my table of refractive indices in my article 'Light,' *Encyclopædia Metropolitana*). It was, however, too soft for optical use as an object glass. This Faraday overcame, at least to a considerable degree, by the introduction of silica.

6. Regarding Anderson, Faraday writes thus in 1845: "I cannot resist the occasion

In 1831 Faraday published a paper, "On a Peculiar Class of Optical Deceptions," to which I believe the beautiful optical toy called the chromatrope owes its origin. In the same year he published a paper on vibrating surfaces, in which he solved an acoustical problem which, though of extreme simplicity *when solved*, appears to have baffled many eminent men. The problem was to account for the fact that light bodies, such as the seed of lycopodium, collected at the vibrating parts of sounding plates, while sand ran to the nodal lines. Faraday showed that the light bodies were entangled in the little whirlwinds formed in the air over the places of vibration, and through which the heavier sand was readily projected. Faraday's resources as an experimentalist were so wonderful, and his delight in experiment was so great, that he sometimes almost ran into excess in this direction. I have heard him say that this paper on vibrating surfaces was too heavily laden with experiments.

The work thus referred to, though sufficient of itself to secure no mean scientific reputation, forms but the vestibule of Faraday's achievements. He had been engaged within these walls for eighteen years. During part of the time he had drunk in knowledge from Davy, and during the remainder he continually exercised his capacity for independent inquiry. In 1831 we have him at the climax of his intellectual strength, forty years of age, stored with knowledge and full of original power. Through reading, lecturing, and experimenting, he had become thoroughly familiar with electrical science; he saw where light was needed and expansion possible. The phenomena of ordinary electric induction belonged, as it were, to the alphabet of his knowledge; he knew that under ordinary circumstances the presence of an electrified body was sufficient to excite, by induction, an unelectrified body. He knew that the wire which carried an electric current was an electrified body, and still that all attempts had failed to make it excite in other wires a state similar to its own.

What was the reason of this failure? Faraday never could work from the experiments of others, however clearly described. He knew well that from every experiment issues a kind of radiation, luminous in different degrees in different minds, and he hardly trusted himself to reason upon

that is thus offered to me of mentioning the name of Mr. Anderson, who came to me as an assistant in the glass experiments, and has remained ever since in the laboratory of the Royal Institution. He assisted me in all the researches into which I have entered since that time; and to his care, steadiness, exactitude, and faithfulness in the performance of all that has been committed to his charge, I am much indebted.—M. F." [See *Experimental Researches, Great Books of the Western World*, Vol. 45, p. 596 (Ed.).]

an experiment that he had not seen. In the autumn of 1831 he began to repeat the experiments with electric currents, which, up to that time, had produced no positive result. And here, for the sake of younger inquirers, if not for the sake of us all, it is worth while to dwell for a moment on a power which Faraday possessed in an extraordinary degree. He united vast strength with perfect flexibility. His momentum was that of a river, which combines weight and directness with the ability to yield to the flexures of its bed. The intentness of his vision in any direction did not apparently diminish his power of perception in other directions; and when he attacked a subject, expecting results, he had the faculty of keeping his mind alert, so that results different from those which he expected should not escape him through preoccupation.

He began his experiments on the induction of electric currents by composing a helix of two insulated wires which were wound side by side round the same wooden cylinder. One of these wires he connected with a voltaic battery of ten cells, and the other with a sensitive galvanometer. When connection with the battery was made, and while the current flowed, no effect whatever was observed at the galvanometer. But he never accepted an experimental result until he had applied to it the utmost power at his command. He raised his battery from 10 cells to 120 cells, but without avail. The current flowed calmly through the battery wire without producing, during its flow, any sensible result upon the galvanometer.

"During its flow," and this was the time when an effect was expected— but here Faraday's power of lateral vision, separating, as it were, from the line of expectation, came into play. He noticed that a feeble move-

Two completely independent coils of insulated wire were wound side by side on a wooden cylinder. One coil was connected to a voltaic battery, the current flowing when the battery wires were touched together. The other coil was connected to a sensitive galvanometer. At the moment that the battery wires were touched, the galvanometer moved, though the circuits were separate.

ment of the needle always occurred at the moment when he made contact with the battery; that the needle would afterwards return to its former position and remain quietly there unaffected by the *flowing* current. At the moment, however, when the circuit was interrupted the needle again moved, and in a direction opposed to that observed on the completion of the circuit.

This result, and others of a similar kind, led him to the conclusion that the battery current through the one wire did in reality induce a similar current through the other; but that it continued for an instant only, and partook more of the nature of the electric wave from a common Leyden jar than of the current from a voltaic battery. The momentary currents thus generated were called *induced* currents, while the current which generated them was called the *inducing* current. It was immediately proved that the current generated at making the circuit was always opposed in direction to its generator, while that developed on the rupture of the circuit coincided in direction with the inducing current. It appeared as if the current on its first rush through the primary wire sought a purchase in the secondary one, and, by a kind of kick, impelled backward through the latter an electric wave, which subsided as soon as the primary current was fully established.

Faraday, for a time, believed that the secondary wire, though quiescent when the primary current had been once established, was not in its natural condition, its return to that condition being declared by the current observed at breaking the circuit. He called this hypothetical state of the wire the *electrotonic state;* he afterwards abandoned this hypothesis, but seemed to return to it in later life. The term electrotonic is also preserved by Professor Du Bois Reymond to express a certain electric condition of the nerves, and Professor Clerk Maxwell has ably defined and illustrated the hypothesis in the tenth volume of the *Transactions of the Cambridge Philosophical Society.*

The mere approach of a wire forming a closed curve to a second wire through which a voltaic current flowed was then shown by Faraday to be sufficient to arouse in the neutral wire an induced current, opposed in direction to the inducing current; the withdrawal of the wire also generated a current having the same direction as the inducing current; those currents existed only during the time of approach or withdrawal, and when neither the primary nor the secondary wire was in motion, no matter how close their proximity might be, no induced current was generated.

Faraday has been called a purely inductive philosopher. A great deal

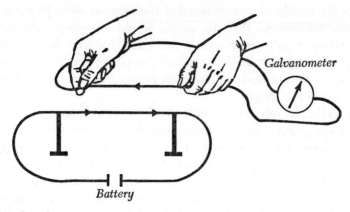

An induced current was produced when a wire forming a closed circuit
through a galvanometer was brought near a wire carrying a voltaic current.
The direction of the induced current was opposed to that
of the inducing current.

of nonsense is, I fear, uttered in this land of England about induction and
deduction. Some profess to befriend the one, some the other, while the
real vocation of an investigator, like Faraday, consists in the incessant
marriage of both. He was at this time full of the theory of Ampère, and
it cannot be doubted that numbers of his experiments were executed
merely to test his deductions from that theory. Starting from the dis-
covery of Oersted, the illustrious French philosopher had shown that
all the phenomena of magnetism then known might be reduced to the
mutual attractions and repulsions of electric currents. Magnetism had
been produced from electricity, and Faraday, who all his life long enter-
tained a strong belief in such reciprocal actions, now attempted to effect
the evolution of electricity from magnetism. Round a welded iron ring he
placed two distinct coils of covered wire, causing the coils to occupy op-
posite halves of the ring. Connecting the ends of one of the coils with
a galvanometer, he found that the moment the ring was magnetized,
by sending a current through *the other coil* the galvanometer needle
whirled round four or five times in succession. The action, as before, was
that of a pulse, which vanished immediately. On interrupting the circuit,
a whirl of the needle in the opposite direction occurred. It was only dur-
ing the time of magnetization or demagnetization that these effects were
produced. The induced currents declared a *change* of condition only, and
they vanished the moment the act of magnetization or demagnetization
was complete.

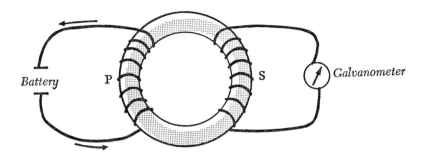

Two coils, P and S, were wound on an iron ring. The primary coil, P,
was connected to a battery; the secondary coil, S, to a galvanometer.
When a current was started in P, a current was induced in S
in a direction opposite to that in P. With the current flowing in P,
there was no current in S. When the current in P was interrupted,
there was a reverse current in S.

The effects obtained with the welded ring were also obtained with
straight bars of iron. Whether the bars were magnetized by the electric
current, or were excited by the contact of permanent steel magnets, in-
duced currents were always generated during the rise, and during the
subsidence of the magnetism. The use of iron was then abandoned, and
the same effects were obtained by merely thrusting a permanent steel
magnet into a coil of wire. A rush of electricity through the coil accom-
panied the insertion of the magnet; an equal rush in the opposite direction
accompanied its withdrawal. The precision with which Faraday describes
these results, and the completeness with which he defines the boundaries
of his facts, are wonderful. The magnet, for example, must not be passed
quite through the coil, but only half through; for if passed wholly through,
the needle is stopped as by a blow, and then he shows how this blow re-
sults from a reversal of the electric wave in the helix. He next operated
with the powerful permanent magnet of the Royal Society, and obtained
with it, in an exalted degree, all the foregoing phenomena.

And now he turned the light of these discoveries upon the darkest
physical phenomenon of that day. Arago had discovered, in 1824, that a
disk of nonmagnetic metal had the power of bringing a vibrating mag-
netic needle suspended over it rapidly to rest; and that on causing the
disk to rotate the magnetic needle rotated along with it. When both were
quiescent, there was not the slightest measurable attraction or repulsion
exerted between the needle and the disk; still, when in motion the disk
was competent to drag after it not only a light needle, but a heavy mag-
net. The question had been probed and investigated with admirable skill

*An induced current was produced by the mere motion
of a permanent steel magnet in a coil of wire. A rush of electricity
through the coil occurred when the magnet was inserted. An equal rush
in the opposite direction occurred when the magnet was withdrawn.*

by both Arago and Ampère, and Poisson had published a theoretic
memoir on the subject; but no cause could be assigned for so extraordi-
nary an action. It had also been examined in this country by two cele-
brated men, Mr. Babbage and Sir John Herschel; but it still remained
a mystery. Faraday always recommended the suspension of judgment in
cases of doubt. "I have always admired," he said, "the prudence and
philosophical reserve shown by M. Arago in resisting the temptation to
give a theory of the effect he had discovered, so long as he could not
devise one which was perfect in its application, and in refusing to assent
to the imperfect theories of others." Now, however, the time for theory
had come. Faraday saw mentally the rotating disk, under the operation of
the magnet, flooded with his induced currents, and from the known laws
of interaction between currents and magnets he hoped to deduce the
motion observed by Arago. That hope he realized, showing by actual ex-
periment that, when his disk rotated, currents passed through it, their
position and direction being such as must, in accordance with the es-
tablished laws of electromagnetic action, produce the observed rotation.

 Introducing the edge of his disk between the poles of the large horse-
shoe magnet of the Royal Society, and connecting the axis and the edge

*Faraday's electrical generator to produce a steady current
by rotating a copper disk between the poles of a magnet.*

of the disk, each by a wire with a galvanometer, he obtained, when the disk was turned round, a constant flow of electricity. The direction of the current was determined by the direction of the motion, the current being reversed when the rotation was reversed. He now states the law which rules the production of currents in both disks and wires, and in so doing used, for the first time, a phrase which has since become famous. When iron filings are scattered over a magnet, the particles of iron arrange themselves in certain determinate lines called magnetic curves. In 1831, Faraday for the first time called these curves "lines of magnetic force"; and he showed that to produce induced currents neither approach to nor withdrawal from a magnetic source, or center, or pole, was essential, but that it was only necessary to cut appropriately the lines of magnetic force. Faraday's first paper on magnetoelectric induction, which I have here endeavoured to condense, was read before the Royal Society on the 24th of November, 1831.

On January 12, 1832, he communicated to the Royal Society a second paper on terrestrial magnetoelectric induction, which was chosen as the Bakerian Lecture for the year. He placed a bar of iron in a coil of wire, and lifting the bar into the direction of the dipping needle, he excited by this action a current in the coil. On reversing the bar, a current in the opposite direction rushed through the wire. The same effect was produced when, on holding the helix in the line of dip, a bar of iron was thrust into it. Here, however, the earth acted on the coil through the intermediation of the bar of iron. He abandoned the bar and simply set a copper plate spinning in a horizontal plane; he knew that the earth's lines of magnetic force then crossed the plate at an angle of about 70°.

*Lines of magnetic force pass out of the north pole of a magnet,
and in at the south pole. To produce induced currents in a coil
it was only necessary to cut appropriately the lines of magnetic force.
For the arrangement shown, the coil may be spun around on its vertical axis
or drawn back and forth across the end of the magnet.*

When the plate spun round, the lines of force were intersected and in-
duced currents generated, which produced their proper effect when
carried from the plate to the galvanometer. "When the plate was in the
magnetic meridian, or in any other plane coinciding with the magnetic
dip, then its rotation produced no effect upon the galvanometer."

At the suggestion of a mind fruitful in suggestions of a profound and
philosophic character—I mean that of Sir John Herschel—Mr. Barlow,
of Woolwich, had experimented with a rotating iron shell. Mr. Christie
had also performed an elaborate series of experiments on a rotating iron
disk. Both of them had found that when in rotation the body exercised a
peculiar action upon the magnetic needle, deflecting it in a manner which
was not observed during quiescence; but neither of them was aware at
the time of the agent which produced this extraordinary deflection. They
ascribed it to some change in the magnetism of the iron shell and disk.

But Faraday at once saw that his induced currents must come into
play here, and he immediately obtained them from an iron disk. With a
hollow brass ball, moreover, he produced the effects obtained by Mr.
Barlow. Iron was in no way necessary; the only condition of success was
that the rotating body should be of a character to admit of the formation
of currents in its substance; it must, in other words, be a conductor of
electricity. The higher the conducting power the more copious were the
currents. He now passes from his little brass globe to the globe of the
earth. He plays like a magician with the earth's magnetism. He sees the
invisible lines along which its magnetic action is exerted, and sweeping
his wand across these lines evokes this new power. Placing a simple loop

Galvanometer

A dipping needle, shown in the background, is so balanced
that it points slantingly downward toward the earth's north magnetic pole.
[At Washington, D.C., the inclination, or dip, is 70 degrees.]
Faraday found that, when an iron bar was thrust into a coil
in the direction of the dip, a momentary current was induced.

of wire round a magnetic needle he bends its upper portion to the west;
the north pole of the needle immediately swerves to the east; he bends
his loop to the east, and the north pole moves to the west. Suspending a
common bar magnet in a vertical position, he causes it to spin round its
own axis. Its pole being connected with one end of a galvanometer wire,
and its equator with the other end, electricity rushes round the galva-
nometer from the rotating magnet. He remarks upon the "singular inde-
pendence" of the magnetism and the body of the magnet which carries
it. The steel behaves as if it were isolated from its own magnetism.

And then his thoughts suddenly widen, and he asks himself whether
the rotating earth does not generate induced currents as it turns round
its axis from west to east. In his experiment with the twirling magnet the
galvanometer wire remained at rest; one portion of the circuit was in
motion *relatively* to *another portion*. But in the case of the twirling planet
the galvanometer wire would necessarily be carried along with the
earth; there would be no relative motion. What must be the conse-
quence? Take the case of a telegraph wire with its two terminal plates
dipped into the earth, and suppose the wire to lie in the magnetic merid-
ian. The ground underneath the wire is influenced like the wire itself by
the earth's rotation; if a current from south to north be generated in the
wire, a similar current from south to north would be generated in the

earth under the wire; these currents would run against the same terminal plate, and thus neutralize each other.

This inference appears inevitable, but his profound vision perceived its possible invalidity. He saw that it was at least possible that the difference of conducting power between the earth and the wire might give one an advantage over the other, and that thus a residual or differential current might be obtained. He combined wires of different materials, and caused them to act in opposition to each other, but found the combination ineffectual. The more copious flow in the better conductor was exactly counterbalanced by the resistance of the worse. Still, though experiment was thus emphatic, he would clear his mind of all discomfort by operating on the earth itself. He went to the round lake near Kensington Palace, and stretched 480 feet of copper wire, north and south, over the lake, causing plates soldered to the wire at its ends to dip into the water. The copper wire was severed at the middle, and the severed ends connected with a galvanometer. No effect whatever was observed. But though quiescent water gave no effect, moving water might. He therefore worked at London Bridge for three days during the ebb and flow of the tide, but without any satisfactory result. Still he urges, "Theoretically it seems a necessary consequence, that where water is flowing there electric currents should be formed. If a line be imagined passing from Dover to Calais through the sea, and returning through the land, beneath the water to Dover, it traces out a circuit of conducting matter one part of which, when the water moves up or down the channel, is cutting the magnetic curves of the earth, whilst the other is relatively at rest. . . .

"There is every reason to believe that currents do run in the general direction of the circuit described, either one way or the other, according as the passage of the water is up or down the channel." This was written before the submarine cable was thought of, and he once informed me that actual observation upon that cable had been found to be in accordance with his theoretic deduction.[7]

7. I am indebted to a friend for the following exquisite morsel: "A short time after the publication of Faraday's first researches in magnetoelectricity, he attended the meeting of the British Association at Oxford, in 1832. On this occasion he was requested by some of the authorities to repeat the celebrated experiment of eliciting a spark from a magnet, employing for this purpose the large magnet in the Ashmolean Museum. To this he consented, and a large party assembled to witness the experiments, which, I need not say, were perfectly successful. While he was repeating them a dignitary of the university entered the room, and addressing himself to Professor Daniell, who was standing near Faraday, inquired what was going on. The Professor explained to him as popularly as possible this striking result of Faraday's great discovery. The Dean listened with attention and looked earnestly at the brilliant spark, but a moment after he assumed a serious counte-

Three years subsequent to the publication of these researches—that is to say, on January 29, 1835—Faraday read before the Royal Society a paper "on the influence by induction of an electric current upon itself." A shock and spark of a peculiar character had been observed by a young man named William Jenkin, who must have been a youth of some scientific promise, but who, as Faraday once informed me, was dissuaded by his own father from having anything to do with science. The investigation of the fact noticed by Mr. Jenkin led Faraday to the discovery of the *extra current*, or the current *induced in the primary wire itself* at the moments of making and breaking contact, the phenomena which he described and illustrated in the beautiful and exhaustive paper referred to.

Seven and thirty years have passed since the discovery of magneto-electricity; but if we except the *extra current*, until quite recently nothing of moment was added to the subject. Faraday entertained the opinion that the discoverer of a great law of principle had a right to the "spoils"—this was his term—arising from its illustration; and guided by the principle he had discovered, his wonderful mind, aided by his wonderful ten fingers, overran in a single autumn this vast domain, and hardly left behind him the shred of a fact to be gathered by his successors.

And here the question may arise in some minds: What is the use of it all? The answer is, that if man's intellectual nature thirsts for knowledge, then knowledge is useful because it satisfies this thirst. If you demand practical ends, you must, I think, expand your definition of the term practical, and make it include all that elevates and enlightens the intellect, as well as all that ministers to the bodily health and comfort of men. Still, if needed, an answer of another kind might be given to the question "What is its use?" As far as electricity has been applied for medical purposes, it has been almost exclusively Faraday's electricity. You have noticed those lines of wire which cross the streets of London. It is Faraday's currents that speed from place to place through these wires. Approaching the point of Dungeness, the mariner sees an unusually brilliant light, and from the noble *phares* of La Hève the same light flashes across the sea. These are Faraday's sparks exalted by suitable machinery to sunlike splendor. At the present moment the Board of Trade and the

nance and shook his head; 'I am sorry for it,' said he, as he walked away. In the middle of the room he stopped for a moment and repeated, 'I am sorry for it,' then, walking towards the door, when the handle was in his hand he turned round and said, '*Indeed* I am sorry for it; it is putting new arms into the hands of the incendiary.' This occurred a short time after the papers had been filled with the doings of the hayrick burners. An erroneous statement of what fell from the Dean's mouth was printed at the time in one of the Oxford papers. He is there wrongly stated to have said, 'It is putting new arms into the hands of the infidel.' "

Brethren of the Trinity House, as well as the Commissioners of Northern Lights, are contemplating the introduction of the magnetoelectric light at numerous points upon our coasts; and future generations will be able to refer to those guiding stars in answer to the question, what has been the practical use of the labours of Faraday? But I would again emphatically say, that his work needs no such justification, and that if he had allowed his vision to be disturbed by considerations regarding the practical use of his discoveries, those discoveries would never have been made by him. "I have rather," he writes in 1831, "been desirous of discovering new facts and new relations dependent on magnetoelectric induction, than of exalting the force of those already obtained, being assured that the latter would find their full development hereafter."

In 1817, when lecturing before a private society in London on the element chlorine, Faraday thus expressed himself with reference to this question of utility: "Before leaving this subject, I will point out the history of this substance, as an answer to those who are in the habit of saying to every new fact, 'What is its use?' Dr. Franklin says to such, 'What is the use of an infant?' The answer of the experimentalist is, 'Endeavour to make it useful.' When Scheele discovered this substance, it appeared to have no use; it was in its infancy and useless state, but having grown up to maturity, witness its powers, and see what endeavours to make it useful have done."

The foregoing consists of Chapters I–III of Tyndall's FARADAY AS A DISCOVERER.

Eve Curie

1904–

Eve Curie was born in Paris in 1904, the daughter of Pierre and Marie Curie. She began early to study music, and though she received the degree of bachelor of science and philosophy from Sévigné College, she became a concert pianist. She made her debut at Paris in 1925 and subsequently played in many cities, chiefly in France. After her mother's death she began collecting and classifying all the papers, manuscripts, and documents left by Mme Curie; she went to Poland to obtain material on her mother's youth; and she interrogated all those friends and acquaintances of the scientist who could be reached. Her biography, titled *Madame Curie,* was published in 1937. It was described as one of the great biographies of our time and was translated into many languages.

Eve Curie gave vigorous support to the activities of the Free French in World War II. She visited, as a correspondent, some of the most active battlefronts and wrote a book about her experiences called *Journey Among Warriors* (1943). She later became one of the publishers of the newspaper *Paris Presse.* With her husband, Henri Labouisse, she now resides in Washington, D.C.

The Curie family would have delighted Galton, the author of *Hereditary Genius.* Pierre and Marie Curie received the Nobel Prize in physics for 1903, in association with Henri Becquerel, for the discovery of radiation. Mme Curie herself won the Nobel Prize in Chemistry for 1911, for the discovery of radium. Her daughter Irène, in association with the latter's husband, Frédéric Joliot-Curie, won the Nobel Prize in chemistry for 1935, for their production of artificially induced radiation. And Eve Curie attained the first rank

among biographers upon the publication of *Madame Curie.* If genius is hereditary in any family, it would appear to have been so in this one.

Mme Curie not only received two Nobel Prizes; she also received innumerable other prizes and medals and was made a corresponding honorary member of almost every scientific society on earth. The curie, a unit of measurement for radium emanation, was named after her, as was the element curium.

Despite this public acclaim (there were, however, also violent attacks on her), Mme Curie remained a simple, kind, almost timid woman. "Marie Curie is, of all celebrated beings," said her lifelong friend Albert Einstein, "the only one whom fame has not corrupted."

The problem which thus faced her biographer was, though it might seem simple, in fact extremely complex and difficult. On the one hand, there was the temptation to do no more than recount the troubles and obstacles of Mme Curie's youth, to tell how each of these was in turn overcome, to applaud the great discoveries, to describe the personal anguish, to narrate the series of triumphs, and to close with a rousing paean of praise. But the risk in that case was to create a cold and quite unbelievable character.

On the other hand, Eve Curie might have been tempted to tell no more than a "human interest" story; she might have emphasized the naïveté of her subject. But the risk in this case was to fall into pathos and sentimentality.

The young biographer of Mme Curie avoided both dangers. Eve Curie's picture of her mother is as warm, as human, as paradoxical as the woman herself; but that woman is also a great scientist. In a short introduction to the book Eve Curie tells us how she managed to do this. "It would have been a crime," she writes, "to add the slightest ornament to this story, so like a myth. I have not related a single anecdote of which I am not sure. I have not deformed a single essential phrase or so much as invented the color of a dress. The facts are as stated; the quoted words were actually pronounced."

In other words, she wrote about her mother's life in much the same way that her mother wrote about her discoveries. Mme Curie did not add anything, either; she too was objective in the best sense, she too was patient and willing to allow the truth to speak for itself. Both of these remarkable women lend considerable credence to the proposition that truth is not only stranger than fiction but also much more interesting.

It hardly needs saying that the chapter reprinted below, *The Discovery of Radium,* has the virtues of the whole book. Here is the story of Mme Curie in miniature. In particular, the reader is urged to note especially the three notebook entries quoted at the end of the chapter. Therein, the author seems to be saying, lies the essence of Marie Curie, who could be equally happy about the discovery of radium and about the fact that her daughter has fifteen teeth.

The Discovery of Radium

While a young wife kept house, washed her baby daughter and put pans on the fire, in a wretched laboratory at the School of Physics a woman physicist was making the most important discovery of modern science.

At the end of 1897 the balance sheet of Marie's activity showed two university degrees, a fellowship and a monograph on the magnetization of tempered steel. No sooner had she recovered from childbirth than she was back again at the laboratory.

The next stage in the logical development of her career was the doctor's degree. Several weeks of indecision came in here. She had to choose a subject of research which would furnish fertile and original material. Like a writer who hesitates and asks himself questions before settling the subject of his next novel, Marie, reviewing the most recent work in physics with Pierre, was in search of a subject for a thesis.

At this critical moment Pierre's advice had an importance which cannot be neglected. With respect to her husband, the young woman regarded herself as an apprentice: he was an older physicist, much more experienced than she. He was even, to put it exactly, her chief, her "boss."

But without a doubt Marie's character, her intimate nature, had a great part in this all-important choice. From childhood the Polish girl had carried the curiosity and daring of an explorer within her. This was the instinct that had driven her to leave Warsaw for Paris and the Sorbonne, and had made her prefer a solitary room in the Latin Quarter to the Dluskis' downy nest. In her walks in the woods she always chose the wild trail or the unfrequented road.

At this moment she was like a traveler musing on a long voyage. Bent over the globe and pointing out, in some far country, a strange name that excites his imagination, the traveler suddenly decides to go there and nowhere else: so Marie, going through the reports of the latest experi-

mental studies, was attracted by the publication of the French scientist Henri Becquerel of the preceding year. She and Pierre already knew this work; she read it over again and studied it with her usual care.

After Roentgen's discovery of X rays, Henri Poincaré conceived the idea of determining whether rays like the X ray were emitted by "fluorescent" bodies under the action of light. Attracted by the same problem, Henri Becquerel examined the salts of a "rare metal," uranium. Instead of finding the phenomenon he had expected, he observed another, altogether different and incomprehensible: he found that uranium salts *spontaneously* emitted, without exposure to light, some rays of unknown nature. A compound of uranium, placed on a photographic plate surrounded by black paper, made an impression on the plate through the paper. And, like the X ray, these astonishing "uranic" salts discharged an electroscope by rendering the surrounding air a conductor.

Henri Becquerel made sure that these surprising properties were not caused by a preliminary exposure to the sun and that they persisted when the uranium compound had been maintained in darkness for several months. For the first time, a physicist had observed the phenomenon to which Marie Curie was later to give the name of *radioactivity*. But the nature of the radiation and its origin remained an enigma.

Becquerel's discovery fascinated the Curies. They asked themselves whence came the energy—tiny, to be sure—which uranium compounds constantly disengaged in the form of radiation. And what was the nature of this radiation? Here was an engrossing subject of research, a doctor's thesis! The subject tempted Marie most because it was a virgin field: Becquerel's work was very recent and so far as she knew nobody in the laboratories of Europe had yet attempted to make a fundamental study of uranium rays. As a point of departure, and as the only bibliography, there existed some communications presented by Henri Becquerel at the Academy of Science during the year 1896. It was a leap into great adventure, into an unknown realm.

There remained the question of where she was to make her experiments—and here the difficulties began. Pierre made several approaches to the director of the School of Physics with practically no results: Marie was given the free use of a little glassed-in studio on the ground floor of the school. It was a kind of storeroom, sweating with damp, where unused machines and lumber were put away. Its technical equipment was rudimentary and its comfort nil.

Deprived of an adequate electrical installation and of everything that forms material for the beginning of scientific research, she kept her

patience, sought and found a means of making her apparatus work in this hole.

It was not easy. Instruments of precision have sneaking enemies: humidity, changes of temperature. Incidentally the climate of this little workroom, fatal to the sensitive electrometer, was not much better for Marie's health. But this had no importance. When she was cold, the young woman took her revenge by noting the degrees of temperature in centigrade in her notebook. On February 6, 1898, we find, among the formulas and figures: "Temperature here 6°25." Six degrees . . . ! [1] Marie, to show her disapproval, added ten little exclamation points.

The candidate for the doctor's degree set her first task to be the measurement of the "power of ionization" of uranium rays—that is to say, their power to render the air a conductor of electricity and so to discharge an electroscope. The excellent method she used, which was to be the key to the success of her experiments, had been invented for the study of other phenomena by two physicists well known to her: Pierre and Jacques Curie. Her technical installation consisted of an "ionization chamber," a Curie electrometer and a piezoelectric quartz.

At the end of several weeks the first result appeared: Marie acquired the certainty that the intensity of this surprising radiation was proportional to the quantity of uranium contained in the samples under examination, and that this radiation, which could be measured with precision, was not affected either by the chemical state of combination of the uranium or by external factors such as lighting or temperature.

These observations were perhaps not very sensational to the uninitiated, but they were of passionate interest to the scientist. It often happens in physics that an inexplicable phenomenon can be subjected, after some investigation, to laws already known, and by this very fact loses its interest for the research worker. Thus, in a badly constructed detective story, if we are told in the third chapter that the woman of sinister appearance who might have committed the crime is in reality only an honest little housewife who leads a life without secrets, we feel discouraged and cease to read.

Nothing of the kind happened here. The more Marie penetrated into intimacy with uranium rays, the more they seemed without precedent, essentially unknown. They were like nothing else. Nothing affected them. In spite of their very feeble power, they had an extraordinary individuality.

1. About 44° Fahrenheit.

Turning this mystery over and over in her head, and pointing toward the truth, Marie felt and could soon affirm that the incomprehensible radiation was an *atomic* property. She questioned: Even though the phenomenon had only been observed with uranium, nothing proved that uranium was the only chemical element capable of emitting such radiation. Why should not other bodies possess the same power? Perhaps it was only by chance that this radiation had been observed in uranium first, and had remained attached to uranium in the minds of physicists. Now it must be sought for elsewhere. . . .

No sooner said than done. Abandoning the study of uranium, Marie undertook to examine *all known chemical bodies,* either in the pure state or in compounds. And the result was not long in appearing: compounds of another element, thorium, also emitted spontaneous rays like those of uranium and of similar intensity. The physicist had been right: the surprising phenomenon was by no means the property of uranium alone, and it became necessary to give it a distinct name. Mme Curie suggested the name of *radioactivity.* Chemical substances like uranium and thorium, endowed with this particular "radiance," were called *radio elements.*

Radioactivity so fascinated the young scientist that she never tired of examining the most diverse forms of matter, always by the same method. Curiosity, a marvelous feminine curiosity, the first virtue of a scientist, was developed in Marie to the highest degree. Instead of limiting her observation to simple compounds, salts and oxides, she had the desire to assemble samples of minerals from the collection at the School of Physics, and of making them undergo almost at hazard, for her own amusement, a kind of customs inspection which is an electrometer test. Pierre approved, and chose with her the veined fragments, hard or crumbly, oddly shaped, which she wanted to examine.

Marie's idea was simple—simple as the stroke of genius. At the crossroads where Marie now stood, hundreds of research workers might have remained, nonplussed, for months or even years. After examining all known chemical substances, and discovering—as Marie had done—the radiation of thorium, they would have continued to ask themselves in vain whence came this mysterious radioactivity. Marie, too, questioned and wondered. But her surprise was translated into fruitful acts. She had used up all evident possibilities. Now she turned toward the unplumbed and the unknown.

She knew in advance what she would learn from an examination of the minerals, or rather she thought she knew. The specimens which contained neither uranium nor thorium would be revealed as totally "in-

active." The others, containing uranium or thorium, would be radioactive.

Experiment confirmed this prevision. Rejecting the inactive minerals, Marie applied herself to the others and measured their radioactivity. Then came a dramatic revelation: the radioactivity was a *great deal stronger* than could have been normally foreseen by the quantity of uranium or thorium contained in the products examined!

"It must be an error in experiment," the young woman thought; for doubt is the scientist's first response to an unexpected phenomenon.

She started her measurements over again, unmoved, using the same products. She started over again ten times, twenty times. And she was forced to yield to the evidence: the quantities of uranium and of thorium found in these minerals were by no means sufficient to justify the exceptional intensity of the radiation she observed.

Where did this excessive and abnormal radiation come from? Only one explanation was possible: the minerals must contain, in small quantity, a *much more powerfully radioactive substance* than uranium and thorium.

But what substance? In her preceding experiments, Marie had already examined *all known chemical elements.*

The scientist replied to the question with the sure logic and the magnificent audaciousness of a great mind: The minerals certainly contained a radioactive substance, which was at the same time a chemical element unknown until this day: *a new element.*

A new element! It was a fascinating and alluring hypothesis—but still a hypothesis. For the moment this powerfully radioactive substance existed only in the imagination of Marie and of Pierre. But it did exist there. It existed strongly enough to make the young woman go to see Bronya one day and tell her in a restrained, ardent voice:

"You know, Bronya, the radiation that I couldn't explain comes from a new chemical element. The element is there and I've got to find it. We are sure! The physicists we have spoken to believe we have made an error in experiment and advise us to be careful. But I am convinced that I am not mistaken."

These were unique moments in her unique life. The layman forms a theatrical—and wholly false—idea of the research worker and of his discoveries. "The moment of discovery" does not always exist: the scientist's work is too tenuous, too divided, for the certainty of success to crackle out suddenly in the midst of his laborious toil like a stroke of lightning, dazzling him by its fire. Marie, standing in front of her apparatus, perhaps never experienced the sudden intoxication of triumph.

This intoxication was spread over several days of decisive labor, made feverish by a magnificent hope. But it must have been an exultant moment when, convinced by the rigorous reasoning of her brain that she was on the trail of new matter, she confided the secret to her elder sister, her ally always. . . . Without exchanging one affectionate word, the two sisters must have lived again, in a dizzying breath of memory, their years of waiting, their mutual sacrifices, their bleak lives as students, full of hope and faith.

It was barely four years before that Marie had written:

> Life is not easy for any of us. But what of that? We must have perseverance and above all confidence in ourselves. We must believe that we are gifted for something, and that this thing, at whatever cost, must be attained.

That "something" was to throw science upon a path hitherto unsuspected.

In a first communication to the Academy, presented by Prof. Lippmann and published in the *Proceedings* on April 12, 1898, Marie Sklodovska Curie announced the probable presence in pitchblende ores of a new element endowed with powerful radioactivity. This was the first stage of the discovery of radium.

By the force of her own intuition the physicist had shown to herself that the wonderful substance must exist. She decreed its existence. But its incognito still had to be broken. Now she would have to verify hypothesis by experiment, isolate this material and see it. She must be able to announce with certainty: "It is there."

Pierre Curie had followed the rapid progress of his wife's experiments with passionate interest. Without directly taking part in Marie's work, he had frequently helped her by his remarks and advice. In view of the stupefying character of her results, he did not hesitate to abandon his study of crystals for the time being in order to join his efforts to hers in the search for the new substance.

Thus, when the immensity of a pressing task suggested and exacted collaboration, a great physicist was at Marie's side—a physicist who was the companion of her life. Three years earlier, love had joined this exceptional man and woman together—love, and perhaps some mysterious foreknowledge, some sublime instinct for the work in common.

The available force was now doubled. Two brains, four hands, now sought the unknown element in the damp little workroom in the Rue

Lhomond. From this moment onward it is impossible to distinguish each one's part in the work of the Curies. We know that Marie, having chosen to study the radiation of uranium as the subject of her thesis, discovered that other substances were also radioactive. We know that after the examination of minerals she was able to announce the existence of a new chemical element, powerfully radioactive, and that it was the capital importance of this result which decided Pierre Curie to interrupt his very different research in order to try to isolate this element with his wife. At that time—May or June 1898—a collaboration began which was to last for eight years, until it was destroyed by a fatal accident.

We cannot and must not attempt to find out what should be credited to Marie and what to Pierre during these eight years. It would be exactly what the husband and wife did not want. The personal genius of Pierre Curie is known to us by the original work he had accomplished before this collaboration. His wife's genius appears to us in the first intuition of discovery, the brilliant start; and it was to reappear to us again, solitary, when Marie Curie the widow unflinchingly carried the weight of a new science and conducted it, through research, step by step, to its harmonious expansion. We therefore have formal proof that in the fusion of their two efforts, in this superior alliance of man and woman, the exchange was equal.

Let this certainty suffice for our curiosity and admiration. Let us not attempt to separate these creatures full of love, whose handwriting alternates and combines in the working notebooks covered with formulas, these creatures who were to sign nearly all their scientific publications together. They were to write "We found" and "We observed"; and when they were constrained by fact to distinguish between their parts, they were to employ this moving locution:

> Certain minerals containing uranium and thorium (pitchblende, chalcolite, uranite) are very active from the point of view of the emission of Becquerel rays. In a preceding communication, *one of us* showed that their activity was even greater than that of uranium and thorium, and stated the opinion that this effect was due to some other very active substance contained in small quantity in these minerals.
>
> (Pierre and Marie Curie: *Proceedings of the Academy of Science,* July 18, 1898.)

Marie and Pierre looked for this "very active" substance in an ore of uranium called pitchblende, which in the crude state had shown itself to be four times more radioactive than the pure oxide of uranium that could be extracted from it. But the composition of this ore had been known for

a long time with considerable precision. The new element must therefore
be present in very small quantity or it would not have escaped the notice
of scientists and their chemical analysis.

According to their calculations—"pessimistic" calculations, like those of
true physicists, who always take the less attractive of two probabilities—
the collaborators thought the ore should contain the new element to a
maximum quantity of one per cent. They decided that this was very
little. They would have been in consternation if they had known that the
radioactive element they were hunting down did not count for more than
a millionth part of pitchblende ore.

They began their prospecting patiently, using a method of chemical
research invented by themselves, based on radioactivity: they separated
all the elements in pitchblende by ordinary chemical analysis and then
measured the radioactivity of each of the bodies thus obtained. By suc-
cessive eliminations they saw the "abnormal" radioactivity take refuge in
certain parts of the ore. As they went on, the field of investigation was
narrowed. It was exactly the technique used by the police when they
search the houses of a neighborhood, one by one, to isolate and arrest a
malefactor.

But there was more than one malefactor here: the radioactivity was
concentrated principally in two different chemical fractions of the pitch-
blende. For M. and Mme Curie it indicated the existence of two new
elements instead of one. By July, 1898, they were able to announce the
discovery of one of these substances with certainty.

"You will have to name it," Pierre said to his young wife, in the same
tone as if it were a question of choosing a name for little Irène.

The one-time Mlle Sklodovska reflected in silence for a moment. Then,
her heart turning toward her own country which had been erased from
the map of the world, she wondered vaguely if the scientific event would
be published in Russia, Germany and Austria—the oppressor countries—
and answered timidly: "Could we call it 'polonium'?"

In the *Proceedings of the Academy* for July, 1898, we read:

> We believe the substance we have extracted from pitchblende con-
> tains a metal not yet observed, related to bismuth by its analytical prop-
> erties. If the existence of this new metal is confirmed we propose to call
> it *polonium,* from the name of the original country of one of us.

The choice of this name proves that in becoming a Frenchwoman and
a physicist Marie had not disowned her former enthusiasms. Another
thing proves it for us: even before the note "On a New Radioactive

Substance Contained in Pitchblende" had appeared in the *Proceedings of the Academy,* Marie had sent the manuscript to her native country, to that Joseph Boguski who directed the little laboratory at the Museum of Industry and Agriculture where she had made her first experiments. The communication was published in Warsaw in a monthly photographic review called *Swiatlo* almost as soon as in Paris.

Life was unchanged in the little flat in the Rue de la Glacière. Marie and Pierre worked even more than usual; that was all. When the heat of summer came, the young wife found time to buy some baskets of fruit in the markets and, as usual, she cooked and put away preserves for the winter, according to the recipes used in the Curie family. Then she locked the shutters on her windows, which gave on burned leaves; she registered their two bicycles at the Orleans station, and, like thousands of other young women in Paris, went off on holiday with her husband and her child.

This year the couple had rented a peasant's house at Auroux, in Auvergne. Happy to breathe good air after the noxious atmosphere of the Rue Lhomond, the Curies made excursions to Mende, Puy, Clermont, Mont-Dore. They climbed hills, visited grottoes, bathed in rivers. Every day, alone in the country, they spoke of what they called their "new metals," polonium and "the other"—the one that remained to be found. In September they would go back to the damp workroom and the dull minerals; with freshened ardor they would take up their search again. . . .

One grief interfered with Marie's intoxication for work: the Dluskis were on the point of leaving Paris. They had decided to settle in Austrian Poland and to build a sanatorium for tubercular sufferers at Zakopane in the Carpathian Mountains. The day of separation arrived: Marie and Bronya exchanged brokenhearted farewells; Marie was losing her friend and protector, and for the first time she had the feeling of exile.

Marie to Bronya, December 2, 1898:

You can't imagine what a hole you have made in my life. With you two, I have lost everything I clung to in Paris except my husband and child. It seems to me that Paris no longer exists, aside from our lodging and the school where we work.

Ask Mme Dluska if the green plant you left behind should be watered, and how many times a day. Does it need a great deal of heat and sun?

We are well, in spite of the bad weather, the rain and the mud. Irène

is getting to be a big girl. She is very difficult about her food, and aside from milk tapioca she will eat hardly anything regularly, not even eggs. Write me what would be a suitable menu for persons of her age. . . .

In spite of their prosaic character—or perhaps because of it—some notes written by Mme Curie in that memorable year 1898 seem to us worth quoting. Some are to be found in the margins of a book called *Family Cooking*, with respect to a recipe for gooseberry jelly:

> I took eight pounds of fruit and the same weight in crystallized sugar. After an ebullition of ten minutes, I passed the mixture through a rather fine sieve. I obtained fourteen pots of very good jelly, not transparent, which "took" perfectly.

In a school notebook covered with gray linen, in which the young mother had written little Irène's weight day by day, her diet and the appearance of her first teeth, we read under the date of July 20, 1898, some days after the publication of the discovery of polonium:

> Irène says "thanks" with her hand. She can walk very well now on all fours. She says "Gogli, gogli, go." She stays in the garden all day at Sceaux on a carpet. She can roll, pick herself up, and sit down.

On August 15, at Auroux:

> Irène has cut her seventh tooth, on the lower left. She can stand for half a minute alone. For the past three days we have bathed her in the river. She cries, but today (fourth bath) she stopped crying and played with her hands in the water.
>
> She plays with the cat and chases him with war cries. She is not afraid of strangers any more. She sings a great deal. She gets up on the table when she is in her chair.

Three months later, on October 17, Marie noted with pride:

> Irène can walk very well, and no longer goes on all fours.

On January 5, 1899:

> Irène has fifteen teeth!

Between these two notes—that of October 17, 1898, in which Irène no longer goes on all fours, and that of January 5 in which Irène has fifteen teeth—and a few months after the note on the gooseberry preserve, we find another note worthy of remark.

It was drawn up by Marie and Pierre Curie and a collaborator called G. Bémont. Intended for the Academy of Science, and published in the

Proceedings of the session of December 26, 1898, it announced the existence of a second new chemical element in pitchblende.

Some lines of this communication read as follows:

> *The various reasons we have just enumerated lead us to believe that the new radioactive substance contains a new element to which we propose to give the name of RADIUM.*
>
> *The new radioactive substance certainly contains a very strong proportion of barium; in spite of that its radioactivity is considerable. The radioactivity of radium therefore must be enormous.*

*The foregoing consists of Chapter XII
of Eve Curie's* MADAME CURIE.

Charles Robert Darwin

1809–1882

Charles Darwin was born, as he tells us in this autobiography, on February 12, 1809, at Shrewsbury, England. On the same day, in a log cabin in the backwoods of the pioneer state of Kentucky, was born Abraham Lincoln. Darwin was the grandson of the poet-naturalist Erasmus Darwin; his mother was the daughter of the great pottery maker Josiah Wedgwood; his cousin was Francis Galton. The family was distinguished in many walks of life, but especially in science; four of Darwin's sons became prominent scientists, and three of them were knighted. He was not knighted himself. Evolution was too scandalous a doctrine for its leading spokesman to be so honored. Of course, he was the recipient of greater and more lasting honor than any English monarch could confer.

Do we not believe him when he says that it was "truly surprising" to him that he "should have influenced to a considerable extent the belief of scientific men on some important points"? That is, we believe in the sincerity of his surprise; no one can doubt the importance of the revolution in thought he brought about. "My name ought to last for a few years," he says. Again the simplicity of the remark seems the best proof of its sincerity. The "few years" have stretched to nearly a century, and it appears probable that the name of Darwin will be known as long as science endures.

Most of the facts of his life are told us by himself. His diffidence may mask the truth that, despite the prior work of Wallace, the *Origin of Species* was as remarkable for its originality as for its eloquence. He charitably omits more than passing references to the attacks that he, as its author, had to suffer for the remainder of his life. And we might not know from Darwin's account of them that

43

his other publications would have been sufficient in themselves to make him the leading naturalist of his time.

Darwin died on April 19, 1882, and was buried in Westminster Abbey. His death occurred less than a year after the last paragraphs of his autobiography were written.

Darwin's *Autobiography* is not a formal work. He wrote it, he says, for amusement, and because it "might possibly interest" his descendants. He took "no pains about (the) style of writing." Yet the little book is fascinating. We cannot put it down. Why is this?

Perhaps it is because the very simplicity and ingenuousness of the account lend credence to it. It has been said that the hardest person to tell the truth about is oneself. Darwin remarks that "no man can . . . correctly" describe the state of his own mind. Yet there are some things that a man knows about himself that no one else knows. These things are here.

Three items, among many, are of particular interest. They are minutiae, perhaps, in the life of this great man, but significant ones. First, there is the fact that, in his old age, he had "wholly lost, to (his) great regret, all pleasure from poetry of any kind." His mind, he felt, had "become a kind of machine for grinding general laws out of large collections of facts."

Darwin himself was concerned and puzzled by this. "Why this should have caused the atrophy of that part of the brain alone, on which the higher tastes depend," he writes, "I cannot conceive." He suggests that the loss might be due to weakness of intellect. Leaving aside this explanation, which seems unapt in his case, it is indeed something to ponder. In other words, are science and art really so deeply opposed? Do they depend for their existence and appreciation on two quite different kinds of minds?

Notes from the artist: "Surrounding the seated figure of Darwin are some of the objects he studied while preparing his theory of evolution: primitive vertebrate, amphibian, finches, skull of Toxodon, *jaw of* Mylodon, *foot of* Macrauchenia, *beetle, mollusk, flatworms. Also included is the 'Beagle,' the ship on which he voyaged for nearly five years while making his investigations. The quotation is from the* Origin of Species."

Charles Darwin

I have called this principle, by which each slight variation, if useful, is preserved, by the term Natural Selection

Second, what he tells us about his methods of work is instructive. When writing a book, he made outline after outline, each longer and more detailed than those that preceded it. This is a good way to compose any expository work. Almost anyone can get guidance from the paragraphs in which he describes his habits of writing.

Finally, there is his reply to the critics who claimed that he had no "power of reasoning." "I do not think that this can be true," he says, "for the *Origin of Species* is one long argument from the beginning to the end . . . No one could have written it without having some power of reasoning." The wonderful charm of the man shines through that last sentence. The reader who does not smile at it would not smile at anything.

Autobiography

A German editor having written to me for an account of
the development of my mind and character with some sketch of my
autobiography, I have thought that the attempt would amuse me, and
might possibly interest my children or their children. I know that it
would have interested me greatly to have read even so short and dull a
sketch of the mind of my grandfather, written by himself, and what he
thought and did, and how he worked. I have attempted to write the
following account of myself, as if I were a dead man in another world
looking back at my own life. Nor have I found this difficult, for life is
nearly over with me. I have taken no pains about my style of writing.

I was born at Shrewsbury on February 12, 1809, and my earliest recol-
lection goes back only to when I was a few months over four years old,
when we went to near Abergele for sea-bathing, and I recollect some
events and places there with some little distinctness.

My mother died in July, 1817, when I was a little over eight years old,
and it is odd that I can remember hardly anything about her except her
death-bed, her black velvet gown, and her curiously constructed work-
table. In the spring of this same year I was sent to a day-school in
Shrewsbury, where I stayed a year. I have been told that I was much
slower in learning than my younger sister Catherine, and I believe that
I was in many ways a naughty boy.

By the time I went to this day-school [1] my taste for natural history, and
more especially for collecting, was well developed. I tried to make out

1. Kept by Rev. G. Case, minister of the Unitarian Chapel in the High Street.
Mrs. Darwin was a Unitarian and attended Mr. Case's chapel, and my father
as a little boy went there with his elder sisters. But both he and his brother
were christened and intended to belong to the Church of England; and after
his early boyhood he seems usually to have gone to church and not to Mr.
Case's. It appears (*St. James' Gazette*, Dec. 15, 1883) that a mural tablet has
been erected to his memory in the chapel, which is now known as the "Free
Christian Church."—Sir Francis Darwin.

the names of plants,[2] and collected all sorts of things, shells, seals, franks, coins, and minerals. The passion for collecting, which leads a man to be a systematic naturalist, a virtuoso, or a miser, was very strong in me, and was clearly innate, as none of my sisters or brother ever had this taste.

One little event during this year has fixed itself very firmly in my mind, and I hope that it has done so from my conscience having been afterwards sorely troubled by it; it is curious as showing that apparently I was interested at this early age in the variability of plants! I told another little boy (I believe it was Leighton, who afterwards became a well-known lichenologist and botanist) that I could produce variously coloured polyanthuses and primroses by watering them with certain coloured fluids, which was of course a monstrous fable, and had never been tried by me. I may here also confess that as a little boy I was much given to inventing deliberate falsehoods, and this was always done for the sake of causing excitement. For instance, I once gathered much valuable fruit from my father's trees and hid it in the shrubbery, and then ran in breathless haste to spread the news that I had discovered a hoard of stolen fruit.

I must have been a very simple little fellow when I first went to the school. A boy of the name of Garnett took me into a cake-shop one day, and bought some cakes for which he did not pay, as the shopman trusted him. When we came out I asked him why he did not pay for them, and he instantly answered, "Why, do you not know that my uncle left a great sum of money to the town on condition that every tradesman should give whatever was wanted without payment to any one who wore his old hat and moved [it] in a particular manner?" and he then showed me how it was moved. He then went into another shop where he was trusted, and asked for some small article, moving his hat in the proper manner, and of course obtained it without payment. When we came out he said, "Now if you like to go by yourself into that cake-shop (how well I remember its exact position) I will lend you my hat, and you can get whatever you like if you move the hat on your head properly." I gladly accepted the generous offer, and went in and asked for some cakes, moved the old hat and was walking out of the shop, when the shopman made a rush at me, so I dropped the cakes and ran for dear life, and was astonished by being greeted with shouts of laughter by my false friend Garnett.

2. Rev. W. A. Leighton, who was a schoolfellow of my father's at Mr. Case's school, remembers his bringing a flower to school and saying that his mother had taught him by looking at the inside of the blossom the name of the plant could be discovered. Mr. Leighton goes on, "This greatly roused my attention and curiosity, and I inquired of him repeatedly how this could be done"— but his lesson was naturally enough not transmissible.—F. D.

I can say in my own favour that I was as a boy humane, but I owed this entirely to the instruction and example of my sisters. I doubt indeed whether humanity is a natural or innate quality. I was very fond of collecting eggs, but I never took more than a single egg out of a bird's nest, except on one single occasion, when I took all, not for their value, but from a sort of bravado.

I had a strong taste for angling, and would sit for any number of hours on the bank of a river or pond watching the float; when at Maer [3] I was told that I could kill the worms with salt and water, and from that day I never spitted a living worm, though at the expense probably of some loss of success.

Once as a very little boy while at the day-school, or before that time, I acted cruelly, for I beat a puppy, I believe, simply from enjoying the sense of power; but the beating could not have been severe, for the puppy did not howl, of which I feel sure, as the spot was near the house. This act lay heavily on my conscience, as is shown by my remembering the exact spot where the crime was committed. It probably lay all the heavier from my love of dogs being then, and for a long time afterwards, a passion. Dogs seemed to know this, for I was an adept in robbing their love from their masters.

I remember clearly only one other incident during this year while at Mr. Case's daily school, namely, the burial of a dragoon soldier; and it is surprising how clearly I can still see the horse with the man's empty boots and carbine suspended to the saddle, and the firing over the grave. This scene deeply stirred whatever poetic fancy there was in me.

In the summer of 1818 I went to Dr. Butler's great school in Shrewsbury, and remained there for seven years till midsummer 1825, when I was sixteen years old. I boarded at this school, so that I had the great advantage of living the life of a true schoolboy; but as the distance was hardly more than a mile to my home, I very often ran there in the longer intervals between the callings over and before locking up at night. This, I think, was in many ways advantageous to me by keeping up home affections and interests. I remember in the early part of my school-life that I often had to run very quickly to be in time, and from being a fleet runner was generally successful; but when in doubt I prayed earnestly to God to help me, and I well remember that I attributed my success to the prayers and not to my quick running, and marvelled how generally I was aided.

I have heard my father and elder sister say that I had, as a very young

3. The house of his uncle, Josiah Wedgwood.

boy, a strong taste for long solitary walks; but what I thought about I know not. I often became quite absorbed, and once, while returning to school on the summit of the old fortifications round Shrewsbury, which had been converted into a public foot-path with no parapet on one side, I walked off and fell to the ground, but the height was only seven or eight feet. Nevertheless the number of thoughts which passed through my mind during this very short, but sudden and wholly unexpected, fall was astonishing, and seems hardly compatible with what physiologists have, I believe, proved about each thought requiring quite an appreciable amount of time.

Nothing could have been worse for the development of my mind than Dr. Butler's school, as it was strictly classical, nothing else being taught, except a little ancient geography and history. The school as a means of education to me was simply a blank. During my whole life I have been singularly incapable of mastering any language. Especial attention was paid to verse-making, and this I could never do well. I had many friends, and got together a good collection of old verses, which by patching together, sometimes aided by other boys, I could work into any subject. Much attention was paid to learning by heart the lessons of the previous day; this I could effect with great facility, learning forty or fifty lines of Virgil or Homer, while I was in morning chapel; but this exercise was utterly useless, for every verse was forgotten in forty-eight hours. I was not idle, and, with the exception of versification, generally worked conscientiously at my classics, not using cribs. The sole pleasure I ever received from such studies was from some of the odes of Horace, which I admired greatly.

When I left the school I was for my age neither high nor low in it; and I believe that I was considered by all my masters and by my father as a very ordinary boy, rather below the common standard in intellect. To my deep mortification my father once said to me, "You care for nothing but shooting, dogs, and rat-catching, and you will be a disgrace to yourself and all your family." But my father, who was the kindest man I ever knew and whose memory I love with all my heart, must have been angry and somewhat unjust when he used such words.

Looking back as well as I can at my character during my school-life, the only qualities which at this period promised well for the future were, that I had strong and diversified tastes, much zeal for whatever interested me, and a keen pleasure in understanding any complex subject or thing. I was taught Euclid by a private tutor, and I distinctly remember the intense satisfaction which the clear geometrical proofs gave me. I re-

member, with equal distinctness, the delight which my uncle gave me (the father of Francis Galton) by explaining the principle of the vernier of a barometer. With respect to diversified tastes, independently of science, I was fond of reading various books, and I used to sit for hours reading the historical plays of Shakespeare, generally in an old window in the thick walls of the school. I read also other poetry, such as Thomson's *Seasons*, and the recently published poems by Byron and Scott. I mention this because later in life I wholly lost, to my great regret, all pleasure from poetry of any kind, including Shakespeare. In connection with pleasure from poetry, I may add that in 1822 a vivid delight in scenery was first awakened in my mind, during a riding tour on the borders of Wales, and this has lasted longer than any other aesthetic pleasure.

Early in my school-days a boy had a copy of the *Wonders of the World*, which I often read, and disputed with other boys about the veracity of some of the statements; and I believe that this book first gave me a wish to travel in remote countries, which was ultimately fulfilled by the voyage of the *Beagle*. In the latter part of my school-life I became passionately fond of shooting; I do not believe that any one could have shown more zeal for the most holy cause than I did for shooting birds. How well I remember killing my first snipe, and my excitement was so great that I had much difficulty in reloading my gun from the trembling of my hands. This taste long continued, and I became a very good shot. When at Cambridge I used to practise throwing up my gun to my shoulder before a looking-glass to see that I threw it up straight. Another and better plan was to get a friend to wave about a lighted candle, and then to fire at it with a cap on the nipple, and if the aim was accurate the little puff of air would blow out the candle. The explosion of the cap caused a sharp crack, and I was told that the tutor of the college remarked, "What an extraordinary thing it is, Mr. Darwin seems to spend hours in cracking a horsewhip in his room, for I often hear the crack when I pass under his windows."

I had many friends among the schoolboys, whom I loved dearly, and I think that my disposition was then very affectionate.

With respect to science, I continued collecting minerals with much zeal, but quite unscientifically—all that I cared about was a new-*named* mineral, and I hardly attempted to classify them. I must have observed insects with some little care, for when ten years old (1819) I went for three weeks to Plas Edwards on the sea-coast in Wales, I was very much interested and surprised at seeing a large black and scarlet Hemipterous

insect, many moths (Zygaena), and a Cicindela, which are not found in Shropshire. I almost made up my mind to begin collecting all the insects which I could find dead, for on consulting my sister I concluded that it was not right to kill insects for the sake of making a collection. From reading White's *Selborne,* I took much pleasure in watching the habits of birds, and even made notes on the subject. In my simplicity I remember wondering why every gentleman did not become an ornithologist.

Towards the close of my school-life, my brother worked hard at chemistry, and made a fair laboratory with proper apparatus in the tool-house in the garden, and I was allowed to aid him as a servant in most of his experiments. He made all the gases and many compounds, and I read with great care several books on chemistry, such as Henry and Parkes's *Chemical Catechism.* The subject interested me greatly, and we often used to go on working till rather late at night. This was the best part of my education at school, for it showed me practically the meaning of experimental science. The fact that we worked at chemistry somehow got known at school, and as it was an unprecedented fact, I was nicknamed "Gas." I was also once publicly rebuked by the head master, Dr. Butler, for thus wasting my time on such useless subjects; and he called me very unjustly a *poco curante* [little concerned], and as I did not understand what he meant, it seemed to me a fearful reproach.

As I was doing no good at school, my father wisely took me away at a rather earlier age than usual, and sent me (October, 1825) to Edinburgh University with my brother, where I stayed for two years or sessions. My brother was completing his medical studies, though I do not believe he ever really intended to practise, and I was sent there to commence them. But soon after this period I became convinced from various small circumstances that my father would leave me property enough to subsist on with some comfort, though I never imagined that I should be so rich a man as I am; but my belief was sufficient to check any strenuous efforts to learn medicine.

The instruction at Edinburgh was altogether by lectures, and these were intolerably dull, with the exception of those on chemistry by Hope; but to my mind there are no advantages and many disadvantages in lectures compared with reading. Dr. Duncan's lectures on *materia medica* at 8 o'clock on a winter's morning are something fearful to remember. Dr. Munro made his lectures on human anatomy as dull as he was himself, and the subject disgusted me. It has proved one of the greatest evils in my life that I was not urged to practise dissection, for I should soon have got over my disgust; and the practice would have been invaluable

for all my future work. This has been an irremediable evil, as well as my incapacity to draw. I also attended regularly the clinical wards in the hospital. Some of the cases distressed me a good deal, and I still have vivid pictures before me of some of them; but I was not so foolish as to allow this to lessen my attendance. I cannot understand why this part of my medical course did not interest me in a greater degree; for during the summer before coming to Edinburgh I began attending some of the poor people, chiefly children and women in Shrewsbury: I wrote down as full an account as I could of the case with all the symptoms, and read them aloud to my father, who suggested further inquiries and advised me what medicines to give, which I made up myself. At one time I had at least a dozen patients, and I felt a keen interest in the work. My father, who was by far the best judge of character whom I ever knew, declared that I should make a successful physician, meaning by this one who would get many patients. He maintained that the chief element of success was exciting confidence; but what he saw in me which convinced him that I should create confidence I know not. I also attended on two occasions the operating theatre in the hospital at Edinburgh, and saw two very bad operations, one on a child, but I rushed away before they were completed. Nor did I ever attend again, for hardly any inducement would have been strong enough to make me do so, this being long before the blessed days of chloroform. The two cases fairly haunted me for many a long year.

My brother stayed only one year at the University, so that during the second year I was left to my own resources; and this was an advantage, for I became well acquainted with several young men fond of natural science. One of these was Ainsworth, who afterwards published his travels in Assyria; he was a Wernerian geologist, and knew a little about many subjects. Dr. Coldstream was a very different young man, prim, formal, highly religious, and most kindhearted; he afterwards published some good zoological articles. A third young man was Hardie, who would, I think, have made a good botanist, but died early in India. Lastly, Dr. Grant, my senior by several years, but how I became acquainted with him I cannot remember; he published some first-rate zoological papers, but after coming to London as professor in University College, he did nothing more in science, a fact which has always been inexplicable to me. I knew him well; he was dry and formal in manner, with much enthusiasm beneath this outer crust. He one day, when we were walking together, burst forth in high admiration of Lamarck and his views on evolution. I listened in silent astonishment, and as far as I can judge without

any effect on my mind. I had previously read the *Zoonomia* of my grand-father, in which similar views are maintained, but without producing any effect on me. Nevertheless it is probable that the hearing rather early in life such views maintained and praised may have favoured my upholding them under a different form in my *Origin of Species*. At this time I admired greatly the *Zoonomia;* but on reading it a second time after an interval of ten or fifteen years, I was much disappointed, the proportion of speculation being so large to the facts given.

Drs. Grant and Coldstream attended much to marine zoology, and I often accompanied the former to collect animals in the tidal pools, which I dissected as well as I could. I also became friends with some of the Newhaven fishermen, and sometimes accompanied them when they trawled for oysters, and thus got many specimens. But from not having had any regular practice in dissection, and from possessing only a wretched microscope, my attempts were very poor. Nevertheless I made one interesting little discovery, and read, about the beginning of the year 1826, a short paper on the subject before the Plinian Society. This was that the so-called ova of Flustra had the power of independent movement by means of cilia, and were in fact larvae. In another short paper I showed that the little globular bodies which had been supposed to be the young state of *Fucus loreus* were the egg-cases of the wormlike *Pontobdella muricata*.

The Plinian Society was encouraged and, I believe, founded by Professor Jameson: it consisted of students and met in an underground room in the University for the sake of reading papers on natural science and discussing them. I used regularly to attend, and the meeting had a good effect on me in stimulating my zeal and giving me new congenial acquaintances. One evening a poor young man got up, and after stammering for a prodigious length of time, blushing crimson, he at last slowly got out the words, "Mr. President, I have forgotten what I was going to say." The poor fellow looked quite overwhelmed, and all the members were so surprised that no one could think of a word to say to cover his confusion. The papers which were read to our little society were not printed, so that I had not the satisfaction of seeing my paper in print; but I believe Dr. Grant noticed my small discovery in his excellent memoir on Flustra.

I was also a member of the Royal Medical Society, and attended pretty regularly; but as the subjects were exclusively medical, I did not much care about them. Much rubbish was talked there, but there were some

good speakers, of whom the best was the present Sir J. Kay-Shuttleworth. Dr. Grant took me occasionally to the meetings of the Wernerian Society, where various papers on natural history were read, discussed, and afterwards published in the *Transactions*. I heard Audubon deliver there some interesting discourses on the habits of North American birds, sneering somewhat unjustly at Waterton. By the way, a Negro lived in Edinburgh who had travelled with Waterton, and gained his livelihood by stuffing birds, which he did excellently; he gave me lessons for payment, and I used often to sit with him, for he was a very pleasant and intelligent man.

Mr. Leonard Horner also took me once to a meeting of the Royal Society of Edinburgh, where I saw Sir Walter Scott in the chair as president, and he apologized to the meeting as not feeling fitted for such a position. I looked at him and at the whole scene with some awe and reverence, and I think it was owing to this visit during my youth, and to my having attended the Royal Medical Society, that I felt the honour of being elected a few years ago an honorary member of both these societies more than any other similar honour. If I had been told at that time that I should one day have been thus honoured, I declare that I should have thought it as ridiculous and improbable as if I had been told that I should be elected king of England.

During my second year at Edinburgh I attended Jameson's lectures on geology and zoology, but they were incredibly dull. The sole effect they produced on me was the determination never as long as I lived to read a book on geology, or in any way to study the science. Yet I feel sure that I was prepared for a philosophical treatment of the subject; for an old Mr. Cotton in Shropshire, who knew a good deal about rocks, had pointed out to me two or three years previously a well-known large erratic boulder in the town of Shrewsbury, called the "bell-stone"; he told me that there was no rock of the same kind nearer than Cumberland or Scotland, and he solemnly assured me that the world would come to an end before any one would be able to explain how this stone came where it now lay. This produced a deep impression on me, and I meditated over this wonderful stone. So I felt the keenest delight when I first read of the action of icebergs in transporting boulders, and I gloried in the progress of geology. Equally striking is the fact that I, though now only sixty-seven years old, heard the professor, in a field lecture at Salisbury Craigs, discoursing on a trap-dike, with amygdaloidal margins and the strata indurated on each side, with volcanic rocks all around us, say that it was a fissure filled with sediment from above, adding with a sneer that

there were men who maintained that it had been injected from beneath in a molten condition. When I think of this lecture, I do not wonder that I determined never to attend to geology.

From attending Jameson's lectures, I became acquainted with the curator of the museum, Mr. Macgillivray, who afterwards published a large and excellent book on the birds of Scotland. I had much interesting natural-history talk with him, and he was very kind to me. He gave me some rare shells, for I at that time collected marine mollusca, but with no great zeal.

My summer vacations during these two years were wholly given up to amusements, though I always had some book in hand, which I read with interest. During the summer of 1826 I took a long walking tour with two friends with knapsacks on our backs through North Wales. We walked thirty miles most days, including one day the ascent of Snowdon. I also went with my sister on a riding tour in North Wales, a servant with saddle-bags carrying our clothes. The autumns were devoted to shooting chiefly at Mr. Owens', at Woodhouse, and at my Uncle Jos's,[4] at Maer. My zeal was so great that I used to place my shooting-boots open by my bed-side when I went to bed, so as not to lose half a minute in putting them on in the morning; and on one occasion I reached a distant part of the Maer estate, on the 20th of August for black-game shooting, before I could see: I then toiled on with the gamekeeper the whole day through thick heath and young Scotch firs.

I kept an exact record of every bird which I shot throughout the whole season. One day when shooting at Woodhouse with Captain Owen, the eldest son, and Major Hill, his cousin, afterwards Lord Berwick, both of whom I liked very much, I thought myself shamefully used, for every time after I had fired and thought that I had killed a bird, one of the two acted as if loading his gun, and cried out, "You must not count that bird, for I fired at the same time," and the gamekeeper, perceiving the joke, backed them up. After some hours they told me the joke, but it was no joke to me, for I had shot a large number of birds, but did not know how many, and could not add them to my list, which I used to do by making a knot in a piece of string tied to a button-hole. This my wicked friends had perceived.

How I did enjoy shooting! but I think that I must have been half-consciously ashamed of my zeal, for I tried to persuade myself that shooting was almost an intellectual employment: it required so much skill to judge where to find most game and to hunt the dogs well.

4. Josiah Wedgwood, the son of the founder of the Etruria Works.

One of my autumnal visits to Maer in 1827 was memorable from meeting there Sir J. Mackintosh, who was the best converser I ever listened to. I heard afterwards with a glow of pride that he had said, "There is something in that young man that interests me." This must have been chiefly due to his perceiving that I listened with much interest to everything which he said, for I was as ignorant as a pig about his subjects of history, politics, and moral philosophy. To hear of praise from an eminent person, though no doubt apt or certain to excite vanity, is, I think, good for a young man, as it helps to keep him in the right course.

My visits to Maer during these two or three succeeding years were quite delightful, independently of the autumnal shooting. Life there was perfectly free; the country was very pleasant for walking or riding; and in the evening there was much very agreeable conversation, not so personal as it generally is in large family parties, together with music. In the summer the whole family used often to sit on the steps of the old portico, with the flower-garden in front, and with the steep wooded bank opposite the house reflected in the lake, with here and there a fish rising or a waterbird paddling about. Nothing has left a more vivid picture on my mind than these evenings at Maer. I was also attached to and greatly revered my Uncle Jos; he was silent and reserved, so as to be a rather awful man; but he sometimes talked openly with me. He was the very type of an upright man, with the clearest judgment. I do not believe that any power on earth could have made him swerve an inch from what he considered the right course. I used to apply to him in my mind the well-known ode of Horace, now forgotten by me, in which the words *nec vultus tyranni* [nor the frown of the tyrant], etc.,[5] come in.

Cambridge 1828–1831. After having spent two sessions in Edinburgh, my father perceived, or he heard from my sisters, that I did not like the thought of being a physician, so he proposed that I should become a clergyman. He was very properly vehement against my turning into an idle sporting man, which then seemed my probable destination. I asked for some time to consider, as from what little I had heard or thought on the subject I had scruples about declaring my belief in all the dogmas of

5. Justum et tenacem propositi virum
 Non civium ardor prava jubentium
 Non vultus instantis tyranni
 Mente quatit solida.

 [A just man and steadfast in his purpose is not shaken in his strong resolve by the wicked ardour of the mob's command or the menacing tyrant's frown.—Horace, *Odes*.]

the Church of England; though otherwise I liked the thought of being a country clergyman. Accordingly I read with care Pearson on the *Creed*, and a few other books on divinity; and as I did not then in the least doubt the strict and literal truth of every word in the Bible, I soon persuaded myself that our Creed must be fully accepted.

Considering how fiercely I have been attacked by the orthodox, it seems ludicrous that I once intended to be a clergyman. Nor was this intention and my father's wish ever formally given up, but died a natural death when, on leaving Cambridge, I joined the *Beagle* as naturalist. If the phrenologists are to be trusted, I was well fitted in one respect to be a clergyman. A few years ago the secretaries of a German psychological society asked me earnestly by letter for a photograph of myself; and some time afterwards I received the proceedings of one of the meetings, in which it seemed that the shape of my head had been the subject of a public discussion, and one of the speakers declared that I had the bump of reverence developed enough for ten priests.

As it was decided that I should be a clergyman, it was necessary that I should go to one of the English universities and take a degree; but as I had never opened a classical book since leaving school, I found to my dismay that in the two intervening years I had actually forgotten, incredible as it may appear, almost everything which I had learned, even to some few of the Greek letters. I did not therefore proceed to Cambridge at the usual time in October, but worked with a private tutor in Shrewsbury, and went to Cambridge after the Christmas vacation, early in 1828. I soon recovered my school standard of knowledge, and could translate easy Greek books, such as Homer and the Greek Testament, with moderate facility.

During the three years which I spent at Cambridge my time was wasted, as far as the academical studies were concerned, as completely as at Edinburgh and at school. I attempted mathematics, and even went during the summer of 1828 with a private tutor (a very dull man) to Barmouth, but I got on very slowly. The work was repugnant to me, chiefly from my not being able to see any meaning in the early steps in algebra. This impatience was very foolish, and in after years I have deeply regretted that I did not proceed far enough at least to understand something of the great leading principles of mathematics, for men thus endowed seem to have an extra sense. But I do not believe that I should ever have succeeded beyond a very low grade. With respect to classics I did nothing except attend a few compulsory college lectures, and the attendance was almost nominal. In my second year I had to work for a

month or two to pass the little-go,[6] which I did easily. Again, in my last year I worked with some earnestness for my final degree of B.A., and brushed up my classics, together with a little algebra and Euclid, which latter gave me much pleasure, as it did at school. In order to pass the B.A. examination, it was also necessary to get up Paley's *Evidences of Christianity*, and his *Moral Philosophy*. This was done in a thorough manner, and I am convinced that I could have written out the whole of the *Evidences* with perfect correctness, but not of course in the clear language of Paley. The logic of this book and, as I may add, of his *Natural Theology* gave me as much delight as did Euclid. The careful study of these works, without attempting to learn any part by rote, was the only part of the academical course which, as I then felt and as I still believe, was of the least use to me in the education of my mind. I did not at that time trouble myself about Paley's premises; and taking these on trust, I was charmed and convinced by the long line of argumentation. By answering well the examination questions in Paley, by doing Euclid well, and by not failing miserably in classics, I gained a good place among the hoi polloi or crowd of men who do not go in for honours. Oddly enough, I cannot remember how high I stood, and my memory fluctuates between the fifth, tenth, or twelfth name on the list.[7]

Public lectures on several branches were given in the University, attendance being quite voluntary; but I was so sickened with lectures at Edinburgh that I did not even attend Sedgwick's eloquent and interesting lectures. Had I done so I should probably have become a geologist earlier than I did. I attended, however, Henslow's lectures on botany, and liked them much for their extreme clearness, and the admirable illustrations; but I did not study botany. Henslow used to take his pupils, including several of the older members of the University, on field excursions, on foot or in coaches, to distant places, or in a barge down the river, and lectured on the rarer plants and animals which were observed. These excursions were delightful.

Although, as we shall presently see, there were some redeeming features in my life at Cambridge, my time was sadly wasted there, and worse than wasted. From my passion for shooting and for hunting, and, when this failed, for riding across country, I got into a sporting set, including some dissipated low-minded young men. We used often to dine together in the evening, though these dinners often included men of a higher

6. The popular name, then in use, for the first examination for the B.A. degree.
7. Tenth in the list of January, 1831.

stamp, and we sometimes drank too much, with jolly singing and playing at cards afterwards. I know that I ought to feel ashamed of days and evenings thus spent, but as some of my friends were very pleasant, and we were all in the highest spirits, I cannot help looking back to these times with much pleasure.

But I am glad to think that I had many other friends of a widely different nature. I was very intimate with Whitley,[8] who was afterwards senior wrangler, and we used continually to take long walks together. He inoculated me with a taste for pictures and good engravings, of which I bought some. I frequently went to the Fitzwilliam Gallery, and my taste must have been fairly good, for I certainly admired the best pictures, which I discussed with the old curator. I read also with much interest Sir Joshua Reynolds' book. This taste, though not natural to me, lasted for several years, and many of the pictures in the National Gallery in London gave me much pleasure, that of Sebastiano del Piombo exciting in me a sense of sublimity.

I also got into a musical set, I believe by means of my warm-hearted friend Herbert,[9] who took a high wrangler's degree. From associating with these men, and hearing them play, I acquired a strong taste for music, and used very often to time my walks so as to hear on weekdays the anthem in King's College Chapel. This gave me intense pleasure, so that my backbone would sometimes shiver. I am sure that there was no affectation or mere imitation in this taste, for I used generally to go by myself to King's College, and I sometimes hired the chorister boys to sing in my rooms. Nevertheless I am so utterly destitute of an ear that I cannot perceive a discord, or keep time and hum a tune correctly; and it is a mystery how I could possibly have derived pleasure from music.

My musical friends soon perceived my state, and sometimes amused themselves by making me pass an examination which consisted in ascertaining how many tunes I could recognize when they were played rather more quickly or slowly than usual. "God Save the King," when thus played, was a sore puzzle. There was another man with almost as bad an ear as I had, and strange to say he played a little on the flute. Once I had the triumph of beating him in one of our musical examinations.

But no pursuit at Cambridge was followed with nearly so much earnestness or gave me so much pleasure as collecting beetles. It was the

8. Rev. C. Whitley, Hon. Canon of Durham, formerly Reader in Natural Philosophy in Durham University.
9. The late John Maurice Herbert, County Court Judge of Cardiff and the Monmouth Circuit.

mere passion for collecting, for I did not dissect them, and rarely compared their external characters with published descriptions, but got them named anyhow. I will give a proof of my zeal: one day, on tearing off some old bark, I saw two rare beetles, and seized one in each hand; then I saw a third and new kind, which I could not bear to lose, so that I popped the one which I held in my right hand into my mouth. Alas! it ejected some intensely acrid fluid, which burnt my tongue so that I was forced to spit the beetle out, which was lost, as was the third one.

I was very successful in collecting, and invented two new methods: I employed a labourer to scrape, during the winter, moss off old trees and place it in a large bag, and likewise to collect the rubbish at the bottom of the barges in which reeds are brought from the fens, and thus I got some very rare species. No poet ever felt more delighted at seeing his first poem published than I did at seeing, in Stephens' *Illustrations of British Insects*, the magic words, "captured by C. Darwin, Esq." I was introduced to entomology by my second cousin, W. Darwin Fox, a clever and most pleasant man, who was then at Christ's College, and with whom I became extremely intimate. Afterwards I became well acquainted, and went out collecting, with Albert Way of Trinity, who in after years became a well-known archaeologist; also with H. Thompson of the same college, afterwards a leading agriculturist, chairman of a great railway, and member of Parliament. It seems therefore that a taste for collecting beetles is some indication of future success in life!

I am surprised what an indelible impression many of the beetles which I caught at Cambridge have left on my mind. I can remember the exact appearance of certain posts, old trees and banks where I made a good capture. The pretty *Panagaeus crux-major* was a treasure in those days, and here at Down I saw a beetle running across a walk, and on picking it up instantly perceived that it differed slightly from *P. crux-major*, and it turned out to be *P. quadripunctatus*, which is only a variety or closely allied species, differing from it very slightly in outline. I had never seen in those old days Licinus alive, which to an uneducated eye hardly differs from many of the black Carabidous beetles; but my sons found here a specimen, and I instantly recognized that it was new to me; yet I had not looked at a British beetle for the last twenty years.

I have not as yet mentioned a circumstance which influenced my whole career more than any other. This was my friendship with Professor Henslow. Before coming up to Cambridge, I had heard of him from my brother as a man who knew every branch of science, and I was accordingly pre-

pared to reverence him. He kept open house once every week, when all undergraduates, and some older members of the university, who were attached to science used to meet in the evening. I soon got, through Fox, an invitation, and went there regularly. Before long I became well acquainted with Henslow, and during the latter half of my time at Cambridge took long walks with him on most days, so that I was called by some of the dons "the man who walks with Henslow"; and in the evening I was very often asked to join his family dinner. His knowledge was great in botany, entomology, chemistry, mineralogy, and geology. His strongest taste was to draw conclusions from long-continued minute observations. His judgment was excellent, and his whole mind well balanced; but I do not suppose that any one would say that he possessed much original genius. He was deeply religious, and so orthodox that he told me one day he should be grieved if a single word of the Thirty-nine Articles were altered. His moral qualities were in every way admirable. He was free from every tinge of vanity or other petty feeling; and I never saw a man who thought so little about himself or of his own concerns. His temper was imperturbably good, with the most winning and courteous manners; yet, as I have seen, he could be roused by any bad action to the warmest indignation and prompt action.

I once saw in his company in the streets of Cambridge almost as horrid a scene as could have been witnessed during the French Revolution. Two body-snatchers had been arrested, and while being taken to prison had been torn from the constable by a crowd of the roughest men, who dragged them by their legs along the muddy and stony road. They were covered from head to foot with mud, and their faces were bleeding either from having been kicked or from the stones; they looked like corpses, but the crowd was so dense that I got only a few momentary glimpses of the wretched creatures. Never in my life have I seen such wrath painted on a man's face as was shown by Henslow at this horrid scene. He tried repeatedly to penetrate the mob; but it was simply impossible. He then rushed away to the mayor, telling me not to follow him but to get more policemen. I forget the issue, except that the two men were got into the prison without being killed.

Henslow's benevolence was unbounded, as he proved by his many excellent schemes for his poor parishioners when in after years he held the living of Hitcham. My intimacy with such a man ought to have been, and I hope was, an inestimable benefit. I cannot resist mentioning a trifling incident which showed his kind consideration. While examining some pollen-grains on a damp surface, I saw the tubes exserted, and instantly

rushed off to communicate my surprising discovery to him. Now I do not suppose any other professor of botany could have helped laughing at my coming in such a hurry to make such a communication. But he agreed how interesting the phenomenon was, and explained its meaning, but made me clearly understand how well it was known; so I left him not in the least mortified, but well pleased at having discovered for myself so remarkable a fact, but determined not to be in such a hurry again to communicate my discoveries.

Dr. Whewell was one of the older and distinguished men who sometimes visited Henslow, and on several occasions I walked home with him at night. Next to Sir J. Mackintosh he was the best converser on grave subjects to whom I ever listened. Leonard Jenyns,[10] who afterwards published some good essays in natural history,[11] often stayed with Henslow, who was his brother-in-law. I visited him at his parsonage on the borders of the Fens [Swaffham Bulbeck] and had many a good walk and talk with him about natural history. I became also acquainted with several other men older than me, who did not care much about science, but were friends of Henslow. One was a Scotchman, brother of Sir Alexander Ramsay, and tutor of Jesus College; he was a delightful man, but did not live for many years. Another was Dr. Dawes, afterwards Dean of Hereford, and famous for his success in the education of the poor. These men and others of the same standing, together with Henslow, used sometimes to take distant excursions into the country, which I was allowed to join, and they were most agreeable.

Looking back, I infer that there must have been something in me a little superior to the common run of youths, otherwise the above-mentioned men, so much older than me and higher in academical position, would never have allowed me to associate with them. Certainly I was not aware of any such superiority, and I remember one of my sporting friends, Turner, who saw me at work with my beetles, saying that I should some day be a fellow of the Royal Society, and the notion seemed to me preposterous.

During my last year at Cambridge, I read with care and profound interest Humboldt's *Personal Narrative*. This work, and Sir J. Herschel's *Introduction to the Study of Natural Philosophy*, stirred up in me a burning zeal to add even the most humble contribution to the noble structure of natural science. No one or a dozen other books influenced me nearly so

10. The well-known Soame Jenyns was cousin to Mr. Jenyns' father.
11. Mr. Jenyns (now Blomefield) described the fish for the zoology of the *Beagle;* and is author of a long series of papers, chiefly zoological.

much as these two. I copied out from Humboldt long passages about Tenerife, and read them aloud on one of the above-mentioned excursions to (I think) Henslow, Ramsay, and Dawes, for on a previous occasion I had talked about the glories of Tenerife, and some of the party declared they would endeavour to go there; but I think that they were only half in earnest. I was, however, quite in earnest, and got an introduction to a merchant in London to inquire about ships; but the scheme was, of course, knocked on the head by the voyage of the *Beagle*.

My summer vacations were given up to collecting beetles, to some reading, and short tours. In the autumn my whole time was devoted to shooting, chiefly at Woodhouse and Maer, and sometimes with young Eyton of Eyton. Upon the whole the three years which I spent at Cambridge were the most joyful in my happy life; for I was then in excellent health, and almost always in high spirits.

As I had at first come up to Cambridge at Christmas, I was forced to keep two terms after passing my final examination, at the commencement of 1831; and Henslow then persuaded me to begin the study of geology. Therefore on my return to Shropshire I examined sections, and coloured a map of parts round Shrewsbury. Professor Sedgwick intended to visit North Wales in the beginning of August to pursue his famous geological investigations among the older rocks, and Henslow asked him to allow me to accompany him.[12] Accordingly he came and slept at my father's house.

A short conversation with him during this evening produced a strong impression on my mind. While examining an old gravel-pit near Shrewsbury, a labourer told me that he had found in it a large worn tropical volute shell, such as may be seen on the chimney-pieces of cottages; and as he would not sell the shell, I was convinced that he had really found it in the pit. I told Sedgwick of the fact, and he at once said (no doubt truly) that it must have been thrown away by some one into the pit; but then added, if really embedded there it would be the greatest misfortune to geology, as it would overthrow all that we know about the superficial deposits of the Midland counties. These gravel-beds belong in fact to the Glacial period, and in after years I found in them broken arctic shells.

12. In connection with this tour my father used to tell a story about Sedgwick: They had started from their inn one morning, and had walked a mile or two, when Sedgwick suddenly stopped, and vowed that he would return, being certain "that damned scoundrel" (the waiter) had not given the chambermaid the sixpence entrusted to him for the purpose. He was ultimately persuaded to give up the project, seeing that there was no reason for suspecting the waiter of especial perfidy.—F. D.

But I was then utterly astonished at Sedgwick not being delighted at so wonderful a fact as a tropical shell being found near the surface in the middle of England. Nothing before had ever made me thoroughly realize, though I had read various scientific books, that science consists in grouping facts so that general laws or conclusions may be drawn from them.

Next morning we started for Llangollen, Conway, Bangor, and Capel Curig. This tour was of decided use in teaching me a little how to make out the geology of a country. Sedgwick often sent me on a line parallel to his, telling me to bring back specimen of the rocks and to mark the stratification on a map. I have little doubt that he did this for my good, as I was too ignorant to have aided him. On this tour I had a striking instance of how easy it is to overlook phenomena, however conspicuous, before they have been observed by any one. We spent many hours in Cwm Idwal, examining all the rocks with extreme care, as Sedgwick was anxious to find fossils in them; but neither of us saw a trace of the wonderful glacial phenomena all around us: we did not notice the plainly scored rocks, the perched boulders, the lateral and terminal moraines. Yet these phenomena are so conspicuous that, as I declared in a paper published many years afterwards in the *Philosophical Magazine*, a house burnt down by fire did not tell its story more plainly than did this valley. If it had still been filled by a glacier, the phenomena would have been less distinct than they now are.

At Capel Curig I left Sedgwick and went in a straight line by compass and map across the mountains to Barmouth, never following any track unless it coincided with my course. I thus came on some strange wild places, and enjoyed much this manner of travelling. I visited Barmouth to see some Cambridge friends who were reading there, and thence returned to Shrewsbury and to Maer for shooting; for at that time I should have thought myself mad to give up the first days of partridge-shooting for geology or any other science.

VOYAGE OF THE "BEAGLE"
FROM DECEMBER 27, 1831, TO OCTOBER 2, 1836

On returning home from my short geological tour in North Wales, I found a letter from Henslow, informing me that Captain Fitz-Roy was willing to give up part of his own cabin to any young man who would volunteer to go with him without pay as naturalist to the voyage of the *Beagle*. I have given, as I believe, in my MS. Journal an account of all the circumstances which then occurred; I will here only say that I was

instantly eager to accept the offer, but my father strongly objected, add-
ing the words, fortunate for me, "If you can find any man of common
sense who advises you to go I will give my consent." So I wrote that eve-
ning and refused the offer. On the next morning I went to Maer to be
ready for September 1, and, while out shooting, my uncle [13] sent for me,
offering to drive me over to Shrewsbury and talk with my father, as my
uncle thought it would be wise in me to accept the offer. My father al-
ways maintained that he was one of the most sensible men in the world,
and he at once consented in the kindest manner. I had been rather ex-
travagant at Cambridge, and to console my father, said, "that I should
be deuced clever to spend more than my allowance while on board the
Beagle"; but he answered with a smile, "But they tell me you are very
clever."

Next day I started for Cambridge to see Henslow, and thence to Lon-
don to see Fitz-Roy, and all was soon arranged. Afterwards, on becoming
very intimate with Fitz-Roy, I heard that I had run a very narrow risk
of being rejected, on account of the shape of my nose! He was an ardent
disciple of Lavater, and was convinced that he could judge of a man's
character by the outline of his features; and he doubted whether any one
with my nose could possess sufficient energy and determination for the
voyage. But I think he was afterwards well satisfied that my nose had
spoken falsely.

Fitz-Roy's character was a singular one, with very many noble fea-
tures: he was devoted to his duty, generous to a fault, bold, determined,
and indomitably energetic, and an ardent friend to all under his sway.
He would undertake any sort of trouble to assist those whom he thought
deserved assistance. He was a handsome man, strikingly like a gentleman,
with highly courteous manners, which resembled those of his maternal
uncle, the famous Lord Castlereagh, as I was told by the minister at Rio.
Nevertheless he must have inherited much in his appearance from
Charles II, for Dr. Wallich gave me a collection of photographs which
he had made, and I was struck with the resemblance of one to Fitz-Roy;
and on looking at the name, I found it Ch. E. Sobieski Stuart, Count
d'Albanie, a descendant of the same monarch.

Fitz-Roy's temper was a most unfortunate one. It was usually worst in
the early morning, and with his eagle eye he could generally detect some-
thing amiss about the ship, and was then unsparing in his blame. He was
very kind to me, but was a man very difficult to live with on the intimate
terms which necessarily followed from our messing by ourselves in the
same cabin. We had several quarrels; for instance, early in the voyage

13. Josiah Wedgwood.

at Bahia, in Brazil, he defended and praised slavery, which I abominated, and told me that he had just visited a great slave-owner, who had called up many of his slaves and asked them whether they were happy, and whether they wished to be free, and all answered "No." I then asked him, perhaps with a sneer, whether he thought that the answer of slaves in the presence of their master was worth anything. This made him excessively angry, and he said that as I doubted his word we could not live any longer together. I thought that I should have been compelled to leave the ship; but as soon as the news spread, which it did quickly, as the captain sent for the first lieutenant to assuage his anger by abusing me, I was deeply gratified by receiving an invitation from all the gun-room officers to mess with them. But after a few hours Fitz-Roy showed his actual magnanimity by sending an officer to me with an apology and a request that I would continue to live with him.

His character was in several respects one of the most noble which I have ever known.

The voyage of the *Beagle* has been by far the most important event in my life, and has determined my whole career; yet it depended on so small a circumstance as my uncle offering to drive me thirty miles to Shrewsbury, which few uncles would have done, and on such a trifle as the shape of my nose. I have always felt that I owe to the voyage the first real training or education of my mind; I was led to attend closely to several branches of natural history, and thus my powers of observation were improved, though they were always fairly developed.

The investigation of the geology of all the places visited was far more important, as reasoning here comes into play. On first examining a new district nothing can appear more hopeless than the chaos of rocks; but by recording the stratification and nature of the rocks and fossils at many points, always reasoning and predicting what will be found elsewhere, light soon begins to dawn on the district, and the structure of the whole becomes more or less intelligible. I had brought with me the first volume of Lyell's *Principles of Geology*, which I studied attentively; and the book was of the highest service to me in many ways. The very first place which I examined, namely St. Jago in the Cape de Verde Islands, showed me clearly the wonderful superiority of Lyell's manner of treating geology, compared with that of any other author whose works I had with me or ever afterwards read.

Another of my occupations was collecting animals of all classes, briefly describing and roughly dissecting many of the marine ones; but from not being able to draw, and from not having sufficient anatomical knowledge, a great pile of MS. which I made during the voyage has proved almost

useless. I thus lost much time, with the exception of that spent in acquiring some knowledge of the crustaceans, as this was of service when in after years I undertook a monograph of the Cirripedia.

During some part of the day I wrote my Journal, and took much pains in describing carefully and vividly all that I had seen; and this was good practice. My Journal served also, in part, as letters to my home, and portions were sent to England whenever there was an opportunity.

The above various special studies were, however, of no importance compared with the habit of energetic industry and of concentrated attention to whatever I was engaged in, which I then acquired. Everything about which I thought or read was made to bear directly on what I had seen or was likely to see; and this habit of mind was continued during the five years of the voyage. I feel sure that it was this training which has enabled me to do whatever I have done in science.

Looking backwards, I can now perceive how my love for science gradually preponderated over every other taste. During the first two years my old passion for shooting survived in nearly full force, and I shot myself all the birds and animals for my collection; but gradually I gave up my gun more and more, and finally altogether, to my servant, as shooting interfered with my work, more especially with making out the geological structure of a country. I discovered, though unconsciously and insensibly, that the pleasure of observing and reasoning was a much higher one than that of skill and sport. That my mind became developed through my pursuits during the voyage is rendered probable by a remark made by my father, who was the most acute observer whom I ever saw, of a sceptical disposition, and far from being a believer in phrenology; for on first seeing me after the voyage, he turned round to my sisters, and exclaimed, "Why, the shape of his head is quite altered."

To return to the voyage. On September 11 (1831), I paid a flying visit with Fitz-Roy to the *Beagle* at Plymouth. Thence to Shrewsbury to wish my father and sisters a long farewell. On October 24 I took up my residence at Plymouth, and remained there until December 27, when the *Beagle* finally left the shores of England for her circumnavigation of the world. We made two earlier attempts to sail, but were driven back each time by heavy gales. These two months at Plymouth were the most miserable which I ever spent, though I exerted myself in various ways. I was out of spirits at the thought of leaving all my family and friends for so long a time, and the weather seemed to me inexpressibly gloomy. I was also troubled with palpitation and pain about the heart, and like many a young ignorant man, especially one with a smattering of medical knowledge, was convinced that I had heart disease. I did not consult any doc-

tor, as I fully expected to hear the verdict that I was not fit for the voyage, and I was resolved to go at all hazards.

I need not here refer to the events of the voyage—where we went and what we did—as I have given a sufficiently full account in my published Journal. The glories of the vegetation of the Tropics rise before my mind at the present time more vividly than anything else, though the sense of sublimity, which the great deserts of Patagonia and the forest-clad mountains of Tierra del Fuego excited in me, has left an indelible impression on my mind. The sight of a naked savage in his native land is an event which can never be forgotten. Many of my excursions on horse-back through wild countries, or in the boats, some of which lasted several weeks, were deeply interesting; their discomfort and some degree of danger were at that time hardly a drawback, and none at all afterwards. I also reflect with high satisfaction on some of my scientific work, such as solving the problem of coral islands, and making out the geological structure of certain islands, for instance, St. Helena. Nor must I pass over the discovery of the singular relations of the animals and plants inhabiting the several islands of the Galapagos Archipelago, and of all of them to the inhabitants of South America.

As far as I can judge of myself, I worked to the utmost during the voyage from the mere pleasure of investigation, and from my strong desire to add a few facts to the great mass of facts in natural science. But I was also ambitious to take a fair place among scientific men—whether more ambitious or less so than most of my fellow-workers, I can form no opinion.

The geology of St. Jago is very striking, yet simple: a stream of lava formerly flowed over the bed of the sea, formed of triturated recent shells and corals, which it has baked into a hard white rock. Since then the whole island has been upheaved. But the line of white rock revealed to me a new and important fact, namely, that there had been afterwards subsidence round the craters, which had since been in action, and had poured forth lava. It then first dawned on me that I might perhaps write a book on the geology of the various countries visited, and this made me thrill with delight. That was a memorable hour to me, and how distinctly I can call to mind the low cliff of lava beneath which I rested, with the sun glaring hot, a few strange desert plants growing near, and with living corals in the tidal pools at my feet. Later in the voyage, Fitz-Roy asked me to read some of my Journal, and declared it would be worth publishing; so here was a second book in prospect!

Towards the close of our voyage I received a letter while at Ascension, in which my sisters told me that Sedgwick had called on my father, and

said that I should take a place among the leading scientific men. I could not at the time understand how he could have learnt anything of my proceedings, but I heard (I believe afterwards) that Henslow had read some of the letters which I wrote to him before the Philosophical Society of Cambridge,[14] and had printed them for private distribution. My collection of fossil bones, which had been sent to Henslow, also excited considerable attention among palaeontologists. After reading this letter, I clambered over the mountains of Ascension with a bounding step, and made the volcanic rocks resound under my geological hammer. All this shows how ambitious I was; but I think that I can say with truth that in after years, though I cared in the highest degree for the approbation of such men as Lyell and Hooker, who were my friends, I did not care much about the general public. I do not mean to say that a favourable review or a large sale of my books did not please me greatly, but the pleasure was a fleeting one, and I am sure that I have never turned one inch out of my course to gain fame.

FROM MY RETURN TO ENGLAND (OCTOBER 2, 1836) TO MY MARRIAGE (JANUARY 29, 1839)

These two years and three months were the most active ones which I ever spent, though I was occasionally unwell, and so lost some time. After going backwards and forwards several times between Shrewsbury, Maer, Cambridge, and London, I settled in lodgings at Cambridge [15] on December 13, where all my collections were under the care of Henslow. I stayed here three months, and got my minerals and rocks examined by the aid of Professor Miller.

I began preparing my *Journal of Travels*, which was not hard work, as my MS. Journal had been written with care, and my chief labour was making an abstract of my more interesting scientific results. I sent also, at the request of Lyell, a short account of my observations on the elevation of the coast of Chile to the Geological Society.

On March 7, 1837, I took lodgings in Great Marlborough Street in London, and remained there for nearly two years, until I was married. During these two years I finished my Journal, read several papers before the Geological Society, began preparing the MS. for my *Geological Observations*, and arranged for the publication of the *Zoology of the Voyage of the Beagle*. In July I opened my first note-book for facts in relation to the

14. Read at the meeting held November 16, 1835, and printed in a pamphlet of 31 pages for distribution among the members of the society.
15. In Fitzwilliam Street.

Origin of Species, about which I had long reflected, and never ceased working for the next twenty years.

During these two years I also went a little into society, and acted as one of the honorary secretaries of the Geological Society. I saw a great deal of Lyell. One of his chief characteristics was his sympathy with the work of others, and I was as much astonished as delighted at the interest which he showed when, on my return to England, I explained to him my views on coral reefs. This encouraged me greatly, and his advice and example had much influence on me. During this time I saw also a good deal of Robert Brown; I used often to call and sit with him during his breakfast on Sunday mornings, and he poured forth a rich treasure of curious observations and acute remarks, but they almost always related to minute points, and he never with me discussed large or general questions in science.

During these two years I took several short excursions as a relaxation, and one longer one to the Parallel Roads of Glen Roy, an account of which was published in the *Philosophical Transactions.* This paper was a great failure, and I am ashamed of it. Having been deeply impressed with what I had seen of the elevation of the land of South America, I attributed the parallel lines to the action of the sea; but I had to give up this view when Agassiz propounded his glacier-lake theory. Because no other explanation was possible under our then state of knowledge, I argued in favour of sea action; and my error has been a good lesson to me never to trust in science to the principle of exclusion.

As I was not able to work all day at science, I read a good deal during these two years on various subjects, including some metaphysical books; but I was not well fitted for such studies. About this time I took much delight in Wordsworth's and Coleridge's poetry; and can boast that I read the *Excursion* twice through. Formerly Milton's *Paradise Lost* had been my chief favourite, and in my excursions during the voyage of the *Beagle,* when I could take only a single volume, I always chose Milton.

FROM MY MARRIAGE, JANUARY 29, 1839,
AND RESIDENCE IN UPPER GOWER STREET, TO OUR
LEAVING LONDON AND SETTLING AT DOWN,
SEPTEMBER 14, 1842

[*After speaking of his happy married life, and of his children, he continues:*]

During the three years and eight months while we resided in London, I did less scientific work, though I worked as hard as I possibly could,

than during any other equal length of time in my life. This was owing to frequently recurring unwellness, and to one long and serious illness. The greater part of my time, when I could do anything, was devoted to my work on *Coral Reefs,* which I had begun before my marriage, and of which the last proof-sheet was corrected on May 6, 1842. This book, though a small one, cost me twenty months of hard work, as I had to read every work on the islands of the Pacific and to consult many charts. It was thought highly of by scientific men, and the theory therein given is, I think, now well established.

No other work of mine was begun in so deductive a spirit as this, for the whole theory was thought out on the west coast of South America before I had seen a true coral reef. I had therefore only to verify and extend my views by a careful examination of living reefs. But it should be observed that I had during the two previous years been incessantly attending to the effects on the shores of South America of the intermittent elevation of the land, together with denudation and the deposition of sediment. This necessarily led me to reflect much on the effects of subsidence, and it was easy to replace in imagination the continued deposition of sediment by the upward growth of corals. To do this was to form my theory of the formation of barrier-reefs and atolls.

Besides my work on coral reefs, during my residence in London, I read before the Geological Society papers on the Erratic Boulders of South America, on Earthquakes, and on the Formation by the Agency of Earthworms of Mould. I also continued to superintend the publication of the *Zoology of the Voyage of the Beagle.* Nor did I ever intermit collecting facts bearing on the *Origin of Species;* and I could sometimes do this when I could do nothing else from illness.

In the summer of 1842 I was stronger than I had been for some time, and took a little tour by myself in North Wales, for the sake of observing the effects of the old glaciers which formerly filled all the larger valleys. I published a short account of what I saw in the *Philosophical Magazine.* This excursion interested me greatly, and it was the last time I was ever strong enough to climb mountains or to take long walks such as are necessary for geological work.

During the early part of our life in London, I was strong enough to go into general society, and saw a good deal of several scientific men, and other more or less distinguished men. I will give my impressions with respect to some of them, though I have little to say worth saying.

I saw more of Lyell than of any other man, both before and after my marriage. His mind was characterized, as it appeared to me, by clearness, caution, sound judgment, and a good deal of originality. When I made

any remark to him on geology, he never rested until he saw the whole case clearly, and often made me see it more clearly than I had done before. He would advance all possible objections to my suggestion, and even after these were exhausted would long remain dubious. A second characteristic was his hearty sympathy with the work of other scientific men.[16]

On my return from the voyage of the *Beagle*, I explained to him my views on coral reefs, which differed from his, and I was greatly surprised and encouraged by the vivid interest which he showed. His delight in science was ardent, and he felt the keenest interest in the future progress of mankind. He was very kind hearted, and thoroughly liberal in his religious beliefs, or rather disbeliefs, but he was a strong theist. His candour was highly remarkable. He exhibited this by becoming a convert to the Descent theory, though he had gained much fame by opposing Lamarck's views, and this after he had grown old. He reminded me that I had many years before said to him, when discussing the opposition of the old school of geologists to his new views, "What a good thing it would be if every scientific man was to die when sixty years old, as afterwards he would be sure to oppose all new doctrines." But he hoped that now he might be allowed to live.

The science of geology is enormously indebted to Lyell—more so, as I believe, than to any other man who ever lived. When [I was] starting on the voyage of the *Beagle*, the sagacious Henslow, who, like all other geologists, believed at that time in successive cataclysms, advised me to get and study the first volume of the *Principles*, which had then just been published, but on no account to accept the views therein advocated. How differently would any one now speak of the *Principles!* I am proud to remember that the first place, namely, St. Jago, in the Cape de Verde Archipelago, in which I geologized convinced me of the infinite superiority of Lyell's views over those advocated in any other work known to me.

The powerful effects of Lyell's works could formerly be plainly seen in the different progress of the science in France and England. The present total oblivion of Elie de Beaumont's wild hypotheses, such as his *Craters of Elevation* and *Lines of Elevation* (which latter hypothesis I heard Sedgwick at the Geological Society lauding to the skies), may be largely attributed to Lyell.

I saw a good deal of Robert Brown, "facile Princeps Botanicorum," as

16. The slight repetition here observable is accounted for by the notes on Lyell, etc., having been added in April, 1881, a few years after the rest of the *Recollections* were written.

he was called by Humboldt. He seemed to me to be chiefly remarkable for the minuteness of his observations, and their perfect accuracy. His knowledge was extraordinarily great, and much died with him, owing to his excessive fear of ever making a mistake. He poured out his knowledge to me in the most unreserved manner, yet was strangely jealous on some points. I called on him two or three times before the voyage of the *Beagle,* and on one occasion he asked me to look through a microscope and describe what I saw. This I did, and believe now that it was the marvellous currents of protoplasm in some vegetable cell. I then asked him what I had seen but he answered me, "That is my little secret."

He was capable of the most generous actions. When old, much out of health, and quite unfit for any exertion, he daily visited (as Hooker told me) an old man-servant, who lived at a distance (and whom he supported), and read aloud to him. This is enough to make up for any degree of scientific penuriousness or jealousy.

I may here mention a few other eminent men whom I have occasionally seen, but I have little to say about them worth saying. I felt a high reverence for Sir J. Herschel, and was delighted to dine with him at his charming house at the Cape of Good Hope, and afterwards at his London house. I saw him, also, on a few other occasions. He never talked much, but every word which he uttered was worth listening to.

I once met at breakfast at Sir R. Murchison's house the illustrious Humboldt, who honoured me by expressing a wish to see me. I was a little disappointed with the great man, but my anticipations probably were too high. I can remember nothing distinctly about our interview, except that Humboldt was very cheerful and talked much.

[Speaking of H. Spencer] reminds me of Buckle, whom I once met at Hensleigh Wedgwood's. I was very glad to learn from him his system of collecting facts. He told me that he bought all the books which he read, and made a full index, to each, of the facts which he thought might prove serviceable to him, and that he could always remember in what book he had read anything, for his memory was wonderful. I asked him how at first he could judge what facts would be serviceable, and he answered that he did not know, but that a sort of instinct guided him. From this habit of making indexes, he was enabled to give the astonishing number of references on all sorts of subjects, which may be found in his *History of Civilisation.* This book I thought most interesting, and read it twice, but I doubt whether his generalizations are worth anything. Buckle was a great talker, and I listened to him saying hardly a word, nor indeed could I have done so for he left no gaps. When Mrs. Farrer began to sing, I jumped up

and said that I must listen to her; after I had moved away he turned around to a friend and said (as was overheard by my brother), "Well, Mr. Darwin's books are much better than his conversation."

Of other great literary men, I once met Sydney Smith at Dean Milman's house. There was something inexplicably amusing in every word which he uttered. Perhaps this was partly due to the expectation of being amused. He was talking about Lady Cork, who was then extremely old. This was the lady who, as he said, was once so much affected by one of his charity sermons that she *borrowed* a guinea from a friend to put in the plate. He now said, "It is generally believed that my dear old friend Lady Cork has been overlooked," and he said this in such a manner that no one could for a moment doubt that he meant that his dear old friend had been overlooked by the devil. How he managed to express this I know not.

I likewise once met Macaulay at Lord Stanhope's (the historian's) house, and as there was only one other man at dinner, I had a grand opportunity of hearing him converse, and he was very agreeable. He did not talk at all too much; nor indeed could such a man talk too much as long as he allowed others to turn the stream of his conversation, and this he did allow.

Lord Stanhope once gave me a curious little proof of the accuracy and fullness of Macaulay's memory: many historians used often to meet at Lord Stanhope's house, and in discussing various subjects they would sometimes differ from Macaulay, and formerly they often referred to some book to see who was right; but latterly, as Lord Stanhope noticed, no historian ever took this trouble, and whatever Macaulay said was final.

On another occasion I met at Lord Stanhope's house one of his parties of historians and other literary men, and among them were Motley and Grote. After luncheon I walked about Chevening Park for nearly an hour with Grote, and was much interested by his conversation and pleased by the simplicity and absence of all pretension in his manners.

Long ago I dined occasionally with the old Earl, the father of the historian; he was a strange man, but what little I knew of him I liked much. He was frank, genial, and pleasant. He had strongly marked features, with a brown complexion, and his clothes, when I saw him, were all brown. He seemed to believe in everything which was to others utterly incredible. He said one day to me, "Why don't you give up your fiddle-faddle of geology and zoology, and turn to the occult sciences?" The historian, then Lord Mahon, seemed shocked at such a speech to me, and his charming wife much amused.

The last man whom I will mention is Carlyle, seen by me several times at my brother's house, and two or three times at my own house. His talk was very racy and interesting, just like his writings, but he sometimes went on too long on the same subject. I remember a funny dinner at my brother's, where, among a few others, were Babbage and Lyell, both of whom liked to talk. Carlyle, however, silenced every one by haranguing during the whole dinner on the advantages of silence. After dinner Babbage, in his grimmest manner, thanked Carlyle for his very interesting lecture on silence.

Carlyle sneered at almost every one: One day in my house he called Grote's *History* "a fetid quagmire, with nothing spiritual about it." I always thought, until his *Reminiscences* appeared, that his sneers were partly jokes, but this now seems rather doubtful. His expression was that of a depressed, almost despondent yet benevolent, man; and it is notorious how heartily he laughed. I believe that his benevolence was real, though stained by not a little jealousy. No one can doubt about his extraordinary power of drawing pictures of things and men—far more vivid, as it appears to me, than any drawn by Macaulay. Whether his pictures of men were true ones is another question.

He has been all-powerful in impressing some grand moral truths on the minds of men. On the other hand, his views about slavery were revolting. In his eyes might was right. His mind seemed to me a very narrow one; even if all branches of science, which he despised, are excluded. It is astonishing to me that Kingsley should have spoken of him as a man well fitted to advance science. He laughed to scorn the idea that a mathematician, such as Whewell, could judge, as I maintained he could, of Goethe's views on light. He thought it a most ridiculous thing that any one should care whether a glacier moved a little quicker or a little slower, or moved at all. As far as I could judge, I never met a man with a mind so ill adapted for scientific research.

While living in London, I attended as regularly as I could the meetings of several scientific societies, and acted as secretary to the Geological Society. But such attendance, and ordinary society, suited my health so badly that we resolved to live in the country, which we both preferred and have never repented of.

RESIDENCE AT DOWN FROM SEPTEMBER 14, 1842, TO THE PRESENT TIME, 1876

After several fruitless searches in Surrey and elsewhere, we found this house and purchased it. I was pleased with the diversified appearance of

vegetation proper to a chalk district, and so unlike what I had been accustomed to in the Midland counties; and still more pleased with the extreme quietness and rusticity of the place. It is not, however, quite so retired a place as a writer in a German periodical makes it, who says that my house can be approached only by a mule track! Our fixing ourselves here has answered admirably in one way which we did not anticipate, namely, by being very convenient for frequent visits from our children.

Few persons can have lived a more retired life than we have done. Besides short visits to the houses of relations, and occasionally to the seaside or elsewhere, we have gone nowhere. During the first part of our residence we went a little into society, and received a few friends here; but my health almost always suffered from the excitement, violent shivering and vomiting attacks being thus brought on. I have therefore been compelled for many years to give up all dinner-parties; and this has been somewhat of a deprivation to me, as such parties always put me into high spirits. From the same cause I have been able to invite here very few scientific acquaintances.

My chief enjoyment and sole employment throughout life has been scientific work; and the excitement from such work makes me for the time forget, or drives away, my daily discomfort. I have therefore nothing to record during the rest of my life, except the publication of my several books. Perhaps a few details how they arose may be worth giving.

My several Publications. In the early part of 1844, my observations on the volcanic islands visited during the voyage of the *Beagle* were published. In 1845, I took much pains in correcting a new edition of my *Journal of Researches,* which was originally published in 1839 as part of Fitz-Roy's work. The success of this, my first literary child, always tickles my vanity more than that of any of my other books. Even to this day it sells steadily in England and the United States, and has been translated for the second time into German, and into French and other languages. This success of a book of travels, especially of a scientific one, so many years after its first publication is surprising. Ten thousand copies have been sold in England of the second edition. In 1846 my *Geological Observations on South America* were published. I record in a little diary, which I have always kept, that my three geological books (*Coral Reefs* included) consumed four and a half years' steady work; "and now it is ten years since my return to England. How much time have I lost by illness?" I have nothing to say about these three books except that to my surprise new editions have lately been called for.

In October, 1846, I began to work on *Cirripedia.* When on the coast of Chile, I found a most curious form, which burrowed into the shells of

Concholepas, and which differed so much from all other Cirripedes that I had to form a new suborder for its sole reception. Lately an allied burrowing genus has been found on the shores of Portugal. To understand the structure of my new Cirripede I had to examine and dissect many of the common forms; and this gradually led me on to take up the whole group. I worked steadily on this subject for the next eight years, and ultimately published two thick volumes, describing all the known living species, and two thin quartos on the extinct species. I do not doubt that Sir E. Lytton Bulwer had me in his mind when he introduced in one of his novels a Professor Long, who had written two huge volumes on limpets.

Although I was employed during eight years on this work, yet I record in my diary that about two years out of this time was lost by illness. On this account I went in 1848 for some months to Malvern for hydropathic treatment, which did me much good, so that on my return home I was able to resume work. So much was I out of health that when my dear father died on November 13, 1848, I was unable to attend his funeral or to act as one of his executors.

My work on the Cirripedia possesses, I think, considerable value, as besides describing several new and remarkable forms, I made out the homologies of the various parts—I discovered the cementing apparatus, though I blundered dreadfully about the cement glands—and lastly I proved the existence in certain genera of minute males complemental to and parasitic on the hermaphrodites. This latter discovery has at last been fully confirmed; though at one time a German writer was pleased to attribute the whole account to my fertile imagination. The Cirripedes form a highly varying and difficult group of species to class; and my work was of considerable use to me when I had to discuss in the *Origin of Species* the principles of a natural classification. Nevertheless, I doubt whether the work was worth the consumption of so much time.

From September, 1854, I devoted my whole time to arranging my huge pile of notes, to observing, and to experimenting in relation to the transmutation of species. During the voyage of the *Beagle* I had been deeply impressed by discovering in the Pampean formation great fossil animals covered with armour like that on the existing armadillos; secondly, by the manner in which closely allied animals replace one another in proceeding southwards over the continent; and thirdly, by the South American character of most of the productions of the Galapagos Archipelago, and more especially by the manner in which they differ slightly on each island of the group, none of the islands appearing to be very ancient in a geological sense.

It was evident that such facts as these, as well as many others, could only be explained on the supposition that species gradually become modified; and the subject haunted me. But it was equally evident that neither the action of the surrounding conditions nor the will of the organisms (especially in the case of plants) could account for the numerable cases in which organisms of every kind are beautifully adapted to their habits of life—for instance, a woodpecker or a tree-frog to climb trees, or a seed for dispersal by hooks or plumes. I had always been much struck by such adaptations, and until these could be explained it seemed to me almost useless to endeavour to prove by indirect evidence that species have been modified.

After my return to England it appeared to me that by following the example of Lyell in geology, and by collecting all facts which bore in any way on the variation of animals and plants under domestication and nature, some light might perhaps be thrown on the whole subject. My first note-book was opened in July, 1837. I worked on true Baconian principles, and without any theory collected facts on a wholesale scale, more especially with respect to domesticated productions, by printed inquiries, by conversation with skilful breeders and gardeners, and by extensive reading. When I see the list of books of all kinds which I read and abstracted, including whole series of Journals and Transactions, I am surprised at my industry. I soon perceived that selection was the keystone of man's success in making useful races of animals and plants. But how selection could be applied to organisms living in a state of nature remained for some time a mystery to me.

In October, 1838, that is, fifteen months after I had begun my systematic inquiry, I happened to read for amusement Malthus on *Population,* and being well prepared to appreciate the struggle for existence which everywhere goes on from long-continued observation of the habits of animals and plants, it at once struck me that under these circumstances favourable variations would tend to be preserved, and unfavourable ones to be destroyed. The result of this would be the formation of new species. Here then I had at last got a theory by which to work; but I was so anxious to avoid prejudice that I determined not for some time to write even the briefest sketch of it. In June, 1842, I first allowed myself the satisfaction of writing a very brief abstract of my theory in pencil in 35 pages; and this was enlarged during the summer of 1844 into one of 230 pages, which I had fairly copied out and still possess.

But at that time I overlooked one problem of great importance; and it is astonishing to me, except on the principle of Columbus and his egg, how I could have overlooked it and its solution. This problem is the tend-

ency in organic beings descended from the same stock to diverge in char-
acter as they become modified. That they have diverged greatly is obvious
from the manner in which species of all kinds can be classed under genera,
genera under families, families under suborders and so forth; and I can
remember the very spot in the road, while in my carriage, when to my joy
the solution occurred to me; and this was long after I had come to Down.
The solution, as I believe, is that the modified offspring of all dominant
and increasing forms tend to become adapted to many and highly diver-
sified places in the economy of nature.

Early in 1856 Lyell advised me to write out my views pretty fully, and
I began at once to do so on a scale three or four times as extensive as that
which was afterwards followed in my *Origin of Species;* yet it was only
an abstract of the materials which I had collected, and I got through
about half the work on this scale. But my plans were overthrown, for
early in the summer of 1858 Mr. Wallace, who was then in the Malay
Archipelago, sent me an essay, "On the Tendency of Varieties to depart
indefinitely from the Original Type"; and this essay contained exactly
the same theory as mine. Mr. Wallace expressed the wish that if I thought
well of his essay I should send it to Lyell for perusal.

The circumstances under which I consented at the request of Lyell and
Hooker to allow of an abstract from my MS., together with a letter to Asa
Gray, dated September 5, 1857, to be published at the same time with
Wallace's essay are given in the *Journal of the Proceedings of the Linnean
Society,* 1858, p. 45. I was at first very unwilling to consent, as I thought
Mr. Wallace might consider my doing so unjustifiable, for I did not then
know how generous and noble was his disposition. The extract from my
MS. and the letter to Asa Gray had neither been intended for publication,
and were badly written. Mr. Wallace's essay, on the other hand, was ad-
mirably expressed and quite clear. Nevertheless, our joint productions
excited very little attention, and the only published notice of them which
I can remember was by Professor Haughton of Dublin, whose verdict
was that all that was new in them was false, and what was true was old.
This shows how necessary it is that any new view should be explained at
considerable length in order to arouse public attention.

In September, 1858, I set to work by the strong advice of Lyell and
Hooker to prepare a volume on the transmutation of species, but was
often interrupted by ill health, and short visits to Dr. Lane's delightful
hydropathic establishment at Moor Park. I abstracted the MS. begun on
a much larger scale in 1856, and completed the volume on the same re-
duced scale. It cost me thirteen months and ten days' hard labour. It was

published under the title of the *Origin of Species*, in November, 1859. Though considerably added to and corrected in the later editions, it has remained substantially the same book.

It is no doubt the chief work of my life. It was from the first highly successful. The first small edition of 1,250 copies was sold on the day of publication, and a second edition of 3,000 copies soon afterwards. Sixteen thousand copies have now (1876) been sold in England; and considering how stiff a book it is, this is a large sale. It has been translated into almost every European tongue, even into such languages as Spanish, Bohemian, Polish, and Russian. It has also, according to Miss Bird, been translated into Japanese,[17] and is there much studied. Even an essay in Hebrew has appeared on it, showing that the theory is contained in the Old Testament! The reviews were very numerous; for some time I collected all that appeared on the *Origin* and on my related books, and these amount (excluding newspaper reviews) to 265; but after a time I gave up the attempt in despair. Many separate essays and books on the subject have appeared; and in Germany a catalogue or bibliography on "Darwinismus" has appeared every year or two.

The success of the *Origin* may, I think, be attributed in large part to my having long before written two condensed sketches, and to my having finally abstracted a much larger manuscript, which was itself an abstract. By this means I was enabled to select the more striking facts and conclusions. I had, also, during many years followed a golden rule, namely, that whenever a published fact, a new observation or thought came across me, which was opposed to my general results, to make a memorandum of it without fail and at once; for I had found by experience that such facts and thoughts were far more apt to escape from the memory than favourable ones. Owing to this habit, very few objections were raised against my views which I had not at least noticed and attempted to answer.

It has sometimes been said that the success of the *Origin* proved "that the subject was in the air," or "that men's minds were prepared for it." I do not think that this is strictly true, for I occasionally sounded not a few naturalists, and never happened to come across a single one who seemed to doubt about the permanence of species. Even Lyell and Hooker, though they would listen with interest to me, never seemed to agree. I tried once or twice to explain to able men what I meant by Natural Selection, but signally failed. What I believe was strictly true is that innumerable well-observed facts were stored in the minds of naturalists

17. Miss Bird is mistaken, as I learn from Professor Mitsukuri.—F. D.

ready to take their proper places as soon as any theory which would receive them was sufficiently explained. Another element in the success of the book was its moderate size; and this I owe to the appearance of Mr. Wallace's essay; had I published on the scale in which I began to write in 1856, the book would have been four or five times as large as the *Origin*, and very few would have had the patience to read it.

I gained much by my delay in publishing from about 1839, when the theory was clearly conceived, to 1859; and I lost nothing by it, for I cared very little whether men attributed most originality to me or Wallace; and his essay no doubt aided in the reception of the theory. I was forestalled in only one important point, which my vanity has always made me regret, namely, the explanation by means of the Glacial period of the presence of the same species of plants and of some few animals on distant mountain summits and in the Arctic Regions. This view pleased me so much that I wrote it out *in extenso*, and I believe that it was read by Hooker some years before E. Forbes published his celebrated memoir on the subject. In the very few points in which we differed, I still think that I was in the right. I have never, of course, alluded in print to my having independently worked out this view.

Hardly any point gave me so much satisfaction when I was at work on the *Origin* as the explanation of the wide difference in many classes between the embryo and the adult animal, and of the close resemblance of the embryos within the same class. No notice of this point was taken, as far as I remember, in the early reviews of the *Origin*, and I recollect expressing my surprise on this head in a letter to Asa Gray. Within late years several reviewers have given the whole credit to Fritz Müller and Häckel, who undoubtedly have worked it out much more fully, and in some respects more correctly than I did. I had materials for a whole chapter on the subject, and I ought to have made the discussion longer; for it is clear that I failed to impress my readers; and he who succeeds in doing so deserves, in my opinion, all the credit.

This leads me to remark that I have almost always been treated honestly by my reviewers, passing over those without scientific knowledge as not worthy of notice. My views have often been grossly misrepresented, bitterly opposed and ridiculed, but this has been generally done, as I believe, in good faith. On the whole I do not doubt that my works have been over and over again greatly overpraised. I rejoice that I have avoided controversies, and this I owe to Lyell, who many years ago, in reference to my geological works, strongly advised me never to get entangled in a controversy, as it rarely did any good and caused a miserable loss of time and temper.

Whenever I have found out that I have blundered, or that my work has been imperfect, and when I have been contemptuously criticized, and even when I have been overpraised, so that I have felt mortified, it has been my greatest comfort to say hundreds of times to myself that "I have worked as hard and as well as I could, and no man can do more than this." I remember when in Good Success Bay, in Tierra del Fuego, thinking (and, I believe, that I wrote home to the effect) that I could not employ my life better than in adding a little to natural science. This I have done to the best of my abilities, and critics may say what they like, but they cannot destroy this conviction.

During the last two months of 1859 I was fully occupied in preparing a second edition of the *Origin*, and by an enormous correspondence. On January 1, 1860, I began arranging my notes for my work on the *Variation of Animals and Plants under Domestication;* but it was not published until the beginning of 1868, the delay having been caused partly by frequent illnesses, one of which lasted seven months, and partly by being tempted to publish on other subjects which at the time interested me more.

On May 15, 1862, my little book on the *Fertilisation of Orchids*, which cost me ten months' work, was published; most of the facts had been slowly accumulated during several previous years. During the summer of 1839, and, I believe, during the previous summer, I was led to attend to the cross-fertilisation of flowers by the aid of insects, from having come to the conclusion in my speculations on the origin of species that crossing played an important part in keeping specific forms constant. I attended to the subject more or less during every subsequent summer; and my interest in it was greatly enhanced by having procured and read in November, 1841, through the advice of Robert Brown, a copy of C. K. Sprengel's wonderful book *Das entdeckte Geheimnis der Natur* [The Newly Revealed Mystery of Nature]. For some years before 1862 I had specially attended to the fertilisation of our British orchids; and it seemed to me the best plan to prepare as complete a treatise on this group of plants as well as I could, rather than to utilize the great mass of matter which I had slowly collected with respect to other plants.

My resolve proved a wise one, for since the appearance of my book, a surprising number of papers and separate works on the fertilisation of all kinds of flowers have appeared; and these are far better done than I could possibly have effected. The merits of poor old Sprengel, so long overlooked, are now fully recognized many years after his death.

During the same year I published in the *Journal of the Linnean Society*

a paper "On the Two Forms, or Dimorphic Condition of Primula," and during the next five years, five other papers on dimorphic and trimorphic plants. I do not think anything in my scientific life has given me so much satisfaction as making out the meaning of the structure of these plants. I had noticed in 1838 or 1839 the dimorphism of *Linum flavum,* and had at first thought it was merely a case of unmeaning variability. But on examining the common species of Primula I found that the two forms were much too regular and constant to be thus viewed. I therefore became almost convinced that the common cowslip and primrose were on the high road to become dioecious; that the short pistil in the one form and the short stamens in the other form were tending towards abortion. The plants were therefore subjected under this point of view to trial; but as soon as the flowers with short pistils fertilised with pollen from the short stamens were found to yield more seeds than any other of the four possible unions, the abortion theory was knocked on the head. After some additional experiment, it became evident that the two forms, though both were perfect hermaphrodites, bore almost the same relation to one another as do the two sexes of an ordinary animal. With Lythrum we have the still more wonderful case of three forms standing in a similar relation to one another. I afterwards found that the offspring from the union of two plants belonging to the same forms presented a close and curious analogy with hybrids from the union of two distinct species.

In the autumn of 1864 I finished a long paper on *Climbing Plants,* and sent it to the Linnean Society. The writing of this paper cost me four months; but I was so unwell when I received the proof-sheets that I was forced to leave them very badly and often obscurely expressed. The paper was little noticed, but when in 1875 it was corrected and published as a separate book it sold well. I was led to take up this subject by reading a short paper by Asa Gray, published in 1858. He sent me seeds, and on raising some plants I was so much fascinated and perplexed by the revolving movements of the tendrils and stems, which movements are really very simple, though appearing at first sight very complex, that I procured various other kinds of climbing plants, and studied the whole subject. I was all the more attracted to it, from not being at all satisfied with the explanation which Henslow gave us in his lectures about twining plants, namely, that they had a natural tendency to grow up in a spire. This explanation proved quite erroneous. Some of the adaptations displayed by climbing plants are as beautiful as those of orchids for ensuring cross-fertilisation.

My *Variation of Animals and Plants under Domestication* was begun, as already stated, in the beginning of 1860, but was not published until

the beginning of 1868. It was a big book, and cost me four years and two months' hard labour. It gives all my observations and an immense number of facts, collected from various sources, about our domestic productions. In the second volume the causes and laws of variation, inheritance, etc., are discussed as far as our present state of knowledge permits. Towards the end of the work I give my well-abused hypothesis of pangenesis. An unverified hypothesis is of little or no value; but if any one should hereafter be led to make observations by which some such hypothesis could be established, I shall have done good service, as an astonishing number of isolated facts can be thus connected together and rendered intelligible. In 1875 a second and largely corrected edition, which cost me a good deal of labour, was brought out.

My *Descent of Man* was published in February, 1871. As soon as I had become, in the year 1837 or 1838, convinced that species are mutable productions, I could not avoid the belief that man must come under the same law. Accordingly I collected notes on the subject for my own satisfaction, and not for a long time with any intention of publishing. Although in the *Origin of Species* the derivation of any particular species is never discussed, yet I thought it best, in order that no honourable man should accuse me of concealing my views, to add that by the work "light would be thrown on the origin of man and his history." It would have been useless and injurious to the success of the book to have paraded, without giving any evidence, my conviction with respect to his origin.

But when I found that many naturalists fully accepted the doctrine of the evolution of species, it seemed to me advisable to work up such notes as I possessed, and to publish a special treatise on the origin of man. I was the more glad to do so, as it gave me an opportunity of fully discussing sexual selection—a subject which had always greatly interested me. This subject, and that of the variation of our domestic productions, together with the causes and laws of variation, inheritance, and the intercrossing of plants, are the sole subjects which I have been able to write about in full, so as to use all the materials which I have collected. The *Descent of Man* took me three years to write, but then as usual some of this time was lost by ill health, and some was consumed by preparing new editions and other minor works. A second and largely corrected edition of the *Descent* appeared in 1874.

My book on the *Expression of the Emotions in Men and Animals* was published in the autumn of 1872. I had intended to give only a chapter on the subject in the *Descent of Man*, but as soon as I began to put my notes together, I saw that it would require a separate treatise.

My first child was born on December 27, 1839, and I at once commenced to make notes on the first dawn of the various expressions which he exhibited, for I felt convinced, even at this early period, that the most complex and fine shades of expression must all have had a gradual and natural origin. During the summer of the following year, 1840, I read Sir C. Bell's admirable work on expression, and this greatly increased the interest which I felt in the subject, though I could not at all agree with his belief that various muscles had been specially created for the sake of expression. From this time forward I occasionally attended to the subject, both with respect to man and our domesticated animals. My book sold largely, 5,267 copies having been disposed of on the day of publication.

In the summer of 1860 I was idling and resting near Hartfield, where two species of Drosera abound; and I noticed that numerous insects had been entrapped by the leaves. I carried home some plants, and on giving them insects saw the movements of the tentacles, and this made me think it probable that the insects were caught for some special purpose. Fortunately a crucial test occurred to me, that of placing a large number of leaves in various nitrogenous and non-nitrogenous fluids of equal density; and as soon as I found that the former alone excited energetic movements, it was obvious that here was a fine new field for investigation.

During subsequent years, whenever I had leisure, I pursued my experiments, and my book on *Insectivorous Plants* was published in July, 1875— that is, sixteen years after my first observations. The delay in this case, as with all my other books, has been a great advantage to me; for a man after a long interval can criticize his own work, almost as well as if it were that of another person. The fact that a plant should secrete, when properly excited, a fluid containing an acid and ferment, closely analogous to the digestive fluid of an animal, was certainly a remarkable discovery.

During this autumn of 1876 I shall publish on the *Effects of Cross and Self-Fertilisation in the Vegetable Kingdom*. This book will form a complement to that on the *Fertilisation of Orchids,* in which I showed how perfect were the means for cross-fertilisation, and here I shall show how important are the results. I was led to make, during eleven years, the numerous experiments recorded in this volume, by a mere accidental observation; and indeed it required the accident to be repeated before my attention was thoroughly aroused to the remarkable fact that seedlings of self-fertilised parentage are inferior, even in the first generation, in height and vigour to seedlings of cross-fertilised parentage. I hope also to republish a revised edition of my book on orchids, and hereafter my

papers on dimorphic and trimorphic plants, together with some additional observations on allied points which I never have had time to arrange. My strength will then probably be exhausted, and I shall be ready to exclaim "*Nunc dimittis.*"

Written May 1, 1881. The Effects of Cross and Self-Fertilisation was published in the autumn of 1876; and the results there arrived at explain, as I believe, the endless and wonderful contrivances for the transportal of pollen from one plant to another of the same species. I now believe, however, chiefly from the observations of Hermann Müller, that I ought to have insisted more strongly than I did on the many adaptations for self-fertilisation; though I was well aware of many such adaptations. A much enlarged edition of my *Fertilisation of Orchids* was published in 1877.

In this same year *The Different Forms of Flowers,* etc., appeared, and in 1880 a second edition. This book consists chiefly of the several papers on heterostyled flowers originally published by the Linnean Society, corrected, with much new matter added, together with observations on some other cases in which the same plant bears two kinds of flowers. As before remarked, no little discovery of mine ever gave me so much pleasure as the making out the meaning of heterostyled flowers. The results of crossing such flowers in an illegitimate manner I believe to be very important, as bearing on the sterility of hybrids; although these results have been noticed by only a few persons.

In 1879, I had a translation of Dr. Ernst Krause's *Life of Erasmus Darwin* published, and I added a sketch of his character and habits from material in my possession. Many persons have been much interested by this little life, and I am surprised that only 800 or 900 copies were sold.

In 1880 I published, with [my son] Frank's assistance, our *Power of Movement in Plants.* This was a tough piece of work. The book bears somewhat the same relation to my little book on *Climbing Plants* which *Cross-Fertilisation* did to the *Fertilisation of Orchids;* for in accordance with the principle of evolution it was impossible to account for climbing plants having been developed in so many widely different groups unless all kinds of plants possess some slight power of movement of an analogous kind. This I proved to be the case; and I was further led to a rather wide generalization, viz., that the great and important classes of movements, excited by light, the attraction of gravity, etc., are all modified forms of the fundamental movement of circumnutation. It has always pleased me to exalt plants in the scale of organized beings; and I therefore felt an especial pleasure in showing how many and what admirably well-adapted movements the tip of a root possesses.

I have now (May 1, 1881) sent to the printers the MS. of a little book on *The Formation of Vegetable Mould through the Action of Worms.* This is a subject of but small importance; and I know not whether it will interest any readers,[18] but it has interested me. It is the completion of a short paper read before the Geological Society more than forty years ago, and has revived old geological thoughts.

I have now mentioned all the books which I have published, and these have been the milestones in my life, so that little remains to be said. I am not conscious of any change in my mind during the last thirty years, excepting in one point presently to be mentioned; nor, indeed, could any change have been expected unless one of general deterioration. But my father lived to his eighty-third year with his mind as lively as ever it was, and all his faculties undimmed; and I hope that I may die before my mind fails to a sensible extent. I think that I have become a little more skilful in guessing right explanations and in devising experimental tests; but this may probably be the result of mere practice, and of a larger store of knowledge. I have as much difficulty as ever in expressing myself clearly and concisely; and this difficulty has caused me a very great loss of time; but it has had the compensating advantage of forcing me to think long and intently about every sentence, and thus I have been led to see errors in reasoning and in my own observations or those of others.

There seems to be a sort of fatality in my mind leading me to put at first my statement or proposition in a wrong or awkward form. Formerly I used to think about my sentences before writing them down; but for several years I have found that it saves time to scribble in a vile hand whole pages as quickly as I possibly can, contracting half the words; and then correct deliberately. Sentences thus scribbled down are often better ones than I could have written deliberately.

Having said thus much about my manner of writing, I will add that with my large books I spend a good deal of time over the general arrangement of the matter. I first make the rudest outline in two or three pages, and then a larger one in several pages, a few words or one word standing for a whole discussion or series of facts. Each one of these headings is again enlarged and often transferred before I begin to write *in extenso.* As in several of my books facts observed by others have been very extensively used, and as I have always had several quite distinct subjects in hand at the same time, I may mention that I keep from thirty to forty large portfolios, in cabinets with labelled shelves, into which I

18. Between November, 1881, and February, 1884, 8,500 copies have been sold.

can at once put a detached reference or memorandum. I have bought many books, and at their ends I make an index of all the facts that concern my work; or, if the book is not my own, write out a separate abstract, and of such abstracts I have a large drawer full. Before beginning on any subject I look to all the short indexes and make a general and classified index, and by taking the one or more proper portfolios I have all the information collected during my life ready for use.

I have said that in one respect my mind has changed during the last twenty or thirty years. Up to the age of thirty, or beyond it, poetry of many kinds, such as the works of Milton, Gray, Byron, Wordsworth, Coleridge, and Shelley, gave me great pleasure, and even as a schoolboy I took intense delight in Shakespeare, especially in the historical plays. I have also said that formerly pictures gave me considerable, and music very great, delight. But now for many years I cannot endure to read a line of poetry: I have tried lately to read Shakespeare, and found it so intolerably dull that it nauseated me. I have also almost lost my taste for pictures or music. Music generally sets me thinking too energetically on what I have been at work on, instead of giving me pleasure. I retain some taste for fine scenery, but it does not cause me the exquisite delight which it formerly did. On the other hand, novels which are works of the imagination, though not of a very high order, have been for years a wonderful relief and pleasure to me, and I often bless all novelists. A surprising number have been read aloud to me, and I like all if moderately good, and if they do not end unhappily—against which a law ought to be passed. A novel, according to my taste, does not come into the first class unless it contains some person whom one can thoroughly love, and if a pretty woman all the better.

This curious and lamentable loss of the higher aesthetic tastes is all the odder, as books on history, biographies, and travels (independently of any scientific facts which they may contain), and essays on all sorts of subjects interest me as much as ever they did. My mind seems to have become a kind of machine for grinding general laws out of large collections of facts, but why this should have caused the atrophy of that part of the brain alone on which the higher tastes depend I cannot conceive. A man with a mind more highly organized or better constituted than mine would not, I suppose, have thus suffered; and if I had to live my life again, I would have made a rule to read some poetry and listen to some music at least once every week; for perhaps the parts of my brain now atrophied would thus have been kept active through use. The loss of these tastes is a loss of happiness, and may possibly be injurious to the

intellect, and more probably to the moral character, by enfeebling the emotional part of our nature.

My books have sold largely in England, have been translated into many languages, and passed through several editions in foreign countries. I have heard it said that the success of a work abroad is the best test of its enduring value. I doubt whether this is at all trustworthy; but judged by this standard my name ought to last for a few years. Therefore it may be worth-while to try to analyse the mental qualities and the conditions on which my success has depended; though I am aware that no man can do this correctly.

I have no great quickness of apprehension or wit which is so remarkable in some clever men, for instance, Huxley. I am therefore a poor critic: a paper or book, when first read, generally excites my admiration, and it is only after considerable reflection that I perceive the weak points. My power to follow a long and purely abstract train of thought is very limited; and therefore I could never have succeeded with metaphysics or mathematics. My memory is extensive, yet hazy: it suffices to make me cautious by vaguely telling me that I have observed or read something opposed to the conclusion which I am drawing, or on the other hand in favour of it; and after a time I can generally recollect where to search for my authority. So poor in one sense is my memory that I have never been able to remember for more than a few days a single date or a line of poetry.

Some of my critics have said, "Oh, he is a good observer, but he has no power of reasoning!" I do not think that this can be true, for the *Origin of Species* is one long argument from the beginning to the end, and it has convinced not a few able men. No one could have written it without having some power of reasoning. I have a fair share of invention, and of common sense or judgment, such as every fairly successful lawyer or doctor must have, but not, I believe, in any higher degree.

On the favourable side of the balance, I think that I am superior to the common run of men in noticing things which easily escape attention, and in observing them carefully. My industry has been nearly as great as it could have been in the observation and collection of facts. What is far more important, my love of natural science has been steady and ardent.

This pure love has, however, been much aided by the ambition to be esteemed by my fellow naturalists. From my early youth I have had the strongest desire to understand or explain whatever I observed—that is, to group all facts under some general laws. These causes combined have given me the patience to reflect or ponder for any number of years over

any unexplained problem. As far as I can judge, I am not apt to follow blindly the lead of other men. I have steadily endeavoured to keep my mind free so as to give up any hypothesis, however much beloved (and I cannot resist forming one on every subject), as soon as facts are shown to be opposed to it. Indeed, I have had no choice but to act in this manner, for with the exception of the coral reefs, I cannot remember a single first-formed hypothesis which had not after a time to be given up or greatly modified. This has naturally led me to distrust greatly deductive reasoning in the mixed sciences. On the other hand, I am not very sceptical—a frame of mind which I believe to be injurious to the process of science. A good deal of scepticism in a scientific man is advisable to avoid much loss of time, but I have met with not a few men who, I feel sure, have often thus been deterred from experiment or observations which would have proved directly or indirectly serviceable.

In illustration, I will give the oddest case which I have known. A gentleman (who, as I afterwards heard, is a good local botanist) wrote to me from the eastern counties that the seed or beans of the common field-bean had this year everywhere grown on the wrong side of the pod. I wrote back asking for further information, as I did not understand what was meant; but I did not receive any answer for a very long time. I then saw in two newspapers, one published in Kent and the other in Yorkshire, paragraphs stating that it was a most remarkable fact that "the beans this year had all grown on the wrong side." So I thought there must be some foundation for so general a statement. Accordingly, I went to my gardener, an old Kentish man, and asked him whether he had heard anything about it, and he answered, "Oh, no, Sir, it must be a mistake, for the beans grow on the wrong side only on leap year, and this is not leap year." I then asked him how they grew in common years and how on leap years, but soon found that he knew absolutely nothing of how they grew at any time, but he stuck to his belief.

After a time I heard from my first informant, who, with many apologies, said that he should not have written to me had he not heard the statement from several intelligent farmers; but that he had since spoken again to every one of them, and not one knew in the least what he had himself meant. So that here a belief—if indeed a statement with no definite idea attached to it can be called a belief—had spread over almost the whole of England without any vestige of evidence.

I have known in the course of my life only three intentionally falsified statements, and one of these may have been a hoax (and there have been several scientific hoaxes), which, however, took in an American agricul-

tural journal. It related to the formation in Holland of a new breed of oxen by the crossing of distinct species of *Bos* (some of which I happen to know are sterile together), and the author had the impudence to state that he had corresponded with me, and that I had been deeply impressed with the importance of his result. The article was sent to me by the editor of an English agricultural journal, asking for my opinion before republishing it.

A second case was an account of several varieties raised by the author from several species of Primula, which had spontaneously yielded a full complement of seed, although the parent plants had been carefully protected from the access of insects. This account was published before I had discovered the meaning of heterostylism, and the whole statement must have been fraudulent, or there was neglect in excluding insects so gross as to be scarcely credible.

The third case was more curious: Mr. Huth published in his book on *Consanguineous Marriage* some long extracts from a Belgian author who stated that he had interbred rabbits in the closest manner for very many generations without the least injurious effects. The account was published in a most respectable journal, that of the Royal Society of Belgium; but I could not avoid feeling doubts—I hardly know why, except that there were no accidents of any kind, and my experience in breeding animals made me think this very improbable.

So with much hesitation I wrote to Professor Van Beneden, asking him whether the author was a trustworthy man. I soon heard in answer that the society had been greatly shocked by discovering that the whole account was a fraud.[19] The writer had been publicly challenged in the journal to say where he had resided and kept his large stock of rabbits while carrying on his experiments, which must have consumed several years, and no answer could be extracted from him.

My habits are methodical, and this has been of not a little use for my particular line of work. Lastly, I have had ample leisure from not having to earn my own bread. Even ill health, though it has annihilated several years of my life, has saved me from the distractions of society and amusement.

Therefore my success as a man of science, whatever this may have amounted to, has been determined, as far as I can judge, by complex and

19. The falseness of the published statements on which Mr. Huth relied has been pointed out by himself in a slip inserted in all the copies of his book which then remained unsold.

diversified mental qualities and conditions. Of these, the most important have been—the love of science—unbounded patience in long reflecting over any subject—industry in observing and collecting facts—and a fair share of invention as well as of common sense. With such moderate abilities as I possess, it is truly surprising that I should have influenced to a considerable extent the belief of scientific men on some important points.

Jean Henri Fabre

1823–1915

J. Henri Fabre was born at St. Léons, in southern France, in 1823, the son of humble parents who could afford to give him only an elementary education. He studied at the normal school at Vaucluse, supporting himself, and became a teacher. He took a position in Corsica but had to leave it when he contracted malaria. In 1852 he began to teach at Avignon, where he remained for 20 years. During this period his salary never exceeded $320 a year. His ideas on pedagogy were in advance of his time; when he finally admitted girls to his science classes he was denounced and dismissed from his post. He was ejected, with his wife and five children, from his home, and was saved only by a loan from John Stuart Mill, with whom he had made a number of botanical excursions.

Fabre now retired from teaching and supported himself by writing books of popular science. He paid back the loan and, after nine years, in 1879, bought the first piece of land he had ever owned. Its two and one-half sandy, scrubby acres, and his joy in their acquisition, are described in the first of the selections that follow. Here, at Sérignan, he gathered together the notes of a quarter of a century and began to produce his great work, the *Souvenirs entomologiques,* whose ten volumes were not completed till 1907. His laboratory, fitted with the most primitive equipment, gave evidence of his extraordinary industry. Not only were there the ten volumes, comprising 2,500 pages and 850,000 words, but in the floor of the laboratory a path had been worn in the tiles by Fabre as he circled his table in his heavy peasant shoes.

Upon the completion of his *Souvenirs,* Fabre, who had worked in almost total obscurity, was suddenly discovered by the leading literary figures of the time. He was showered with homage, and a jubilee in his honor was held at Sérignan in 1910, when he was 86.

He was nearly blind, and he was hardly able to recognize the President of France who had journeyed from Paris to pay his respects. Fabre died at Sérignan, saddened by the war that had overwhelmed his beloved country, on October 11, 1915.

Here, surely—and the list is far from complete—is a company both numerous and select, whose conversation will not fail to charm my solitude, if I succeed in drawing it out." Thus Fabre describes the insect population of his little farm at Sérignan, his "abandoned, barren, sun-scorched bit of land, favored by thistles and by wasps and bees." It has been doubted whether any man ever appreciated such a worthless piece of land more. For Fabre, it was certainly not worthless. It was, in his words, "a laboratory in the open fields." And it was in a laboratory, whether open or enclosed, that he was happiest. Despite the suffering of his life, Fabre gives the impression of being one of the happiest men who ever lived. He who loves insects is fortunate, for there are so many of them.

To Fabre, of course, insects were not what they are to most people. Each was almost an individual; certainly each species was distinct. It is said that he overemphasized the importance of instinct in insect life. He thought wasps and bees were more limited in their freedom to adapt to circumstances than certain modern entomologists believe. But he came to his conclusions as a result of observation so patient and painstaking that it almost seems incredible.

The Sacred Beetle, the second selection reprinted here, is, as its title suggests, about one kind of insect rather than many. The scarab, or dung-beetle (the nearest American relative is the june-bug), was one of Fabre's favorite insects. He spent nearly half a century studying this thieving, lazy, but also unbelievably industrious little animal. He seemed never to grow tired of dung-beetles, nor did he, evidently, ever become unaware of how funny the fact might appear to some people. "What excitement over a single patch of cow-dung!" he writes, knowing full well that the reader will smile not only at the beetle's enthusiasm, but at the author's, too. To Fabre the beetle's world was part of that "most wonderful of festivals, life's springtime awakening." Life, any kind of life, no matter how humble, was to Fabre a festival. Others might think this silly or sad, but he could only watch and wonder.

Fabre's scientific purity must be defended. He appears, from one

point of view, to interject too much human morality into his history
of the dung-beetle. "These dung-rollers rob one another with a calm
effrontery which, to my knowledge, is without a parallel," he writes.
The beetle's "breach of trust rouses (his) indignation," and he ob-
serves that, in general, "the insect cares for nothing but itself." But
it is also apparent that his moralizing is done with tongue in cheek.
In fact, he seems to accept the dung-beetle for what it is and makes
no judgments for or against. He loves the insect in that sense—he
does not want to change it.

Fabre is a naturalist. What he observes, he studies in the round,
as a whole. "To know thoroughly the history of the destroyer of our
vines," he writes, "might perhaps be more important than to know
how this or that nerve-fibre of a Cirriped ends." His is a laboratory
of "living entomology," and his data are histories, not isolated facts.
He does not seek for causes; it is enough for him that he discover
what happens, not how it happens. That can come later, he seems
to imply, when patient men like him have done their work.

A Laboratory
of the Open Fields [1]

To travel the world, by land and sea, from pole to pole; to cross-question life, under every clime, in the infinite variety of its manifestations: that surely would be glorious luck for him that has eyes to see; and it formed the radiant dreams of my young years, at the time when *Robinson Crusoe* was my delight. These rosy illusions, rich in voyages, were soon succeeded by dull, stay-at-home reality. The jungles of India, the virgin forests of Brazil, the towering crests of the Andes, beloved by the condor, were reduced, as a field for exploration, to a patch of pebbles enclosed within four walls.

I go the circuit of my enclosure over and over again, a hundred times, by short stages; I stop here and I stop there; patiently, I put questions and, at long intervals, I receive some scrap of a reply. The smallest insect village has become familiar to me: I know each fruit-branch where the praying mantis perches; each bush where the pale Italian cricket strums amid the calmness of the summer nights; each downy plant scraped by the Anthidium, that maker of cotton bags; each cluster of lilac worked by the Megachile, the leaf-cutter.

This is what I wished for, *hoc erat in votis:* a bit of land, oh, not so very large, but fenced in, to avoid the drawbacks of a public way; an abandoned, barren, sun-scorched bit of land, favoured by thistles and by wasps and bees. Here, without fear of being troubled by the passersby, I could consult the Ammophila and the Sphex and engage in that difficult conversation whose questions and answers have experiment for their

1. Among the insects named by Fabre, the Cicadella is a froghopper; the Scarab, Lamellicorns, Oryctes and Cetoniae are beetles; the Sphex, Ammophila, Cerceris, Stizus, Pompilus, Pelopaeus, Polistes, Eumenes, Scoliae and Bembeces are wasps; the Ephippiger is a green grasshopper and the Halicti, Megachiles, Chalcicodomae, Osmiae, Anthophorae, Anthidium, Eucerae, Macrocerae, Dasypodae and Andrenae are all wild bees.

97

language; here, without distant expeditions that take up my time, without tiring rambles that strain my nerves, I could contrive my plans of attack, lay my ambushes and watch their effects at every hour of the day. *Hoc erat in votis.* Yes, this was my wish, my dream, always cherished, always vanishing into the mists of the future.

And it is no easy matter to acquire a laboratory in the open fields, when harassed by a terrible anxiety about one's daily bread. For forty years have I fought, with steadfast courage, against the paltry plagues of life; and the long-wished-for laboratory has come at last. What it has cost me in perseverance and relentless work I will not try to say. It has come; and, with it—a more serious condition—perhaps a little leisure. I say perhaps, for my leg is still hampered with a few links of the convict's chain.

The wish is realized. It is a little late, O my pretty insects! I greatly fear that the peach is offered to me when I am beginning to have no teeth wherewith to eat it. Yes, it is a little late: the wide horizons of the outset have shrunk into a low and stifling canopy, more and more straitened day by day. Regretting nothing in the past, save those whom I have lost; regretting nothing, not even my first youth; hoping nothing either, I have reached the point at which, worn out by the experience of things, we ask ourselves if life be worth the living.

Amid the ruins that surround me, one strip of wall remains standing, immovable upon its solid base: my passion for scientific truth. Is that enough, O my busy insects, to enable me to add yet a few seemly pages to your history? Will my strength not cheat my good intentions? Why, indeed, did I forsake you so long? Friends have reproached me for it. Ah, tell them, tell those friends, who are yours as well as mine, tell them that it was not forgetfulness on my part, not weariness, nor neglect: I thought of you; I was convinced that the Cerceris cave had more fair secrets to reveal to us, that the chase of the Sphex held fresh surprises in store. But time failed me; I was alone, deserted, struggling against misfortune. Before philosophizing, one had to live. Tell them that; and they will pardon me.

Others again have reproached me with my style, which has not the solemnity, nay, better, the dryness of the schools. They fear lest a page that is read without fatigue should not always be the expression of the truth. Were I to take their word for it, we are profound only on condition of being obscure. Come here, one and all of you—you, the sting-bearers, and you, the wing-cased armour-clads—take up my defence and bear witness in my favour. Tell of the intimate terms on which I live

with you, of the patience with which I observe you, of the care with which I record your actions. Your evidence is unanimous: yes, my pages, though they bristle not with hollow formulas nor learned smatterings, are the exact narrative of facts observed, neither more nor less; and whoso cares to question you in his turn will obtain the same replies.

And then, my dear insects, if you cannot convince those good people, because you do not carry the weight of tedium, I, in my turn, will say to them:

"You rip up the animal and I study it alive; you turn it into an object of horror and pity, whereas I cause it to be loved; you labour in a torture-chamber and dissecting-room, I make my observations under the blue sky to the song of the cicadas, you subject cell and protoplasm to chemical tests, I study instinct in its loftiest manifestations; you pry into death, I pry into life. And why should I not complete my thought: the boars have muddied the clear stream; natural history, youth's glorious study, has, by dint of cellular improvements, become a hateful and repulsive thing. Well, if I write for men of learning, for philosophers, who, one day, will try to some extent to unravel the tough problem of instinct, I write also, I write above all things for the young. I want to make them love the natural history which you make them hate; and that is why, while keeping strictly to the domain of truth, I avoid your scientific prose, which too often, alas seems borrowed from some Iroquois idiom!"

But this is not my business for the moment: I want to speak of the bit of land long cherished in my plans to form a laboratory of living entomology, the bit of land which I have at last obtained in the solitude of a little village. It is a *harmas*, the name given, in this district, to an untilled, pebbly expanse abandoned to the vegetation of the thyme. It is too poor to repay the work of the plough; but the sheep passes there in spring, when it has chanced to rain and a little grass shoots up.

My harmas, however, because of its modicum of red earth swamped by a huge mass of stones, has received a rough first attempt at cultivation: I am told that vines once grew here. And, in fact, when we dig the ground before planting a few trees, we turn up, here and there, remains of the precious stock, half-carbonized by time. The three-pronged fork, therefore, the only implement of husbandry that can penetrate such a soil as this, has entered here; and I am sorry, for the primitive vegetation has disappeared. No more thyme, no more lavender, no more clumps of kermes-oak, the dwarf oak that forms forests across which we step by lengthening our stride a little. As these plants, especially the first two, might be of use to me by offering the bees and wasps a spoil to forage, I am

compelled to reinstate them in the ground whence they were driven by the fork.

What abounds without my mediation is the invaders of any soil that is first dug up and then left for a long time to its own resources. We have, in the first rank, the couch-grass, that execrable weed which three years of stubborn warfare have not succeeded in exterminating. Next, in respect of number, come the centauries, grim-looking one and all, bristling with prickles or starry halberds. They are the yellow-flowered centaury, the mountain centaury, the star-thistle and the rough centaury: the first predominates. Here and there, amid their inextricable confusion, stands, like a chandelier with spreading, orange flowers for lights, the fierce Spanish oyster-plant, whose spikes are strong as nails. Above it, towers the Illyrian cotton-thistle, whose straight and solitary stalk soars to a height of three to six feet and ends in large pink tufts. Its armour hardly yields before that of the oyster-plant. Nor must we forget the lesser thistle-tribe, with first of all, the prickly or "cruel" thistle, which is so well armed that the plant-collector knows not where to grasp it; next, the spear-thistle, with its ample foliage, ending each of its veins with a spear-head; lastly, the black knap-weed, which gathers itself into a spiky knot. In among these, in long lines armed with hooks, the shoots of the blue dewberry creep along the ground. To visit the prickly thicket when the wasp goes foraging, you must wear boots that come to mid-leg or else resign yourself to a smarting in the calves. As long as the ground retains a few remnants of the vernal rains, this rude vegetation does not lack a certain charm, when the pyramids of the oyster-plant and the slender branches of the cotton-thistle rise above the wide carpet formed by the yellow-flowered centaury saffron heads; but let the droughts of summer come and we see but a desolate waste, which the flame of a match would set ablaze from one end to the other. Such is, or rather was, when I took possession of it, the Eden of bliss where I mean to live henceforth alone with the insect. Forty years of desperate struggle have won it for me.

Eden, I said; and, from the point of view that interests me, the expression is not out of place. This cursed ground, which no one would have had at a gift to sow with a pinch of turnip-seed, is an earthly paradise for the bees and wasps. Its mighty growth of thistles and centauries draws them all to me from everywhere around. Never, in my insect-hunting memories, have I seen so large a population at a single spot; all the trades have made it their rallying-point. Here come hunters of every kind of game, builders in clay, weavers of cotton goods, collectors of pieces cut from a leaf or the petals of a flower, architects in pasteboard, plasterers

mixing mortar, carpenters boring wood, miners digging underground galleries, workers handling goldbeater's skin and many more.

Who is this one? An Anthidium. She scrapes the cobwebby stalk of the yellow-flowered centaury and gathers a ball of wadding which she carries off proudly in the tips of her mandibles. She will turn it, under ground, into cotton-felt satchels to hold the store of honey and the egg. And these others, so eager for plunder? They are Megachiles, carrying under their bellies their black, white or blood-red reaping-brushes. They will leave the thistles to visit the neighbouring shrubs and there cut from the leaves oval pieces which will be made into a fit receptacle to contain the harvest. And these, clad in black velvet? They are Chalcicodomae, who work with cement and gravel. We could easily find their masonry on the stones in the harmas. And these, noisily buzzing with a sudden flight? They are the Anthophorae, who live in the old walls and the sunny banks of the neighbourhood.

Now come the Osmiae. One stacks her cells in the spiral staircase of an empty snail-shell; another, attacking the pith of a dry bit of bramble, obtains for her grubs a cylindrical lodging and divides it into floors by means of partition-walls; a third employs the natural channel of a cut reed; a fourth is a rent-free tenant of the vacant galleries of some mason-bee. Here are the Macrocerae and the Eucerae, whose males are proudly horned; the Dasypodae, who carry an ample brush of bristles on their hind-legs for a reaping implement; the Andrenae, so manifold in species; the slender-bellied Halicti. I omit a host of others. If I tried to continue this record of the guests of my thistles, it would muster almost the whole of the honey-yielding tribe. A learned entomologist of Bordeaux, Professor Pérez, to whom I submit the naming of my prizes, once asked me if I had any special means of hunting, to send him so many rarities and even novelties. I am not at all an experienced and, still less, a zealous hunter, for the insect interests me much more when engaged in its work than when stuck on a pin in a cabinet. The whole secret of my hunting is reduced to my dense nursery of thistles and centauries.

By a most fortunate chance, with this populous family of honey-gatherers was allied the whole hunting tribe. The builders' men had distributed here and there in the harmas great mounds of sand and heaps of stones, with a view to running up some surrounding walls. The work dragged on slowly; and the materials found occupants from the first year. The mason-bees had chosen the interstices between the stones as a dormitory where to pass the night, in serried groups. The powerful eyed lizard, who, when close-pressed, attacks both man and dog, wide-mouthed,

had selected a cave wherein to lie in wait for the passing scarab; the black-eared chat, garbed like a Dominican, white-frocked with black wings, sat on the top stone, singing his short rustic lay: his nest, with its sky-blue eggs, must be somewhere in the heap. The little Dominican disappeared with the loads of stones. I regret him: he would have been a charming neighbour. The eyed lizard I do not regret at all.

The sand sheltered a different colony. Here, the Bembeces were sweeping the threshold of their burrows, flinging a curve of dust behind them; the Languedocian Sphex was dragging her Ephippigera by the antennae; a Stizus was storing her preserves of Cicadellae. To my sorrow, the masons ended by evicting the sporting tribe; but, should I ever wish to recall it, I have but to renew the mounds of sand: they will soon all be there.

Hunters that have not disappeared, their homes being different, are the Ammophilae, whom I see fluttering, one in spring, the others in autumn, along the garden-walks and over the lawns, in search of a caterpillar; the Pompili, who travel alertly, beating their wings and rummaging in every corner in quest of a spider. The largest of them waylays the Narbonne Lycosa, whose burrow is not infrequent in the harmas. This burrow is a vertical well, with a curb of fescue-grass intertwined with silk. You can see the eyes of the mighty spider gleam at the bottom of the den like little diamonds, an object of terror to most. What a prey and what dangerous hunting for the Pompilus! And here, on a hot summer afternoon, is the Amazon-ant, who leaves her barrack-rooms in long battalions and marches far afield to hunt for slaves. We will follow her in her raids when we find time. Here again, around a heap of grasses turned to mould, are Scoliae an inch and a half long, who fly gracefully and dive into the heap, attracted by a rich prey, the grubs of Lamellicorns, Oryctes and Cetoniae.

What subjects for study! And there are more to come. The house was as utterly deserted as the ground. When man was gone and peace assured, the animal hastily seized on everything. The warbler took up his abode in the lilac-shrubs; the greenfinch settled in the thick shelter of the cypresses; the sparrow carted rags and straw under every slate; the serin-finch, whose downy nest is no bigger than half an apricot, came and chirped in the plane-tree-tops; the Scops made a habit of uttering his monotonous, piping note here, of an evening; the bird of Pallas Athene, the owl, came hurrying along to hoot and hiss.

In front of the house is a large pond, fed by the aqueduct that supplies the village-pumps with water. Here, from half a mile and more around, come the frogs and toads in the lovers' season. The natterjack,

sometimes as large as a plate, with a narrow stripe of yellow down his back, makes his appointments here to take his bath; when the evening twilight falls, we see hopping along the edge the midwife toad, the male, who carries a cluster of eggs, the size of peppercorns, wrapped round his hindlegs: the genial paterfamilias has brought his precious packet from afar, to leave it in the water and afterwards retire under some flat stone, whence he will emit a sound like a tinkling bell. Lastly, when not croaking amid the foliage, the tree-frogs indulge in the most graceful dives. And so, in May, as soon as it is dark, the pond becomes a deafening orchestra: it is impossible to talk at table, impossible to sleep. We had to remedy this by means perhaps a little too rigorous. What could we do? He who tries to sleep and cannot needs becomes ruthless.

Bolder still, the wasp has taken possession of the dwelling-house. On my door-sill, in a soil of rubbish, nestles the white-banded Sphex: when I go indoors, I must be careful not to damage her burrows, not to tread upon the miner absorbed in her work. It is quite a quarter of a century since I last saw the saucy cricket-hunter. When I made her acquaintance, I used to visit her at a few miles' distance: each time, it meant an expedition under the blazing August sun. To-day, I find her at my door; we are intimate neighbours. The embrasure of the closed window provides an apartment of a mild temperature for the Pelopaeus. The earthbuilt nest is fixed against the freestone wall. To enter her home, the spider-huntress uses a little hole left open by accident in the shutters. On the mouldings of the Venetian blinds, a few stray mason-bees build their group of cells; inside the outer shutters, left ajar, a Eumenes constructs her little earthen dome, surmounted by a short, bell-mouthed neck. The common wasp and the Polistes are my dinner-guests: they visit my table to see if the grapes served are as ripe as they look.

Here, surely—and the list is far from complete—is a company both numerous and select, whose conversation will not fail to charm my solitude, if I succeed in drawing it out. My dear beasts of former days, my old friends, and others, more recent acquaintances, all are here, hunting, foraging, building in close proximity. Besides, should we wish to vary the scene of observation, the mountain is but a few hundred steps away, with its tangle of arbutus, rock-roses and arborescent heather; with its sandy spaces dear to the Bembeces; with its marly slopes exploited by different wasps and bees. And that is why, foreseeing these riches, I have abandoned the town for the village and come to Sérignan to weed my turnips and water my lettuces.

Laboratories are being founded, at great expense, on our Atlantic and Mediterranean coasts, where people cut up small sea-animals, of but

meagre interest to us; they spend a fortune on powerful microscopes, delicate dissecting-instruments, engines of capture, boats, fishing-crews, aquariums, to find out how the yolk of an Annelid's egg is constructed, a question whereof I have never yet been able to grasp the full importance; and they scorn the little land-animal, which lives in constant touch with us, which provides universal psychology with documents of inestimable value, which too often threatens the public wealth by destroying our crops. When shall we have an entomological laboratory for the study not of the dead insect, steeped in alcohol, but of the living insect; a laboratory having for its object the instinct, the habits, the manner of living, the work, the struggles, the propagation of that little world, with which agriculture and philosophy have most seriously to reckon?

To know thoroughly the history of the destroyer of our vines might perhaps be more important than to know how this or that nerve-fibre of a Cirriped ends; to establish by experiment the line of demarcation between intellect and instinct; to prove, by comparing facts in the zoological progression, whether human reason be an irreducible faculty or not: all this ought surely to take precedence of the number of joints in a crustacean's antenna. These enormous questions would need an army of workers; and we have not one. The fashion is all for the mollusc and the zoophytes. The depths of the sea are explored with many dragnets; the soil which we tread is consistently disregarded. While waiting for the fashion to change, I open my harmas laboratory of living entomology; and this laboratory shall not cost the ratepayers one farthing.

*The foregoing consists of two paragraphs
from Fabre's* THE GLOW-WORM
and Chapter I from Fabre's THE LIFE OF THE FLY.

The Sacred Beetle

I t happened like this. There were five or six of us: myself, the oldest, officially their master but even more their friend and comrade; they, lads with warm hearts and joyous imaginations, overflowing with that youthful vitality which makes us so enthusiastic and so eager for knowledge. We started off one morning down a path fringed with dwarf elder and hawthorn, whose clustering blossoms were already a paradise for the rose chafer ecstatically drinking in their bitter perfumes. We talked as we went. We were going to see whether the sacred beetle had yet made his appearance on the sandy plateau of Les Angles, whether he was rolling that pellet of dung in which ancient Egypt beheld an image of the world; we were going to find out whether the stream at the foot of the hill was not hiding under its mantle of duckweed young newts with gills like tiny branches of coral; whether that pretty little fish of our rivulets, the stickleback, had donned his wedding scarf of purple and blue; whether the newly arrived swallow was skimming the meadows on pointed wing, chasing the craneflies, who scatter their eggs as they dance through the air; if the eyed lizard was sunning his blue-speckled body on the threshold of a burrow dug in the sandstone; if the laughing gull, travelling from the sea in the wake of the legions of fish that ascend the Rhône to milt in its waters, was hovering in his hundreds over the river, ever and anon uttering his cry so like a maniac's laughter; if . . . but that will do. To be brief, let us say that, like good simple folk who find pleasure in all living things, we were off to spend a morning at the most wonderful of festivals, life's springtime awakening.

Our expectations were fulfilled. The stickleback was dressed in his best: his scales would have paled the lustre of silver; his throat was flashing with the brightest vermilion. On the approach of the great black horse-leech, the spines on his back and sides started up, as though worked

by a spring. In the face of this resolute attitude, the bandit turns tail and slips ignominiously down among the water-weeds. The placid mollusc tribe—Planorbes, Limnaei and other water-snails—were sucking in the air on the surface of the water. The Hydrophilus [a predaceous water-beetle] and her hideous larva, those pirates of the ponds, darted amongst them, wringing a neck or two as they passed. The stupid crowd did not seem even to notice it. But let us leave the plain and its waters and clamber up the bluff to the plateau above us. Up there, sheep are grazing and horses being exercised for the approaching races, while all are distributing manna to the enraptured dung-beetles.

What excitement over a single patch of cow-dung! Never did adventurers hurrying from the four corners of the earth display such eagerness in working a Californian claim. Before the sun becomes too hot, they are there in their hundreds, large and small, of every sort, shape and size, hastening to carve themselves a slice of the common cake. There are some that labour in the open air and scrape the surface; there are others that dig themselves galleries in the thick of the heap, in search of choice veins; some work the lower stratum and bury their spoil without delay in the ground just below; others again, the smallest, keep on one side and crumble a morsel that has slipped their way during the mighty excavations of their more powerful fellows. Some, newcomers and doubtless the hungriest, consume their meal on the spot; but the greater number dream of accumulating stocks that will allow them to spend long days in affluence, down in some safe retreat. A nice, fresh patch of dung is not found just when you want it, in the barren plains overgrown with thyme; a windfall of this sort is as manna from the sky; only fortune's favourites receive so fair a portion. Wherefore the riches of to-day are prudently hoarded for the morrow. The stercoraceous scent has carried the glad tidings half a mile around; and all have hastened up to get a store of provisions. A few laggards are still arriving, on the wing or on foot.

Who is this that comes trotting towards the heap, fearing lest he reach it too late? His long legs move with awkward jerks, as though driven by some mechanism within his belly; his little red antennae unfurl their fan, a sign of anxious greed. He is coming, he has come, not without sending a few banqueters sprawling. It is the sacred beetle, clad all in black, the biggest and most famous of our dung-beetles. Behold him at table, beside his fellow-guests, each of whom is giving the last touches to his ball with the flat of his broad forelegs or else enriching it with yet one

more layer before retiring to enjoy the fruit of his labours in peace. Let us follow the construction of the famous ball in all its phases.

The clypeus, or shield, that is, the edge of the broad, flat head, is notched with six angular teeth arranged in a semicircle. This constitutes the tool for digging and cutting up, the rake that lifts and casts aside the unnutritious vegetable fibres, goes for something better, scrapes and collects it. A choice is thus made, for these connoisseurs differentiate between one thing and another, making a rough selection when the beetle is occupied with his own provender, but an extremely scrupulous one when it is a case of constructing the maternal ball, which has a central cavity in which the egg will hatch. Then every scrap of fibre is conscientiously rejected and only the stercoral quintessence is gathered as the material for building the inner layer of the cell. The young larva, on issuing from the egg, thus finds in the very walls of its lodging a food of special delicacy which strengthens its digestion and enables it afterwards to attack the coarse outer layers.

Where his own needs are concerned, the beetle is less particular and contents himself with a very general sorting. The notched shield then does its scooping and digging, its casting aside and scraping together more or less at random. The forelegs play a mighty part in the work. They are flat, bow-shaped, supplied with powerful nervures and armed on the outside with five strong teeth. If a vigorous effort be needed to remove an obstacle or to force a way through the thickest part of the heap, the dung-beetle makes use of his elbows, that is to say, he flings his toothed legs to right and left and clears a semicircular space with an energetic sweep. Room once made, a different kind of work is found for these same limbs: they collect armfuls of the stuff raked together by the shield and push it under the insect's belly, between the four hinder legs. These are formed for the turner's trade. They are long and slender, especially the last pair, slightly bowed and finished with a very sharp claw. They are at once recognized as compasses, capable of embracing a globular body in their curved branches and of verifying and correcting its shape. Their function is, in fact, to fashion the ball.

Armful by armful, the material is heaped up under the belly, between the four legs, which, by a slight pressure, impart their own curve to it and give it a preliminary outline. Then, every now and again, the rough-hewn pill is set spinning between the four branches of the double pair of spherical compasses; it turns under the dung-beetle's belly until it is rolled into a perfect ball. Should the surface layer lack plasticity and threaten to

peel off, should some too stringy part refuse to yield to the action of the lathe, the forelegs touch up the faulty places; their broad paddles pat the ball to give consistency to the new layer and to work the recalcitrant bits into the mass.

Under a hot sun, when time presses, one stands amazed at the turner's feverish activity. And so the work proceeds apace: what a moment ago was a tiny pellet is now a ball the size of a walnut; soon it will be the size of an apple. I have seen some gluttons manufacture a ball the size of a man's fist. This indeed means food in the larder for days to come!

The beetle has his provisions. The next thing is to withdraw from the fray and transport the victuals to a suitable place. Here the scarab's most striking characteristics begin to show themselves. Straightway he begins his journey; he clasps his sphere with his two long hind-legs, whose terminal claws, planted in the mass, serve as pivots; he obtains a purchase with the middle pair of legs; and, with his toothed forearms, pressing in turn upon the ground, to do duty as levers, he proceeds with his load, he himself moving backwards, body bent, head down and hind-quarters in the air. The rear legs, the principal factor in the mechanism, are in continual movement backwards and forwards, shifting the claws to change the axis of rotation, to keep the load balanced and to push it along by alternate thrusts to right and left. In this way, the ball finds itself touching the ground by turns with every point of its surface, a process which perfects its shape and gives an even consistency to its outer layer by means of pressure uniformly distributed.

And now to work with a will! The thing moves, it begins to roll; we shall get there, though not without difficulty. Here is a first awkward place: the Beetle is wending his way athwart a slope and the heavy mass tends to follow the incline; the insect, however, for reasons best known to itself, prefers to cut across this natural road, a bold project which may be brought to naught by a false step or by a grain of sand which disturbs the balance of the load. The false step is made: down goes the ball to the bottom of the valley; and the insect, toppled over by the shock, is lying on its back, kicking. It is soon up again and hastens to harness itself once more to its load. The machine works better than ever. But look out, you dunderhead! Follow the dip of the valley: that will save labour and mishaps; the road is good and level; your ball will roll quite easily. Not a bit of it! The beetle prepares once again to mount the slope that has already been his undoing. Perhaps it suits him to return to the heights. Against that I have nothing to say: the scarab's judgment is better than mine as to the advisability of keeping to lofty regions; he can see farther than I can in these matters. But at least take this path, which will lead you up

by a gentle incline! Certainly not! Let him find himself near some very
steep slope, impossible to climb, and that is the very path which the ob-
stinate fellow will choose. Now begins a Sisyphean labour. The ball,
that enormous burden, is painfully hoisted, step by step, with infinite
precautions, to a certain height, always backwards. We wonder by what
miracle of statics a mass of this size can be kept upon the slope. Oh! An
ill-advised movement frustrates all this toil: the ball rolls down, dragging
the beetle with it. Once more the heights are scaled and another fall is
the sequel. The attempt is renewed, with greater skill this time at the
difficult points; a wretched grass-root, the cause of the previous falls, is
carefully got over. We are almost there; but steady now, steady! It is a
dangerous ascent and the merest trifle may yet ruin everything. For see,
a leg slips on a smooth bit of gravel! Down come ball and beetle, all mixed
up together. And the insect begins over again, with indefatigable obsti-
nacy. Ten times, twenty times, he will attempt the hopeless ascent, until
his persistence vanquishes all obstacles, or until, wisely recognizing the
futility of his efforts, he adopts the level road.

The scarab does not always push his precious ball alone: sometimes
he takes a partner; or, to be accurate, the partner takes him. This is the
way in which things usually happen: once his ball is ready, a dung-beetle
issues from the crowd and leaves the work-yard, pushing his prize back-
wards. A neighbour, a newcomer, whose own task is hardly begun,
abruptly drops his work and runs to the moving ball, to lend a hand to
the lucky owner, who seems to accept the proffered aid kindly. Hence-
forth the two work in partnership. Each does his best to push the pellet to
a place of safety. Was a compact really concluded in the work-yard, a tacit
agreement to share the cake between them? While one was kneading and
moulding the ball, was the other tapping rich veins whence to extract
choice materials and add them to the common store? I have never ob-
served any such collaboration; I have always seen each dung-beetle oc-
cupied solely with his own affairs in the works. The last-comer, therefore,
has no acquired rights.

Can it then be a partnership between the two sexes, a couple intending
to set up house? I thought so for a time.

The evidence of the scalpel compelled me to abandon my belief in this
domestic idyll. There is no outward difference between the two sexes in
the Scarabaei. I therefore dissected the pair of dung-beetles engaged in
trundling one and the same ball; and they very often proved to be of the
same sex.

Neither community of family nor community of labour! Then what
is the motive for this apparent partnership? It is purely and simply an

attempt at robbery. The zealous fellow-worker, on the false plea of lend-
ing a helping hand, cherishes a plan to purloin the ball at the first op-
portunity. To make one's own ball at the heap means hard work and pa-
tience; to steal one ready-made, or at least to foist one's self as a guest,
is a much easier matter. Should the owner's vigilance slacken, you can
run away with his property; should you be too closely watched, you can
sit down to table uninvited, pleading services rendered. It is "Heads I
win, tails you lose" in these tactics, so that pillage is practised as one of
the most lucrative of trades. Some go to work craftily, in the way which
I have described: they come to the aid of a comrade who has not the
least need of them and hide the most barefaced greed under the cloak
of charitable assistance. Others, bolder perhaps, more confident in their
strength, go straight to their goal and commit robbery with violence.

Scenes are constantly happening such as this: a scarab goes off, peace-
fully, by himself, rolling his ball, his lawful property, acquired by con-
scientious work. Another comes flying up, I know not whence, drops
down heavily, folds his dingy wings under their cases and, with the back
of his toothed forearms, knocks over the owner, who is powerless to ward
off the attack in his awkward position, harnessed as he is to his property.
While the victim struggles to his feet, the other perches himself atop the
ball, the best position from which to repel an assailant. With his forearms
crossed over his breast, ready to hit back, he awaits events. The dispos-
sessed one moves round the ball, seeking a favourable spot at which to
make the assault; the usurper spins round on the roof of the citadel, fac-
ing his opponent all the time. If the latter raise himself in order to scale
the wall, the robber gives him a blow that stretches him on his back.
Safe at the top of his fortress, the besieged beetle could foil his adver-
sary's attempts indefinitely if the latter did not change his tactics. He
turns sapper so as to reduce the citadel with the garrison. The ball, shaken
from below, totters and begins rolling, carrying with it the thieving dung-
beetle, who makes violent efforts to maintain his position on the top. This
he succeeds in doing—though not invariably—thanks to hurried gymnas-
tic feats which land him higher on the ball and make up for the ground
which he loses by its rotation. Should a false movement bring him to
earth, the chances become equal and the struggle turns into a wrestling-
match. Robber and robbed grapple with each other, breast to breast.
Their legs lock and unlock, their joints intertwine, their horny armour
clashes and grates with the rasping sound of metal under the file. Then
the one who succeeds in throwing his opponent and releasing himself
scrambles to the top of the ball and there takes up his position. The siege

is renewed, now by the robber, now by the robbed, as the chances of the hand-to-hand conflict may decree. The former, a brawny desperado, no novice at the game, often has the best of the fight. Then, after two or three unsuccessful attempts, the defeated beetle wearies and returns philosophically to the heap, to make himself a new pellet. As for the other, with all fear of a surprise attack at an end, he harnesses himself to the conquered ball and pushes it whither he pleases. I have sometimes seen a third thief appear upon the scene and rob the robber. Nor can I honestly say that I was sorry.

I ask myself in vain what Proudhon introduced into scarabaean morality the daring paradox that "property means plunder," or what diplomatist taught the dung-beetle the savage maxim that "might is right." I have no data that would enable me to trace the origin of these spoliations, which have become a custom, of this abuse of strength to capture a lump of ordure. All that I can say is that theft is a general practice among the scarabs. These dung-rollers rob one another with a calm effrontery which, to my knowledge, is without a parallel. I leave it to future observers to elucidate this curious problem in animal psychology and I go back to the two partners rolling their ball in concert.

But first let me dispel a current error in the text-books. I find in M. Émile Blanchard's magnificent work, *Métamorphoses, mœurs et instincts des insectes* [Metamorphoses, the habits and instincts of the insects], the following passage:

> Sometimes our insect is stopped by an insurmountable obstacle; the ball has fallen into a hole. At such moments the Ateuchus gives evidence of a really astonishing grasp of the situation as well as of a system of ready communication between individuals of the same species which is even more remarkable. Recognizing the impossibility of coaxing the ball out of the hole, the Ateuchus seems to abandon it and flies away. If you are sufficiently endowed with that great and noble virtue called patience, stay by the forsaken ball: after a while, the Ateuchus will return to the same spot and will not return alone; he will be accompanied by two, three, four or five companions, who will all alight at the place indicated and will combine their efforts to raise the load. The Ateuchus has been to fetch reinforcements; and this explains why it is such a common sight, in the dry fields, to see several Ateuchi joining in the removal of a single ball.

Finally, I read in Illiger's *Entomological Magazine:*

> A *Gymnopleurus pilularius* [a smaller dung-beetle], while constructing the ball of dung destined to contain her eggs, let it roll into a hole,

whence she strove for a long time to extract it unaided. Finding that she was wasting her time in vain efforts, she ran to a neighbouring heap of manure to fetch three individuals of her own species, who, uniting their strength to hers, succeeded in withdrawing the ball from the cavity into which it had fallen and then returned to their manure to continue their work.

I crave a thousand pardons of my illustrious master, M. Blanchard, but things certainly do not happen as he says. To begin with, the two accounts are so much alike that they must have had a common origin. Illiger, on the strength of observations not continuous enough to deserve blind confidence, put forward the case of his Gymnopleurus; and the same story was repeated about the Scarabaei because it is, in fact, quite usual to see two of these insects occupied together either in rolling a ball or in getting it out of a troublesome place. But this cooperation in no way proves that the dung-beetle who found himself in difficulties went to requisition the aid of his mates. I have had no small measure of the patience recommended by M. Blanchard; I have lived laborious days in close intimacy, if I may say so, with the sacred beetle; I have done everything that I could think of in order to enter into his ways and habits as thoroughly as possible and to study them from life; and I have never seen anything that suggested either nearly or remotely the idea of companions summoned to lend assistance. As I shall presently relate, I have subjected the dung-beetle to far more serious trials than that of getting his ball into a hole; I have confronted him with much graver difficulties than that of mounting a slope, which is sheer sport to the obstinate Sisyphus, who seems to delight in the rough gymnastics involved in climbing steep places, as if the ball thereby grew firmer and accordingly increased in value; I have created artificial situations in which the insect had the uttermost need of help; and never did my eyes detect any evidence of friendly services being rendered by comrade to comrade. I have seen beetles robbed and beetles robbing and nothing more. If a number of them were gathered around the same pill, it meant that a battle was taking place. My humble opinion, therefore, is that the incident of a number of Scarabaei collected around the same ball with thieving intentions has given rise to these stories of comrades called in to lend a hand. Imperfect observations are responsible for this transformation of the bold highwayman into a helpful companion who has left his work to do another a friendly turn.

It is no light matter to attribute to an insect a really astonishing grasp of a situation, combined with an even more amazing power of communi-

cation between individuals of the same species. Such an admission involves more than one imagines. That is why I insist on my point. What! Are we to believe that a beetle in distress will conceive the idea of going in quest of help? We are to imagine him flying off and scouring the country to find fellow-workers on some patch of dung; when he has found them, we are to suppose that he addresses them, in some sort of pantomime, by gestures with his antennae more particularly, in some such words as these:

"I say, you fellows, my load's upset in a hole over there; come and help me get it out. I'll do as much for you one day!"

And we are to believe that his comrades understand! And, more incredible still, that they straightway leave their work, the pellet which they have just begun, the beloved pill exposed to the cupidity of others and certain to be filched in their absence, and go to the help of the suppliant! I am profoundly incredulous of such unselfishness; and my incredulity is confirmed by what I have witnessed for years and years, not in glass-cases but in the very places where the scarab works. Apart from its maternal solicitude, in which respect it is nearly always admirable, the insect cares for nothing but itself, unless it lives in societies, like the hive-bees, the ants and the rest.

But let me end this digression, which is excused by the importance of the subject. I was saying that a sacred beetle, in possession of a ball which he is pushing backwards, is often joined by another, who comes hurrying up to lend an assistance which is anything but disinterested, his intention being to rob his companion if the opportunity present itself. Let us call the two workers partners, though that is not the proper name for them, seeing that the one forces himself upon the other, who probably accepts outside help only for fear of a worse evil. The meeting, by the way, is absolutely peaceful. The owner of the ball does not cease work for an instant on the arrival of the newcomer; and his uninvited assistant seems animated by the best intentions and sets to work on the spot. The way in which the two partners harness themselves differs. The proprietor occupies the chief position, the place of honour: he pushes at the rear, with his hind-legs in the air and his head down. His subordinate is in front, in the reverse posture, head up, toothed arms on the ball, long hind-legs on the ground. Between the two, the ball rolls along, one driving it before him, the other pulling it towards him.

The efforts of the couple are not always very harmonious, the more so as the assistant has his back to the road to be traversed, while the owner's view is impeded by the load. The result is that they are constantly

having accidents, absurd tumbles, taken cheerfully and in good part: each picks himself up quickly and resumes the same position as before. On level ground, this system of traction does not correspond with the dynamic force expended, through lack of precision in the combined movements: the scarab at the back would do as well and better if left to himself. And so the helper, having given a proof of his good-will at the risk of throwing the machinery out of gear, now decides to keep still, without letting go of the precious ball, of course. He already looks upon that as his: a ball touched is a ball gained. He won't be so silly as not to stick to it: the other might give him the slip!

So he gathers his legs flat under his belly, encrusting himself, so to speak, on the ball and becoming one with it. Henceforth, the whole concern—the ball and the beetle clinging to its surface—is rolled along by the efforts of the lawful owner. The intruder sits tight and lies low, heedless whether the load pass over his body, whether he be at the top, bottom or side of the rolling ball. A queer sort of assistant, who gets a free ride so as to make sure of his share of the victuals!

But a steep ascent heaves in sight and gives him a fine part to play. He takes the lead now, holding up the heavy mass with his toothed arms, while his mate seeks a purchase in order to hoist the load a little higher. In this way, by a combination of well-directed efforts, the beetle above gripping, the one below pushing, I have seen a couple mount hills which would have been too much for a single porter, however persevering. But in times of difficulty not all show the same zeal: there are some who, on awkward slopes where their assistance is most needed, seem blissfully unaware of the trouble. While the unhappy Sisyphus exhausts himself in attempts to get over the bad part, the other quietly leaves him to it: imbedded in the ball, he rolls down with it if it comes to grief and is hoisted up with it when they start afresh.

I have often tried the following experiment on the two partners in order to judge their inventive faculties when placed in a serious predicament. Suppose them to be on level ground, number two seated motionless on the ball, number one busy pushing. Without disturbing the latter, I nail the ball to the ground with a long, strong pin. It stops suddenly. The beetle, unaware of my perfidy, doubtless believes that some natural obstacle, a rut, a tuft of couch-grass, a pebble, bars the way. He redoubles his efforts, struggles his hardest; nothing happens.

"What can the matter be? Let's go and see."

The beetle walks two or three times round his pellet. Discovering noth-

ing to account for its immobility, he returns to the rear and starts pushing again. The ball remains stationary.

"Let's look up above."

The beetle goes up to find nothing but his motionless colleague, for I had taken care to drive in the pin so deep that the head disappeared in the ball. He explores the whole upper surface and comes down again. Fresh thrusts are vigorously applied in front and at the sides, with the same absence of success. There is not a doubt about it: never before was dung-beetle confronted with such a problem in inertia.

Now is the time, the very time, to claim assistance, which is all the easier as his mate is there, close at hand, squatting on the summit of the ball. Will the scarab rouse him? Will he talk to him like this:

"What are you doing there, lazybones? Come and look at the thing: it's broken down!"

Nothing proves that he does anything of the kind, for I see him steadily shaking the unshakable, inspecting his stationary machine on every side, while all this time his companion sits resting. At long last, however, the latter becomes aware that something unusual is happening; he is apprised of it by his mate's restless tramping and by the immobility of the ball. He comes down, therefore, and in his turn examines the machine. Double harness does no better than single harness. This is beginning to look serious. The little fans of the beetles' antennae open and shut, open again, betraying by their agitation acute anxiety. Then a stroke of genius ends the perplexity:

"Who knows what's underneath?"

They now start exploring below the ball; and a little digging soon reveals the presence of the pin. They recognize at once that the trouble is there.

If I had had a voice in their deliberations, I should have said:

"We must make a hole in the ball and pull out that skewer which is holding it down."

This most elementary of all proceedings and one so easy to such expert diggers was not adopted, was not even tried. The dung-beetle was shrewder than man. The two colleagues, one on this side, one on that, slip under the ball, which begins to slide up the pin, getting higher and higher in proportion as the living wedges make their way underneath. The clever operation is made possible by the softness of the material, which gives easily and makes a channel under the head of the immovable stake. Soon the pellet is suspended at a height equal to the thickness of

the scarabs' bodies. The rest is not such plain sailing. The dung-beetles, who at first were lying flat, rise gradually to their feet, still pushing with their backs. The work becomes harder and harder as the legs, in straightening out, lose their strength; but none the less they do it. Then comes a time when they can no longer push with their backs, the limit of their height having been reached. A last resource remains, but one much less favourable to the development of motive power. This is for the insect to adopt one or other of its postures when harnessed to the ball, head down or up, and to push with its hind- or forelegs, as the case may be. Finally the ball drops to the ground, unless we have used too long a pin. The gash made by our stake is repaired more or less and the carting of the precious pellet is at once resumed.

But, should the pin really be too long, then the ball, which remains firmly fixed, ends by being suspended at a height above that of the insect's full stature. In that case, after vain evolutions around the unconquerable greased pole, the dung-beetles throw up the sponge, unless we are sufficiently kind hearted to finish the work ourselves and restore their treasure to them. Or again we can help them by raising the floor with a small flat stone, a pedestal from the top of which it is possible for the beetle to continue his labours. Its use does not appear to be immediately understood, for neither of the two is in any hurry to take advantage of it. Nevertheless, by accident or design, one or other at last finds himself on the stone. Oh, joy! As he passed, he felt the ball touch his back. At that contact, courage returns; and his efforts begin once more. Standing on his helpful platform, the scarab stretches his joints, rounds his shoulders, as one might say, and shoves the pellet upwards. When his shoulders no longer avail, he works with his legs, now upright, now head downwards. There is a fresh pause, accompanied by fresh signs of uneasiness, when the limit of extension is reached. Thereupon, without disturbing the creature, we place a second little stone on the top of the first. With the aid of this new step, which provides a fulcrum for its levers, the insect pursues its task. Thus adding story upon story as required, I have seen the scarab, hoisted to the summit of a tottering pile three or four fingers'-breadth in height, persevere in his work until the ball was completely detached.

Had he some vague consciousness of the service performed by the gradual raising of the pedestal? I venture to doubt it, though he cleverly took advantage of my platform of little stones. As a matter of fact, if the very elementary idea of using a higher support in order to reach something placed above one's grasp were not beyond the beetle's comprehension,

how is it that, when there are two of them, neither thinks of lending the other his back so as to raise him by that much and make it possible for him to go on working? If one helped the other in this way, they could reach twice as high. They are very far, however, from any such co-opera-tion. Each pushes the ball, with all his might, I admit, but he pushes as if he were alone and seems to have no notion of the happy result that would follow a combined effort. In this instance, when the ball is nailed to the ground by a pin, they do exactly what they do in corresponding circumstances, as, for example, when the load is brought to a standstill by some obstacle, caught in a loop of couch-grass or transfixed by some spiky bit of stalk that has run into the soft, rolling mass. I produced artifi-cially a stoppage which is not really very different from those occurring naturally when the ball is being rolled amid the thousand and one irregu-larities of the ground; and the beetle behaves, in my experimental tests, as he would have behaved in any other circumstances in which I had no part. He uses his back as a wedge and a lever and pushes with his feet, without introducing anything new into his methods, even when he has a companion and can avail himself of his assistance.

When he is all alone in face of the difficulty, when he has no assistant, his dynamic operations remain absolutely the same; and his efforts to move his transfixed ball end in success, provided that we give him the indispensable support of a platform, built up little by little. If we deny him this succour, then, no longer encouraged by the contact of his be-loved ball, he loses heart and sooner or later flies away, doubtless with many regrets, and disappears. Where to? I do not know. What I do know is that he does not return with a gang of fellow-labourers whom he has begged to help him. What would he do with them, he who cannot make use of even one comrade?

But perhaps my experiment, which leaves the ball suspended at an inaccessible height and the insect with its means of action exhausted, is a little too far removed from ordinary conditions. Let us try instead a miniature pit, deep enough and steep enough to prevent the dung-bee-tle, when placed at the bottom, from rolling his load up the side. These are exactly the conditions stated by Messrs. Blanchard and Illiger. Well, what happens? When dogged but utterly fruitless efforts have convinced him of his helplessness, the beetle takes wing and disappears. Relying upon what these learned writers said, I have waited long hours for the insect to return reinforced by a few friends. I have always waited in vain. Many a time also I have found the pellet several days later just where I left it, stuck at the top of a pin or in a hole, proving that nothing fresh

had happened in my absence. A ball abandoned from necessity is a ball abandoned for good, with no attempt at salvage with the aid of others. A dexterous use of wedge and lever to set the ball rolling again is therefore, when all is said, the greatest intellectual effort which I have observed in the sacred beetle. To make up for what the experiment refutes, namely an appeal for help among fellow-workers, I gladly chronicle this feat of mechanical prowess for the dung-beetles' greater glory.

Directing their steps at random, over sandy plains thick with thyme, over cart-ruts and steep places, the two beetle brethren roll the ball along for some time, thus giving its substance a certain consistency which may be to their liking. While still on the road, they select a favourable spot. The rightful owner, the beetle who throughout has kept the place of honour, behind the ball, the one in short who has done almost all the carting by himself, sets to work to dig the dining-room. Beside him is the ball, with number two clinging to it, shamming dead. Number one attacks the sand with his sharp-edged forehead and his toothed legs; he flings armfuls of it behind him; and the work of excavating proceeds apace. Soon the beetle has disappeared from view in the half-dug cavern. Whenever he returns to the upper air with a load, he invariably glances at his ball to see if all is well. From time to time, he brings it nearer the threshold of the burrow; he feels it and seems to acquire new vigour from the contact. The other, lying demure and motionless on the ball, continues to inspire confidence. Meanwhile the underground hall grows larger and deeper; and the digger's field of operations is now too vast for any but very occasional appearances. Now is the time. The crafty sleeper awakens and hurriedly decamps with the ball, which he pushes behind him with the speed of a pickpocket anxious not to be caught in the act. This breach of trust rouses my indignation, but the historian triumphs for the moment over the moralist and I leave him alone: I shall have time enough to intervene on the side of law and order if things threaten to turn out badly.

The thief is already some yards away. His victim comes out of the burrow, looks around and finds nothing. Doubtless an old hand himself, he knows what this means. Scent and sight soon put him on the track. He makes haste and catches up the robber; but the artful dodger, when he feels his pursuer close on his heels, promptly changes his posture, gets on his hind-legs and clasps the ball with his toothed arms, as he does when acting as an assistant.

You rogue, you! I see through your tricks: you mean to plead as an excuse that the pellet rolled down the slope and that you are only trying to stop it and bring it back home. I, however, an impartial witness, declare

that the ball was quite steady at the entrance to the burrow and did not roll of its own accord. Besides, the ground is level. I declare that I saw you set the thing in motion and make off with unmistakable intentions. It was an attempt at larceny, or I've never seen one!

My evidence is not admitted. The owner cheerfully accepts the other's excuses; and the two bring the ball back to the burrow as though nothing had happened.

If the thief, however, has time to get far enough away, or if he manages to cover his trail by adroitly doubling back, the injury is irreparable. To collect provisions under a blazing sun, to cart them a long distance, to dig a comfortable banqueting-hall in the sand and then—just when everything is ready and your appetite, whetted by exercise, lends an added charm to the approaching feast—suddenly to find yourself cheated by a crafty partner is, it must be admitted, a reverse of fortune that would dishearten most of us. The dung-beetle does not allow himself to be cast down by this piece of ill-luck; he rubs his cheeks, spreads his antennae, sniffs the air and flies to the nearest heap to begin all over again.

The foregoing is taken
from Fabre's THE SACRED BEETLE AND OTHERS.

Loren Eiseley

1907–

Loren Eiseley was born in Lincoln, Nebraska, in 1907. He studied at the University of Nebraska and received his Ph.D. in anthropology from the University of Pennsylvania. He taught at the University of Kansas, at Oberlin College, and at the University of Pennsylvania, where, from 1947, he was head of the department of anthropology, and, from 1959, provost of the university.

He has lectured at many universities and has written articles for most of the leading scientific journals as well as for a number of magazines. He has ranged over much of the western United States in search of remains of early postglacial man. *The Immense Journey,* his first book, appeared in 1957. It is a collection of papers on various subjects, all of them linked together by their common concern with time. *Darwin's Century,* an account of the impact of the idea of evolution, was published in 1958, and his remarkable lecture, *The Mind as Nature,* in 1962.

The following selection is a chapter from *The Immense Journey.* The title refers to the journey through time from the beginning. Not the beginning of man—that occurred only a moment ago, Eiseley says. It is his concern to remind men that there is more to the world than themselves, both in space and time.

Man "is rooted in his particular century," Eiseley writes. "Out of it—forward or backward—he cannot run." Later in the book he writes: "There is something wrong with our world view. It is still Ptolemaic, though the sun is no longer believed to revolve around the earth." He seems to be suggesting that there is in our thinking, despite all that we have learned about the past, a kind of

temporal parochialism. The sun is no longer thought to revolve about the earth, but man, Eiseley is saying, still conceives of himself as somehow at the center of the universe. And if this is true, his argument runs, how much more difficult it must be for us to give up the illusion that the human epoch is the be-all and end-all of time.

We are fixed, in other words, even more irremovably in the Now than in the Here. Only by an effort of the imagination can we break out of our temporal strait jackets. But there is a great reluctance, Eiseley suggests, to do so. If we are to succeed, we must use words in new ways.

Eiseley's words in the following selection have a strange quality. He uses many surprising metaphors, and most of them have a special character. If it is read carefully, his text is seen to use terms standing for more or less violent spatial movements in order to force us to feel temporal movements. At the beginning, for example, he sets the scene: it is, typically, in no definite place, for its purpose is to make us see change in time. He descends into the Slit, and it is at once obvious that this spatial descent is a movement backward in time. "The Slit was a little sinister . . . for over me the sky seemed already as far off as some future century I would never see." The word "far" in that sentence has two meanings, in space and time, and so does the word "see."

One can find other examples of Eiseley's attempt to bring us, by the use of unexpected metaphors, to an understanding of the vastness, and indeterminacy, of time. He points to that place of "converging roads where . . . cat and man and weasel must leap into a single shape." The word "leap" in that sentence is one of these metaphors. He conceives of himself as "already caught a few feet above (the skull) in the strata," and thus caught, as it were, in a long-past epoch. "Living creatures flow," he says, again using a surprising word to produce his effect, "with little more consistency than clouds from age to age." He remembers "lifting, as I always did, a figurative lantern to some ambiguous crossroads sign within my brain." There are crossroads, he is saying, in time as well as space. And when he emerges from the crack in the earth, which is also a crack in time, he is cautious, lest he might have strayed into an era different from the one he knew. "I looked all about carefully," he says, "in a sudden anxiety that it might not be a grazing horse that I would see." For the moment, at least, it was conceivable that it

might have been a mammoth—or some strange animal that does not yet walk the earth.

It is clear that Eiseley's language is special, and also that it is different from that of most of the other scientists in this volume. Strictly speaking, he is not here recounting observations of nature or telling us the results of experiments on it. Indeed, he is perhaps not telling us anything that we do not already know. Rather, he is telling us what we do know, but what, he seems to be insisting, we nevertheless refuse to accept. *The Immense Journey* is not in itself a scientific work; it is a work, by a distinguished scientist, that is a result of the scientific world view. As such, it is a representative of an important body of modern writing. And it is of course, in itself, extremely fine.

On Time

from *The Immense Journey*

Some lands are flat and grass covered, and smile so evenly up at the sun that they seem forever youthful, untouched by man or time. Some are torn, ravaged and convulsed like the features of profane old age. Rocks are wrenched up and exposed to view; black pits receive the sun but give back no light.

It was to such a land I rode, but I rode to it across a sunlit, timeless prairie over which nothing passed but antelope or a wandering bird. On the verge where that prairie halted before a great wall of naked sandstone and clay, I came upon the Slit. A narrow crack worn by some descending torrent had begun secretly, far back in the prairie grass, and worked itself deeper and deeper into the fine sandstone that led by devious channels into the broken waste beyond. I rode back along the crack to a spot where I could descend into it, dismounted, and left my horse to graze.

The crack was only about body width and, as I worked my way downward, the light turned dark and green from the overhanging grass. Above me the sky became a narrow slit of distant blue, and the sandstone was cool to my hands on either side. The Slit was a little sinister—like an open grave, assuming the dead were enabled to take one last look—for over me the sky seemed already as far off as some future century I would never see.

I ignored the sky, then, and began to concentrate on the sandstone walls that had led me into this place. It was tight and tricky work, but that cut was a perfect cross section through perhaps ten million years of time. I hoped to find at least a bone, but I was not quite prepared for the sight I finally came upon. Staring straight out at me, as I slid farther and deeper into the green twilight, was a skull embedded in the solid sandstone. I had come at just the proper moment when it was fully to be seen, the

white bone gleaming there in a kind of ashen splendor, water worn, and about to be ground away in the next long torrent.

It was not, of course, human. I was deep, deep below the time of man in a remote age near the beginning of the reign of mammals. I squatted on my heels in the narrow ravine, and we stared a little blankly at each other, the skull and I. There were marks of generalized primitiveness in that low, pinched brain case and grinning jaw that marked it as lying far back along those converging roads where, as I shall have occasion to establish elsewhere, cat and man and weasel must leap into a single shape.

It was the face of a creature who had spent his days following his nose, who was led by instinct rather than memory, and whose power of choice was very small. Though he was not a man, nor a direct human ancestor, there was yet about him, even in the bone, some trace of that low, snuffling world out of which our forebears had so recently emerged. The skull lay tilted in such a manner that it stared, sightless, up at me as though I, too, were already caught a few feet above him in the strata and, in my turn, were staring upward at that strip of sky which the ages were carrying farther away from me beneath the tumbling debris of falling mountains. The creature had never lived to see a man, and I, what was it I was never going to see?

I restrained a panicky impulse to hurry upward after that receding sky that was outlined above the Slit. Probably, I thought, as I patiently began the task of chiseling into the stone around the skull, I would never again excavate a fossil under conditions which led to so vivid an impression that I was already one myself. The truth is that we are all potential fossils still carrying within our bodies the crudities of former existences, the marks of a world in which living creatures flow with little more consistency than clouds from age to age.

As I tapped and chiseled there in the foundations of the world, I had ample time to consider the cunning manipulability of the human fingers. Experimentally I crooked one of the long slender bones. It might have been silica, I thought, or aluminum, or iron—the cells would have made it possible. But no, it is calcium, carbonate of lime. Why? Only because of its history. Elements more numerous than calcium in the earth's crust could have been used to build the skeleton. Our history is the reason—we came from the water. It was there the cells took the lime habit, and they kept it after we came ashore.

It is not a bad symbol of that long wandering, I thought again—the human hand that has been fin and scaly reptile foot and furry paw. If a

stone should fall (I cocked an eye at the leaning shelf above my head
and waited, fatalistically) let the bones lie here with their message, for
those who might decipher it, if they come down late among us from the
stars.

Above me the great crack seemed to lengthen.

Perhaps there is no meaning in it at all, the thought went on inside me,
save that of journey itself, so far as men can see. It has altered with the
chances of life, and the chances brought us here; but it was a good jour-
ney—long, perhaps—but a good journey under a pleasant sun. Do not
look for the purpose. Think of the way we came and be a little proud.
Think of this hand—the utter pain of its first venture on the pebbly shore.

Or consider its later wanderings.

I ceased my tappings around the sand-filled sockets of the skull and
wedged myself into a crevice for a smoke. As I tamped a load of tobacco
into my pipe, I thought of a town across the valley that I used sometimes
to visit, a town whose little inhabitants never welcomed me. No sign
points to it and I rarely go there any more. Few people know about it
and fewer still know that in a sense we, or rather some of the creatures
to whom we are related, were driven out of it once, long ago. I used to
park my car on a hill and sit silently observant, listening to the talk ring-
ing out from neighbor to neighbor, seeing the inhabitants drowsing in
their doorways, taking it all in with nostalgia—the sage smell on the wind,
the sunlight without time, the village without destiny. We can look, but
we can never go back. It is prairie-dog town.

"Whirl is king," said Aristophanes, and never since life began was Whirl
more truly king than eighty million years ago in the dawn of the Age of
Mammals. It would come as a shock to those who believe firmly that the
scroll of the future is fixed and the roads determined in advance, to ob-
serve the teetering balance of earth's history through the age of the Pa-
leocene. The passing of the reptiles had left a hundred uninhabited life
zones and a scrambling variety of newly radiating forms. Unheard-of spe-
cies of giant ground birds threatened for a moment to dominate the
earthly scene. Two separate orders of life contended at slightly different
intervals for the pleasant grasslands—for the seeds and the sleepy bur-
rows in the sun.

Sometimes, sitting there in the mountain sunshine above prairie-dog
town, I could imagine the attraction of that open world after the fern
forest damp or the croaking gloom of carboniferous swamps. There by
a tree root I could almost make him out, that shabby little Paleocene rat,

eternal tramp and world wanderer, father of all mankind. He ruffed his
coat in the sun and hopped forward for a seed. It was to be a long time
before he would be seen on the grass again, but he was trying to make
up his mind. For good or ill there was to be one more chance, but that
chance was fifty million years away.

Here in the Paleocene occurred the first great radiation of the placental
mammals, and among them were the earliest primates—the zoological
order to which man himself belongs. Today, with a few unimportant ex-
ceptions, the primates are all arboreal in habit except man. For this rea-
son we have tended to visualize all of our remote relatives as tree dwellers.
Recent discoveries, however, have begun to alter this one-sided picture.
Before the rise of the true rodents, the highly successful order to which
present-day prairie dogs and chipmunks belong, the environment which
they occupy had remained peculiarly open to exploitation. Into this zone
crowded a varied assemblage of our early relatives.

"In habitat," comments one scholar, "many of these early primates may
be thought of as the rats of the Paleocene. With the later appearance of
true rodents, the primate habitat was markedly restricted." The bone hunt-
ers, in other words, have succeeded in demonstrating that numerous pri-
mates reveal a remarkable development of rodentlike characteristics in
the teeth and skull during this early period of mammalian evolution. The
movement is progressive and distributed in several different groups. One
form, although that of a true primate, shows similarities to the modern
kangaroo rat, which is, of course, a rodent. There is little doubt that it
was a burrower.

It is this evidence of a lost chapter in the history of our kind that I used
to remember on the sunny slope above prairie-dog town, and that enables
me to say in a somewhat figurative fashion that we were driven out of it
once ages ago. We are not, except very remotely as mammals, related to
prairie dogs. Nevertheless, through several million years of Paleocene
time, the primate order, instead of being confined to trees, was experi-
menting to some extent with the same grassland burrowing life that the
rodents later perfected. The success of these burrowers crowded the pri-
mates out of this environment and forced them back into the domain of
the branches. As a result, many primates, by that time highly specialized
for a ground life, became extinct.

In the restricted world of the trees, a "refuge area," as the zoologist
would say, the others lingered on in diminished numbers. Our ancient
relatives, it appeared, were beaten in their attempt to expand upon the

ground; they were dying out in the temperate zone, and their significance as a widespread and diversified group was fading. The shabby pseudo rat I had seen ruffling his coat to dry after the night damps of the reptile age, had ascended again into the green twilight of the rain forest. The chatterers with the ever growing teeth were his masters. The sunlight and the grass belonged to them.

It is conceivable that except for the invasion of the rodents, the primate line might even have abandoned the trees. We might be there on the grass, you and I, barking in the high-plains sunlight. It is true we came back in fifty million years with the cunning hands and the eyes that the tree world gave us, but was it victory? Once more in memory I saw the high blue evening fall sleepily upon that village, and once more swung the car to leave, lifting, as I always did, a figurative lantern to some ambiguous crossroads sign within my brain. The pointing arms were nameless and nameless were the distances to which they pointed. One took one's choice.

I ceased my daydreaming then, squeezed myself out of the crevice, shook out my pipe, and started chipping once more, the taps sounding along the inward-leaning walls of the Slit like the echo of many footsteps ascending and descending. I had come a long way down since morning; I had projected myself across a dimension I was not fitted to traverse in the flesh. In the end I collected my tools and climbed painfully up through the colossal debris of ages. When I put my hands on the surface of the crack I looked all about carefully in a sudden anxiety that it might not be a grazing horse that I would see.

He had not visibly changed, however, and I mounted in some slight trepidation and rode off, having a memory for a camp—if I had gotten a foot in the right era—which should lie somewhere over to the west. I did not, however, escape totally from that brief imprisonment.

Perhaps the Slit, with its exposed bones and its far-off vanishing sky, has come to stand symbolically in my mind for a dimension denied to man, the dimension of time. Like the wistaria on the garden wall he is rooted in his particular century. Out of it—forward or backward—he cannot run. As he stands on his circumscribed pinpoint of time, his sight for the past is growing longer, and even the shadowy outlines of the galactic future are growing clearer, though his own fate he cannot yet see. Along the dimension of time, man, like the rooted vine in space, may never pass in person. Considering the innumerable devices by which the mindless root has evaded the limitations of its own stability, however, it may well be

that man himself is slowly achieving powers over a new dimension—a dimension capable of presenting him with a wisdom he has barely begun to discern.

Through how many dimensions and how many media will life have to pass? Down how many roads among the stars must man propel himself in search of the final secret? The journey is difficult, immense, at times impossible, yet that will not deter some of us from attempting it. We cannot know all that has happened in the past, or the reason for all of these events, any more than we can with surety discern what lies ahead. We have joined the caravan, you might say, at a certain point; we will travel as far as we can, but we cannot in one lifetime see all that we would like to see or learn all that we hunger to know.

The reader who would pursue such a journey with me is warned that the essays in this book have not been brought together as a guide but are offered rather as a somewhat unconventional record of the prowlings of one mind which has sought to explore, to understand, and to enjoy the miracles of this world, both in and out of science. It is, without doubt, an inconsistent record in many ways, compounded of fear and hope, for it has grown out of the seasonal jottings of a man preoccupied with time. It involves, I see now as I come to put it together, the four ancient elements of the Greeks: mud and the fire within it we call life, vast waters, and something—space, air, the intangible substance of hope which at the last proves unanalyzable by science, yet out of which the human dream is made.

Forward and backward I have gone, and for me it has been an immense journey. Those who accompany me need not look for science in the usual sense, though I have done all in my power to avoid errors in fact. I have given the record of what one man thought as he pursued research and pressed his hands against the confining walls of scientific method in his time. It is not, I must confess at the outset, an account of discovery so much as a confession of ignorance and of the final illumination that sometimes comes to a man when he is no longer careful of his pride. In the last three chapters of the book I have tried to put down such miracles as can be evoked from common earth. But men see differently. I can at best report only from my own wilderness. The important thing is that each man possess such a wilderness and that he consider what marvels are to be observed there.

Finally, I do not pretend to have set down, in Baconian terms, a true, or even a consistent model of the universe. I can only say that here is a bit of my personal universe, the universe traversed in a long and uncom-

pleted journey. If my record, like those of the sixteenth-century voyagers, is confused by strange beasts or monstrous thoughts or sights of abortive men, these are no more than my eyes saw or my mind conceived. On the world island we are all castaways, so that what is seen by one may often be dark or obscure to another.

*The foregoing is the first essay
in Eiseley's* THE IMMENSE JOURNEY.

Rachel L. Carson

1907–

Rachel Carson was born at Springdale, Pennsylvania, in 1907. She studied at Pennsylvania College for Women (Chatham College) and received an M.A. from Johns Hopkins University, in Baltimore, Maryland, in 1932. She was an assistant in zoology at the University of Maryland (1931–36), and an assistant in zoology at Johns Hopkins during the summers of the same years. She undertook research at the Marine Biological Laboratory at Woods Hole, Massachusetts. From 1952 she was an associate of the Woods Hole Oceanographic Institution.

In 1936 she joined what is now called the U.S. Fish and Wildlife Service, a branch of the Department of the Interior. In 1949 she became the service's editor-in-chief.

The Sea around Us, from which the following selection is taken, was published in 1951. The book won many prizes, including the National Book Award. A prize-winning documentary movie was made from it. Miss Carson is also the author of *Under the Sea Wind* (1941), *The Edge of the Sea* (1955), and *Silent Spring* (1962). The last is a brilliantly written polemic against the indiscriminate use of insecticides which have the effect of producing irreversible changes in the ecological balance. It has been the cause of much discussion and controversy.

It has been claimed that the scientist and the poet have much in common and should be friends. They seldom are; and it is even more rare, as is the case with Miss Carson, to find them combined in one single person. Miss Carson has published poems and scientific papers. *The Sea around Us* partakes of both forms of communication between human beings.

Poetry may, perhaps should, contradict itself; the theory is, at least, that science should not. By her use of metaphor and of exaggeration, or of hyperbole, Miss Carson proclaims her poetic inclinations. She speaks of that "half the earth that is covered by miles-deep, lightless water, that has been dark since the world began." Earlier in the volume, however, she had recounted how the world— by this she means the earth—existed for hundreds of millions of years before there was any ocean at all. Nevertheless, "dark since the world began" is an effective phrase, and it gives the reader exactly the impression desired: that is, of an environment that is unchangingly, "eternally" dark.

Again, Miss Carson refers to the "endless night" of this same portion of the deep, or "sunless," sea. She speaks of the "abysmal depths" of the sea, and of the "abyssal creatures" that live there. Such words are forcefully connotative; they remind the reader of those descriptions which are common among poets, and which emphasize the beauty, terror, and mystery of the sea.

The Sea around Us is a superior work of scientific popularization, and the chapter from it reprinted below is noteworthy for the amount of knowledge it disseminates, as well as for the charming and, indeed, awe-inspiring way in which it does so. But it should be pointed out that much research has been done, much investigation undertaken, in the deep sea since 1951. The puzzling question of the "phantom bottom" has been answered: it *is* plankton, after all. The true bottom of the deep ocean has in many places now been mapped. Nevertheless, it is still correct, as Miss Carson says, that "this region has withheld its secrets more obstinately than any other." It is claimed that more is known about the depths of space than about the ocean depths of our own planet.

Why this should be so is not entirely clear. The sea is, of course, dangerous to land animals, and to man. But so are the high mountains, and they have been explored for a century. And so is space. The darkness of the deep sea—the "endless night" to which Miss Carson refers, and which she makes so vivid—may be at the heart of the problem. Men are even more animals of the light than of the land. Is there not something intrinsically frightening about dark water? So at least the dreams of human beings would seem to indicate. If so, then Miss Carson's poetic language may be just right for talking about the deep sea. Poetry has been from time immemorial man's way of dealing with the terrors of the dark unknown.

The Sunless Sea

Where great whales come sailing by,
Sail and sail, with unshut eye.
Matthew Arnold.

Between the sunlit surface waters of the open sea and the hidden hills and valleys of the ocean floor lies the least known region of the sea. These deep, dark waters, with all their mysteries and their unsolved problems, cover a very considerable part of the earth. The whole world ocean extends over about three-fourths of the surface of the globe. If we subtract the shallow areas of the continental shelves and the scattered banks and shoals, where at least the pale ghost of sunlight moves over the underlying bottom, there still remains about half the earth that is covered by miles-deep, lightless water, that has been dark since the world began.

This region has withheld its secrets more obstinately than any other. Man, with all his ingenuity, has been able to venture only to its threshold. Carrying tanks of compressed air, he can swim down to depths of about 300 feet. He can descend about 500 feet wearing a diving helmet and a rubberized suit. Only a few men in all the history of the world have had the experience of descending, alive, beyond the range of visible light. The first to do so were William Beebe and Otis Barton; in the bathysphere, they reached a depth of 3,028 feet in the open ocean off Bermuda, in the year 1934. Barton alone, in the summer of 1949, descended to a depth of 4,500 feet off California, in a steel sphere of somewhat different design; and in 1953 French divers penetrated depths greater than a mile, existing for several hours in a zone of cold and darkness where the presence of living man had never before been known.

Although only a fortunate few can ever visit the deep sea, the precise instruments of the oceanographer, recording light penetration, pressure, salinity, and temperature, have given us the materials with which to reconstruct in imagination these eerie, forbidding regions. Unlike the sur-

face waters, which are sensitive to every gust of wind, which know day and night, respond to the pull of sun and moon, and change as the seasons change, the deep waters are a place where change comes slowly, if at all. Down beyond the reach of the sun's rays, there is no alternation of light and darkness. There is rather an endless night, as old as the sea itself. For most of its creatures, groping their way endlessly through its black waters, it must be a place of hunger, where food is scarce and hard to find, a shelterless place where there is no sanctuary from ever present enemies, where one can only move on and on, from birth to death, through the darkness, confined as in a prison to his own particular layer of the sea.

They used to say that nothing could live in the deep sea. It was a belief that must have been easy to accept, for without proof to the contrary, how could anyone conceive of life in such a place?

A century ago the British biologist Edward Forbes wrote: "As we descend deeper and deeper into this region, the inhabitants become more and more modified, and fewer and fewer, indicating our approach to an abyss where life is either extinguished, or exhibits but a few sparks to mark its lingering presence." Yet Forbes urged further exploration of "this vast deep-sea region" to settle forever the question of the existence of life at great depths.

Even then, the evidence was accumulating. Sir John Ross, during his exploration of the arctic seas in 1818, had brought up from a depth of 1,000 fathoms mud in which there were worms, "thus proving there was animal life in the bed of the ocean notwithstanding the darkness, stillness, silence, and immense pressure produced by more than a mile of superincumbent water."

Then from the surveying ship *Bulldog*, examining a proposed northern route for a cable from Faeroe to Labrador in 1860, came another report. The *Bulldog's* sounding line, which at one place had been allowed to lie for some time on the bottom at a depth of 1,260 fathoms, came up with 13 starfish clinging to it. Through these starfish, the ship's naturalist wrote, "the deep has sent forth the long coveted message." But not all the zoologists of the day were prepared to accept the message. Some doubters asserted that the starfish had "convulsively embraced" the line somewhere on the way back to the surface.

In the same year, 1860, a cable in the Mediterranean was raised for repairs from a depth of 1,200 fathoms. It was found to be heavily encrusted with corals and other sessile animals that had attached themselves at an early stage of development and grown to maturity over

a period of months or years. There was not the slightest chance that they had become entangled in the cable as it was being raised to the surface.

Then the *Challenger,* the first ship ever equipped for oceanographic exploration, set out from England in the year 1872 and traced a course around the globe. From bottoms lying under miles of water, from silent deeps carpeted with red clay ooze, and from all the lightless intermediate depths, net-haul after net-haul of strange and fantastic creatures came up and were spilled out on the decks. Poring over the weird beings thus brought up for the first time into the light of day, beings no man had ever seen before, the *Challenger* scientists realized that life existed even on the deepest floor of the abyss.

The recent discovery that a living cloud of some unknown creatures is spread over much of the ocean at a depth of several hundred fathoms below the surface is the most exciting thing that has been learned about the ocean for many years.

When, during the first quarter of the twentieth century, echo sounding was developed to allow ships while under way to record the depth of the bottom, probably no one suspected that it would also provide a means of learning something about deep-sea life. But operators of the new instruments soon discovered that the sound waves, directed downward from the ship like a beam of light, were reflected back from any solid object they met. Answering echoes were returned from intermediate depths, presumably from schools of fish, whales, or submarines; then a second echo was received from the bottom.

These facts were so well established by the late 1930's that fishermen had begun to talk about using their fathometers to search for schools of herring. Then the war brought the whole subject under strict security regulations, and little more was heard about it. In 1946, however, the United States Navy issued a significant bulletin. It was reported that several scientists, working with sonic equipment in deep water off the California coast, had discovered a widespread "layer" of some sort, which gave back an answering echo to the sound waves. This reflecting layer, seemingly suspended between the surface and the floor of the Pacific, was found over an area 300 miles wide. It lay from 1,000 to 1,500 feet below the surface. The discovery was made by three scientists, C. F. Eyring, R. J. Christensen, and R. W. Raitt, aboard the U.S.S. *Jasper* in 1942, and for a time this mysterious phenomenon, of wholly unknown nature, was called the ECR layer. Then in 1945 Martin W. Johnson, marine biologist of the Scripps Institution of Oceanography, made a further discovery which gave the first clue to the nature of the layer. Working aboard the vessel *E. W. Scripps,* Johnson found that whatever sent back the echoes

moved upward and downward in rhythmic fashion, being found near the surface at night, in deep water during the day. This discovery disposed of speculations that the reflections came from something inanimate, perhaps a mere physical discontinuity in the water, and showed that the layer is composed of living creatures capable of controlled movement.

From this time on, discoveries about the sea's "phantom bottom" came rapidly. With widespread use of echo-sounding instruments, it has become clear that the phenomenon is not something peculiar to the coast of California alone. It occurs almost universally in deep ocean basins—drifting by day at a depth of several hundred fathoms, at night rising to the surface, and again, before sunrise, sinking into the depths.

On the passage of the U.S.S. *Henderson* from San Diego to the Antarctic in 1947, the reflecting layer was detected during the greater part of each day, at depths varying from 150 to 450 fathoms, and on a later run from San Diego to Yokosuka, Japan, the *Henderson's* fathometer again recorded the layer every day, suggesting that it exists almost continuously across the Pacific.

During July and August 1947, the U.S.S. *Nereus* made a continuous fathogram from Pearl Harbor to the Arctic and found the scattering layer over all deep waters along this course. It did not develop, however, in the shallow Bering and Chuckchee seas. Sometimes in the morning, the *Nereus'* fathogram showed two layers, responding in different ways to the growing illumination of the water; both descended into deep water, but there was an interval of twenty miles between the two descents.

Despite attempts to sample it or photograph it, no one is sure what the layer is, although the discovery may be made any day. There are three principal theories, each of which has its group of supporters. According to these theories, the sea's phantom bottom may consist of small planktonic shrimps, of fishes, or of squids.

As for the plankton theory, one of the most convincing arguments is the well-known fact that many plankton creatures make regular vertical migrations of hundreds of feet, rising toward the surface at night, sinking down below the zone of light penetration very early in the morning. This is, of course, exactly the behavior of the scattering layer. Whatever composes it is apparently strongly repelled by sunlight. The creatures of the layer seem almost to be held prisoner at the end—or beyond the end—of the sun's rays throughout the hours of daylight, waiting only for the welcome return of darkness to hurry upward into the surface waters. But what is the power that repels; and what the attraction that draws them surfaceward once the inhibiting force is removed? Is it comparative safety from enemies that makes them seek darkness? Is it more

abundant food near the surface that lures them back under cover of night?

Those who say that fish are the reflectors of the sound waves usually account for the vertical migrations of the layer as suggesting that the fish are feeding on planktonic shrimp and are following their food. They believe that the air bladder of a fish is, of all structures concerned, most likely from its construction to return a strong echo. There is one outstanding difficulty in the way of accepting this theory: we have no other evidence that concentrations of fish are universally present in the oceans. In fact, almost everything else we know suggests that the really dense populations of fish live over the continental shelves or in certain very definite determined zones of the open ocean where food is particularly abundant. If the reflecting layer is eventually proved to be composed of fish, the prevailing views of fish distribution will have to be radically revised.

The most startling theory (and the one that seems to have the fewest supporters) is that the layer consists of concentrations of squid, "hovering below the illuminated zone of the sea and awaiting the arrival of darkness in which to resume their raids into the plankton-rich surface waters." Proponents of this theory argue that squid are abundant enough, and of wide enough distribution, to give the echoes that have been picked up almost everywhere from the equator to the two poles. Squid are known to be the sole food of the sperm whale, found in the open oceans in all temperate and tropical waters. They also form the exclusive diet of the bottlenosed whale and are eaten extensively by most other toothed whales, by seals, and by many sea birds. All these facts argue that they must be prodigiously abundant.

It is true that men who have worked close to the sea surface at night have received vivid impressions of the abundance and activity of squids in the surface waters in darkness. Long ago Johan Hjort wrote:

> One night we were hauling long lines on the Faeroe slope, working with an electric lamp hanging over the side in order to see the line, when like lightning flashes one squid after another shot towards the light. . . . In October, 1902, we were one night steaming outside the slopes of the coast banks of Norway, and for many miles we could see the squids moving in the surface waters like luminous bubbles, resembling large milky white electric lamps being constantly lit and extinguished.

Thor Heyerdahl reports that at night his raft was literally bombarded by squids; and Richard Fleming says that in his oceanographic work off

the coast of Panamá it was common to see immense schools of squid gathering at the surface at night and leaping upward toward the lights that were used by the men to operate their instruments. But equally spectacular surface displays of shrimp have been seen, and most people find it difficult to believe in the ocean-wide abundance of squid.

Deep-water photography holds much promise for the solution of the mystery of the phantom bottom. There are technical difficulties, such as the problem of holding a camera still as it swings at the end of a long cable, twisting and turning, suspended from a ship which itself moves with the sea. Some of the pictures so taken look as though the photographer has pointed his camera at a starry sky and swung it in an arc as he exposed the film. Yet the Norwegian biologist Gunnar Rollefson had an encouraging experience in correlating photography with echograms. On the research ship *Johan Hjort* off the Lofoten Islands, he persistently got reflection of sound from schools of fish in 20 to 30 fathoms. A specially constructed camera was lowered to the depth indicated by the echogram. When developed, the film showed moving shapes of fish at a distance, and a large and clearly recognizable cod appeared in the beam of light and hovered in front of the lens.

Direct sampling of the layer is the logical means of discovering its identity, but the problem is to develop large nets that can be operated rapidly enough to capture swift-moving animals. Scientists at Woods Hole, Massachusetts, have towed ordinary plankton nets in the layer and have found that euphausiid shrimps, glassworms, and other deep-water plankton are concentrated there; but there is still a possibility that the layer itself may actually be made up of larger forms feeding on the shrimps—too large or swift to be taken in the presently used nets. New nets may give the answer. Television is another possibility.

Shadowy and indefinite though they be, these recent indications of an abundant life at mid-depths agree with the reports of the only observers who have actually visited comparable depths and brought back eyewitness accounts of what they saw. William Beebe's impressions from the bathysphere were of a life far more abundant and varied than he had been prepared to find, although, over a period of six years, he had made many hundreds of net hauls in the same area. More than a quarter of a mile down, he reported aggregations of living things "as thick as I have ever seen them." At half a mile—the deepest descent of the bathysphere —Dr. Beebe recalled that "there was no instant when a mist of plankton . . . was not swirling in the path of the beam."

The existence of an abundant deep-sea fauna was discovered, prob-

ably millions of years ago, by certain whales and also, it now appears, by seals. The ancestors of all whales, we know by fossil remains, were land mammals. They must have been predatory beasts, if we are to judge by their powerful jaws and teeth. Perhaps in their foragings about the deltas of great rivers or around the edges of shallow seas, they discovered the abundance of fish and other marine life and over the centuries formed the habit of following them farther and farther into the sea. Little by little their bodies took on a form more suitable for aquatic life; their hind limbs were reduced to rudiments, which may be discovered in a modern whale by dissection, and the forelimbs were modified into organs for steering and balancing.

Eventually the whales, as though to divide the sea's food resources among them, became separated into three groups: the plankton-eaters, the fish-eaters, and the squid-eaters. The plankton-eating whales can exist only where there are dense masses of small shrimp or copepods to supply their enormous food requirements. This limits them, except for scattered areas, to arctic and antarctic waters and the high temperate latitudes. Fish-eating whales may find food over a somewhat wider range of ocean, but they are restricted to places where there are enormous populations of schooling fish. The blue water of the tropics and of the open ocean basins offers little to either of these groups. But that immense, square-headed, formidably toothed whale known as the cachalot or sperm whale discovered long ago what men have known for only a short time—that hundreds of fathoms below the almost untenanted surface waters of these regions there is an abundant animal life. The sperm whale has taken these deep waters for his hunting grounds; his quarry is the deep-water population of squids including the giant squid Architeuthis, which lives pelagically at depths of 1,500 feet or more. The head of the sperm whale is often marked with long stripes, which consist of a great number of circular scars made by the suckers of the squid. From this evidence we can imagine the battles that go on, in the darkness of the deep water, between these two huge creatures—the sperm whale with its 70-ton bulk, the squid with a body as long as 30 feet, and writhing, grasping arms extending the total length of the animal to perhaps 50 feet.

The greatest depth at which the giant squid lives is not definitely known, but there is one instructive piece of evidence about the depth to which sperm whales descend, presumably in search of the squids. In April, 1932, the cable repair ship *All America* was investigating an apparent break in the submarine cable between Balboa in the Canal Zone

and Esmeraldas, Ecuador. The cable was brought to the surface off the coast of Colombia. Entangled in it was a dead 45-foot male sperm whale. The submarine cable was twisted around the lower jaw and was wrapped around one flipper, the body, and the caudal flukes. The cable was raised from a depth of 540 fathoms, or 3,240 feet.

Some of the seals also appear to have discovered the hidden food reserves of the deep ocean. It has long been something of a mystery where, and on what, the northern fur seals of the eastern Pacific feed during the winter, which they spend off the coast of North America from California to Alaska. There is no evidence that they are feeding to any great extent on sardines, mackerel, or other commercially important fishes. Presumably four million seals could not compete with commercial fishermen for the same species without the fact being known. But there is some evidence on the diet of the fur seals, and it is highly significant. Their stomachs have yielded the bones of a species of fish that has never been seen alive. Indeed, not even its remains have been found anywhere except in the stomachs of seals. Ichthyologists say that this "seal fish" belongs to a group that typically inhabits very deep water, off the edge of the continental shelf.

How either whales or seals endure the tremendous pressure changes involved in dives of several hundred fathoms is not definitely known. They are warm-blooded mammals like ourselves. Caisson disease, which is caused by the rapid accumulation of nitrogen bubbles in the blood with sudden release of pressure, kills human divers if they are brought up rapidly from depths of 200 feet or so. Yet, according to the testimony of whalers, a baleen whale, when harpooned, can dive straight down to a depth of half a mile, as measured by the amount of line carried out. From these depths, where it has sustained a pressure of half a ton on every inch of body, it returns almost immediately to the surface. The most plausible explanation is that, unlike the diver, who has air pumped to him while he is under water, the whale has in its body only the limited supply it carries down, and does not have enough nitrogen in its blood to do serious harm. The plain truth is, however, that we really do not know, since it is obviously impossible to confine a living whale and experiment on it, and almost as difficult to dissect a dead one satisfactorily.

At first thought it seems a paradox that creatures of such great fragility as the glass sponge and the jellyfish can live under the conditions of immense pressure that prevail in deep water. For creatures at home in the deep sea, however, the saving fact is that the pressure inside their tissues is the same as that without, and as long as this balance is preserved,

they are no more inconvenienced by a pressure of a ton or so than we are by ordinary atmospheric pressure. And most abyssal creatures, it must be remembered, live out their whole lives in a comparatively restricted zone, and are never required to adjust themselves to extreme changes of pressure.

But of course there are exceptions, and the real miracle of sea life in relation to great pressure is not the animal that lives its whole life on the bottom, bearing a pressure of perhaps five or six tons, but those that regularly move up and down through hundreds or thousands of feet of vertical change. The small shrimps and other planktonic creatures that descend into deep water during the day are examples. Fish that possess air bladders, on the other hand, are vitally affected by abrupt changes of pressure, as anyone knows who has seen a trawler's net raised from a hundred fathoms. Apart from the accident of being captured in a net and hauled up through waters of rapidly diminishing pressures, fish may sometimes wander out of the zone to which they are adjusted and find themselves unable to return. Perhaps in their pursuit of food they roam upward to the ceiling of the zone that is theirs, and beyond whose invisible boundary they may not stray without meeting alien and inhospitable conditions. Moving from layer to layer of drifting plankton as they feed, they may pass beyond the boundary. In the lessened pressure of these upper waters the gas enclosed within the air bladder expands. The fish becomes lighter and more buoyant. Perhaps he tries to fight his way down again, opposing the upward lift with all the power of his muscles. If he does not succeed, he "falls" to the surface, injured and dying, for the abrupt release of pressure from without causes distension and rupture of the tissues.

The compression of the sea under its own weight is relatively slight, and there is no basis for the old and picturesque belief that, at the deeper levels, the water resists the downward passage of objects from the surface. According to this belief, sinking ships, the bodies of drowned men, and presumably the bodies of the larger sea animals not consumed by hungry scavengers, never reach the bottom, but come to rest at some level determined by the relation of their own weight to the compression of the water, there to drift forever. The fact is that anything will continue to sink as long as its specific gravity is greater than that of the surrounding water, and all large bodies descend, in a matter of a few days, to the ocean floor. As mute testimony to this fact, we bring up from the deepest ocean basins the teeth of sharks and the hard ear bones of whales.

Nevertheless the weight of sea water—the pressing down of miles of water upon all the underlying layers—does have a certain effect upon the water itself. If this downward compression could suddenly be relaxed by some miraculous suspension of natural laws, the sea level would rise about 93 feet all over the world. This would shift the Atlantic coastline of the United States westward a hundred miles or more and alter other familiar geographic outlines all over the world.

Immense pressure, then, is one of the governing conditions of life in the deep sea; darkness is another. The unrelieved darkness of the deep waters has produced weird and incredible modifications of the abyssal fauna. It is a blackness so divorced from the world of the sunlight that probably only the few men who have seen it with their own eyes can visualize it. We know that light fades out rapidly with descent below the surface. The red rays are gone at the end of the first 200 or 300 feet, and with them all the orange and yellow warmth of the sun. Then the greens fade out, and at 1,000 feet only a deep, dark, brilliant blue is left. In very clear waters the violet rays of the spectrum may penetrate another thousand feet. Beyond this is only the blackness of the deep sea.

In a curious way, the colors of marine animals tend to be related to the zone in which they live. Fishes of the surface waters, like the mackerel and herring, often are blue or green; so are the floats of the Portuguese men-of-war and the azure-tinted wings of the swimming snails. Down below the diatom meadows and the drifting sargassum weed, where the water becomes ever more deeply, brilliantly blue, many creatures are crystal clear. Their glassy, ghostly forms blend with their surroundings and make it easier for them to elude the ever-present, ever-hungry enemy. Such are the transparent hordes of the arrowworms or glass-worms, the comb jellies, and the larvae of many fishes.

At a thousand feet, and on down to the very end of the sun's rays, silvery fishes are common, and many others are red, drab brown, or black. Pteropods are a dark violet. Arrowworms, whose relatives in the upper layers are colorless, are here a deep red. Jellyfish medusae, which above would be transparent, at a depth of 1,000 feet are a deep brown.

At depths greater than 1,500 feet, all the fishes are black, deep violet, or brown, but the prawns wear amazing hues of red, scarlet, and purple. Why, no one can say. Since all the red rays are strained out of the water far above this depth, the scarlet raiment of these creatures can only look black to their neighbors.

The deep sea has its stars, and perhaps here and there an eerie and transient equivalent of moonlight, for the mysterious phenomenon of

luminescence is displayed by perhaps half of all the fishes that live in dimly lit or darkened waters, and by many of the lower forms as well. Many fishes carry luminous torches that can be turned on or off at will, presumably helping them find or pursue their prey. Others have rows of lights over their bodies, in patterns that vary from species to species and may be a sort of recognition mark or badge by which the bearer can be known as friend or enemy. The deep-sea squid ejects a spurt of fluid that becomes a luminous cloud, the counterpart of the "ink" of his shallow-water relative.

Down beyond the reach of even the longest and strongest of the sun's rays, the eyes of fishes become enlarged, as though to make the most of any chance illumination of whatever sort, or they may become telescopic, large of lens, and protruding. In deep-sea fishes, hunting always in dark waters, the eyes tend to lose the "cones" or color-perceiving cells of the retina, and to increase the "rods," which perceive dim light. Exactly the same modification is seen on land among the strictly nocturnal prowlers which, like abyssal fish, never see the sunlight.

In their world of darkness, it would seem likely that some of the animals might have become blind, as has happened to some cave fauna. So, indeed, many of them have, compensating for the lack of eyes with marvelously developed feelers and long, slender fins and processes with which they grope their way, like so many blind men with canes, their whole knowledge of friends, enemies, or food coming to them through the sense of touch.

The last traces of plant life are left behind in the thin upper layer of water, for no plant can live below about 600 feet even in very clear water, and few find enough sunlight for their food-manufacturing activities below 200 feet. Since no animal can make its own food, the creatures of the deeper waters live a strange, almost parasitic existence of utter dependence on the upper layers. These hungry carnivores prey fiercely and relentlessly upon each other, yet the whole community is ultimately dependent upon the slow rain of descending food particles from above. The components of this never-ending rain are the dead and dying plants and animals from the surface, or from one of the intermediate layers. For each of the horizontal zones or communities of the sea that lie, in tier after tier, between the surface and the sea bottom, the food supply is different and in general poorer than for the layer above. There is a hint of the fierce and uncompromising competition for food in the saber-toothed jaws of some of the small, dragonlike fishes of the deeper waters, in the immense mouths and in the elastic and distensible

bodies that make it possible for a fish to swallow another several times its size, enjoying swift repletion after a long fast.

Pressure, darkness, and—we should have added only a few years ago —silence, are the conditions of life in the deep sea. But we know now that the conception of the sea as a silent place is wholly false. Wide experience with hydrophones and other listening devices for the detection of submarines has proved that, around the shore lines of much of the world, there is the extraordinary uproar produced by fishes, shrimps, porpoises and probably other forms not yet identified. There has been little investigation as yet of sound in the deep, offshore areas, but when the crew of the *Atlantis* lowered a hydrophone into deep water off Bermuda, they recorded strange mewing sounds, shrieks, and ghostly moans, the sources of which have not been traced. But fish of shallower zones have been captured and confined in aquaria, where their voices have been recorded for comparison with sounds heard at sea, and in many cases satisfactory identification can be made.

During the Second World War the hydrophone network set up by the United States Navy to protect the entrance to Chesapeake Bay was temporarily made useless when, in the spring of 1942, the speakers at the surface began to give forth, every evening, a sound described as being like "a pneumatic drill tearing up pavement." The extraneous noises that came over the hydrophones completely masked the sounds of the passage of ships. Eventually it was discovered that the sounds were the voices of fish known as croakers, which in the spring move into Chesapeake Bay from their offshore wintering grounds. As soon as the noise had been identified and analyzed, it was possible to screen it out with an electric filter, so that once more only the sounds of ships came through the speakers.

Later in the same year, a chorus of croakers was discovered off the pier of the Scripps Institution at La Jolla. Every year from May until late September the evening chorus begins about sunset, and "increases gradually to a steady uproar of harsh froggy croaks, with a background of soft drumming. This continues unabated for two to three hours and finally tapers off to individual outbursts at rare intervals." Several species of croakers isolated in aquaria gave sounds similar to the "froggy croaks," but the authors of the soft background drumming—presumably another species of croaker—have not yet been discovered.

One of the most extraordinarily widespread sounds of the undersea is the crackling, sizzling sound, like dry twigs burning or fat frying, heard near beds of the snapping shrimp. This is a small, round shrimp, about

half an inch in diameter, with one very large claw which it uses to stun its prey. The shrimp are forever clicking the two joints of this claw together, and it is the thousands of clicks that collectively produce the noise known as shrimp crackle. No one had any idea the little snapping shrimps were so abundant or so widely distributed until their signals began to be picked up on hydrophones. They have been heard over a broad band that extends around the world, between latitudes 35° N. and 35° S. (for example, from Cape Hatteras to Buenos Aires) in ocean waters less than 30 fathoms deep.

Mammals as well as fishes and crustaceans contribute to the undersea chorus. Biologists listening through a hydrophone in an estuary of the St. Lawrence River heard "high-pitched resonant whistles and squeals, varied with the ticking and clucking sounds slightly reminiscent of a string orchestra tuning up, as well as mewing and occasional chirps." This remarkable medley of sounds was heard only while schools of the white porpoise were seen passing up or down the river, and so was assumed to be produced by them.

The mysteriousness, the eeriness, the ancient unchangingness of the great depths have led many people to suppose that some very old forms of life—some "living fossils"—may be lurking undiscovered in the deep ocean. Some such hope may have been in the minds of the *Challenger* scientists. The forms they brought up in their nets were weird enough, and most of them had never before been seen by man. But basically they were modern types. There was nothing like the trilobites of Cambrian time or the sea scorpions of the Silurian, nothing reminiscent of the great marine reptiles that invaded the sea in the Mesozoic. Instead, there were modern fishes, squids, and shrimps, strangely and grotesquely modified, to be sure, for life in the difficult deep-sea world, but clearly types that have developed in rather recent geologic time.

Far from being the original home of life, the deep sea has probably been inhabited for a relatively short time. While life was developing and flourishing in the surface waters, along the shores, and perhaps in the rivers and swamps, two immense regions of the earth still forbade invasion by living things. These were the continents and the abyss. As we have seen, the immense difficulties of surviving on land were first overcome by colonists from the sea about 300 million years ago. The abyss, with its unending darkness, its crushing pressures, its glacial cold, presented even more formidable difficulties. Probably the successful invasion of this region—at least by higher forms of life—occurred somewhat later.

Yet in recent years there have been one or two significant happenings

that have kept alive the hope that the deep sea may, after all, conceal strange links with the past. In December, 1938, off the southeast tip of Africa, an amazing fish was caught alive in a trawl—a fish that was supposed to have been dead for at least 60 million years! This is to say, the last known fossil remains of its kind date from the Cretaceous, and no living example had been recognized in historic time until this lucky nethaul.

The fishermen who brought it up in their trawl from a depth of only 40 fathoms realized that this five-foot, bright blue fish, with its large head and strangely shaped scales, fins, and tail, was different from anything that they ever caught before, and on their return to port they took it to the nearest museum, where it was christened Latimeria. It was identified as a coelacanth, or one of an incredibly ancient group of fishes that first appeared in the seas some 300 million years ago. Rocks representing the next 200 million and more years of earth history yielded fossil coelacanths; then, in the Cretaceous, the record of these fishes came to an end. After 60 million years of mysterious oblivion, one of the group, Latimeria, then appeared before the eyes of the South African fishermen, apparently little changed in structure from its ancient ancestors. But where had these fishes been in the meantime?

The story of the coelacanths did not end in 1938. Believing there must be other such fish in the sea, an ichthyologist in South Africa, Professor J. L. B. Smith, began a patient search that lasted 14 years before it was successful. Then, in December, 1952, a second coelacanth was captured near the island of Anjouan, off the northwestern tip of Madagascar. It differed enough from Latimeria to be placed in a separate genus, but like the first coelacanth known in modern times, it can tell us much of a shadowy chapter in the evolution of living things.

Occasionally a very primitive type of shark, known from its puckered gills as a "frillshark," is taken in waters between a quarter of a mile and half a mile down. Most of these have been caught in Norwegian and Japanese waters—there are only about 50 preserved in the museums of Europe and America—but recently one was captured off Santa Barbara, California. The frillshark has many anatomical features similar to those of the ancient sharks that lived 25 to 30 million years ago. It has too many gills and too few dorsal fins for a modern shark, and its teeth, like those of fossil sharks, are three-pronged and briarlike. Some ichthyologists regard it as a relic derived from very ancient shark ancestors that have died out in the upper waters but, through this single species, are still carrying on their struggle for earthly survival, in the quiet of the deep sea.

Possibly there are other such anachronisms lurking down in these regions of which we know so little, but they are likely to be few and scattered. The terms of existence in these deep waters are far too uncompromising to support life unless that life is plastic, molding itself constantly to the harsh conditions, seizing every advantage that makes possible the survival of living protoplasm in a world only a little less hostile than the black reaches of interplanetary space.

*The foregoing consists of Chapter 4
from Rachel Carson's* THE SEA AROUND US.

J. B. S. Haldane

1892–

John Burdon Sanderson Haldane was born on November 5, 1892, studied at Eton and at New College, Oxford, and was elected a fellow of New College in 1919. He became reader in biochemistry at Cambridge in 1922 and was appointed professor of genetics at London University in 1933. From 1937 to 1957 he was professor of biometry at London.

He has published papers on subjects in biology, botany, statistical theory, physiology, and chemistry, as well as a number of popular books. He has done numerous experiments on the effects of various chemical and physical agents on the human body. In the course of such experiments, he has often used himself as subject, subjecting his own body to extreme stresses and strains. He has a wide knowledge of mathematics, as the following selection indicates, and he has made contributions to physics, particularly to aspects of the theory of relativity. He is by profession a geneticist. In short, he is remarkably versatile as well as prolific.

He is also a Marxist, and he was from 1940 to 1949 the chairman of the editorial board of the *London Daily Worker*. It has been claimed that his political views have sometimes influenced his scientific ones. If this is so, it is not evident in the famous little essay reprinted here.

The main point of the essay is probably perfectly clear. It is that we are ruled, in our physical existence, by mathematics, and in a way that we may never have suspected. "For every type of animal there is a most convenient size, and a large change in size inevitably carries with it a change of form." We are prisoners of gravity; we

could not much alter ourselves without first altering the mathematical laws of nature. Since the latter alteration seems impossible, at least on this planet, it is likely that we will have to be content with our six feet and 180 pounds for a good many eons to come.

Haldane does not content himself with pointing out what is, if you think about it, an obvious fact. He explains that "just as there is a best size for every animal, so the same is true for every human institution." He points out that the Greeks "held that a small city was the largest possible democratic state." However, he goes on to say that "the English invention of representative government made a democratic nation possible." Is there an apparent contradiction here?

"The higher animals are not larger than the lower because they are more complicated," says Haldane. "They are more complicated because they are larger." The surface of something increases as the square of a dimension, the volume as the cube of it. The least "numerate" person will recognize what a dramatic difference this is, when the dimension in question increases markedly. The difference, indeed, might be called tyrannical. Not only are we ruled by mathematics—we are the slaves of mathematics. "Comparative anatomy is largely the story of the struggle to increase surface in proportion to volume."

Haldane's little essay, a classic, forces us to think about such seemingly obvious matters as size and weight—but in fresh ways. Every paragraph is packed with unexpected ideas. The whole discussion is a perfect example of how a good scientist who is also a good writer can lead the layman to see the world of nature from a novel angle.

On Being the Right Size

T he most obvious differences between different animals are differences of size, but for some reason the zoologists have paid singularly little attention to them. In a large textbook of zoology before me I find no indication that the eagle is larger than the sparrow, or the hippopotamus bigger than the hare, though some grudging admissions are made in the case of the mouse and the whale. But yet it is easy to show that a hare could not be as large as a hippopotamus, or a whale as small as a herring. For every type of animal there is a most convenient size, and a large change in size inevitably carries with it a change of form.

Let us take the most obvious of possible cases, and consider a giant man sixty feet high—about the height of Giant Pope and Giant Pagan in the illustrated *Pilgrim's Progress* of my childhood. These monsters were not only ten times as high as Christian, but ten times as wide and ten times as thick, so that their total weight was a thousand times his, or about eighty to ninety tons. Unfortunately the cross sections of their bones were only a hundred times those of Christian, so that every square inch of giant bone had to support ten times the weight borne by a square inch of human bone. As the human thigh-bone breaks under about ten times the human weight, Pope and Pagan would have broken their thighs every time they took a step. This was doubtless why they were sitting down in the picture I remember. But it lessens one's respect for Christian and Jack the Giant-Killer.

To turn to zoology, suppose that a gazelle, a graceful little creature with long thin legs, is to become large, it will break its bones unless it does one of two things. It may make its legs short and thick, like the rhinoceros, so that every pound of weight has still about the same area of bone to support it. Or it can compress its body and stretch out its legs obliquely to gain stability, like the giraffe. I mention these two beasts because they happen to belong to the same order as the gazelle, and both are quite successful mechanically, being remarkably fast runners.

Gravity, a mere nuisance to Christian, was a terror to Pope, Pagan, and Despair. To the mouse and any smaller animal it presents practically no dangers. You can drop a mouse down a thousand-yard mine-shaft; and, on arriving at the bottom, it gets a slight shock and walks away. A rat would probably be killed, though it can fall safely from the eleventh story of a building; a man is killed, a horse splashes. For the resistance presented to movement by the air is proportional to the surface of the moving object. Divide an animal's length, breadth, and height each by ten; its weight is reduced to a thousandth, but its surface only to a hundredth. So the resistance to falling in the case of the small animal is relatively ten times greater than the driving force.

An insect, therefore, is not afraid of gravity; it can fall without danger, and can cling to the ceiling with remarkably little trouble. It can go in for elegant and fantastic forms of support like that of the daddy-long-legs. But there is a force which is as formidable to an insect as gravitation to a mammal. This is surface tension. A man coming out of a bath carries with him a film of water of about one-fiftieth of an inch in thickness. This weighs roughly a pound. A wet mouse has to carry about its own weight of water. A wet fly has to lift many times its own weight and, as every one knows, a fly once wetted by water or any other liquid is in a very serious position indeed. An insect going for a drink is in as great danger as a man leaning out over a precipice in search of food. If it once falls into the grip of the surface tension of the water—that is to say, gets wet—it is likely to remain so until it drowns. A few insects, such as water-beetles, contrive to be unwettable: the majority keep well away from their drink by means of a long proboscis.

Of course tall land animals have other difficulties. They have to pump their blood to greater heights than a man and, therefore, require a larger blood pressure and tougher blood-vessels. A great many men die from burst arteries, especially in the brain, and this danger is presumably still greater for an elephant or a giraffe. But animals of all kinds find difficulties in size for the following reason. A typical small animal, say a microscopic worm or rotifer, has a smooth skin through which all the oxygen it requires can soak in, a straight gut with sufficient surface to absorb its food, and a simple kidney. Increase its dimensions tenfold in every direction, and its weight is increased a thousand times, so that if it is to use its muscles as efficiently as its miniature counterpart, it will need a thousand times as much food and oxygen per day and will excrete a thousand times as much of waste products.

Now if its shape is unaltered its surface will be increased only a hun-

dredfold, and ten times as much oxygen must enter per minute through each square millimetre of skin, ten times as much food through each square millimetre of intestine. When a limit is reached to their absorptive powers their surface has to be increased by some special device. For example, a part of the skin may be drawn out into tufts to make gills or pushed in to make lungs, thus increasing the oxygen-absorbing surface in proportion to the animal's bulk. A man, for example, has a hundred square yards of lung. Similarly, the gut, instead of being smooth and straight, becomes coiled and develops a velvety surface, and other organs increase in complication. The higher animals are not larger than the lower because they are more complicated. They are more complicated because they are larger. Just the same is true of plants. The simplest plants, such as the green algae growing in stagnant water or on the bark of trees, are mere round cells. The higher plants increase their surface by putting out leaves and roots. Comparative anatomy is largely the story of the struggle to increase surface in proportion to volume.

Some of the methods of increasing the surface are useful up to a point, but not capable of a very wide adaptation. For example, while vertebrates carry the oxygen from the gills or lungs all over the body in the blood, insects take air directly to every part of their body by tiny blind tubes called tracheae which open to the surface at many different points. Now, although by their breathing movements they can renew the air in the outer part of the tracheal system, the oxygen has to penetrate the finer branches by means of diffusion. Gases can diffuse easily through very small distances, not many times larger than the average length travelled by a gas molecule between collisions with other molecules. But when such vast journeys—from the point of view of a molecule— as a quarter of an inch have to be made, the process becomes slow. So the portions of an insect's body more than a quarter of an inch from the air would always be short of oxygen. In consequence hardly any insects are much more than half an inch thick. Land crabs are built on the same general plan as insects, but are much clumsier. Yet like ourselves they carry oxygen around in their blood, and are therefore able to grow far larger than any insects. If the insects had hit on a plan for driving air through their tissues instead of letting it soak in, they might well have become as large as lobsters, though other considerations would have prevented them from becoming as large as man.

Exactly the same difficulties attach to flying. It is an elementary principle of aeronautics that the minimum speed needed to keep an aeroplane of a given shape in the air varies as the square root of its length. If its

linear dimensions are increased four times, it must fly twice as fast. Now the power needed for the minimum speed increases more rapidly than the weight of the machine. So the larger aeroplane, which weighs sixty-four times as much as the smaller, needs one hundred and twenty-eight times its horsepower to keep up. Applying the same principles to the birds, we find that the limit to their size is soon reached. An angel whose muscles developed no more power weight for weight than those of an eagle or a pigeon would require a breast projecting for about four feet to house the muscles engaged in working its wings, while to economize in weight, its legs would have to be reduced to mere stilts. Actually a large bird such as an eagle or kite does not keep in the air mainly by moving its wings. It is generally to be seen soaring, that is to say balanced on a rising column of air. And even soaring becomes more and more difficult with increasing size. Were this not the case eagles might be as large as tigers and as formidable to man as hostile aeroplanes.

But it is time that we passed to some of the advantages of size. One of the most obvious is that it enables one to keep warm. All warm-blooded animals at rest lose the same amount of heat from a unit area of skin, for which purpose they need a food-supply proportional to their surface and not to their weight. Five thousand mice weigh as much as a man. Their combined surface and food or oxygen consumption are about seventeen times a man's. In fact a mouse eats about one quarter its own weight of food every day, which is mainly used in keeping it warm. For the same reason small animals cannot live in cold countries. In the arctic regions there are no reptiles or amphibians, and no small mammals. The smallest mammal in Spitsbergen is the fox. The small birds fly away in the winter, while the insects die, though their eggs can survive six months or more of frost. The most successful mammals are bears, seals, and walruses.

Similarly, the eye is a rather inefficient organ until it reaches a large size. The back of the human eye on which an image of the outside world is thrown, and which corresponds to the film of a camera, is composed of a mosaic of "rods and cones" whose diameter is little more than a length of an average light-wave. Each eye has about half a million, and for two objects to be distinguishable their images must fall on separate rods or cones. It is obvious that with fewer but larger rods and cones we should see less distinctly. If they were twice as broad, two points would have to be twice as far apart before we could distinguish them at a given distance. But if their size were diminished and their number increased we should see no better. For it is impossible to form a definite image

smaller than a wave-length of light. Hence a mouse's eye is not a small-scale model of a human eye. Its rods and cones are not much smaller than ours, and therefore there are far fewer of them. A mouse could not distinguish one human face from another six feet away. In order that they should be of any use at all the eyes of small animals have to be much larger in proportion to their bodies than our own. Large animals on the other hand only require relatively small eyes, and those of the whale and elephant are little larger than our own.

For rather more recondite reasons the same general principle holds true of the brain. If we compare the brain-weights of a set of very similar animals such as the cat, cheetah, leopard, and tiger, we find that as we quadruple the body-weight the brain-weight is only doubled. The larger animal with proportionately larger bones can economize on brain, eyes, and certain other organs.

Such are a very few of the considerations which show that for every type of animal there is an optimum size. Yet although Galileo demonstrated the contrary more than three hundred years ago, people still believe that if a flea were as large as a man it could jump a thousand feet into the air. As a matter of fact the height to which an animal can jump is more nearly independent of its size than proportional to it. A flea can jump about two feet, a man about five. To jump a given height, if we neglect the resistance of the air, requires an expenditure of energy proportional to the jumper's weight. But if the jumping muscles form a constant fraction of the animal's body, the energy developed per ounce of muscle is independent of the size, provided it can be developed quickly enough in the small animal. As a matter of fact an insect's muscles, although they can contract more quickly than our own, appear to be less efficient; as otherwise a flea or grasshopper could rise six feet into the air.

And just as there is a best size for every animal, so the same is true for every human institution. In the Greek type of democracy all the citizens could listen to a series of orators and vote directly on questions of legislation. Hence their philosophers held that a small city was the largest possible democratic state. The English invention of representative government made a democratic nation possible, and the possibility was first realized in the United States, and later elsewhere. With the development of broadcasting it has once more become possible for every citizen to listen to the political views of representative orators, and the future may perhaps see the return of the national state to the Greek form of democracy. Even the referendum has been made possible only by the institution of daily newspapers.

To the biologist the problem of socialism appears largely as a problem of size. The extreme socialists desire to run every nation as a single business concern. I do not suppose that Henry Ford would find much difficulty in running Andorra or Luxembourg on a socialistic basis. He has already more men on his pay-roll than their population. It is conceivable that a syndicate of Fords, if we could find them, would make Belgium Ltd. or Denmark Inc. pay their way. But while nationalization of certain industries is an obvious possibility in the largest of states, I find it no easier to picture a completely socialized British Empire or United States than an elephant turning somersaults or a hippopotamus jumping a hedge.

Thomas Henry Huxley

1825–1895

T. H. Huxley was born at Ealing, England, on May 4, 1825. He was the son of a schoolmaster, but he received no formal education. "I had . . . neither help nor sympathy in any intellectual direction till I reached manhood," he later wrote. He wanted to become an engineer; he studied the subject, and found that he preferred the "mechanical engineering of living machines"—*i.e.*, biology. At seventeen he was much struck by the works of Carlyle, and from him learned "to make things clear and get rid of cant and shows of all sorts." At the same age he commenced regular medical studies at Charing Cross Hospital, in London, graduating in 1845.

He became a surgeon and entered the Navy. He was assigned to H. M. S. "Rattlesnake," about to start for surveying work in Torres Strait. In the course of the long voyage he made a study of the tropical seas. He united the Medusae and certain polyps to form a class that he called Hydrozoa, and he noted that all members of the class consisted of two membranes enclosing a central cavity. He then suggested that the two membranes correspond to two layers which appear in the embryos of higher animals. This "prophetic generalization" of the ectoderm and endoderm was later used in support of the theory of evolution. After his return in 1850 to England, he was elected a fellow of the Royal Society (1851); the following year he received the Royal Medal. Thus at the age of twenty-six, with no assistance from anybody, he had placed himself in the first rank of English scientists.

Huxley at this stage of his life accepted the idea of evolution within a type but not from a lower type to a higher one. *The Origin of Species* changed his mind. He found in Darwin's theory what he had failed to find in Lamarck and Lyell, namely, an intelligible and

persuasive hypothesis: natural selection. By 1892 he could write: "The doctrine of evolution is no speculation, but a generalization of certain facts." In the meantime he had written many answers to the attacks on Darwin and himself for their advocacy of evolution. Among them were *Man's Place in Nature and Other Anthropological Essays* (1863), from which the first of the following selections is taken. *On a Piece of Chalk* (1868) was inspired by similar aims.

Huxley served on ten Royal commissions in twenty-two years, was secretary and then president of the Royal Society, was a member of the London School Board, and in 1892 became a Privy Councillor. He died, after a long and painful illness, on June 29, 1895.

O*n the Relations of Man to the Lower Animals* opens with the proposition that "the question of questions for mankind—the problem which underlies all others, and is more deeply interesting than any other—is the ascertainment of the place which man occupies in nature and of his relations to the universe of things." This is a sweeping assertion and it is perhaps wise to understand from the beginning what it means.

Does man have a place in nature? Or is his place, essentially, out of, or above, nature? If he does have a place, is it unique, distinct from the place that all other things have? And does man, even if he has a definite place in nature, have one out of nature, too? These are some of the important questions raised by Huxley's assertion.

To Huxley, nature is a continuum and it includes everything that exists. If man has existence, he must have a place in nature. Huxley here ignores any other mode of existence that man might have. As to the place man occupies, however, Huxley is impartial. He imagines himself and his reader to be visiting scientists from another planet. They come upon a new mammal, man, and wish to decide where it belongs in their classification of terrestrial animals. "Being happily free," he writes, "from all real, or imaginary, personal

Notes from the artist: "A young Huxley, with an orangutan perched on the back of his chair. In the background, superimposed on the body of a primitive lungfish, the head of Bishop Wilberforce— who challenged Huxley's defense of the theory of evolution—glares at the young scientist. The quotation is from Science and Culture."

T.H.
Huxley

"Irrationally held truths
may be more harmful
than reasoned
errors."

interest in the results of the inquiry thus set afoot, we should pro-
ceed to weigh the arguments on one side and on the other, with as
much judicial calmness as if the question related to a new opossum."

The visiting scientists would have to conclude, Huxley says,
that man belongs to the order of Primates. What is the evidence
that this is so? Huxley displays it to us, carefully, calmly, and at
length. It is not primarily to be found, he says, in the physiology of
the brain, or in man's special functions and productions. Rather, it
consists in a comparison of structure, of morphology—in the struc-
ture of the hands and feet and pelvis, in the relative proportions of
the limbs, and, perhaps most important of all, in the structure and
number of the teeth. All of these elements of man's physiognomy
show, upon impartial and objective consideration, that man is less
different from the higher apes than the higher apes are from the
monkeys and lower primates. Since it is admitted that the apes and
monkeys belong together and form one order of living things, then
man belongs to it, too.

Huxley is not denying that man's place is at the top of nature.
Nothing he says belittles or ignores the immense differences of an-
other kind between man and all the other animals. But these differ-
ences, he says, are not the result, primarily, of structure and
morphology. They are the result of language. Man's larger brain may
make language possible, but it does not guarantee it. Once man in-
vents language, he makes strides forward that no other animal can
match.

On a Piece of Chalk is simpler and broader in its approach to a
problem in the study of nature. We discover that the chalk which
covers much of England and Europe must be the product of living
animals in a long since dried-up sea. That sea must have lain over
Europe for thousands—we would say millions—of years. The chalk
is "vastly older," Huxley says, "than Adam himself." The question
whether any natural thing could be "vastly older" than Adam was a
serious question in Huxley's day. For if nothing were, then it was
difficult to see how the earth could be "the theatre of a series of
changes as vast in their amount as they were slow in their progress."
But if the earth were really very old, then there was time for these
vast changes to have occurred, and there was no need to have re-
course to the hypothesis of a "grand catastrophe." [1]

1. For a discussion of "catastrophism," see the introductory note to the selection from
Lyell's *The Principles of Geology*, in Vol. 8, pp. 315–318, in this set.

Huxley ends his lecture in a way that is reminiscent of the end of Faraday's *Chemical History of a Candle*. Huxley suggests that a piece of chalk could be put "into the hot but obscure flame of burning hydrogen," in which case "it would presently shine like the sun." This would symbolize, he implies, what he has been trying to do in the lecture; but the symbol has a wider meaning than that. The chalk "has become luminous," he writes, "and its clear rays, penetrating the abyss of the remote past, have brought within our ken some stages of the evolution of the earth." Huxley's final intention is to show how science shines its light on nature itself. Nature, submitted to the flame of thought, becomes luminous, and is brought within our ken.

On the Relations of Man to the Lower Animals

T he question of questions for mankind—the problem which underlies all others, and is more deeply interesting than any other—is the ascertainment of the place which man occupies in nature and of his relations to the universe of things. Whence our race has come; what are the limits of our power over nature, and of nature's power over us; to what goal we are tending; are the problems which present themselves anew and with undiminished interest to every man born into the world. Most of us, shrinking from the difficulties and dangers which beset the seeker after original answers to these riddles, are contented to ignore them altogether, or to smother the investigating spirit under the feather-bed of respected and respectable tradition. But, in every age, one or two restless spirits, blessed with that constructive genius, which can only build on a secure foundation, or cursed with the spirit of mere scepticism, are unable to follow in the well-worn and comfortable track of their forefathers and contemporaries, and unmindful of thorns and stumbling-blocks, strike out into paths of their own. The sceptics end in the infidelity which asserts the problem to be insoluble, or in the atheism which denies the existence of any orderly progress and governance of things: the men of genius propound solutions which grow into systems of theology or of philosophy, or veiled in musical language which suggests more than it asserts, take the shape of the poetry of an epoch.

Each such answer to the great question, invariably asserted by the followers of its propounder, if not by himself, to be complete and final, remains in high authority and esteem, it may be for one century, or it may be for twenty: but, as invariably, time proves each reply to have been a mere approximation to the truth—tolerable chiefly on account of the ignorance of those by whom it was accepted, and wholly intolerable when tested by the larger knowledge of their successors.

GIBBON ORANG CHIMPANZEE GORILLA MAN

SKELETONS OF THE

Fig. 1. *Skeletons photographically reduced from diagrams of the natural size (except that of the gibbon, which was twice as large as nature), after drawings by Waterhouse Hawkins from specimens in the Museum of the Royal College of Surgeons.*

In a well-worn metaphor, a parallel is drawn between the life of man and the metamorphosis of the caterpillar into the butterfly; but the comparison may be more just as well as more novel, if for its former term we take the mental progress of the race. History shows that the human mind, fed by constant accessions of knowledge, periodically grows too large for its theoretical coverings, and bursts them asunder to appear in new habiliments, as the feeding and growing grub, at intervals, casts its too narrow skin and assumes another, itself but temporary. Truly the imago state of man seems to be terribly distant, but every moult is a step gained, and of such there have been many.

Since the revival of learning, whereby the Western races of Europe were enabled to enter upon that progress towards true knowledge, which was commenced by the philosophers of Greece, but was almost arrested in subsequent long ages of intellectual stagnation, or, at most, gyration, the human larva has been feeding vigorously, and moulting in proportion. A skin of some dimension was cast in the 16th century, and another towards the end of the 18th, while, within the last fifty years, the extraordinary growth of every department of physical science has spread among us mental food of so nutritious and stimulating a character that a new ecdysis seems imminent. But this is a process not unusually accompanied by many throes and some sickness and debility, or, it may be, by graver disturbances; so that every good citizen must feel bound to facilitate the process, and even if he have nothing but a scalpel to work withal, to ease the cracking integument to the best of his ability.

In this duty lies my excuse for the publication of these essays. For it will be admitted that some knowledge of man's position in the animate world is an indispensable preliminary to the proper understanding of his relations to the universe; and this again resolves itself, in the long run, into an inquiry into the nature and the closeness of the ties which connect him with those singular creatures whose history has been sketched in the preceding pages.

The importance of such an inquiry is indeed intuitively manifest. Brought face to face with these blurred copies of himself, the least thoughtful of men is conscious of a certain shock, due perhaps, not so much to disgust at the aspect of what looks like an insulting caricature, as to the awakening of a sudden and profound mistrust of time-honoured theories and strongly-rooted prejudices regarding his own position in nature, and his relations to the underworld of life; while that which remains a dim suspicion for the unthinking, becomes a vast argument, fraught with the deepest consequences, for all who are acquainted

with the recent progress of the anatomical and physiological sciences.

I now propose briefly to unfold that argument, and to set forth, in a form intelligible to those who possess no special acquaintance with anatomical science, the chief facts upon which all conclusions respecting the nature and the extent of the bonds which connect man with the brute world must be based: I shall then indicate the one immediate conclusion which, in my judgment, is justified by those facts, and I shall finally discuss the bearing of that conclusion upon the hypotheses which have been entertained respecting the origin of man.

The facts to which I would first direct the reader's attention, though ignored by many of the professed instructors of the public mind, are easy of demonstration and are universally agreed to by men of science; while their significance is so great, that whoso has duly pondered over them will, I think, find little to startle him in the other revelations of biology. I refer to those facts which have been made known by the study of development.

It is a truth of very wide, if not of universal, application, that every living creature commences its existence under a form different from, and simpler than, that which it eventually attains.

The oak is a more complex thing than the little rudimentary plant contained in the acorn; the caterpillar is more complex than the egg; the butterfly than the caterpillar; and each of these beings, in passing from its rudimentary to its perfect condition, runs through a series of changes, the sum of which is called its development. In the higher animals these changes are extremely complicated; but, within the last half century, the labours of such men as Von Baer, Rathke, Reichert, Bischoff, and Remak, have almost completely unravelled them, so that the successive stages of development which are exhibited by a dog, for example, are now as well known to the embryologist as are the steps of the metamorphosis of the silkworm moth to the schoolboy. It will be useful to consider with attention the nature and the order of the stages of canine development, as an example of the process in the higher animals generally.

The dog, like all animals, save the very lowest (and further inquiries may not improbably remove the apparent exception), commences its existence as an egg: as a body which is, in every sense, as much an egg as that of a hen, but is devoid of that accumulation of nutritive matter which confers upon the bird's egg its exceptional size and domestic utility; and wants the shell, which would not only be useless to an ani-

mal incubated within the body of its parent, but would cut it off from access to the source of that nutriment which the young creature requires, but which the minute egg of the mammal does not contain within itself.

The dog's egg is, in fact, a little spheroidal bag (Fig. 2), formed of a delicate transparent membrane called the *vitelline membrane,* and about $\frac{1}{130}$ to $\frac{1}{120}$ of an inch in diameter. It contains a mass of viscid nutritive matter—the *yolk*—within which is enclosed a second much more delicate spheroidal bag, called the *germinal vesicle* (*a*). In this, lastly, lies a more solid rounded body, termed the *germinal spot* (*b*).

The egg, or *ovum* is originally formed within a gland, from which, in due season, it becomes detached, and passes into the living chamber fitted for its protection and maintenance during the protracted process

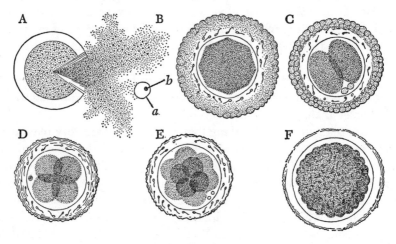

Fig. 2. A. *Egg of the dog,*
with the vitelline membrane burst, so as to give exit
to the yolk, the germinal vesicle (a), *and its included spot* (b).
B, C, D, E, F. *Successive changes of the yolk indicated in the text.*
After Bischoff.

of gestation. Here, when subjected to the required conditions, this minute and apparently insignificant particle of living matter becomes animated by a new and mysterious activity. The germinal vesicle and spot cease to be discernible (their precise fate being one of the yet unsolved problems of embryology), but the yolk becomes circumferentially indented, as if an invisible knife had been drawn round it, and thus appears divided into two hemispheres (Fig. 2, C).

By the repetition of this process in various planes, these hemispheres

become subdivided, so that four segments are produced (D); and these, in like manner, divide and subdivide again, until the whole yolk is converted into a mass of granules, each of which consists of a minute spheroid of yolk-substance, enclosing a central particle, the so-called *nucleus* (F). Nature, by this process, has attained much the same result as that which a human artificer arrives at by his operations in a brick-field. She takes the rough plastic material of the yolk and breaks it up into well-shaped tolerably even-sized masses—handy for building up into any part of the living edifice.

Next, the mass of organic bricks, or *cells* as they are technically called, thus formed, acquires an orderly arrangement, becoming converted into a hollow spheroid with double walls. Then, upon one side of this spheroid, appears a thickening, and, by and by, in the centre of the area of thickening, a straight shallow groove (Fig. 3, A) marks the central line of the edifice which is to be raised, or, in other words, indicates the position of the middle line of the body of the future dog. The substance bounding the groove on each side next rises up into a fold, the rudiment of the side wall of that long cavity, which will eventually lodge the spinal marrow and the brain; and in the floor of this chamber appears a solid cellular cord, the so-called *notochord*. One end of the enclosed cavity dilates to form the head (Fig. 3, B), the other remains narrow, and eventually becomes the tail; the side walls of the body are fashioned out of the downward continuation of the walls of the groove; and from them, by and by, grow out little buds which, by degrees, assume the shape of limbs. Watching the fashioning process stage by stage, one is forcibly reminded of the modeller in clay. Every part, every organ, is at first, as it were pinched up rudely, and sketched out in the rough; then shaped more accurately; and only, at last, receives the touches which stamp its final character.

Thus, at length, the young puppy assumes such a form as is shown in Fig. 3, C. In this condition it has a disproportionately large head, as dissimilar to that of a dog as the bud-like limbs are unlike his legs.

The remains of the yolk, which have not yet been applied to the nutrition and growth of the young animal, are contained in a sac attached to the rudimentary intestine, and termed the yolk-sac, or *umbilical vesicle*. Two membranous bags, intended to subserve respectively the protection and nutrition of the young creature, have been developed from the skin and from the under and hinder surface of the body; the former, the so-called *amnion*, is a sac filled with fluid, which invests the whole body of the embryo, and plays the part of a sort of water-bed for it; the

other, termed the *allantois*, grows out, loaded with blood-vessels, from the ventral region, and eventually applying itself to the walls of the cavity, in which the developing organism is contained, enables these vessels to become the channel by which the stream of nutriment, required to supply the wants of the offspring, is furnished to it by the parent.

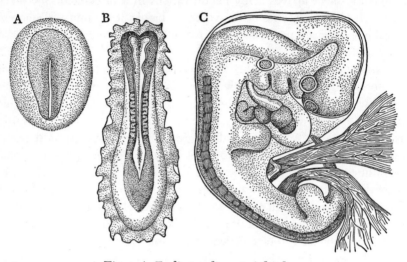

Fig. 3. A. *Earliest rudiment of the dog.*
B. *Rudiment further advanced, showing the foundations
of the head, tail, and vertebral column.*
C. *The very young puppy, with attached ends of the yolk-sac and allantois,
and invested in the amnion.*

The structure which is developed by the interlacement of the vessels of the offspring with those of the parent, and by means of which the former is enabled to receive nourishment and to get rid of effete matters, is termed the *placenta.*

It would be tedious, and it is unnecessary for my present purpose, to trace the process of development further; suffice it to say, that, by a long and gradual series of changes, the rudiment here depicted and described, becomes a puppy, is born, and then, by still slower and less perceptible steps, passes into the adult dog.

There is not much apparent resemblance between a barn-door fowl and the dog who protects the farm-yard. Nevertheless the student of development finds, not only that the chick commences its existence as an egg, primarily identical, in all essential respects, with that of the dog, but that the yolk of this egg undergoes division—that the primitive groove arises, and that the contiguous parts of the germ are fashioned, by

precisely similar methods, into a young chick, which, at one stage of its existence, is so like the nascent dog, that ordinary inspection would hardly distinguish the two.

The history of the development of any other vertebrate animal, lizard, snake, frog, or fish, tells the same story. There is always, to begin with, an egg having the same essential structure as that of the dog—the yolk of that egg always undergoes division, or *segmentation* as it is often called: the ultimate products of that segmentation constitute the building materials for the body of the young animal; and this is built up round a primitive groove, in the floor of which a notochord is developed. Furthermore, there is a period in which the young of all these animals resemble one another, not merely in outward form, but in all essentials of structure, so closely, that the differences between them are inconsiderable, while, in their subsequent course they diverge more and more widely from one another. And it is a general law that, the more closely any animals resemble one another in adult structure, the longer and the more intimately do their embryos resemble one another: so that, for example, the embryos of a snake and of a lizard remain like one another longer than do those of a snake and of a bird; and the embryo of a dog and of a cat remain like one another for a far longer period than do those of a dog and a bird; or of a dog and an opossum; or even than those of a dog and a monkey.

Thus the study of development affords a clear test of closeness of structural affinity, and one turns with impatience to inquire what results are yielded by the study of the development of Man. Is he something apart? Does he originate in a totally different way from dog, bird, frog, and fish, thus justifying those who assert him to have no place in nature and no real affinity with the lower world of animal life? Or does he originate in a similar germ, pass through the same slow and gradually progressive modifications, depend on the same contrivances for protection and nutrition, and finally enter the world by the help of the same mechanism? The reply is not doubtful for a moment, and has not been doubtful any time these thirty years. Without question, the mode of origin and the early stages of the development of man are identical with those of the animals immediately below him in the scale—without a doubt, in these respects, he is far nearer the apes, than the apes are to the dog.

The human ovum is about $\frac{1}{125}$ of an inch in diameter, and might be described in the same terms as that of the dog, so that I need only refer to the figure illustrative (4, A) of its structure. It leaves the organ

in which it is formed in a similar fashion and enters the organic chamber
prepared for its reception in the same way, the conditions of its de-
velopment being in all respects the same. It has not yet been possible
(and only by some rare chance can it ever be possible) to study the
human ovum in so early a developmental stage as that of yolk division,

Fig. 4. A. *Human ovum (after Kölliker)*.
a. germinal vesicle, b. germinal spot.
B. A very early condition of man,
with yolk-sac, allantois and amnion (original).
C. *A more advanced stage (after Kölliker), compare* Fig. 3, C.

but there is every reason to conclude that the changes it undergoes are
identical with those exhibited by the ova of other vertebrated animals;
for the formative materials of which the rudimentary human body is
composed, in the earliest conditions in which it has been observed, are
the same as those of other animals. Some of these earliest stages are
figured above and, as will be seen, they are strictly comparable
to the very early states of the dog, the marvellous correspondence be-
tween the two which is kept up, even for some time, as development ad-
vances, becoming apparent by the simple comparison of the figures with
those on page 166.

Indeed, it is very long before the body of the young human being
can be readily discriminated from that of the young puppy; but, at a
tolerably early period, the two become distinguishable by the different
form of their adjuncts, the yolk-sac and the allantois. The former, in
the dog, becomes long and spindle-shaped, while in man it remains
spherical: the latter, in the dog, attains an extremely large size, and the
vascular processes which are developed from it and eventually give rise
to the formation of the placenta (taking root, as it were, in the parental
organism, so as to draw nourishment therefrom, as the root of a tree ex-
tracts it from the soil) are arranged in an encircling zone, while in man,

the allantois remains comparatively small, and its vascular rootlets are eventually restricted to one disk-like spot. Hence, while the placenta of the dog is like a girdle, that of man has the cake-like form, indicated by the name of the organ.

But, exactly in those respects in which the developing man differs from the dog, he resembles the ape, which, like man, has a spheroidal yolk-sac and a discoidal, sometimes partially lobed, placenta. So that it is only quite in the later stages of development that the young human being presents marked differences from the young ape, while the latter departs as much from the dog in its development, as the man does.

Startling as the last assertion may appear to be, it is demonstrably true, and it alone appears to me sufficient to place beyond all doubt the structural unity of man with the rest of the animal world, and more particularly and closely with the apes.

Thus, identical in the physical processes by which he originates—identical in the early stages of his formation—identical in the mode of his nutrition before and after birth, with the animals which lie immediately below him in the scale—man, if his adult and perfect structure be compared with theirs, exhibits, as might be expected, a marvellous likeness of organization. He resembles them as they resemble one another—he differs from them as they differ from one another. And, though these differences and resemblances cannot be weighed and measured, their value may be readily estimated; the scale or standard of judgment, touching that value being afforded and expressed by the system of classification of animals now current among zoologists.

A careful study of the resemblances and differences presented by animals has, in fact, led naturalists to arrange them into groups, or assemblages, all the members of each group presenting a certain amount of definable resemblance, and the number of points of similarity being smaller as the group is larger and vice versa. Thus, all creatures which agree only in presenting the few distinctive marks of animality form the kingdom Animalia. The numerous animals which agree only in possessing the special characters of vertebrates form one sub-kingdom of this kingdom. Then the sub-kingdom Vertebrata is subdivided into the five classes, fishes, amphibians, reptiles, birds, and mammals, and these into smaller groups called orders; these into families and genera; while the last are finally broken up into the smallest assemblages, which are distinguished by the possession of constant, not-sexual, characters. These ultimate groups are species.

Every year tends to bring about a greater uniformity of opinion through-

out the zoological world as to the limits and characters of these groups, great and small. At present, for example, no one has the least doubt regarding the characters of the classes Mammalia, Aves, or Reptilia; nor does the question arise whether any thoroughly well-known animal should be placed in one class or the other. Again, there is a very general agreement respecting the characters and limits of the orders of mammals, and as to the animals which are structurally necessitated to take a place in one or another order.

No one doubts, for example, that the sloth and the ant-eater, the kangaroo and the opossum, the tiger and the badger, the tapir and the rhinoceros, are respectively members of the same orders. These successive pairs of animals may, and some do, differ from one another immensely, in such matters as the proportions and structure of their limbs; the number of their dorsal and lumbar vertebrae; the adaptation of their frames to climbing, leaping, or running; the number and form of their teeth; and the characters of their skulls and of the contained brain. But, with all these differences, they are so closely connected in all the more important and fundamental characters of their organization, and so distinctly separated by these same characters from other animals, that zoologists find it necessary to group them together as members of one order. And if any new animal were discovered, and were found to present no greater difference from the kangaroo or from the opossum, for example, than these animals do from one another, the zoologist would not only be logically compelled to rank it in the same order with these, but he would not think of doing otherwise.

Bearing this obvious course of zoological reasoning in mind, let us endeavour for a moment to disconnect our thinking selves from the mask of humanity; let us imagine ourselves scientific Saturnians, if you will, fairly acquainted with such animals as now inhabit the earth, and employed in discussing the relations they bear to a new and singular "erect and featherless biped," which some enterprising traveller, overcoming the difficulties of space and gravitation, has brought from that distant planet for our inspection, well preserved, maybe, in a cask of rum. We should all, at once, agree upon placing him among the mammalian vertebrates; and his lower jaw, his molars, and his brain, would leave no room for doubting the systematic position of the new genus among those mammals, whose young are nourished during gestation by means of a placenta, or what are called the "placental mammals."

Further, the most superficial study would at once convince us that, among the orders of placental mammals, neither the whales, nor the

hoofed creatures, nor the sloths and ant-eaters, nor the carnivorous cats, dogs, and bears, still less the rodent rats and rabbits, or the insectivorous moles and hedgehogs, or the bats, could claim our *Homo*, as one of themselves.

There would remain then, but one order for comparison, that of the apes (using that word in its broadest sense), and the question for discussion would narrow itself to this—is man so different from any of these apes that he must form an order by himself? Or does he differ less from them than they differ from one another, and hence must take his place in the same order with them?

Being happily free from all real, or imaginary, personal interest in the results of the inquiry thus set afoot, we should proceed to weigh the arguments on one side and on the other, with as much judicial calmness as if the question related to a new opossum. We should endeavour to ascertain, without seeking either to magnify or diminish them, all the characters by which our new mammal differed from the apes; and if we found that these were of less structural value than those which distinguish certain members of the ape order from others universally admitted to be of the same order, we should undoubtedly place the newly discovered tellurian genus with them.

I now proceed to detail the facts which seem to me to leave us no choice but to adopt the last-mentioned course.

It is quite certain that the ape which most nearly approaches man, in the totality of its organization, is either the chimpanzee or the gorilla; and as it makes no practical difference, for the purposes of my present argument, which is selected for comparison, on the one hand, with man, and on the other hand, with the rest of the Primates,[1] I shall select the latter (so far as its organization is known)—as a brute now so celebrated in prose and verse, that all must have heard of him, and have formed some conception of his appearance. I shall take up as many of the most important points of difference between man and this remarkable creature, as the space at my disposal will allow me to discuss, and the necessities of the argument demand; and I shall inquire into the value and magnitude of these differences, when placed side by side with those which separate the gorilla from other animals of the same order.

In the general proportions of the body and limbs there is a remarkable

1. We are not at present thoroughly acquainted with the brain of the gorilla, and therefore, in discussing cerebral characters, I shall take that of the chimpanzee as my highest term among the apes.

difference between the gorilla and man, which at once strikes the eye. The gorilla's brain-case is smaller, its trunk larger, its lower limbs shorter, its upper limbs longer in proportion than those of man.

I find that the vertebral column of a full-grown gorilla, in the Museum of the Royal College of Surgeons, measures 27 inches along its anterior curvature, from the upper edge of the atlas, or first vertebra of the neck, to the lower extremity of the sacrum; that the arm, without the hand, is 31½ inches long; that the leg, without the foot, is 26½ inches long; that the hand is 9¾ inches long; the foot 11¼ inches long.

In other words, taking the length of the spinal column as 100, the arm equals 115, the leg 96, the hand 36, and the foot 41.

In the skeleton of a male Bosjesman, in the same collection, the proportions, by the same measurement, to the spinal column, taken as 100, are —the arm 78, the leg 110, the hand 26, and the foot 32. In a woman of the same race the arm is 83, and the leg 120, the hand and foot remaining the same. In a European skeleton I find the arm to be 80, the leg 117, the hand 26, the foot 35.

Thus the leg is not so different as it looks at first sight, in its proportion to the spine in the gorilla and in the man—being very slightly shorter than the spine in the former, and between $\frac{1}{10}$ and $\frac{1}{5}$ longer than the spine in the latter. The foot is longer and the hand much longer in the gorilla; but the great difference is caused by the arms, which are very much longer than the spine in the gorilla, very much shorter than the spine in the man.

The question now arises how are the other apes related to the gorilla in these respects—taking the length of the spine, measured in the same way, at 100? In an adult chimpanzee, the arm is only 96, the leg 90, the hand 43, the foot 39—so that the hand and the leg depart more from the human proportion and the arm less, while the foot is about the same as in the gorilla.

In the orang, the arms are very much longer than in the gorilla (122), while the legs are shorter (88); the foot is longer than the hand (52 and 48), and both are much longer in proportion to the spine.

In the other man-like apes again, the gibbons, these proportions are still further altered; the length of the arms being to that of the spinal column as 19 to 11; while the legs are also a third longer than the spinal column, so as to be longer than in man, instead of shorter. The hand is half as long as the spinal column, and the foot, shorter than the hand, is about $\frac{5}{11}$ths of the length of the spinal column.

Thus *Hylobates* is as much longer in the arms than the gorilla, as the

gorilla is longer in the arms than man; while, on the other hand, it is as much longer in the legs than the man, as the man is longer in the legs than the gorilla, so that it contains within itself the extremest deviations from the average length of both pairs of limbs.[2]

The mandrill presents a middle condition, the arms and legs being nearly equal in length, and both being shorter than the spinal column; while hand and foot have nearly the same proportions to one another and to the spine, as in man.

In the spider monkey (*Ateles*) the leg is longer than the spine, and the arm than the leg; and, finally, in that remarkable lemurine form, the indri (*Lichanotus*), the leg is about as long as the spinal column, while the arm is not more than $11\frac{1}{18}$ of its length; the hand having rather less and the foot rather more, than one-third the length of the spinal column.

These examples might be greatly multiplied, but they suffice to show that, in whatever proportion of its limbs the gorilla differs from man, the other apes depart still more widely from the gorilla and that, consequently, such differences of proportion can have no ordinal value.

We may next consider the differences presented by the trunk, consisting of the vertebral column, or backbone, and the ribs and pelvis, or bony hip-basin, which are connected with it, in man and in the gorilla respectively.

In man, in consequence partly of the disposition of the articular surfaces of the vertebrae, and largely of the elastic tension of some of the fibrous bands, or ligaments, which connect these vertebrae together, the spinal column, as a whole, has an elegant S-like curvature, being convex forwards in the neck, concave in the back, convex in the loins, or lumbar region, and concave again in the sacral region; an arrangement which gives much elasticity to the whole backbone, and diminishes the jar communicated to the spine, and through it to the head, by locomotion in the erect position.

Furthermore, under ordinary circumstances, man has seven vertebrae in his neck, which are called *cervical;* twelve succeed these, bearing ribs and forming the upper part of the back, whence they are termed *dorsal;* five lie in the loins, bearing no distinct, or free, ribs, and are called *lumbar;* five, united together into a great bone, excavated in front, solidly wedged in between the hip bones, to form the back of the pelvis, and known by the name of the *sacrum,* succeed these; and finally,

2. See the figures of the skeletons of four anthropoid apes and of man, drawn to scale, p. 161.

three or four little more or less movable bones, so small as to be insignificant, constitute the *coccyx* or rudimentary tail.

In the gorilla, the vertebral column is similarly divided into cervical, dorsal, lumbar, sacral, and coccygeal vertebrae, and the total number of cervical and dorsal vertebrae, taken together, is the same as in man; but the development of a pair of ribs to the first lumbar vertebra, which is an exceptional occurrence in man, is the rule in the gorilla; and hence, as lumbar are distinguished from dorsal vertebrae only by the presence or absence of free ribs, the seventeen "dorso-lumbar" vertebrae of the gorilla are divided into thirteen dorsal and four lumbar, while in man they are twelve dorsal and five lumbar.

Not only, however, does man occasionally possess thirteen pair of ribs,[3] but the gorilla sometimes has fourteen pairs, while an orangutan skeleton in the Museum of the Royal College of Surgeons has twelve dorsal and five lumbar vertebrae, as in man. Cuvier notes the same number in a *Hylobates*. On the other hand, among the lower apes, many possess twelve dorsal and six or seven lumbar vertebrae; the douroucouli has fourteen dorsal and eight lumbar, and a lemur (*Stenops tardigradus*) has fifteen dorsal and nine lumbar vertebrae.

The vertebral column of the gorilla, as a whole, differs from that of man in the less marked character of its curves, especially in the slighter convexity of the lumbar region. Nevertheless, the curves are present, and are quite obvious in young skeletons of the gorilla and chimpanzee which have been prepared without removal of the ligaments. In young orangs similarly preserved on the other hand, the spinal column is either straight, or even concave forwards, throughout the lumbar region.

Whether we take these characters then, or such minor ones as those which are derivable from the proportional length of the spines of the cervical vertebrae, and the like, there is no doubt whatsoever as to the marked difference between man and the gorilla; but there is as little, that equally marked differences, of the very same order, obtain between the gorilla and the lower apes.

The pelvis, or bony girdle of the hips, of man is a strikingly human part of his organization; the expanded haunch bones affording support for

3. "More than once," says Peter Camper, "have I met with more than six lumbar vertebrae in man. . . . Once I found thirteen ribs and four lumbar vertebrae." Fallopius noted thirteen pair of ribs and only four lumbar vertebrae; and Eustachius once found eleven dorsal vertebrae and six lumbar vertebrae.— *Oeuvres de Pierre Camper*, T. 1, p. 42. As Tyson states, his "Pygmie" had thirteen pair of ribs and five lumbar vertebrae. The question of the curves of the spinal column in the apes requires further investigation.

his viscera during his habitually erect posture, and giving space for the attachment of the great muscles which enable him to assume and to preserve that attitude. In these respects the pelvis of the gorilla differs very considerably from his (Fig. 5). But go no lower than the gibbon, and see how vastly more he differs from the gorilla than the latter does from man, even in this structure. Look at the flat, narrow haunch-bones—the long and narrow passage—the coarse, outwardly curved, ischiatic prominences on which the gibbon habitually rests, and which are coated by the so-called "callosities," dense patches of skin, wholly absent in the gorilla, in the chimpanzee, and in the orang, as in man!

In the lower monkeys and in the lemurs the difference becomes more striking still, the pelvis acquiring an altogether quadrupedal character.

But now let us turn to a nobler and more characteristic organ—that by which the human frame seems to be, and indeed is, so strongly distinguished from all others—I mean the skull. The differences between a gorilla's skull and a man's are truly immense (Fig. 6). In the former, the face, formed largely by the massive jaw-bones, predominates over the brain-case, or cranium proper: in the latter, the proportions of the two are reversed. In the man, the occipital foramen, through which passes the great nervous cord connecting the brain with the nerves of the body, is placed just behind the centre of the base of the skull, which thus becomes evenly balanced in the erect posture; in the gorilla, it lies in the posterior third of that base. In the man, the surface of the skull is comparatively smooth, and the supraciliary ridges or brow prominences usually project but little—while, in the gorilla, vast crests are developed upon the skull, and the brow ridges overhang the cavernous orbits, like great penthouses.

Sections of the skulls, however, show that some of the apparent defects of the gorilla's cranium arise, in fact, not so much from deficiency of brain-case as from excessive development of the parts of the face. The cranial cavity is not ill-shaped, and the forehead is not truly flattened or very retreating, its really well-formed curve being simply disguised by the mass of bone which is built up against it (Fig. 6).

But the roofs of the orbits rise more obliquely into the cranial cavity, thus diminishing the space for the lower part of the anterior lobes of the brain, and the absolute capacity of the cranium is far less than that of man. So far as I am aware, no human cranium belonging to an adult man has yet been observed with a less cubical capacity than 62 cubic inches, the smallest cranium observed in any race of men by Morton, measuring 63 cubic inches; while, on the other hand, the most capa-

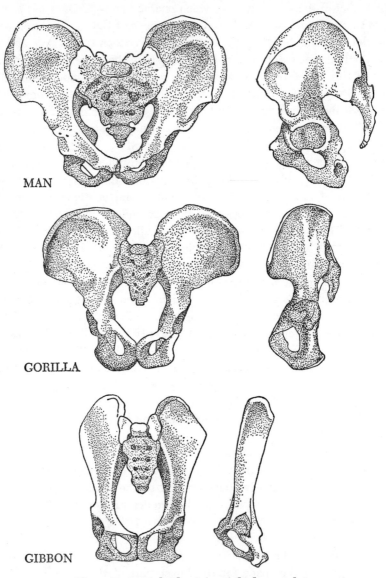

MAN

GORILLA

GIBBON

Fig. 5. *Front and side views of the bony pelvis
of man, the gorilla and gibbon:
after drawings by Waterhouse Hawkins.*

cious gorilla skull yet measured has a content of not more than 34½ cubic inches. Let us assume, for simplicity's sake, that the lowest man's skull has twice the capacity of that of the highest gorilla.[4]

No doubt, this is a very striking difference, but it loses much of its apparent systematic value, when viewed by the light of certain other equally indubitable facts respecting cranial capacities.

The first of these is that the difference in the volume of the cranial cavity of different races of mankind is far greater, absolutely, than that between the lowest man and the highest ape, while, relatively, it is about the same. For the largest human skull measured by Morton contained 114 cubic inches, that is to say, had very nearly double the capacity of the smallest; while its absolute preponderance, of 52 cubic inches—is far greater than that by which the lowest adult male human cranium surpasses the largest of the gorillas $(62 - 34\frac{1}{2} = 27\frac{1}{2})$. Secondly, the adult crania of gorillas which have as yet been measured differ among themselves by nearly one-third, the maximum capacity being 34.5 cubic inches, the minimum 24 cubic inches; and, thirdly, after making all due allowance for difference of size, the cranial capacities of some of the lower apes fall nearly as much, relatively, below those of the higher apes as the latter fall below man.

Thus, even in the important matter of cranial capacity, men differ more widely from one another than they do from the apes; while the lowest apes differ as much, in proportion, from the highest, as the latter

4. It has been affirmed that Hindu crania sometimes contain as little as 27 ounces of water, which would give a capacity of about 46 cubic inches. The minimum capacity which I have assumed above, however, is based upon the valuable tables published by Professor R. Wagner in his *Vorstudien zu einer wissenschaftlichen Morphologie und Physiologie des menschlichen Gehrins.* As the result of the careful weighing of more than 900 human brains, Professor Wagner states that one-half weighed between 1,200 and 1,400 grammes, and that about two-ninths, consisting for the most part of male brains, exceed 1,400 grammes. The lighest brain of an adult male, with sound mental faculties, recorded by Wagner, weighed 1,020 grammes. As a gramme equals 15.4 grains, and a cubic inch of water contains 252.4 grains, this is equivalent to 62 cubic inches of water; so that as brain is heavier than water, we are perfectly safe against erring on the side of diminution in taking this as the smallest capacity of any adult male human brain. The only adult male brain, weighing as little as 970 grammes, is that of an idiot; but the brain of an adult woman, against the soundness of whose faculties nothing appears, weighed as little as 907 grammes (55.3 cubic inches of water); and Reid gives an adult female brain of still smaller capacity. The heaviest brain (1,872 grammes, or about 115 cubic inches) was, however, that of a woman; next to it comes the brain of Cuvier (1,861 grammes), then Byron (1,807 grammes), and then an insane person (1,783 grammes). The lightest adult brain recorded (720 grammes) was that of an idiotic female. The brains of five children, four years old, weighed between 1,275 and 992 grammes. So that it may be safely said that an average European child of four years old has a brain twice as large as that of an adult gorilla.

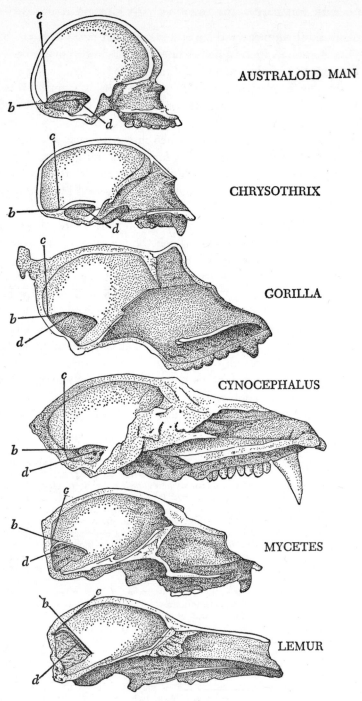

AUSTRALOID MAN

CHRYSOTHRIX

GORILLA

CYNOCEPHALUS

MYCETES

LEMUR

Fig. 6

does from man. The last proposition is still better illustrated by the study of the modifications which other parts of the cranium undergo in the simian series.

It is the large proportional size of the facial bones and the great projection of the jaws which confer upon the gorilla's skull its small facial angle and brutal character.

But if we consider the proportional size of the facial bones to the skull proper only, the little *Chrysothrix* (Fig. 6) differs very widely from the gorilla, and, in the same way, as man does; while the baboons (*Cynocephalus*, Fig. 6) exaggerate the gross proportions of the muzzle of the great anthropoid, so that its visage looks mild and human by comparison with theirs. The difference between the gorilla and the baboon is even greater than it appears at first sight; for the great facial mass of the former is largely due to a downward development of the jaws; an essentially human character, superadded upon that almost purely forward, essentially brutal, development of the same parts which characterises the baboon, and yet more remarkably distinguishes the lemur.

Similarly, the occipital foramen of *Mycetes* (Fig. 6), and still more of the lemurs, is situated completely in the posterior face of the skull, or as much further back than that of the gorilla, as that of the gorilla is further back than that of man; while, as if to render patent the futility of the attempt to base any broad classificatory distinction on such a character, the same group of Platyrhine, or American monkeys, to which the *Mycetes* belongs, contains the *Chrysothrix*, whose occipital foramen is situated far more forward than in any other ape, and nearly approaches the position it holds in man.

Again, the orang's skull is as devoid of excessively developed supraciliary prominences as a man's, though some varieties exhibit great crests elsewhere; and in some of the cebine apes and in the *Chrysothrix*, the cranium is as smooth and rounded as that of man himself.

Fig. 6. *Sections of the skulls of man and various apes, drawn so as to give the cerebral cavity the same length in each case, thereby displaying the varying proportions of the facial bones. The line b indicates the plane of the tentorium, which separates the cerebrum from the cerebellum; d, the axis of the occipital outlet of the skull. The extent of cerebral cavity behind c, which is a perpendicular erected on b at the point where the tentorium is attached posteriorly, indicates the degree to which the cerebrum overlaps the cerebellum—the space occupied by which is roughly indicated by the dark shading. In comparing these diagrams, it must be recollected, that figures on so small a scale as these simply exemplify the statements in the text, the proof of which is to be found in the objects themselves.*

What is true of these leading characteristics of the skull, holds good, as may be imagined, of all minor features; so that for every constant difference between the gorilla's skull and the man's, a similar constant difference of the same order (that is to say, consisting in excess or defect of the same quality) may be found between the gorilla's skull and that of some other ape. So that, for the skull, no less than for the skeleton in general, the proposition holds good that the differences between man and the gorilla are of smaller value than those between the gorilla and some other apes.

In connection with the skull, I may speak of the teeth—organs which have a peculiar classificatory value, and whose resemblances and differences of number, form, and succession, taken as a whole, are usually regarded as more trustworthy indicators of affinity than any others.

Man is provided with two sets of teeth—milk-teeth and permanent teeth. The former consist of four incisors, or cutting teeth; two canines, or eye-teeth; and four molars or grinders, in each jaw, making twenty in all. The latter (Fig. 7) comprise four incisors, two canines, four small grinders, called premolars or false molars, and six large grinders, or true molars in each jaw—making thirty-two in all. The internal incisors are larger than the external pair, in the upper jaw, smaller than the external pair, in the lower jaw. The crowns of the upper molars exhibit four cusps, or blunt-pointed elevations, and a ridge crosses the crown obliquely, from the inner, anterior cusp to the outer, posterior cusp (Fig. 7, m^2). The anterior lower molars have five cusps, three external and two internal. The premolars have two cusps, one internal and one external, of which the outer is the higher.

In all these respects the dentition of the gorilla may be described in the same terms as that of man; but in other matters it exhibits many and important differences (Fig. 7).

Thus the teeth of man constitute a regular and even series—without any break and without any marked projection of one tooth above the level of the rest; a peculiarity which, as Cuvier long ago showed, is shared by no other mammal save one—as different a creature from man as can well be imagined—namely, the long extinct *Anoplotherium*. The teeth of the gorilla, on the contrary, exhibit a break, or interval, termed the *diastema*, in both jaws: in front of the eye-tooth, or between it and the outer incisor, in the upper jaw; behind the eye-tooth, or between it and the front false molar, in the lower jaw. Into this break in the series, in each jaw, fits the canine of the opposite jaw; the size of the eye-tooth in the gorilla being so great that it projects, like a tusk, far beyond the

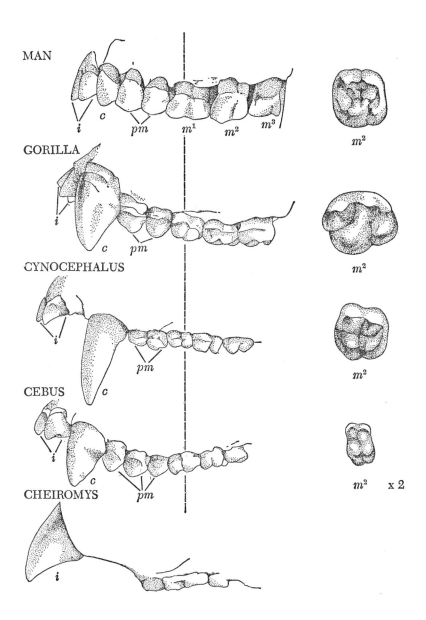

MAN

GORILLA

m^2

CYNOCEPHALUS

m^2

CEBUS

m^2

CHEIROMYS

m^2 x 2

Fig. 7. *Lateral views, of the same length,*
of the upper jaws of various Primates:
i, *incisors;* c, *canines;* pm, *pre-molars;* m, *molars.*
A line is drawn through the first molar
of man, gorilla, Cynocephalus, *and* Cebus,
and the grinding surface of the second molar is shown in each,
its anterior and internal angle being just above the m *of* m^2.

general level of the other teeth. The roots of the false molar teeth of the gorilla, again, are more complex than in man, and the proportional size of the molars is different. The gorilla has the crown of the hindmost grinder of the lower jaw more complex, and the order of eruption of the permanent teeth is different; the permanent canines making their appearance before the second and third molars in man, and after them in the gorilla.

Thus, while the teeth of the gorilla closely resemble those of man in number, kind, and in the general pattern of their crowns, they exhibit marked differences from those of man in secondary respects, such as relative size, number of fangs, and order of appearance.

But, if the teeth of the gorilla be compared with those of an ape, no further removed from it than a *Cynocephalus,* or baboon, it will be found that differences and resemblances of the same order are easily observable; but that many of the points in which the gorilla resembles man are those in which it differs from the baboon; while various respects in which it differs from man are exaggerated in the *Cynocephalus.* The number and the nature of the teeth remain the same in the baboon as in the gorilla and in man. But the pattern of the baboon's upper molars is quite different from that described above (Fig. 7), the canines are proportionally longer and more knife-like; the anterior premolar in the lower jaw is specially modified; the posterior molar of the lower jaw is still larger and more complex than in the gorilla.

Passing from the old-world apes to those of the new world, we meet with a change of much greater importance than any of these. In such a genus as *Cebus,* for example (Fig. 7), it will be found that while in some secondary points, such as the projection of the canines and the diastema, the resemblance to the great ape is preserved; in other and most important respects, the dentition is extremely different. Instead of 20 teeth in the milk set, there are 24: instead of 32 teeth in the permanent set, there are 36, the false molars being increased from eight to twelve. And in form, the crowns of the molars are very unlike those of the gorilla, and differ far more widely from the human pattern.

The marmosets, on the other hand, exhibit the same number of teeth as man and the gorilla; but, notwithstanding this, their dentition is very different, for they have four more false molars, like the other American monkeys—but as they have four fewer true molars, the total remains the same. And passing from the American apes to the lemurs, the dentition becomes still more completely and essentially different from that of the gorilla. The incisors begin to vary both in number and in form. The molars acquire, more and more, a many-pointed, insectivorous character, and in

one genus, the aye-aye (*Cheiromys*), the canines disappear, and the teeth completely simulate those of a rodent (Fig. 7).

Hence it is obvious that, greatly as the dentition of the highest ape differs from that of man, it differs far more widely from that of the lower and lowest apes.

Whatever part of the animal fabric—whatever series of muscles, whatever viscera might be selected for comparison—the result would be the same—the lower apes and the gorilla would differ more than the gorilla and the man. I cannot attempt in this place to follow out all these comparisons in detail, and indeed it is unnecessary I should do so. But certain real, or supposed, structural distinctions between man and the apes remain, upon which so much stress has been laid, that they require careful consideration, in order that the true value may be assigned to those which are real, and the emptiness of those which are fictitious may be exposed. I refer to the characters of the hand, the foot, and the brain.

Man has been defined as the only animal possessed of two hands terminating his fore limbs, and of two feet ending his hind limbs, while it has been said that all the apes possess four hands; and he has been affirmed to differ fundamentally from all the apes in the characters of his brain, which alone, it has been strangely asserted and reasserted, exhibits the structures known to anatomists as the posterior lobe, the posterior cornu of the lateral ventricle, and the hippocampus minor.

That the former proposition should have gained general acceptance is not surprising—indeed, at first sight, appearances are much in its favour: but, as for the second, one can only admire the surpassing courage of its enunciator, seeing that it is an innovation which is not only opposed to generally and justly accepted doctrines, but which is directly negatived by the testimony of all original inquirers, who have specially investigated the matter: and that it neither has been, nor can be, supported by a single anatomical preparation. It would, in fact, be unworthy of serious refutation, except for the general and natural belief that deliberate and reiterated assertions must have some foundation.

Before we can discuss the first point with advantage we must consider with some attention, and compare together, the structure of the human hand and that of the human foot, so that we may have distinct and clear ideas of what constitutes a hand and what a foot.

The external form of the human hand is familiar enough to every one. It consists of a stout wrist followed by a broad palm, formed of flesh, and

tendons, and skin, binding together four bones, and dividing into four long and flexible digits, or fingers, each of which bears on the back of its last joint a broad and flattened nail. The longest cleft between any two digits is rather less than half as long as the hand. From the outer side of the base of the palm a stout digit goes off, having only two joints instead of three; so short, that it only reaches to a little beyond the middle of the first joint of the finger next it; and further remarkable by its great mobility, in consequence of which it can be directed outwards, almost at a right angle to the rest. This digit is called the *pollex*, or thumb; and, like the others, it bears a flat nail upon the back of its terminal joint. In consequence of the proportions and mobility of the thumb, it is what is termed "opposable"; in other words, its extremity can, with the greatest ease, be brought into contact with the extremities of any of the fingers; a property upon which the possibility of our carrying into effect the conceptions of the mind so largely depends.

The external form of the foot differs widely from that of the hand; and yet, when closely compared, the two present some singular resemblances. Thus the ankle corresponds in a manner with the wrist; the sole with the palm; the toes with the fingers; the great toe with the thumb. But the toes, or digits of the foot, are far shorter in proportion than the digits of the hand, and are less moveable, the want of mobility being most striking in the great toe—which, again, is very much larger in proportion to the other toes than the thumb to the fingers. In considering this point, however, it must not be forgotten that the civilized great toe, confined and cramped from childhood upwards, is seen to a great disadvantage, and that in uncivilized and barefooted people it retains a great amount of mobility, and even some sort of opposability. The Chinese boatmen are said to be able to pull an oar; the artisans of Bengal to weave, and the Carajas to steal fish-hooks by its help; though, after all, it must be recollected that the structure of its joints and the arrangement of its bones, necessarily render its prehensile action far less perfect than that of the thumb.

But to gain a precise conception of the resemblances and differences of the hand and foot, and of the distinctive characters of each, we must look below the skin, and compare the bony framework and its motor apparatus in each (Fig. 8).

The skeleton of the hand exhibits, in the region which we term the wrist, and which is technically called the *carpus*—two rows of closely fitted polygonal bones, four in each row, which are tolerably equal in size. The bones of the first row with the bones of the forearm, form the

wrist joint, and are arranged side by side, no one greatly exceeding or overlapping the rest.

Three of the bones of the second row of the carpus bear the four long bones which support the palm of the hand. The fifth bone of the same character is articulated in a much more free and moveable manner than the others, with its carpal bone, and forms the base of the thumb.

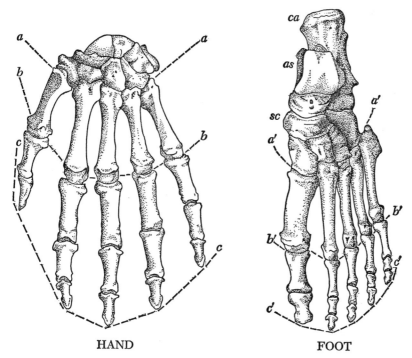

HAND FOOT

Fig. 8. *The skeleton of the hand and foot of man reduced from Dr. Carter's drawings in Gray's* Anatomy. *The hand is drawn to a larger scale than the foot. The line* a a *in the hand indicates the boundary between the carpus and the metacarpus;* b b *that between the latter and the proximal phalanges;* c c *marks the ends of the distal phalanges. The line* a' a' *in the foot indicates the boundary between the tarsus and metatarsus;* b' b' *marks that between the metatarsus and the proximal phalanges; and* c' c' *bounds the ends of the distal phalanges;* ca, *the calcaneum;* as, *the astragalus;* sc, *the scaphoid bone in the tarsus.*

These are called *metacarpal* bones, and they carry the *phalanges,* or bones of the digits, of which there are two in the thumb, and three in each of the fingers.

The skeleton of the foot is very like that of the hand in some respects. Thus there are three phalanges in each of the lesser toes, and only two in the great toe, which answers to the thumb. There is a long bone,

termed *metatarsal,* answering to the metacarpal, for each digit; and the *tarsus* which corresponds with the carpus, presents four short polygonal bones in a row, which correspond very closely with the four carpal bones of the second row of the hand. In other respects the foot differs very widely from the hand. Thus the great toe is the longest digit but one; and its metatarsal is far less moveably articulated with the tarsus than the metacarpal of the thumb with the carpus. But a far more important distinction lies in the fact that, instead of four more tarsal bones there are only three; and, that these three are not arranged side by side, or in one row. One of them, the *os calcis* or heel bone (*ca*), lies externally, and sends back the large projecting heel; another, the *astragalus* (*as*), rests on this by one face, and by another, forms, with the bones of the leg, the ankle joint; while a third face, directed forwards, is separated from the three inner tarsal bones of the row next the metatarsus by a bone called the *scaphoid* (*sc*).

Thus there is a fundamental difference in the structure of the foot and the hand, observable when the carpus and the tarsus are contrasted: and there are differences of degree noticeable when the proportions and the mobility of the metacarpals and metatarsals, with their respective digits, are compared together.

The same two classes of differences become obvious when the muscles of the hand are compared with those of the foot.

Three principal sets of muscles, called "flexors," bend the fingers and thumb, as in clenching the fist, and three sets—the extensors—extend them, as in straightening the fingers. These muscles are all "long muscles"; that is to say, the fleshy part of each, lying in and being fixed to the bones of the arm, is, at the other end, continued into tendons, or rounded cords, which pass into the hand, and are ultimately fixed to the bones which are to be moved. Thus, when the fingers are bent, the fleshy parts of the flexors of the fingers, placed in the arm, contract, in virtue of their peculiar endowment as muscles; and pulling the tendinous cords, connecting with their ends, cause them to pull down the bones of the fingers towards the palm.

Not only are the principal flexors of the fingers and of the thumb long muscles, but they remain quite distinct from one another throughout their whole length.

In the foot, there are also three principal flexor muscles of the digits or toes, and three principal extensors; but one extensor and one flexor are short muscles; that is to say, their fleshy parts are not situated in the leg (which corresponds with the arm), but in the back and in the sole of

the foot—regions which correspond with the back and the palm of the hand.

Again, the tendons of the long flexor of the toes, and of the long flexor of the great toe, when they reach the sole of the foot, do not remain distinct from one another, as the flexors in the palm of the hand do, but they become united and commingled in a very curious manner—while their united tendons receive an accessory muscle connected with the heel-bone.

But perhaps the most absolutely distinctive character about the muscles of the foot is the existence of what is termed the *peronaeus longus*, a long muscle fixed to the outer bone of the leg, and sending its tendon to the outer ankle, behind and below which it passes, and then crosses the foot obliquely to be attached to the base of the great toe. No muscle in the hand exactly corresponds with this, which is eminently a foot muscle.

To resume—the foot of man is distinguished from his hand by the following absolute anatomical differences:

1. By the arrangement of the tarsal bones.
2. By having a short flexor and a short extensor muscle of the digits.
3. By possessing the muscle termed *peronaeus longus*.

And if we desire to ascertain whether the terminal division of a limb, in other Primates, is to be called a foot or a hand, it is by the presence or absence of these characters that we must be guided, and not by the mere proportions and greater or lesser mobility of the great toe, which may vary indefinitely without any fundamental alteration in the structure of the foot.

Keeping these considerations in mind, let us now turn to the limbs of the gorilla. The terminal division of the fore limb presents no difficulty— bone for bone and muscle for muscle, are found to be arranged essentially as in man, or with such minor differences as are found as varieties in man. The gorilla's hand is clumsier, heavier, and has a thumb somewhat shorter in proportion than that of man; but no one has ever doubted it being a true hand.

At first sight, the termination of the hind limb of the gorilla looks very hand-like, and as it is still more so in many of the lower apes, it is not wonderful that the appellation "Quadrumana," or four-handed creatures, adopted from the older anatomists [5] by Blumenbach, and unfortunately

5. In speaking of the foot of his "Pygmie," Tyson remarks, p. 13:
"But this part in the formation and in its function too, being liker a Hand than a Foot: for the distinguishing this sort of animals from others, I have thought whether

rendered current by Cuvier, should have gained such wide acceptance as a name for the simian group. But the most cursory anatomical investigation at once proves that the resemblance of the so-called "hind hand" to a true hand, is only skin deep, and that, in all essential respects, the hind limb of the gorilla is as truly terminated by a foot as that of man. The tarsal bones, in all important circumstances of number, disposition, and form, resemble those of man (Fig. 9). The metatarsals and digits, on the other hand, are proportionally longer and more slender, while the great toe is not only proportionally shorter and weaker, but its metatarsal bone is united by a more moveable joint with the tarsus. At the same time, the foot is set more obliquely upon the leg than in man.

As to the muscles, there is a short flexor, a short extensor, and a *peronaeus longus,* while the tendons of the long flexors of the great toe and of the other toes are united together and with an accessory fleshy bundle.

The hind limb of the gorilla, therefore, ends in a true foot, with a very moveable great toe. It is a prehensile foot, indeed, but is in no sense a hand; it is a foot which differs from that of man not in any fundamental character, but in mere proportions, in the degree of mobility, and in the secondary arrangement of its parts.

It must not be supposed, however, because I speak of these differences as not fundamental, that I wish to underrate their value. They are important enough in their way, the structure of the foot being in strict correlation with that of the rest of the organism in each case. Nor can it be doubted that the greater division of physiological labour in man, so that the function of support is thrown wholly on the leg and foot, is an advance in organization of very great moment to him; but, after all, regarded anatomically, the resemblances between the foot of man and the foot of the gorilla are far more striking and important than the differences.

I have dwelt upon this point at length, because it is one regarding which much delusion prevails; but I might have passed it over without detriment to my argument, which only requires me to show that, be the

it might not be reckoned and called rather Quadru-manus than Quadrupes, *i.e.* a four-handed rather than a four-footed animal."

As this passage was published in 1699, M. I. G. St. Hilaire is clearly in error in ascribing the invention of the term "quadrumanous" to Buffon, though "bimanous" may belong to him. Tyson uses "Quadrumanus" in several places, as at p. 91: "Our *Pygmie* is no Man, nor yet the *common Ape,* but a sort of *Animal* between both; and though a *Biped,* yet of the *Quadrumanus*-kind: though some *Men* too have been observed to use their *Feet* like *Hands* as I have seen several."

differences between the hand and foot of man and those of the gorilla
what they may—the differences between those of the gorilla and those of
the lower apes are much greater.

It is not necessary to descend lower in the scale than the orang for
conclusive evidence on this head.

MAN GORILLA ORANG

Fig. 9. *Foot of man, gorilla, and orangutan*
of the same absolute length,
to show the differences in proportion of each.
Letters as in Fig. 8.
After drawings by Waterhouse Hawkins.

The thumb of the orang differs more from that of the gorilla than the
thumb of the gorilla differs from that of man, not only by its shortness, but
by the absence of any special long flexor muscle. The carpus of the orang,
like that of most lower apes, contains nine bones, while in the gorilla, as
in man and the chimpanzee, there are only eight.

The orang's foot (Fig. 9) is still more aberrant; its very long toes and
short tarsus, short great toe, short and raised heel, great obliquity of
articulation with the leg, and absence of a long flexor tendon to the great
toe, separating it far more widely from the foot of the gorilla than the
latter is separated from that of man.

But, in some of the lower apes, the hand and foot diverge still more from those of the gorilla, than they do in the orang. The thumb ceases to be opposable in the American monkeys; is reduced to a mere rudiment covered by the skin in the spider monkey; and is directed forwards and armed with a curved claw like the other digits, in the marmosets—so that, in all these cases, there can be no doubt but that the hand is more different from that of the gorilla than the gorilla's hand is from man's.

And as to the foot, the great toe of the marmoset is still more insignificant in proportion than that of the orang—while in the lemurs it is very large, and as completely thumb-like and opposable as in the gorilla—but in these animals the second toe is often irregularly modified, and in some species the two principal bones of the tarsus, the *astragalus* and the *os calcis,* are so immensely elongated as to render the foot, so far, totally unlike that of any other mammal.

So with regard to the muscles. The short flexor of the toes of the gorilla differs from that of man by the circumstance that one slip of the muscle is attached, not to the heel-bone, but to the tendons of the long flexors. The lower apes depart from the gorilla by an exaggeration of the same character, two, three, or more, slips becoming fixed to the long flexor tendons—or by a multiplication of the slips. Again, the gorilla differs slightly from man in the mode of interlacing of the long flexor tendons: and the lower apes differ from the gorilla in exhibiting yet other, sometimes very complex, arrangements of the same parts, and occasionally in the absence of the accessory fleshy bundle.

Throughout all these modifications it must be recollected that the foot loses no one of its essential characters. Every monkey and lemur exhibits the characteristic arrangement of tarsal bones, possesses a short flexor and short extensor muscle, and a *peronaeus longus.* Varied as the proportions and appearance of the organ may be, the terminal division of the hind limb remains, in plan and principle of construction, a foot, and never, in those respects, can be confounded with a hand.

Hardly any part of the bodily frame, then, could be found better calculated to illustrate the truth that the structural differences between man and the highest ape are of less value than those between the highest and the lower apes, than the hand or the foot; and yet, perhaps, there is one organ the study of which enforces the same conclusion in a still more striking manner—and that is the brain.

But before entering upon the precise question of the amount of difference between the ape's brain and that of man, it is necessary that we should clearly understand what constitutes a great, and what a small,

difference in cerebral structure; and we shall be best enabled to do this by a brief study of the chief modifications which the brain exhibits in the series of vertebrate animals.

The brain of a fish is very small, compared with the spinal cord into which it is continued, and with the nerves which come off from it: of the segments of which it is composed—the olfactory lobes, the cerebral hemispheres, and the succeeding divisions—no one predominates so much over the rest as to obscure or cover them; and the so-called optic lobes are, frequently, the largest masses of all. In reptiles, the mass of the brain, relatively to the spinal cord, increases and the cerebral hemispheres begin to predominate over the other parts; while in birds this predominance is still more marked. The brain of the lowest mammals, such as the duck-billed platypus and the opossums and kangaroos, exhibits a still more definite advance in the same direction. The cerebral hemispheres have now so much increased in size as, more or less, to hide the representatives of the optic lobes, which remain comparatively small, so that the brain of a marsupial is extremely different from that of a bird, reptile, or fish. A step higher in the scale, among the placental mammals, the structure of the brain acquires a vast modification—not that it appears much altered externally, in a rat or in a rabbit, from what it is in a marsupial—nor that the proportions of its parts are much changed, but an apparently new structure is found between the cerebral hemispheres, connecting them together, as what is called the "great commissure" or "corpus callosum." The subject requires careful re-investigation, but if the currently received statements are correct, the appearance of the "corpus callosum" in the placental mammals is the greatest and most sudden modification exhibited by the brain in the whole series of vertebrated animals—it is the greatest leap anywhere made by Nature in her brain work. For the two halves of the brain being once thus knit together, the progress of cerebral complexity is traceable through a complete series of steps from the lowest rodent, or insectivore, to man; and that complexity consists, chiefly, in the disproportionate development of the cerebral hemispheres and of the cerebellum, but especially of the former, in respect to the other parts of the brain.

In the lower placental mammals, the cerebral hemispheres leave the proper upper and posterior face of the cerebellum completely visible, when the brain is viewed from above; but, in the higher forms, the hinder part of each hemisphere, separated only by the tentorium (p. 193) from the anterior face of the cerebellum, inclines backwards and downwards, and grows out, as the so-called "posterior lobe," so as at length to overlap

and hide the cerebellum. In all mammals, each cerebral hemisphere contains a cavity which is termed the "ventricle"; and as this ventricle is prolonged, on the one hand forwards, and on the other downwards, into the substance of the hemisphere, it is said to have two horns or "cornua," an "anterior cornu," and a "descending cornu." When the posterior lobe is well developed, a third prolongation of the ventricular cavity extends into it, and is called the "posterior cornu."

In the lower and smaller forms of placental mammals the surface of the cerebral hemispheres is either smooth or evenly rounded, or exhibits a very few grooves, which are technically termed "sulci," separating ridges or "convolutions" of the substance of the brain; and the smaller species of all orders tend to a similar smoothness of brain. But, in the higher orders, and especially the larger members of these orders, the grooves, or sulci, become extremely numerous, and the intermediate convolutions proportionately more complicated in their meanderings, until, in the elephant, the porpoise, the higher apes, and man, the cerebral surface appears a perfect labyrinth of tortuous foldings.

Where a posterior lobe exists and presents its customary cavity—the posterior cornu—it commonly happens that a particular sulcus appears upon the inner and under surface of the lobe, parallel with and beneath the floor of the cornu—which is, as it were, arched over the roof of the sulcus. It is as if the groove had been formed by indenting the floor of the posterior horn from without with a blunt instrument, so that the floor should rise as a convex eminence. Now this eminence is what has been termed the "hippocampus minor," the "hippocampus major" being a larger eminence in the floor of the descending cornu. What may be the functional importance of either of these structures we know not.

As if to demonstrate, by a striking example, the impossibility of erecting any cerebral barrier between man and the apes, nature has provided us, in the latter animals, with an almost complete series of gradations from brains little higher than that of a rodent, to brains little lower than that of man. And it is a remarkable circumstance, that though, so far as our present knowledge extends, there *is* one true structural break in the series of forms of simian brains, this hiatus does not lie between man and the man-like apes, but between the lower and the lowest simians; or, in other words, between the old and new world apes and monkeys, and the lemurs. Every lemur which has yet been examined, in fact, has its cerebellum partially visible from above, and its posterior lobe, with the contained posterior cornu and hippocampus minor, more or less rudi-

mentary. Every marmoset, American monkey, old world monkey, baboon, or man-like ape, on the contrary, has its cerebellum entirely hidden, posteriorly, by the cerebral lobes, and possesses a large posterior cornu, with a well-developed hippocampus minor.

In many of these creatures, such as the saimiri (*Chrysothrix*), the cerebral lobes overlap and extend much further behind the cerebellum, in proportion, than they do in man (Fig. 6)—and it is quite certain that, in all, the cerebellum is completely covered behind, by well-developed posterior lobes. The fact can be verified by every one who possesses the skull of any old or new world monkey. For, inasmuch as the brain in all mammals completely fills the cranial cavity, it is obvious that a cast of the interior of the skull will reproduce the general form of the brain, at any rate with such minute and, for the present purpose, utterly unimportant differences as may result from the absence of the enveloping membranes of the brain in the dry skull. But if such a cast be made in plaster, and compared with a similar cast of the interior of a human skull, it will be obvious that the cast of the cerebral chamber, representing the cerebrum of the ape, as completely covers over and overlaps the cast of the cerebellar chamber, representing the cerebellum, as it does in the man (Fig. 10). A careless observer, forgetting that a soft structure like the brain loses its proper shape the moment it is taken out of the skull, may indeed mistake the uncovered condition of the cerebellum of an extracted and distorted brain for the natural relations of the parts; but his error must become patent even to himself if he try to replace the brain within the cranial chamber. To suppose that the cerebellum of an ape is naturally uncovered behind is a miscomprehension comparable only to that of one who should imagine that a man's lungs always occupy but a small portion of the thoracic cavity, because they do so when the chest is opened, and their elasticity is no longer neutralized by the pressure of the air.

And the error is the less excusable, as it must become apparent to every one who examines a section of the skull of any ape above a lemur, without taking the trouble to make a cast of it. For there is a very marked groove in every such skull, as in the human skull—which indicates the line of attachment of what is termed the *tentorium*—a sort of parchment-like shelf, or partition, which, in the recent state, is interposed between the cerebrum and cerebellum, and prevents the former from pressing upon the latter. (See Fig. 6.)

This groove, therefore, indicates the line of separation between that part of the cranial cavity which contains the cerebrum, and that which

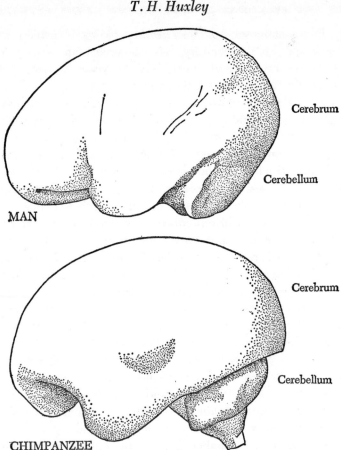

Fig. 10. *Drawings of the internal casts of a man's and of a chimpanzee's skull, of the same absolute length, and placed in corresponding positions. The former drawing is taken from a cast in the Museum of the Royal College of Surgeons, the latter from the photograph of the cast of a chimpanzee's skull, which illustrates the paper by Mr. Marshall "On the Brain of the Chimpanzee" in the Natural History Review for July, 1861. The sharper definition of the lower edge of the cast of the cerebral chamber in the chimpanzee arises from the circumstance that the tentorium remained in that skull and not in the man's. The cast more accurately represents the brain in the chimpanzee than in the man; and the great backward projection of the posterior lobes of the cerebrum of the former, beyond the cerebellum, is conspicuous.*

contains the cerebellum; and as the brain exactly fills the cavity of the skull, it is obvious that the relations of these two parts of the cranial cavity at once informs us of the relations of their contents. Now in man, in all the old world, and in all the new world simiae, with one exception, when the face is directed forwards, this line of attachment of the ten-

torium, or impression for the lateral sinus, as it is technically called, is nearly horizontal, and the cerebral chamber invariably overlaps or projects behind the cerebellar chamber. In the Howler monkey or *Mycetes* (see Fig. 6), the line passes obliquely upwards and backwards, and the cerebral overlap is almost nil; while in the lemurs, as in the lower mammals, the line is much more inclined in the same direction, and the cerebellar chamber projects considerably beyond the cerebral.

When the gravest errors respecting points so easily settled as this question respecting the posterior lobes, can be authoritatively propounded, it is no wonder that matters of observation, of no very complex character, but still requiring a certain amount of care, should have fared worse. Any one who cannot see the posterior lobe in an ape's brain is not likely to give a very valuable opinion respecting the posterior cornu or the hippocampus minor. If a man cannot see a church, it is preposterous to take his opinion about its altar-piece or painted window— so that I do not feel bound to enter upon any discussion of these points, but content myself with assuring the reader that the posterior cornu and the hippocampus minor, have now been seen—usually, at least as well developed as in man, and often better—not only in the chimpanzee, the orang, and the gibbon, but in all the genera of the old world baboons and monkeys, and in most of the new world forms, including the marmosets.

In fact, all the abundant and trustworthy evidence (consisting of the results of careful investigations directed to the determination of these very questions, by skilled anatomists) which we now possess, leads to the conviction that, so far from the posterior lobe, the posterior cornu, and the hippocampus minor, being structures peculiar to and characteristic of man, as they have been over and over again asserted to be, even after the publication of the clearest demonstration of the reverse, it is precisely these structures which are the most marked cerebral characters common to man with the apes. They are among the most distinctly simian peculiarities which the human organism exhibits.

As to the convolutions, the brains of the apes exhibit every stage of progress, from the almost smooth brain of the marmoset, to the orang and the chimpanzee, which fall but little below man. And it is most remarkable that, as soon as all the principal sulci appear, the pattern according to which they are arranged is identical with that of the corresponding sulci of man. The surface of the brain of a monkey exhibits a sort of skeleton map of man's, and in the man-like apes the details become more and more filled in, until it is only in minor characters, such

as the greater excavation of the anterior lobes, the constant presence of fissures usually absent in man, and the different disposition and proportions of some convolutions, that the chimpanzee's or the orang's brain can be structurally distinguished from man's.

So far as cerebral structure goes, therefore, it is clear that man differs less from the chimpanzee or the orang, than these do even from the monkeys, and that the difference between the brains of the chimpanzee and of man is almost insignificant, when compared with that between the chimpanzee brain and that of a lemur [cf. Fig. 11, p. 198].

It must not be overlooked, however, that there is a very striking difference in absolute mass and weight between the lowest human brain and that of the highest ape—a difference which is all the more remarkable when we recollect that a full-grown gorilla is probably pretty nearly twice as heavy as a Bosjesman, or as many a European woman. It may be doubted whether a healthy human adult brain ever weighed less than thirty-one or two ounces, or that the heaviest gorilla brain has exceeded twenty ounces.

This is a very noteworthy circumstance, and doubtless will one day help to furnish an explanation of the great gulf which intervenes between the lowest man and the highest ape in intellectual power;[6] but it has little

6. I say *help* to furnish: for I by no means believe that it was any original difference of cerebral quality, or quantity, which caused that divergence between the human and the pithecoid stirpes, which has ended in the present enormous gulf between them. It is no doubt perfectly true, in a certain sense, that all difference of function is a result of difference of structure; or, in other words, of difference in the combination of the primary molecular forces of living substance; and, starting from this undeniable axiom, objectors occasionally, and with much seeming plausibility, argue that the vast intellectual chasm between the ape and man implies a corresponding structural chasm in the organs of the intellectual functions; so that, it is said, the non-discovery of such vast differences proves, not that they are absent, but that science is incompetent to detect them. A very little consideration, however, will, I think, show the fallacy of this reasoning. Its validity hangs upon the assumption that intellectual power depends altogether on the brain—whereas the brain is only one condition out of many on which intellectual manifestations depend; the others being, chiefly, the organs of the senses and the motor apparatuses, especially those which are concerned in prehension and in the production of articulate speech.

A man born dumb, notwithstanding his great cerebral mass and his inheritance of strong intellectual instincts, would be capable of few higher intellectual manifestations than an orang or a chimpanzee, if he were confined to the society of dumb associates. And yet there might not be the slightest discernible difference between his brain and that of a highly intelligent and cultivated person. The dumbness might be the result of a defective structure of the mouth, or of the tongue, or a mere defective innervation of these parts; or it might result from congenital deafness, caused by some minute defect of the internal ear, which only a careful anatomist could discover.

The argument that because there is an immense difference between a man's intelligence and an ape's, therefore, there must be an equally immense difference between their brains, appears to me to be about as well based as the reasoning by

systematic value, for the simple reason that, as may be concluded from what has been already said respecting cranial capacity, the difference in weight of brain between the highest and the lowest men is far greater, both relatively and absolutely, than that between the lowest man and the highest ape. The latter, as has been seen, is represented by, say twelve, ounces of cerebral substance absolutely, or by 32:20 relatively; but as the largest recorded human brain weighed between 65 and 66 ounces, the former difference is represented by more than 33 ounces absolutely, or by 65:32 relatively. Regarded systematically, the cerebral differences of man and apes, are not of more than generic value; his family distinction resting chiefly on his dentition, his pelvis, and his lower limbs.

Thus, whatever system of organs be studied, the comparison of their modifications in the ape series leads to one and the same result—that the structural differences which separate man from the gorilla and the chimpanzee are not so great as those which separate the gorilla from the lower apes.

But in enunciating this important truth I must guard myself against a form of misunderstanding, which is very prevalent. I find, in fact, that those who endeavour to teach what nature so clearly shows us in this matter, are liable to have their opinions misrepresented and their phraseology garbled, until they seem to say that the structural differences between man and even the highest apes are small and insignificant. Let me take this opportunity then of distinctly asserting, on the contrary, that they are great and significant; that every bone of a gorilla bears marks by which it might be distinguished from the corresponding bone of a man; and that, in the present creation, at any rate, no intermediate link bridges over the gap between *Homo* and *Troglodytes*.

It would be no less wrong than absurd to deny the existence of this chasm; but it is at least equally wrong and absurd to exaggerate its magnitude, and, resting on the admitted fact of its existence, to refuse to

which one should endeavour to prove that, because there is a "great gulf" between a watch that keeps accurate time and another that will not go at all, there is therefore a great structural hiatus between the two watches. A hair in the balance-wheel, a little rust on a pinion, a bend in a tooth of the escapement, a something so slight that only the practised eye of the watchmaker can discover it, may be the source of all the difference.

And believing, as I do, with Cuvier, that the possession of articulate speech is the grand distinctive character of man (whether it be absolutely peculiar to him or not), I find it very easy to comprehend, that some equally inconspicuous structural difference may have been the primary cause of the immeasurable and practically infinite divergence of the human from the simian stirps.

MAN

CHIMPANZEE

Fig. 11. *Drawings of the cerebral hemispheres of a man and of a chimpanzee of the same length, in order to show the relative proportions of the parts: the former taken from a specimen, which Mr. Flower, Conservator of the Museum*

inquire whether it is wide or narrow. Remember, if you will, that there is no existing link between man and the gorilla, but do not forget that there is a no less sharp line of demarcation, a no less complete absence of any transitional form, between the gorilla and the orang, or the orang and the gibbon. I say, not less sharp, though it is somewhat narrower. The structural differences between man and the man-like apes certainly justify our regarding him as constituting a family apart from them; though, inasmuch as he differs less from them than they do from other families of the same order, there can be no justification for placing him in a distinct order.

And thus the sagacious foresight of the great lawgiver of systematic zoology, Linnaeus, becomes justified, and a century of anatomical research brings us back to his conclusion, that man is a member of the same order (for which the Linnaean term Primates ought to be retained) as the apes and lemurs. This order is now divisible into seven families, of about equal systematic value: the first, the Anthropini, contains man alone; the second, the Catarhini, embraces the old world apes; the third, the Platyrhini, all new world apes, except the marmosets; the fourth, the Arctopithecini, contains the marmosets; the fifth, the Lemurini, the lemurs—from which *Cheiromys* should probably be excluded to form a sixth distinct family, the Cheiromyini; while the seventh, the Galeopithecini, contains only the flying lemur *Galeopithecus*—a strange form which almost touches on the bats, as the *Cheiromys* puts on a rodent clothing, and the lemurs simulate insectivora.

Perhaps no order of mammals presents us with so extraordinary a series of gradations as this—leading us insensibly from the crown and summit of the animal creation down to creatures, from which there is but a step, as it seems, to the lowest, smallest, and least intelligent of the placental Mammalia. It is as if nature herself had foreseen the arrogance of man, and with Roman severity had provided that his intellect, by its very triumphs, should call into prominence the slaves, admonishing the conqueror that he is but dust.

These are the chief facts, this the immediate conclusion from them to which I adverted in the commencement of this essay. The facts, I believe, cannot be disputed; and if so, the conclusion appears to me to be inevitable.

of the Royal College of Surgeons, was good enough to dissect for me; the latter, from the photograph of a similarly dissected chimpanzee's brain, given in Mr. Marshall's paper above referred to [p. 194]. a, *posterior lobe;* b, *lateral ventricle;* c, *posterior cornu;* x, *the hippocampus minor.*

But if man be separated by no greater structural barrier from the brutes than they are from one another—then it seems to follow that if any process of physical causation can be discovered by which the genera and families of ordinary animals have been produced, that process of causation is amply sufficient to account for the origin of man. In other words, if it could be shown that the marmosets, for example, have arisen by gradual modification of the ordinary Platyrhini, or that both marmosets and Platyrhini are modified ramifications of a primitive stock—then, there would be no rational ground for doubting that man might have originated, in the one case, by the gradual modification of a man-like ape; or, in the other case, as a ramification of the same primitive stock as those apes.

At the present moment, but one such process of physical causation has any evidence in its favour; or, in other words, there is but one hypothesis regarding the origin of species of animals in general which has any scientific existence—that propounded by Mr. Darwin. For Lamarck, sagacious as many of his views were, mingled them with so much that was crude and even absurd, as to neutralize the benefit which his originality might have effected, had he been a more sober and cautious thinker; and though I have heard of the announcement of a formula touching "the ordained continuous becoming of organic forms," it is obvious that it is the first duty of a hypothesis to be intelligible, and that a quaquaversal proposition of this kind, which may be read backwards, or forwards, or sideways, with exactly the same amount of signification, does not really exist, though it may seem to do so.

At the present moment, therefore, the question of the relation of man to the lower animals resolves itself, in the end, into the larger question of the tenability, or untenability, of Mr. Darwin's views. But here we enter upon difficult ground, and it behoves us to define our exact position with the greatest care.

It cannot be doubted, I think, that Mr. Darwin has satisfactorily proved that what he terms selection, or selective modification, must occur, and does occur, in nature; and he has also proved to superfluity that such selection is competent to produce forms as distinct, structurally, as some genera even are. If the animated world presented us with none but structural differences, I should have no hesitation in saying that Mr. Darwin had demonstrated the existence of a true physical cause, amply competent to account for the origin of living species, and of man among the rest.

But, in addition to their structural distinctions, the species of animals and plants, or at least a great number of them, exhibit physiological characters—what are known as distinct species, structurally, being for the

most part either altogether incompetent to breed one with another; or if they breed, the resulting mule, or hybrid, is unable to perpetuate its race with another hybrid of the same kind.

A true physical cause is, however, admitted to be such only on one condition—that it shall account for all the phenomena which come within the range of its operation. If it is inconsistent with any one phenomenon, it must be rejected; if it fails to explain any one phenomenon, it is so far weak, so far to be suspected; though it may have a perfect right to claim provisional acceptance.

Now, Mr. Darwin's hypothesis is not, so far as I am aware, inconsistent with any known biological fact; on the contrary, if admitted, the facts of development, of comparative anatomy, of geographical distribution, and of palaeontology, become connected together, and exhibit a meaning such as they never possessed before; and I, for one, am fully convinced, that if not precisely true, that hypothesis is as near an approximation to the truth as, for example, the Copernican hypothesis was to the true theory of the planetary motions.

But, for all this, our acceptance of the Darwinian hypothesis must be provisional so long as one link in the chain of evidence is wanting; and so long as all the animals and plants certainly produced by selective breeding from a common stock are fertile, and their progeny are fertile with one another, that link will be wanting. For, so long, selective breeding will not be proved to be competent to do all that is required of it to produce natural species.

I have put this conclusion as strongly as possible before the reader, because the last position in which I wish to find myself is that of an advocate for Mr. Darwin's, or any other views; if by an advocate is meant one whose business it is to smooth over real difficulties, and to persuade where he cannot convince.

In justice to Mr. Darwin, however, it must be admitted that the conditions of fertility and sterility are very ill understood, and that every day's advance in knowledge leads us to regard the hiatus in his evidence as of less and less importance, when set against the multitude of facts which harmonize with, or receive an explanation from, his doctrines.

I adopt Mr. Darwin's hypothesis, therefore, subject to the production of proof that physiological species may be produced by selective breeding; just as a physical philosopher may accept the undulatory theory of light, subject to the proof of the existence of the hypothetical ether; or as the chemist adopts the atomic theory, subject to the proof of the existence of atoms; and for exactly the same reasons, namely, that it has an immense amount of prima facie probability: that it is the only means at

present within reach of reducing the chaos of observed facts to order;
and lastly, that it is the most powerful instrument of investigation which
has been presented to naturalists since the invention of the natural system
of classification, and the commencement of the systematic study of
embryology.

But even leaving Mr. Darwin's views aside, the whole analogy of
natural operations furnishes so complete and crushing an argument
against the intervention of any but what are termed secondary causes, in
the production of all the phenomena of the universe; that, in view of
the intimate relations between man and the rest of the living world, and
between the forces exerted by the latter and all other forces, I can see no
excuse for doubting that all are co-ordinated terms of nature's great
progression, from the formless to the formed—from the inorganic to the
organic—from blind force to conscious intellect and will.

Science has fulfilled her function when she has ascertained and enun-
ciated truth; and were these pages addressed to men of science only, I
should now close this essay, knowing that my colleagues have learned to
respect nothing but evidence, and to believe that their highest duty lies
in submitting to it, however it may jar against their inclinations.

But desiring, as I do, to reach the wider circle of the intelligent public,
it would be unworthy cowardice were I to ignore the repugnance with
which the majority of my readers are likely to meet the conclusions to
which the most careful and conscientious study I have been able to give
to this matter, has led me.

On all sides I shall hear the cry: "We are men and women, not a mere
better sort of apes, a little longer in the leg, more compact in the foot,
and bigger in brain than your brutal chimpanzees and gorillas. The
power of knowledge—the conscience of good and evil—the pitiful tender-
ness of human affections, raise us out of all real fellowship with the brutes,
however closely they may seem to approximate us."

To this I can only reply that the exclamation would be most just and
would have my own entire sympathy, if it were only relevant. But, it is
not I who seek to base man's dignity upon his great toe, or insinuate that
we are lost if an ape has a hippocampus minor. On the contrary, I have
done my best to sweep away this vanity. I have endeavoured to show that
no absolute structural line of demarcation, wider than that between the
animals which immediately succeed us in the scale, can be drawn be-
tween the animal world and ourselves; and I may add the expression of
my belief that the attempt to draw a psychical distinction is equally
futile, and that even the highest faculties of feeling and of intellect begin

to germinate in lower forms of life.[7] At the same time, no one is more strongly convinced than I am of the vastness of the gulf between civilized man and the brutes; or is more certain that whether *from* them or not, he is assuredly not *of* them. No one is less disposed to think lightly of the present dignity, or despairingly of the future hopes, of the only consciously intelligent denizen of this world.

We are indeed told by those who assume authority in these matters, that the two sets of opinions are incompatible, and that the belief in the unity of origin of man and brutes involves the brutalization and degradation of the former. But is this really so? Could not a sensible child confute by obvious arguments, the shallow rhetoricians who would force this conclusion upon us? Is it, indeed, true that the poet, or the philosopher, or the artist whose genius is the glory of his age, is degraded from his high estate by the undoubted historical probability, not to say certainty, that he is the direct descendant of some naked and bestial savage, whose intelligence was just sufficient to make him a little more cunning than the fox, and by so much more dangerous than the tiger? Or is he bound to howl and grovel on all fours because of the wholly unquestionable fact, that he was once an egg, which no ordinary power of discrimination could distinguish from that of a dog? Or is the philanthropist, or the saint, to give up his endeavours to lead a noble life, because the simplest study of man's nature reveals, at its foundations, all the selfish passions, and fierce appetites of the merest quadruped? Is mother love vile because a hen shows it, or fidelity base because dogs possess it?

The common sense of the mass of mankind will answer these questions without a moment's hesitation. Healthy humanity, finding itself hard pressed to escape from real sin and degradation, will leave the brooding over speculative pollution to the cynics and the "righteous over-

7. It is so rare a pleasure for me to find Professor Owen's opinions in entire accordance with my own, that I cannot forbear from quoting a paragraph which appeared in his essay "On the Characters, &c., of the Class Mammalia," in the *Journal of the Proceedings of the Linnean Society of London* for 1857, but is unaccountably omitted in the "Reade Lecture" delivered before the University of Cambridge two years later, which is otherwise nearly a reprint of the paper in question. Prof. Owen writes:

"Not being able to appreciate or conceive of the distinction between the psychical phenomena of a Chimpanzee and of a Boschisman or of an Aztec, with arrested brain growth, as being of a nature so essential as to preclude a comparison between them, or as being other than a difference of degree, I cannot shut my eyes to the significance of that all-pervading similitude of structure—every tooth, every bone, strictly homologous—which makes the determination of the difference between *Homo* and *Pithecus* the anatomist's difficulty."

Surely it is a little singular, that the "anatomist," who finds it "difficult" to determine "the difference" between *Homo* and *Pithecus,* should yet range them on anatomical grounds, in distinct sub-classes.

much" who, disagreeing in everything else, unite in blind insensibility to the nobleness of the visible world, and in inability to appreciate the grandeur of the place man occupies therein.

Nay more, thoughtful men, once escaped from the blinding influences of traditional prejudice, will find in the lowly stock whence man has sprung, the best evidence of the splendour of his capacities; and will discern in his long progress through the past, a reasonable ground of faith in his attainment of a nobler future.

They will remember that in comparing civilized man with the animal world, one is as the Alpine traveller, who sees the mountains soaring into the sky and can hardly discern where the deep shadowed crags and roseate peaks end, and where the clouds of heaven begin. Surely the awe-struck voyager may be excused if, at first, he refuses to believe the geologist, who tells him that these glorious masses are, after all, the hardened mud of primeval seas, or the cooled slag of subterranean furnaces—of one substance with the dullest clay, but raised by inward forces to that place of proud and seemingly inaccessible glory.

But the geologist is right; and due reflection on his teachings, instead of diminishing our reverence and our wonder, adds all the force of intellectual sublimity to the mere aesthetic intuition of the uninstructed beholder.

And after passion and prejudice have died away, the same result will attend the teachings of the naturalist respecting that great Alps and Andes of the living world—man. Our reverence for the nobility of manhood will not be lessened by the knowledge that man is, in substance and in structure, one with the brutes; for, he alone possesses the marvellous endowment of intelligible and rational speech, whereby, in the secular period of his existence, he has slowly accumulated and organized the experience which is almost wholly lost with the cessation of every individual life in other animals; so that, now, he stands raised upon it as on a mountain top, far above the level of his humble fellows, and transfigured from his grosser nature by reflecting, here and there, a ray from the infinite source of truth.

The foregoing is from a collection
of Huxley's essays entitled
MAN'S PLACE IN NATURE AND OTHER ANTHROPOLOGICAL ESSAYS.

On a Piece of Chalk

I f a well were to be sunk at our feet in the midst of the city of Norwich, the diggers would very soon find themselves at work in that white substance, almost too soft to be called rock, with which we are all familiar as "chalk."

Not only here, but over the whole country of Norfolk, the well-sinker might carry his shaft down many hundred feet without coming to the end of the chalk; and on the sea-coast, where the waves have pared away the face of the land which breasts them, the scarped faces of the high cliffs are often wholly formed of the same material. Northward the chalk may be followed as far as Yorkshire; on the south coast it appears abruptly in the picturesque western bays of Dorset, and breaks into the Needles of the Isle of Wight; while on the shores of Kent it supplies that long line of white cliffs to which England owes her name of Albion. Were the thin soil which covers it all washed away, a curved band of white chalk, here broader and there narrower, might be followed diagonally across England from Lulworth in Dorset to Flamborough Head in Yorkshire—a distance of over 280 miles as the crow flies. From this band to the North Sea on the east, and the Channel on the south, the chalk is largely hidden by other deposits; but except in the Weald of Kent and Sussex it enters into the very foundation of all the southeastern counties.

Attaining, as it does in some places, a thickness of more than a thousand feet, the English chalk must be admitted to be a mass of considerable magnitude. Nevertheless it covers but an insignificant portion of the whole area occupied by the chalk formation of the globe, which has precisely the same general characters as ours, and is found in detached patches, some less and others more extensive than the English. Chalk occurs in northwest Ireland; it stretches over a large part of France, the chalk which underlies Paris being, in fact, a continuation of that of the London basin; runs through Denmark and Central Europe, and extends

southward to North Africa; while eastward it appears in the Crimea and in Syria, and may be traced as far as the shores of the Sea of Aral, in Central Asia. If all the points at which true chalk occurs were circumscribed, they would lie within an irregular oval about 3,000 miles in long diameter—the area of which would be as great as that of Europe, and would many times exceed that of the largest existing inland sea, the Mediterranean.

Thus the chalk is no unimportant element in the masonry of the earth's crust, and it impresses a peculiar stamp, varying with the conditions to which it is exposed, on the scenery of the districts in which it occurs. The undulating downs and rounded coombs, covered with sweet-grassed turf, of our inland chalk country, have a peacefully domestic and mutton-suggesting prettiness, but can hardly be called either grand or beautiful. But on our southern coasts the wall-sided cliffs, many hundred feet high, with vast needles and pinnacles standing out in the sea, sharp and solitary enough to serve as perches for the wary cormorant, confer a wonderful beauty and grandeur upon the chalk headlands. And in the East chalk has its share in the formation of some of the most venerable of mountain ranges, such as the Lebanon.

What is this wide-spread component of the surface of the earth? and whence did it come?

You may think this no very hopeful inquiry. You may not unnaturally suppose that the attempt to solve such problems as these can lead to no result save that of entangling the inquirer in vague speculations, incapable of refutation and of verification. If such were really the case, I should have selected some other subject than "a piece of chalk" for my discourse. But in truth, after much deliberation, I have been unable to think of any topic which would so well enable me to lead you to see how solid is the foundation upon which some of the most startling conclusions of physical science rest.

A great chapter of the history of the world is written in the chalk. Few passages in the history of man can be supported by such an overwhelming mass of direct and indirect evidence as that which testifies to the truth of the fragment of the history of the globe which I hope to enable you to read with your own eyes to-night. Let me add that few chapters of human history have a more profound significance for ourselves. I weigh my words well when I assert that the man who should know the true history of the bit of chalk which every carpenter carries about in his breeches-pocket, though ignorant of all other history, is likely, if he will think his knowledge out to its ultimate results, to have a truer and there-

fore a better conception of this wonderful universe, and of man's rela-
tion to it, than the most learned student who is deep read in the records
of humanity and ignorant of those of nature.

The language of the chalk is not hard to learn, not nearly so hard as
Latin, if you only want to get at the broad features of the story it has to
tell; and I propose that we now set to work to spell that story out to-
gether.

We all know that if we "burn" chalk the result is quicklime. Chalk, in
fact, is a compound of carbonic acid gas and lime, and when you make
it very hot the carbonic acid flies away and the lime is left. By this
method of procedure we see the lime, but we do not see the carbonic
acid. If, on the other hand, you were to powder a little chalk and drop it
into a good deal of strong vinegar, there would be a great bubbling and
fizzing, and, finally, a clear liquid, in which no sign of chalk would ap-
pear. Here you see the carbonic acid in the bubbles; the lime, dissolved
in the vinegar, vanishes from sight. There are a great many other ways
of showing that chalk is essentially nothing but carbonic acid and quick-
lime. Chemists enunciate the result of all the experiments which prove
this by stating that chalk is almost wholly composed of "carbonate of
lime."

It is desirable for us to start from the knowledge of this fact, though
it may not seem to help us very far towards what we seek. For carbonate
of lime is a widely-spread substance and is met with under very various
conditions. All sorts of limestones are composed of more or less pure
carbonate of lime. The crust which is often deposited by waters which
have drained through limestone rocks, in the form of what are called
stalagmites and stalactites, is carbonate of lime. Or to take a more familiar
example, the fur on the inside of a tea-kettle is carbonate of lime; and
for anything chemistry tells us to the contrary, the chalk might be a kind
of gigantic fur upon the bottom of the earth-kettle, which is kept pretty
hot below.

Let us try another method of making the chalk tell us its own history.
To the unassisted eye chalk looks simply like a very loose and open kind
of stone. But it is possible to grind a slice of chalk down so thin that you
can see through it—until it is thin enough, in fact, to be examined with
any magnifying power that may be thought desirable. A thin slice of the
fur of a kettle might be made in the same way. If it were examined
microscopically, it would show itself to be a more or less distinctly
laminated mineral substance, and nothing more. But the slice of chalk
presents a totally different appearance when placed under the micro-

scope. The general mass of it is made up of very minute granules; but imbedded in this matrix are innumerable bodies, some smaller and some larger, but on a rough average not more than a hundredth of an inch in diameter, having a well-defined shape and structure. A cubic inch of some specimens of chalk may contain hundreds of thousands of these bodies, compacted together with incalculable millions of the granules.

The examination of a transparent slice gives a good notion of the manner in which the components of the chalk are arranged, and of their relative proportions. But by rubbing up some chalk with a brush in water and then pouring off the milky fluid, so as to obtain sediments of different degrees of fineness, the granules and the minute rounded bodies may be pretty well separated from one another, and submitted to microscopic examination, either as opaque or as transparent objects. By combining the views obtained in these various methods, each of the rounded bodies may be proved to be a beautifully-constructed calcareous fabric, made up of a number of chambers communicating freely with one another. The chambered bodies are of various forms. One of the commonest is something like a badly-grown raspberry, being formed of a number of nearly globular chambers of different sizes congregated together. It is called Globigerina, and some specimens of chalk consist of little else than Globigerinae and granules. Let us fix our attention upon the Globigerina. It is the spoor of the game we are tracking. If we can learn what it is and what are the conditions of its existence, we shall see our way to the origin and past history of the chalk.

A suggestion which may naturally enough present itself is that these curious bodies are the result of some process of aggregation which has taken place in the carbonate of lime; that, just as in winter the rime on our windows simulates the most delicate and elegantly arborescent foliage—proving that the mere mineral, water, may under certain conditions assume the outward form of organic bodies—so this mineral substance, carbonate of lime, hidden away in the bowels of the earth, has taken the shape of these chambered bodies. I am not raising a merely fanciful and unreal objection. Very learned men, in former days, have even entertained the notion that all the formed things found in rocks are of this nature; and if no such conception is at present held to be admissible, it is because long and varied experience has now shown that mineral matter never does assume the form and structure we find in fossils. If anyone were to try to persuade you that an oyster-shell (which is also chiefly composed of carbonate of lime) had crystallized out of seawater, I suppose you would laugh at the absurdity. Your laughter would

be justified by the fact that all experience tends to show that oyster-shells are formed by the agency of oysters, and in no other way. And if there were no better reasons, should be justified, on like grounds, in believing that *Globigerina* is not the product of anything but vital activity.

Happily, however, better evidence in proof of the organic nature of the Globigerinae than that of analogy is forthcoming. It so happens that calcareous skeletons, exactly similar to the Globigerinae of the chalk, are being formed at the present moment by minute living creatures, which flourish in multitudes literally more numerous than the sands of the sea-shore, over a large extent of that part of the earth's surface which is covered by the ocean.

The history of the discovery of these living Globigerinae, and of the part which they play in rock-building, is singular enough. It is a discovery which, like others of no less scientific importance, has arisen incidentally, out of work devoted to very different and exceedingly practical interests. When men first took to the sea, they speedily learned to look out for shoals and rocks; and the more the burden of their ships increased, the more imperatively necessary it became for sailors to ascertain with precision the depth of the waters they traversed. Out of this necessity grew the use of the lead and sounding-line, and, ultimately, marine surveying, which is the recording of the form of coasts and of the depth of the sea, as ascertained by the sounding-lead, upon charts. At the same time it became desirable to ascertain and to indicate the nature of the sea-bottom, since this circumstance greatly affects its goodness as holding-ground for anchors. Some ingenious tar, whose name deserves a better fate than the oblivion into which it has fallen, attained this object by "arming" the bottom of the lead with a lump of grease, to which more or less of the sand or mud or broken shells, as the case might be, adhered, and was brought to the surface. But however well adapted such an apparatus might be for rough nautical purposes, scientific accuracy could not be expected from the armed lead; and to remedy its defects (especially when applied to sounding in great depths) Lieut. Brooke, of the American Navy, some years ago invented a most ingenious machine, by which a considerable portion of the superficial layer of the sea-bottom can be scooped out and brought up from any depth to which the lead descends. In 1853, Lieut. Brooke obtained mud from the bottom of the North Atlantic, between Newfoundland and the Azores, at a depth of more than 10,000 feet, or two miles, by the help of this sounding apparatus. The specimens were sent for examination to Ehrenberg of Berlin, and to Bailey of West Point, and those able microscopists found

that this deep-sea mud was almost entirely composed of the skeletons of living organisms—the greater proportion of these being just like the Globigerinae already known to occur in the chalk.

Thus far the work had been carried on simply in the interests of science, but Lieut. Brooke's method of sounding acquired a high commercial value when the enterprise of laying down the telegraph cable between this country and the United States was undertaken; for it became a matter of immense importance to know, not only the depth of the sea over the whole line along which the cable was to be laid, but the exact nature of the bottom, so as to guard against chances of cutting or fraying the strands of that costly rope. The Admiralty consequently ordered Captain Dayman, an old friend and shipmate of mine, to ascertain the depth over the whole line of the cable and to bring back specimens of the bottom. In former days such a command as this might have sounded very much like one of the impossible things which the young prince in the fairy tales is ordered to do before he can obtain the hand of the princess. However, in the months of June and July, 1857, my friend performed the task assigned to him, with great expedition and precision, without, so far as I know, having met with any reward of that kind. The specimens of Atlantic mud which he procured were sent to me to be examined and reported upon.

The result of all these operations is that we know the contours and nature of the surface soil covered by the North Atlantic for a distance of 1,700 miles from east to west, as well as we know that of any part of the dry land. It is a prodigious plain—one of the widest and most even plains in the world. If the sea were drained off, you might drive a wagon all the way from Valentia, on the west coast of Ireland, to Trinity Bay, in Newfoundland. And, except upon one sharp incline about 200 miles from Valentia, I am not quite sure that it would even be necessary to put the skid on, so gentle are the ascents and descents upon that long route. From Valentia the road would lie downhill for about 200 miles to the point at which the bottom is now covered by 1,700 fathoms of seawater. Then would come the central plain, more than a thousand miles wide, the inequalities of the surface of which would be hardly perceptible, though the depth of water upon it now varies from 10,000 to 15,000 feet, and there are places in which Mont Blanc might be sunk without showing its peak above water. Beyond this the ascent on the American side commences, and gradually leads, for about 300 miles, to the Newfoundland shore.

Almost the whole of the bottom of this central plain (which extends

for many hundred miles in a north and south direction) is covered by a fine mud, which, when brought to the surface, dries into a grayish-white friable substance. You can write with this on a blackboard, if you are so inclined; and to the eye it is quite like very soft grayish chalk. Examined chemically, it proves to be composed almost wholly of carbonate of lime; and if you make a section of it, in the same way as that of the piece of chalk was made, and view it with the microscope, it presents innumerable Globigerinae embedded in a granular matrix. Thus this deep-sea mud is substantially chalk. I say, substantially, because there are a good many minor differences; but as these have no bearing on the question immediately before us—which is the nature of the Globigerinae of the chalk—it is unnecessary to speak of them.

Globigerinae of every size, from the smallest to the largest, are associated together in the Atlantic mud, and the chambers of many are filled by a soft animal matter. This soft substance is, in fact, the remains of the creature to which the Globigerina shell, or rather skeleton, owes its existence—and which is an animal of the simplest imaginable description. It is, in fact, a mere particle of living jelly, without defined parts of any kind—without a mouth, nerves, muscles, or distinct organs, and only manifesting its vitality to ordinary observation by thrusting out and retracting from all parts of its surface long filamentous processes, which serve for arms and legs. Yet this amorphous particle, devoid of everything which, in the higher animals we call organs, is capable of feeding, growing, and multiplying, of separating from the ocean the small proportion of carbonate of lime which is dissolved in sea-water, and of building up that substance into a skeleton for itself, according to a pattern which can be imitated by no other known agency.

The notion that animals can live and flourish in the sea, at the vast depths from which apparently living Globigerinae have been brought up, does not agree very well with our usual conceptions respecting the conditions of animal life; and it is not so absolutely impossible as it might at first sight appear to be that the Globigerinae of the Atlantic sea-bottom do not live and die where they are found.

As I have mentioned, the soundings from the great Atlantic plain are almost entirely made up of Globigerinae, with the granules which have been mentioned, and some few other calcareous shells; but a small percentage of the chalky mud—perhaps at most some five per cent of it —is of a different nature, and consists of shells and skeletons composed of silex, or pure flint. These silicious bodies belong partly to those lowly vegetable organisms which are called Diatomaceae, and partly to those

minute and extremely simple animals termed Radiolariae. It is quite certain that these creatures do not live at the bottom of the ocean, but at its surface—where they may be obtained in prodigious numbers by the use of a properly constructed net. Hence it follows that these silicious organisms, though they are not heavier than the lightest dust, must have fallen, in some cases, through fifteen thousand feet of water, before they reached their final resting-place on the ocean floor. And considering how large a surface these bodies expose in proportion to their weight, it is probable that they occupy a great length of time in making their burial journey from the surface of the Atlantic to the bottom.

But if the Radiolariae and diatoms are thus rained upon the bottom of the sea, from the superficial layer of its waters in which they pass their lives, it is obviously possible that the Globigerinae may be similarly derived; and if they were so, it would be much more easy to understand how they obtain their supply of food than it is at present. Nevertheless the positive and negative evidence all points the other way. The skeletons of the full-grown, deep-sea Globigerinae are so remarkably solid and heavy in proportion to their surface as to seem little fitted for floating; and as a matter of fact they are not to be found along with the diatoms and Radiolariae in the uppermost stratum of the open ocean. It has been observed, again, that the abundance of Globigerinae, in proportion to other organisms of like kind, increases with the depth of the sea, and that deep-water Globigerinae are larger than those which live in shallower parts of the sea; and such facts negative the supposition that these organisms have been swept by currents from the shallows into the deeps of the Atlantic. It therefore seems to be hardly doubtful that these wonderful creatures live and die at the depths in which they are found.

However, the important points for us are that the living Globigerinae are exclusively marine animals, the skeletons of which abound at the bottom of deep seas, and that there is not a shadow of reason for believing that the habits of the Globigerinae of the chalk differed from those of the existing species. But if this be true, there is no escaping the conclusion that the chalk itself is the dried mud of an ancient deep sea.

In working over the soundings collected by Captain Dayman, I was surprised to find that many of what I have called the "granules" of that mud were not, as one might have been tempted to think at first, the mere powder and waste of Globigerinae, but that they had a definite form and size. I termed these bodies "coccoliths," and doubted their organic nature. Dr. Wallich verified my observation, and added the interesting

discovery that not unfrequently bodies similar to these coccoliths were aggregated together into spheroids, which he termed "coccospheres." So far as we knew, these bodies, the nature of which is extremely puzzling and problematical, were peculiar to the Atlantic soundings. But a few years ago Mr. Sorby, in making a careful examination of the chalk by means of thin sections and otherwise, observed, as Ehrenberg had done before him, that much of its granular basis possesses a definite form. Comparing these formed particles with those in the Atlantic soundings, he found the two to be identical, and thus proved that the chalk, like the soundings, contains these mysterious coccoliths and coccospheres. Here was a further and a most interesting confirmation, from internal evidence, of the essential identity of the chalk with modern deep-sea mud. Globigerinae, coccoliths, and coccospheres are found as the chief constituents of both and testify to the general similarity of the conditions under which both have been formed.

The evidence furnished by the hewing, facing, and superposition of the stones of the Pyramids that these structures were built by men has no greater weight than the evidence that the chalk was built by Globig-erinae; and the belief that those ancient pyramid-builders were terrestrial and air-breathing creatures like ourselves is not better based than the conviction that the chalk-makers lived in the sea. But as our belief in the building of the Pyramids by men is not only grounded on the internal evidence afforded by these structures, but gathers strength from multi-tudinous collateral proofs and is clinched by the total absence of any reason for a contrary belief, so the evidence drawn from the Globig-erinae that the chalk is an ancient sea-bottom is fortified by innumerable independent lines of evidence; and our belief in the truth of the conclu-sion to which all positive testimony tends receives the like negative justi-fication from the fact that no other hypothesis has a shadow of founda-tion.

It may be worth while briefly to consider a few of these collateral proofs that the chalk was deposited at the bottom of the sea. The great mass of the chalk is composed, as we have seen, of the skeletons of Globigerinae and other simple organisms, imbedded in granular matter. Here and there, however, this hardened mud of the ancient sea reveals the remains of higher animals which have lived and died and left their hard parts in the mud, just as the oysters die and leave their shells be-hind them in the mud of the present seas.

There are certain groups of animals at the present day which are never found in fresh waters, being unable to live anywhere but in the

sea. Such are the corals; those corallines which are called Polyzoa; those creatures which fabricate the lamp-shells, and are called Brachiopoda; the pearly Nautilus, and all animals allied to it; and all the forms of sea-urchins and star-fishes. Not only are all these creatures confined to salt water at the present day, but, so far as our records of the past go, the conditions of their existence have been the same; hence their occurrence in any deposit is as strong evidence as can be obtained that that deposit was formed in the sea. Now, the remains of animals of all the kinds which have been enumerated occur in the chalk, in greater or less abundance, while not one of those forms of shell-fish which are characteristic of fresh water has yet been observed in it.

When we consider that the remains of more than three thousand distinct species of aquatic animals have been discovered among the fossils of the chalk, that the great majority of them are of such forms as are now met with only in the sea, and that there is no reason to believe that any one of them inhabited fresh water, the collateral evidence that the chalk represents an ancient sea-bottom acquires as great force as the proof derived from the nature of the chalk itself. I think you will now allow that I did not overstate my case when I asserted that we have as strong grounds for believing that all the vast area of dry land at present occupied by the chalk was once at the bottom of the sea as we have for any matter of history whatever; while there is no justification for any other belief.

No less certain is it that the time during which the countries we now call southeast England, France, Germany, Poland, Russia, Egypt, Arabia, Syria were more or less completely covered by a deep sea was of considerable duration. We have already seen that the chalk is in places more than a thousand feet thick. I think you will agree with me that it must have taken some time for the skeletons of animalculae of a hundredth of an inch in diameter to heap up such a mass as that. I have said that throughout the thickness of the chalk the remains of other animals are scattered. These remains are often in the most exquisite state of preservation. The valves of the shell-fishes are commonly adherent; the long spines of some of the sea-urchins, which would be detached by the smallest jar, often remain in their places. In a word, it is certain that these animals have lived and died when the place which they now occupy was the surface of as much of the chalk as had then been deposited, and that each has been covered up by the layer of Globigerina mud, upon which the creatures imbedded a little higher up have in like manner lived and died. But some of these remains prove the existence

of reptiles of vast size in the chalk sea. These lived their time, and had their ancestors and descendants, which assuredly implies time, reptiles being of slow growth.

There is more curious evidence, again, that the process of covering up, or in other words the deposit of Globigerina skeletons, did not go on very fast. It is demonstrable that an animal of the cretaceous sea might die, that its skeleton might lie uncovered upon the sea-bottom long enough to lose all its outward coverings and appendages by putrefaction; and that, after this had happened, another animal might attach itself to the dead and naked skeleton, might grow to maturity, and might itself die before the calcareous mud had buried the whole.

Cases of this kind are admirably described by Sir Charles Lyell. He speaks of the frequency with which geologists find in the chalk a fossilized sea-urchin, to which is attached the lower valve of a Crania. This is a kind of shell-fish, with a shell composed of two pieces, of which, as in the oyster, one is fixed and the other free. "The upper valve is almost invariably wanting, though occasionally found in a perfect state of preservation in the white chalk at some distance. In this case we see clearly that the sea-urchin first lived from youth to age, then died and lost its spines, which were carried away. Then the young *Crania* adhered to the bared shell, grew and perished in its turn; after which the upper valve was separated from the lower before the *Echinus* became enveloped in chalky mud."

A specimen in the Museum of Practical Geology, in London, still further prolongs the period which must have elapsed between the death of the sea-urchin and its burial by the Globigerinae. For the outward face of the valve of a Crania, which is attached to a sea-urchin (Micraster), is itself over-run by an incrusting coralline, which spreads thence over more or less of the surface of the sea-urchin. It follows that, after the upper valve of the Crania fell off, the surface of the attached valve must have remained exposed long enough to allow of the growth of the whole coralline, since corallines do not live imbedded in mud.

The progress of knowledge may one day enable us to deduce from such facts as these the maximum rate at which the chalk can have accumulated, and thus to arrive at the minimum duration of the chalk period. Suppose that the valve of the Crania upon which a coralline has fixed itself, in the way just described, is so attached to the sea-urchin that no part of it is more than an inch above the face upon which the sea-urchin rests. Then, as the coralline could not have fixed itself if the Crania had been covered up with chalk mud, and could not

have lived had itself been so covered, it follows that an inch of chalk
mud could not have accumulated within the time between the death
and decay of the soft parts of the sea-urchin and the growth of the
coralline to the full size which it has attained. If the decay of the soft
parts of the sea-urchin, the attachment, growth to maturity, and decay
of the Crania, and the subsequent attachment and growth of the coral-
line took a year (which is a low estimate enough), the accumulation of the
inch of chalk must have taken more than a year; and the deposit of a
thousand feet of chalk must consequently have taken more than twelve
thousand years. The foundation of all this calculation is of course a
knowledge of the length of time the Crania and the coralline needed to
attain their full size; and on this head precise knowledge is at present
wanting. But there are circumstances which tend to show that nothing
like an inch of chalk has accumulated during the life of a Crania; and on
any probable estimate of the length of that life the chalk period must
have had a much longer duration than that thus roughly assigned to it.

Thus not only is it certain that the chalk is the mud of an ancient sea-
bottom, but it is no less certain that the chalk sea existed during an
extremely long period, though we may not be prepared to give a precise
estimate of the length of that period in years. The relative duration is
clear, though the absolute duration may not be definable. The attempt
to affix any precise date to the period at which the chalk sea began or
ended its existence is baffled by difficulties of the same kind. But the
relative age of the cretaceous epoch may be determined with as great
ease and certainty as the long duration of that epoch.

You will have heard of the interesting discoveries, recently made in
various parts of Western Europe, of flint implements obviously worked
into shape by human hands, under circumstances which show con-
clusively that man is a very ancient denizen of these regions. It has
been proved that the old populations of Europe whose existence has
been revealed to us in this way, consisted of savages, such as the
Esquimaux are now; that in the country which is now France they
hunted the reindeer, and were familiar with the ways of the mammoth
and the bison. The physical geography of France was in those days
different from what it is now—the river Somme, for instance, having cut
its bed a hundred feet deeper between that time and this; and it is
probable that the climate was more like that of Canada or Siberia than
that of Western Europe.

The existence of these people is forgotten even in the traditions of
the oldest historical nations. The name and fame of them had utterly

vanished until a few years back; and the amount of physical change which has been effected since their day renders it more than probable that, venerable as are some of the historical nations, the workers of the chipped flints of Hoxne or of Amiens are to them as they are to us in point of antiquity. But if we assign to these hoar relics of long vanished generations of men the greatest age that can possibly be claimed for them, they are not older than the drift or boulder-clay, which in comparison with the chalk is but a very juvenile deposit. You need go no further than your own seaboard for evidence of this fact. At one of the most charming spots on the coast of Norfolk, Cromer, you will see the boulder-clay forming a vast mass, which lies upon the chalk and must consequently have come into existence after it. Huge boulders of chalk are in fact included in the clay, and have evidently been brought to the position they now occupy by the same agency as that which has planted blocks of syenite from Norway side by side with them.

The chalk, then, is certainly older than the boulder-clay. If you ask how much, I will again take you no further than the same spot upon your own coasts for evidence. I have spoken of the boulder-clay and drift as resting upon the chalk. That is not strictly true. Interposed between the chalk and the drift is a comparatively insignificant layer, containing vegetable matter. But that layer tells a wonderful history. It is full of stumps of trees standing as they grew. Fir-trees are there with their cones, and hazel-bushes with their nuts; there stand the stools of oak- and yew-trees, beeches and alders. Hence this stratum is appropriately called the "forest-bed."

It is obvious that the chalk must have been upheaved and converted into dry land before the timber trees could grow upon it. As the boles of some of these trees are from two to three feet in diameter, it is no less clear that the dry land thus formed remained in the same conditions for long ages. And not only do the remains of stately oaks and well-grown firs testify to the duration of this condition of things, but additional evidence to the same effect is afforded by the abundant remains of elephants, rhinoceroses, hippopotamuses, and other great wild beasts, which it has yielded to the zealous search of such men as the Rev. Mr. Gunn. When you look at such a collection as he has formed, and bethink you that these elephantine bones did veritably carry their owners about, and these great grinders crunch, in the dark woods of which the forest-bed is now the only trace, it is impossible not to feel that they are as good evidence of the lapse of time as the annual rings of the tree stumps.

Thus there is a writing upon the wall of cliffs at Cromer, and whoso runs may read it. It tells us, with an authority which cannot be impeached, that the ancient sea-bed of the chalk sea was raised up, and remained dry land until it was covered with forest stocked with the great game, the spoils of which have rejoiced your geologists. How long it remained in that condition cannot be said; but "the whirligig of time brought its revenges" in those days as in these. That dry land, with the bones and teeth of generations of long-lived elephants, hidden away among the gnarled roots and dried leaves of its ancient trees, sank gradually to the bottom of the icy sea, which covered it with huge masses of drift and boulder-clay. Sea-beasts, such as the walrus, now restricted to the extreme north, paddled about where birds had twittered among the topmost twigs of the fir-trees. How long this state of things endured we know not, but at length it came to an end. The upheaved glacial mud hardened into the soil of modern Norfolk. Forests grew once more, the wolf and the beaver replaced the reindeer and the elephant; and at length what we call the history of England dawned.

Thus you have, within the limits of your own country, proof that the chalk can justly claim a very much greater antiquity than even the oldest physical traces of mankind. But we may go further and demonstrate, by evidence of the same authority as that which testifies to the existence of the father of men, that the chalk is vastly older than Adam himself. The *Book of Genesis* informs us that Adam, immediately upon his creation and before the appearance of Eve, was placed in the Garden of Eden. The problem of the geographical position of Eden has greatly vexed the spirits of the learned in such matters; but there is one point respecting which, so far as I know, no commentator has ever raised a doubt. This is that, of the four rivers which are said to run out of it, Euphrates and Hiddekel are identical with the rivers now known by the names of Euphrates and Tigris. But the whole country in which these mighty rivers take their origin, and through which they run, is composed of rocks which are either of the same age as the chalk or of later date. So that the chalk must not only have been formed, but after its formation the time required for the deposit of these later rocks and for their upheaval into dry land must have elapsed, before the smallest brook which feeds the swift stream of "the great river, the river of Babylon," began to flow.

Thus evidence which cannot be rebutted and which need not be strengthened, though if time permitted I might indefinitely increase its quantity, compels you to believe that the earth, from the time of the chalk to the present day, has been the theatre of a series of changes as

vast in their amount as they were slow in their progress. The area on which we stand has been first sea and then land, for at least four alternations, and has remained in each of these conditions for a period of great length. Nor have these wonderful metamorphoses of sea into land and of land into sea been confined to one corner of England. During the chalk period, or "cretaceous epoch," not one of the present great physical features of the globe was in existence. Our great mountain ranges, Pyrenees, Alps, Himalayas, Andes, have all been upheaved since the chalk was deposited and the cretaceous sea flowed over the sites of Sinai and Ararat. All this is certain, because rocks of cretaceous or still later date have shared in the elevatory movements which gave rise to these mountain chains, and may be found perched up, in some cases, many thousand feet high upon their flanks. And evidence of equal cogency demonstrates that, though in Norfolk the forest-bed rests directly upon the chalk, yet it does so, not because the period at which the forest grew immediately followed that at which the chalk was formed, but because an immense lapse of time, represented elsewhere by thousands of feet of rock, is not indicated at Cromer.

I must ask you to believe that there is no less conclusive proof that a still more prolonged succession of similar changes occurred before the chalk was deposited. Nor have we any reason to think that the first term in the series of these changes is known. The oldest sea-beds preserved to us are sands and mud and pebbles, the wear and tear of rocks which were formed in still older oceans.

But great as is the magnitude of these physical changes of the world, they have been accompanied by a no less striking series of modifications in its living inhabitants. All the great classes of animals, beasts of the field, fowls of the air, creeping things, and things which dwell in the waters, flourished upon the globe long ages before the chalk was deposited. Very few, however, if any, of these ancient forms of animal life were identical with those which now live. Certainly not one of the higher animals was of the same species as any of those now in existence. The beasts of the field, in the days before the chalk, were not our beasts of the field, nor the fowls of the air such as those which the eye of man has seen flying, unless his antiquity dates infinitely further back than we at present surmise. If we could be carried back into those times, we should be as one suddenly set down in Australia before it was colonized. We should see mammals, birds, reptiles, fishes, insects, snails, and the like, clearly recognizable as such, and yet not one of them would be just the same as those with which we are familiar, and many would be extremely different.

From that time to the present the population of the world has under-gone slow and gradual but incessant changes. There has been no grand catastrophe—no destroyer has swept away the forms of life of one period and replaced them by a totally new creation: but one species has vanished, and another has taken its place; creatures of one type of struc-ture have diminished, those of another have increased, as time has passed on. And thus, while the differences between the living creatures of the time before the chalk, and those of the present day, appear startling if placed side by side, we are led from one to the other by the most gradual progress, if we follow the course of Nature through the whole series of those relics of her operations which she has left behind. And it is by the population of the chalk sea that the ancient and the modern inhabit-ants of the world are most completely connected. The groups which are dying out flourish side by side with the groups which are now the dominant forms of life. Thus the chalk contains remains of those strange flying and swimming reptiles, the pterodactyl, the Ichthyosaurus, and the Plesiosaurus, which are found in no later deposits but abounded in preceding ages. The chambered shells called ammonites and belemnites, which are so characteristic of the period preceding the cretaceous, in like manner die with it.

But amongst these fading remainders of a previous state of things are some very modern forms of life, looking like Yankee pedlars among a tribe of Red Indians. Crocodiles of modern type appear; bony fishes, many of them very similar to existing species, almost supplant the forms of fish which predominate in more ancient seas; and many kinds of living shell-fish first became known to us in the chalk. The vegetation acquires a modern aspect. A few living animals are not even distinguish-able, as species, from those which existed at that remote epoch. The Globigerina of the present day, for example, is not different specifically from that of the chalk; and the same may be said of many other Fora-miniferae. I think it probable that critical and unprejudiced examination will show that more than one species of much higher animals have had a similar longevity; but the only example which I can at present give confidently is the snake's-head lamp-shell (*Terebratulina caput serpen-tis*), which lives in our English seas, and abounded (as *Terebratulina striata* of authors) in the chalk. The longest line of human ancestry must hide its diminished head before the pedigree of this insignificant shell-fish. We Englishmen are proud to have an ancestor who was present at the Battle of Hastings. The ancestors of *Terebratulina caput serpentis* may have been present at a battle of Ichthyosauriae in that part of the

sea which, when the chalk was forming, flowed over the site of Hastings. While all around has changed, this *Terebratulina* has peacefully propagated its species from generation to generation, and stands to this day as a living testimony to the continuity of the present with the past history of the globe.

Up to this moment I have stated, so far as I know, nothing but well-authenticated facts and the immediate conclusions which they force upon the mind. But the mind is so constituted that it does not willingly rest in facts and immediate causes, but seeks always after a knowledge of the remoter links in the chain of causation. Taking the many changes of any given spot of the earth's surface, from sea to land and from land to sea, as an established fact, we cannot refrain from asking ourselves how these changes have occurred. And when we have explained them —as they must be explained—by the alternate slow movements of elevation and depression which have affected the crust of the earth, we go still further back and ask, Why these movements?

I am not certain that any one can give you a satisfactory answer to that question. Assuredly I cannot. All that can be said, for certain, is that such movements are part of the ordinary course of nature, inasmuch as they are going on at the present time. Direct proof may be given that some parts of the land of the northern hemisphere are at this moment insensibly rising and others insensibly sinking; and there is indirect but perfectly satisfactory proof that an enormous area now covered by the Pacific has been deepened thousands of feet since the present inhabitants of that sea came into existence. Thus there is not a shadow of a reason for believing that the physical changes of the globe in past times have been effected by other than natural causes. Is there any more reason for believing that the concomitant modifications in the forms of the living inhabitants of the globe have been brought about in other ways?

Before attempting to answer this question let us try to form a distinct mental picture of what has happened in some special case. The crocodiles are animals which, as a group, have a very vast antiquity. They abounded ages before the chalk was deposited; they throng the rivers in warm climates at the present day. There is a difference in the form of the joints of the backbone, and in some minor particulars, between the crocodile of the present epoch and those which lived before the chalk; but in the cretaceous epoch, as I have already mentioned, the crocodiles had assumed the modern type of structure. Notwithstanding this the crocodiles of the chalk are not identically the same as those which lived in the times called "older tertiary," which succeeded the cretaceous

epoch; and the crocodiles of the older tertiaries are not identical with those of the newer tertiaries, nor are these identical with existing forms. (I leave open the question whether particular species may have lived on from epoch to epoch.) Thus each epoch has had its peculiar crocodiles, though all, since the chalk, have belonged to the modern type, and differ simply in their proportions and in such structural particulars as are discernible only to trained eyes.

How is the existence of this long succession of different species of crocodiles to be accounted for? Only two suppositions seem to be open to us—either each species of crocodile has been specially created, or it has arisen out of some pre-existing form by the operation of natural causes. Choose your hypothesis; I have chosen mine. I can find no warranty for believing in the distinct creation of a score of successive species of crocodiles in the course of countless ages of time. Science gives no countenance to such a wild fancy; nor can even the perverse ingenuity of a commentator pretend to discover this sense in the simple words in which the writer of *Genesis* records the proceedings of the fifth and sixth days of the Creation. On the other hand I see no good reason for doubting the necessary alternative that all these varied species have been evolved from pre-existing crocodilian forms by the operation of causes as completely a part of the common order of nature as those which have effected the changes of the inorganic world. Few will venture to affirm that the reasoning which applies to crocodiles loses its force among other animals or among plants. If one series of species has come into existence by the operation of natural causes, it seems folly to deny that all may have arisen in the same way.

A small beginning has led us to a great ending. If I were to put the bit of chalk with which we started, into the hot but obscure flame of burning hydrogen, it would presently shine like the sun. It seems to me that this physical metamorphosis is no false image of what has been the result of our subjecting it to a jet of fervent though nowise brilliant thought tonight. It has become luminous; and its clear rays, penetrating the abyss of the remote past, have brought within our ken some stages of the evolution of the earth; and in the shifting, "without haste but without rest," of the land and sea, as in the endless variation of the forms assumed by living beings, we have observed nothing but the natural product of the forces originally possessed by the substance of the universe.

Sir Francis Galton

1822–1911

Francis Galton was born near Birmingham, England, in 1822. He was educated at London and Cambridge; for a time he thought he would be a doctor, but soon decided to devote himself to science. He traveled to Africa and Spain and added to the geographical and anthropological knowledge of those areas. He was made a member of the Royal Society in 1856; the following year he settled in London and began his life's work on eugenics (a word he invented). He did research also on the weather, inventing the word anticyclone and doing work that led to the modern weather map. He discovered that fingerprints are unique to the person and pointed out their usefulness in the solution of crimes. He developed the composite photograph. In his work on eugenics and human heredity he invented many methods that are now commonplace. Among them were the questionnaire, various apparatus for measuring sensations, and a method of correlating statistical information that is still used.

He was the first "anthropometrist"—that is, man-measurer. He did not only measure man. He tried to measure things that no one thought could be measured, and succeeded in many cases. Thus a remarkably large number of branches of modern science stem from him.

Hereditary Genius, from which the following selection is taken, was published in 1869. It is his most famous book. Second to it, among many publications, is *Inquiries into Human Faculty and Its Development,* which appeared in 1883. He was knighted in 1909, and he died on January 17, 1911. In 1904, he had founded a eugenics laboratory in London and endowed it with forty thousand pounds.

Since the support for the thesis of *Hereditary Genius* is that eminent men tend to be related by blood, it should be noted

that Galton was the grandson of the poet-naturalist Erasmus Darwin, and thus the cousin of Charles Darwin. Descendants of the two men are the leading scientists of our day.

I propose to show," says Galton, "that a man's natural abilities are derived by inheritance, under exactly the same limitations as are the form and physical features of the whole organic world." And he concludes: "I feel convinced that no man can achieve a very high reputation without being gifted with very high abilities; and I trust that reason has been given for the belief, that few who possess these very high abilities can fail in achieving eminence." These statements, and others like them in Galton's work, helped to generate several hotly argued modern controversies.

The first statement raises the question whether abilities are inherited or acquired; whether, that is, it is nature or nurture that determines the intelligence and talents that human beings have. Galton is clearly on the side of nature in this dispute; it is not, therefore, surprising that he has been accused of underestimating the role of environment in individual development. It is equally clear that both sides can be supported by plausible, if not finally convincing, arguments, and the reader might undertake, as an interesting exercise, the refutation of Galton's position as expressed in the following selection. But he should at the same time recognize that Galton's arguments are succinct and carefully marshalled. In particular, he should realize that Galton is admitting that circumstances can bring out in ordinary men talents and attributes that would otherwise not be visible. But it is impossible, Galton is also saying, to make a silk purse out of a sow's ear. The very greatest men of all, he insists, do not, and apparently cannot, spring from absolutely ordinary backgrounds.

Another question raised by Galton is whether genius often goes unnoted by the world. He admits that it may sometimes happen

*Notes from the artist: "A profile portrait of Galton,
with a background figure suggesting his theory of eugenics.
The female figure with the child is from a plate by Julius Casserius,
an Italian anatomist of the sixteenth century."*

Francis Galton

that the extremely talented human being fails to achieve eminence. But the poet Gray's famous dictum—that

> Full many a flower is born to blush unseen,
> And waste its sweetness on the desert air—

that would seem to be pretty emphatically denied by Galton. Again, as in the nature-nurture argument, it would be difficult to prove the proposition either way. Galton cannot prove that the highly talented *never* fail to achieve distinction; on the other hand, it is almost impossible to give convincing examples of persons possessing great talents who failed to achieve it.

Though it may be impossible to make a final decision between the two positions, there may be more wisdom in taking Galton's than its opposite. The idea that genius can exist without recognition is so prone to an obvious kind of abuse—one may, for example, apply it to oneself—that it seems suspect. In the long run it may be more prudent to assume that the world is, after all, the best judge, and if a man does not attain its applause—though this may come after his death—then he never was worthy of it.

Other issues are touched upon by Galton's book. For example, he suggests that the honors examination in mathematics at Cambridge is a pretty fair gauge of abilities of all kinds, not only the mathematical. This assertion, which is also made by some modern framers of tests and examinations, has been hotly disputed—especially by the nonmathematical. But aside from the many controversial positions expressed in the selection, the reader will probably feel that not the least fascinating portions of it deal simply with the achievements of extraordinary human beings.

The Classification of
Human Ability
from *Hereditary Genius*

I propose to show in this book that a man's natural abilities are derived by inheritance, under exactly the same limitations as are the form and physical features of the whole organic world. Consequently, as it is easy, notwithstanding those limitations, to obtain by careful selection a permanent breed of dogs or horses gifted with peculiar powers of running, or of doing anything else, so it would be quite practicable to produce a highly gifted race of men by judicious marriages during several consecutive generations. I shall show that social agencies of an ordinary character, whose influences are little suspected, are at this moment working towards the degradation of human nature, and that others are working towards its improvement. I conclude that each generation has enormous power over the natural gifts of those that follow, and maintain that it is a duty we owe to humanity to investigate the range of that power, and to exercise it in a way that, without being unwise towards ourselves, shall be most advantageous to future inhabitants of the earth.

I am aware that my views, which were first published four years ago in *Macmillan's Magazine* (in June and August 1865), are in contradiction to general opinion; but the arguments I then used have been since accepted, to my great gratification, by many of the highest authorities on heredity. In reproducing them, as I now do, in a much more elaborate form, and on a greatly enlarged basis of induction, I feel assured that, inasmuch as what I then wrote was sufficient to earn the acceptance of Mr. Darwin ("Domestication of Plants and Animals," ii, 7), the increased amount of evidence submitted in the present volume is not likely to be gainsaid.

The general plan of my argument is to show that high reputation is a pretty accurate test of high ability; next to discuss the relationships of a large body of fairly eminent men—namely, the judges of England from 1660 to 1868, the statesmen of the time of George III, and the premiers during the last 100 years—and to obtain from these a general survey of the laws of heredity in respect to genius. Then I shall examine, in order, the kindred of the most illustrious commanders, men of literature and of science, poets, painters, and musicians, of whom history speaks. I shall also discuss the kindred of a certain selection of divines and of modern scholars. Then will follow a short chapter, by way of comparison, on the hereditary transmission of physical gifts, as deduced from the relationships of certain classes of oarsmen and wrestlers. Lastly, I shall collate my results, and draw conclusions.

It will be observed that I deal with more than one grade of ability. Those upon whom the greater part of my volume is occupied, and on whose kinships my argument is most securely based, have been generally reputed as endowed by nature with extraordinary genius. There are so few of these men that, although they are scattered throughout the whole historical period of human existence, their number does not amount to more than 400, and yet a considerable proportion of them will be found to be interrelated.

Another grade of ability with which I deal is that which includes numerous highly eminent, and all the illustrious names of modern English history, whose immediate descendants are living among us, whose histories are popularly known, and whose relationships may readily be traced by the help of biographical dictionaries, peerages, and similar books of reference.

A third and lower grade is that of the English judges, massed together as a whole, for the purpose of the prefatory statistical inquiry of which I have already spoken. No one doubts that many of the ablest intellects of our race are to be found among the judges; nevertheless the *average* ability of a judge cannot be rated as equal to that of the lower of the two grades I have described.

I trust the reader will make allowance for a large and somewhat important class of omissions I have felt myself compelled to make when treating of the eminent men of modern days. I am prevented by a sense of decorum from quoting names of their relations in contemporary life who are not recognized as public characters, although their abilities may be highly appreciated in private life. Still less consistent with decorum would it have been to introduce the names of female relatives that stand

in the same category. My case is so overpoweringly strong that I am perfectly able to prove my point without having recourse to this class of evidence. Nevertheless, the reader should bear in mind that it exists; and I beg he will do me the justice of allowing that I have not over-looked the whole of the evidence that does not appear in my pages. I am deeply conscious of the imperfection of my work, but my sins are those of omission, not of commission. Such errors as I may and must have made, which give a fictitious support to my arguments, are, I am confi-dent, out of all proportion fewer than such omissions of facts as would have helped to establish them.

I have taken little notice in this book of modern men of eminence who are not English, or at least well known to Englishmen. I feared, if I included large classes of foreigners, that I should make glaring errors. It requires a very great deal of labour to hunt out relationships, even with the facilities afforded to a countryman having access to persons acquainted with the various families; much more would it have been difficult to hunt out the kindred of foreigners. I should have especially liked to investigate the biographies of Italians and Jews, both of whom appear to be rich in families of high intellectual breeds. Germany and America are also full of interest. It is a little less so with respect to France, where the Revolution and the guillotine made sad havoc among the progeny of her abler races.

There is one advantage to a candid critic in my having left so large a field untouched; it enables me to propose a test that any well-informed reader may easily adopt who doubts the fairness of my examples. He may most reasonably suspect that I have been unconsciously influenced by my theories to select men whose kindred were most favourable to their support. If so, I beg he will test my impartiality as follows: Let him take a dozen names of his own selection, as the most eminent in whatever profession and in whatever country he knows most about, and let him trace out for himself their relations. It is necessary, as I find by ex-perience, to take some pains to be sure that none, even of the immediate relatives, on either the male or female side, have been overlooked. If he does what I propose, I am confident he will be astonished at the completeness with which the results will confirm my theory. I venture to speak with assurance, because it has often occurred to me to propose this very test to incredulous friends, and invariably, so far as my memory serves me, as large a proportion of the men who were named were dis-covered to have eminent relations, as the nature of my views on heredity would have led me to expect.

CLASSIFICATION OF MEN ACCORDING TO
THEIR REPUTATION

The arguments by which I endeavour to prove that genius is hereditary consist in showing how large is the number of instances in which men who are more or less illustrious have eminent kinsfolk. It is necessary to have clear ideas on the two following matters before my arguments can be rightly appreciated. The first is the degree of selection implied by the words "eminent" and "illustrious." Does "eminent" mean the foremost in a hundred, in a thousand, or in what other number of men? The second is the degree to which reputation may be accepted as a test of ability.

It is essential that I, who write, should have a minimum qualification distinctly before my eyes whenever I employ the phrases "eminent" and the like, and that the reader should understand as clearly as myself the value I attach to those qualifications. An explanation of these words will be the subject of the present chapter. A subsequent chapter will be given to the discussion of how far "eminence" may be accepted as a criterion of natural gifts. It is almost needless for me to insist that the subjects of these two chapters are entirely distinct.

I look upon social and professional life as a continuous examination. All are candidates for the good opinions of others, and for success in their several professions, and they achieve success in proportion as the general estimate is large of their aggregate merits. In ordinary scholastic examinations marks are allotted in stated proportions to various specified subjects—so many for Latin, so many for Greek, so many for English history, and the rest. The world, in the same way, but almost unconsciously, allots marks to men. It gives them for originality of conception, for enterprise, for activity and energy, for administrative skill, for various acquirements, for power of literary expression, for oratory, and much besides of general value, as well as for more specially professional merits. It does not allot these marks according to a proportion that can easily be stated in words, but there is a rough common-sense that governs its practice with a fair approximation to constancy. Those who have gained most of these tacit marks are ranked, by the common judgment of the leaders of opinion, as the foremost men of their day.

The metaphor of an examination may be stretched much further. As there are alternative groups in any one of which a candidate may obtain honours, so it is with reputations—they may be made in law, literature,

science, art, and in a host of other pursuits. Again, as the mere attainment of a general fair level will obtain no honours in an examination, no more will it do so in the struggle for eminence. A man must show conspicuous power in at least one subject in order to achieve a high reputation.

Let us see how the world classifies people, after examining each of them, in her patient, persistent manner, during the years of their manhood. How many men of "eminence" are there, and what proportion do they bear to the whole community?

I will begin by analysing a very painstaking biographical handbook, lately published by Routledge and Co., called "Men of the Time." Its intention, which is very fairly and honestly carried out, is to include none but those whom the world honours for their ability. The catalogue of names is 2,500, and a full half of it consists of American and Continental celebrities. It is well I should give in a foot-note [1] an analysis of its contents, in order to show the exhaustive character of its range. The numbers I have prefixed to each class are not strictly accurate, for I measured them off rather than counted them, but they are quite close enough. The same name often appears under more than one head.

On looking over the book, I am surprised to find how large a proportion of the "Men of the Time" are past middle age. It appears that in the cases of high (but by no means in that of the highest) merit, a man must outlive the age of fifty to be sure of being widely appreciated. It takes time for an able man, born in the humbler ranks of life, to emerge from them and to take his natural position. It would not, therefore, be just to compare the numbers of Englishmen in the book with that of the whole adult male population of the British Isles; but it is necessary to confine our examination to those of the celebrities who are past fifty years of age, and to compare their number with that of the whole male population who are also above fifty years. I estimate, from examining a large part

1. Contents of the *"Dictionary of Men of the Time,"* Ed. 1865:

62 actors, singers, dancers, etc.; 7 agriculturists; 71 antiquaries, archaeologists, numismatists, etc.; 20 architects; 120 artists (painters and designers); 950 authors; 400 divines; 43 engineers and mechanicians; 10 engravers; 140 lawyers, judges, barristers, and legists; 94 medical practitioners, physicians, surgeons, and physiologists; 39 merchants, capitalists, manufacturers, and traders; 168 military officers; 12 miscellaneous; 7 moral and metaphysical philosophers, logicians; 32 musicians and composers; 67 naturalists, botanists, zoologists, etc.; 36 naval officers; 40 philologists and ethnologists; 60 poets (but also included in authors); 60 political and social economists and philanthropists; 154 men of science, astronomers, chemists, geologists, mathematicians, etc.; 29 sculptors; 64 sovereigns, members of royal families, etc.; 376 statesmen, diplomatists, colonial governors, etc.; 76 travellers and geographers.

of the book, that there are about 850 of these men, and that 500 of them are decidedly well known to persons familiar with literary and scientific society. Now, there are about two millions of adult males in the British Isles above fifty years of age; consequently, the total number of the "Men of the Time" are as 425 to a million, and the more select part of them as 250 to a million.

The qualifications for belonging to what I call the more select part are, in my mind, that a man should have distinguished himself pretty frequently either by purely original work, or as a leader of opinion. I wholly exclude notoriety obtained by a single act. This is a fairly well-defined line, because there is not room for many men to be eminent. Each interest or idea has its mouthpiece, and a man who has attained and can maintain his position as the representative of a party or an idea naturally becomes much more conspicuous than his coadjutors who are nearly equal but inferior in ability. This is eminently the case in positions where eminence may be won by official acts. The balance may be turned by a grain that decides whether A, B, or C shall be promoted to a vacant post. The man who obtains it has opportunities of distinction denied to the others. I do not, however, take much note of official rank. People who have left very great names behind them have mostly done so through non-professional labours. I certainly should not include mere officials, except of the highest ranks, and in open professions, among my select list of eminent men.

Another estimate of the proportion of eminent men to the whole population was made on a different basis, and gave much the same result. I took the obituary of the year 1868, published in the *Times* on January 1, 1869, and found in it about fifty names of men of the more select class. This was in one sense a broader, and in another a more rigorous selection than that which I have just described. It was broader, because I included the names of many whose abilities were high, but who died too young to have earned the wide reputation they deserved; and it was more rigorous, because I excluded old men who had earned distinction in years gone by, but had not shown themselves capable in later times to come again to the front. On the first ground, it was necessary to lower the limit of the age of the population with whom they should be compared. Forty-five years of age seemed to me a fair limit, including, as it was supposed to do, a year or two of broken health preceding decease. Now, 210,000 males die annually in the British Isles above the age of forty-five; therefore, the ratio of the more select portion of the "Men of the Time" on these data is as 50 to 210,000, or as 238 to a million.

Thirdly, I consulted obituaries of many years back, when the population of these islands was much smaller, and they appeared to me to lead to similar conclusions, viz. that 250 to a million is an ample estimate.

There would be no difficulty in making a further selection out of these, to any degree of rigour. We could select the 200, the 100, or the fifty best out of the 250, without much uncertainty. But I do not see my way to work downwards. If I were asked to choose the thousand per million best men, I should feel we had descended to a level where there existed no sure data for guidance, where accident and opportunity had undue influence, and where it was impossible to distinguish general eminence from local reputation, or from mere notoriety.

These considerations define the sense in which I propose to employ the word "eminent." When I speak of an eminent man, I mean one who has achieved a position that is attained by only 250 persons in each million of men, or by one person in each 4,000. 4,000 is a very large number—difficult for persons to realize who are not accustomed to deal with great assemblages. On the most brilliant of starlight nights there are never so many as 4,000 stars visible to the naked eye at the same time; yet we feel it to be an extraordinary distinction to a star to be accounted as the brightest in the sky. This, be it remembered, is my narrowest area of selection. I propose to introduce no name whatever into my lists of kinsmen (unless it be marked off from the rest by brackets) that is less distinguished.

The mass of those with whom I deal are far more rigidly selected—many are as one in a million, and not a few as one of many millions. I use the term "illustrious" when speaking of these. They are men whom the whole intelligent part of the nation mourns when they die; who have, or deserve to have, a public funeral; and who rank in future ages as historical characters.

Permit me to add a word upon the meaning of a million, being a number so enormous as to be difficult to conceive. It is well to have a standard by which to realize it. Mine will be understood by many Londoners; it is as follows: One summer day I passed the afternoon in Bushey Park to see the magnificent spectacle of its avenue of horse-chestnut trees, a mile long, in full flower. As the hours passed by, it occurred to me to try to count the number of spikes of flowers facing the drive on one side of the long avenue—I mean all the spikes that were visible in full sunshine on one side of the road. Accordingly, I fixed upon a tree of average bulk and flower, and drew imaginary lines—first halving the tree, then quartering, and so on, until I arrived at a subdivision that was not

too large to allow of my counting the spikes of flowers it included. I did this with three different trees, and arrived at pretty much the same result: as well as I recollect, the three estimates were as nine, ten, and eleven. Then I counted the trees in the avenue, and, multiplying all together, I found the spikes to be just about 100,000 in number. Ever since then, whenever a million is mentioned, I recall the long perspective of the avenue of Bushey Park, with its stately chestnuts clothed from top to bottom with spikes of flowers, bright in the sunshine, and I imagine a similarly continuous floral band, of ten miles in length.

In illustration of the value of the extreme rigour implied by a selection of one in a million, I will take the following instance. The Oxford and Cambridge boat race excites almost a national enthusiasm, and the men who represent their universities as competing crews have good reason to be proud of being the selected champions of such large bodies. The crew of each boat consists of eight men, selected out of about 800 students; namely, the available undergraduates of about two successive years. In other words, the selection that is popularly felt to be so strict, is only as one in a hundred. Now, suppose there had been so vast a number of universities that it would have been possible to bring together 800 men, each of whom had pulled in a university crew, and that from this body the eight best were selected to form a special crew of comparatively rare merit: the selection of each of these would be as 1 to 10,000 ordinary men. Let this process be repeated, and then, and not till then, do you arrive at a superlative crew, representing selections of one in a million. This is a perfectly fair deduction, because the youths at the universities are a haphazard collection of men, so far as regards their thews and sinews. No one is sent to a university on account of his powerful muscle. Or, to put the same facts into another form: it would require a period of no less than 100 years before either university could furnish eight men, each of whom would have sufficient boating eminence to rank as one of the medium crew. Ten thousand years must elapse before eight men could be furnished, each of whom would have the rank of the superlative crew.

It is, however, quite another matter with respect to brain power, for, as I shall have occasion to show, the universities attract to themselves a large proportion of the eminent scholastic talent of all England. There are nearly a quarter of a million males in Great Britain who arrive each year at the proper age for going to the university: therefore, if Cambridge, for example, received only one in every five of the ablest scholastic intellects, she would be able, in every period of twenty

years, to boast of the fresh arrival of an undergraduate, the rank of whose scholastic eminence was that of one in a million.

CLASSIFICATION OF MEN ACCORDING TO THEIR NATURAL GIFTS

I have no patience with the hypothesis occasionally expressed, and often implied, especially in tales written to teach children to be good, that babies are born pretty much alike, and that the sole agencies in creating differences between boy and boy, and man and man, are steady application and moral effort. It is in the most unqualified manner that I object to pretentions of natural equality. The experiences of the nursery, the school, the university, and of professional careers, are a chain of proofs to the contrary. I acknowledge freely the great power of education and social influences in developing the active powers of the mind, just as I acknowledge the effect of use in developing the muscles of a blacksmith's arm, and no further. Let the blacksmith labour as he will, he will find there are certain feats beyond his power that are well within the strength of a man of herculean make, even although the latter may have led a sedentary life. Some years ago, the Highlanders held a grand gathering in Holland Park, where they challenged all England to compete with them in their games of strength. The challenge was accepted, and the well-trained men of the hills were beaten in the foot-race by a youth who was stated to be a pure Cockney, the clerk of a London banker.

Everybody who has trained himself to physical exercises discovers the extent of his muscular powers to a nicety. When he begins to walk, to row, to use the dumb-bells, or to run, he finds to his great delight that his thews strengthen, and his endurance of fatigue increases day after day. So long as he is a novice, he perhaps flatters himself there is hardly an assignable limit to the education of his muscles; but the daily gain is soon discovered to diminish, and at last it vanishes altogether. His maximum performance becomes a rigidly determinate quantity. He learns to an inch, how high or how far he can jump, when he has attained the highest state of training. He learns to half a pound, the force he can exert on the dynamometer, by compressing it. He can strike a blow against the machine used to measure impact, and drive its index to a certain graduation, but no further. So it is in running, in rowing, in walking, and in every other form of physical exertion. There is a definite limit to the muscular powers of every man, which he cannot by any education or exertion overpass.

This is precisely analogous to the experience that every student has had of the working of his mental powers. The eager boy, when he first goes to school and confronts intellectual difficulties, is astonished at his progress. He glories in his newly-developed mental grip and growing capacity for application, and, it may be, fondly believes it to be within his reach to become one of the heroes who have left their mark upon the history of the world. The years go by; he competes in the examinations of school and college, over and over again with his fellows, and soon finds his place among them. He knows he can beat such and such of his competitors; that there are some with whom he runs on equal terms, and others whose intellectual feats he cannot even approach. Probably his vanity still continues to tempt him, by whispering in a new strain. It tells him that classics, mathematics, and other subjects taught in universities, are mere scholastic specialties, and no test of the more valuable intellectual powers. It reminds him of numerous instances of persons who had been unsuccessful in the competitions of youth, but who had shown powers in after-life that made them the foremost men of their age. Accordingly, with newly furbished hopes, and with all the ambition of twenty-two years of age, he leaves his university and enters a larger field of competition. The same kind of experience awaits him here that he has already gone through. Opportunities occur—they occur to every man— and he finds himself incapable of grasping them. He tries, and is tried in many things. In a few years more, unless he is incurably blinded by self-conceit, he learns precisely of what performances he is capable, and what other enterprises lie beyond his compass. When he reaches mature life, he is confident only within certain limits, and knows, or ought to know, himself just as he is probably judged of by the world, with all his unmistakeable weakness and all his undeniable strength. He is no longer tormented into hopeless efforts by the fallacious promptings of overweening vanity, but he limits his undertakings to matters below the level of his reach, and finds true moral repose in an honest conviction that he is engaged in as much good work as his nature has rendered him capable of performing.

There can hardly be a surer evidence of the enormous difference between the intellectual capacity of men, than the prodigious differences in the numbers of marks obtained by those who gain mathematical honours at Cambridge. I therefore crave permission to speak at some length upon this subject, although the details are dry and of little general interest. There are between 400 and 450 students who take their degrees

in each year, and of these, about 100 succeed in gaining honours in mathematics, and are ranged by the examiners in strict order of merit. About the first forty of those who take mathematical honours are distinguished by the title of wranglers, and it is a decidedly creditable thing to be even a low wrangler; it will secure a fellowship in a small college. It must be carefully borne in mind that the distinction of being the first in this list of honours, or what is called the senior wrangler of the year, means a vast deal more than being the foremost mathematician of 400 or 450 men taken at haphazard. No doubt the large bulk of Cambridge men are taken almost at haphazard. A boy is intended by his parents for some profession; if that profession be either the church or the bar, it used to be almost requisite, and it is still important, that he should be sent to Cambridge or Oxford. These youths may justly be considered as having been taken at haphazard. But there are many others who have fairly won their way to the universities, and are therefore selected from an enormous area. Fully one-half of the wranglers have been boys of note at their respective schools, and, conversely, almost all boys of note at schools find their way to the universities. Hence it is that among their comparatively small number of students, the universities include the highest youthful scholastic ability of all England. The senior wrangler, in each successive year, is the chief of these as regards mathematics, and this, the highest distinction, is, or was, continually won by youths who had no mathematical training of importance before they went to Cambridge. All their instruction had been received during the three years of their residence at the university. Now, I do not say anything here about the merits or demerits of Cambridge mathematical studies having been directed along a too narrow groove, or about the presumed disadvantages of ranging candidates in strict order of merit, instead of grouping them, as at Oxford, in classes, where their names appear alphabetically arranged. All I am concerned with here are the results; and these are most appropriate to my argument. The youths start on their three years' race as fairly as possible. They are then stimulated to run by the most powerful inducements, namely, those of competition, of honour, and of future wealth (for a good fellowship *is* wealth); and at the end of the three years they are examined most rigorously according to a system that they all understand and are equally well prepared for. The examination lasts five and a half hours a day for eight days. All the answers are carefully marked by the examiners, who add up the marks at the end and range the candidates in strict order of merit. The fairness

and thoroughness of Cambridge examinations have never had a breath of suspicion cast upon them.

Unfortunately for my purposes, the marks are not published. They are not even assigned on a uniform system, since each examiner is permitted to employ his own scale of marks; but whatever scale he uses, the results as to proportional merit are the same. I am indebted to a Cambridge examiner for a copy of his marks in respect to two examinations, in which the scales of marks were so alike as to make it easy, by a slight proportional adjustment, to compare the two together. This was, to a certain degree, a confidential communication, so that it would be improper for me to publish anything that would identify the years to which these marks refer. I simply give them as groups of

Scale of Merit among the Men
Who Obtain Mathematical Honours at Cambridge

(The results of two years are thrown into a single table.
The total number of marks obtainable in each year was 17,000.)

Number of marks obtained by candidates.	Number of candidates in the two years, taken together, who obtained those marks.[2]
Under 500	24
500 to 1,000	74
1,000 to 1,500	38
1,500 to 2,000	21
2,000 to 2,500	11
2,500 to 3,000	8
3,000 to 3,500	11
3,500 to 4,000	5
4,000 to 4,500	2
4,500 to 5,000	1
5,000 to 5,500	3
5,500 to 6,000	1
6,000 to 6,500	0
6,500 to 7,000	0
7,000 to 7,500	0
7,500 to 8,000	1
	200

2. I have included in this table only the first 100 men in each year. The omitted residue is too small to be important. I have omitted it lest, if the precise numbers of honour men were stated, those numbers would have served to identify the years. For reasons already given, I desire to afford no data to serve that purpose.

figures, sufficient to show the enormous differences of merit. The lowest man in the list of honours gains less than 300 marks; the lowest wrangler gains about 1,500 marks; and the senior wrangler, in one of the lists now before me, gained more than 7,500 marks. Consequently, the lowest wrangler has more than five times the merit of the lowest junior optime, and less than one-fifth the merit of the senior wrangler.

The precise number of marks obtained by the senior wrangler in the more remarkable of these two years was 7,634; by the second wrangler in the same year, 4,123; and by the lowest man in the list of honours, only 237. Consequently, the senior wrangler obtained nearly twice as many marks as the second wrangler, and more than thirty-two times as many as the lowest man. I have received from another examiner the marks of a year in which the senior wrangler was conspicuously eminent. He obtained 9,422 marks, while the second in the same year—whose merits were by no means inferior to those of second wranglers in general—obtained only 5,642. The man at the bottom of the same honour list had only 309 marks, or one-thirtieth the number of the senior wrangler. I have some particulars of a fourth very remarkable year, in which the senior wrangler obtained no less than ten times as many marks as the second wrangler, in the "problem paper." Now, I have discussed with practised examiners the question of how far the numbers of marks may be considered as proportionate to the mathematical power of the candidate, and am assured they are strictly proportionate as regards the lower places, but do not afford full justice to the highest. In other words, the senior wranglers above mentioned had *more* than thirty, or thirty-two times the ability of the lowest men on the lists of honours. They would be able to grapple with problems more than thirty-two times as difficult; or when dealing with subjects of the same difficulty, but intelligible to all, would comprehend them more rapidly in perhaps the square root of that proportion. It is reasonable to expect that marks would do some injustice to the very best men, because a very large part of the time of the examination is taken up by the mechanical labour of writing. Whenever the thought of the candidate outruns his pen, he gains no advantage from his excess of promptitude in conception. I should, however, mention that some of the ablest men have shown their superiority by comparatively little writing. They find their way at once to the root of the difficulty in the problems that are set, and, with a few clean, apposite, powerful strokes, succeed in proving they can overthrow it, and then they go on to another question. Every word they write tells. Thus, the late

Mr. H. Leslie Ellis, who was a brilliant senior wrangler in 1840, and whose name is familiar to many generations of Cambridge men as a prodigy of universal genius, did not even remain during the full period in the examination room: his health was weak, and he had to husband his strength.

The mathematical powers of the last man on the list of honours, which are so low when compared with those of a senior wrangler, are mediocre, or even above mediocrity, when compared with the gifts of Englishmen generally. Though the examination places 100 honour men above him, it puts no less than 300 "poll men" below him. Even if we go so far as to allow that 200 out of the 300 refuse to work hard enough to get honours, there will remain 100 who, even if they worked hard, could not get them. Every tutor knows how difficult it is to drive abstract conceptions, even of the simplest kind, into the brains of most people—how feeble and hesitating is their mental grasp—how easily their brains are mazed —how incapable they are of precision and soundness of knowledge. It often occurs to persons familiar with some scientific subject to hear men and women of mediocre gifts relate to one another what they have picked up about it from some lecture—say at the Royal Institution, where they have sat for an hour listening with delighted attention to an admirably lucid account, illustrated by experiments of the most perfect and beautiful character, in all of which they expressed themselves intensely gratified and highly instructed. It is positively painful to hear what they say. Their recollections seem to be a mere chaos of mist and misapprehension, to which some sort of shape and organization has been given by the action of their own pure fancy, altogether alien to what the lecturer intended to convey. The average mental grasp even of what is called a well-educated audience, will be found to be ludicrously small when rigorously tested.

In stating the differences between man and man, let it not be supposed for a moment that mathematicians are necessarily one-sided in their natural gifts. There are numerous instances of the reverse, of whom the following will be found, as instances of hereditary genius, in the appendix to my chapter on Science. I would especially name Leibnitz, as being universally gifted; but Ampère, Arago, Condorcet, and D'Alembert, were all of them very far more than mere mathematicians. Nay, since the range of examination at Cambridge is so extended as to include other subjects besides mathematics, the differences of ability between the highest and lowest of the successful candidates is yet more glaring than what I have already described. We still find, on the one hand,

mediocre men, whose whole energies are absorbed in getting their 237 marks for mathematics; and, on the other hand, some few senior wranglers who are at the same time high classical scholars and much more besides. Cambridge has afforded such instances. Its lists of classical honours are comparatively of recent date, but other evidence is obtainable from earlier times of their occurrence. Thus, Dr. George Butler, the Head Master of Harrow for very many years, including the period when Byron was a schoolboy (father of the present Head Master, and of other sons, two of whom are also head masters of great public schools), must have obtained that classical office on account of his eminent classical ability; but Dr. Butler was also senior wrangler in 1794, the year when Lord Chancellor Lyndhurst was second. Both Dr. Kaye, the late bishop of Lincoln, and Sir E. Alderson, the late judge, were the senior wranglers and the first classical prizemen of their respective years. Since 1824, when the classical tripos was first established, the late Mr. Goulburn (son of the Right Hon. H. Goulburn, Chancellor of the Exchequer) was second wrangler in 1835, and senior classic of the same year. But in more recent times, the necessary labour of preparation, in order to acquire the highest mathematical places, has become so enormous that there has been a wider differentiation of studies. There is no longer *time* for a man to acquire the necessary knowledge to succeed to the first place in more than one subject. There are, therefore, no instances of a man being absolutely first in both examinations, but a few can be found of high eminence in both classics and mathematics, as a reference to the lists published in the "Cambridge Calendar" will show. The best of these more recent degrees appears to be that of Dr. Barry, late principal of Cheltenham, and now principal of King's College, London (the son of the eminent architect, Sir Charles Barry, and brother of Mr. Edward Barry, who succeeded his father as architect). He was fourth wrangler and seventh classic of his year.

In whatever way we may test ability, we arrive at equally enormous intellectual differences. Lord Macaulay . . . had one of the most tenacious of memories. He was able to recall many pages of hundreds of volumes by various authors, which he had acquired by simply reading them over. An average man could not certainly carry in his memory one thirty-second—ay, or one hundredth—part as much as Lord Macaulay. The father of Seneca had one of the greatest memories on record in ancient times. . . . Porson, the Greek scholar, was remarkable for this gift, and, I may add, the "Porson memory" was hereditary in that family. In statesmanship, generalship, literature, science, poetry, art, just the

same enormous differences are found between man and man; and numerous instances recorded in this book, will show in how small degree, eminence, either in these or any other class of intellectual powers, can be considered as due to purely special powers. They are rather to be considered in those instances as the result of concentrated efforts, made by men who are widely gifted. People lay too much stress on apparent specialities, thinking over rashly that, because a man is devoted to some particular pursuit, he could not possibly have succeeded in anything else. They might just as well say that, because a youth had fallen desperately in love with a brunette, he could not possibly have fallen in love with a blonde. He may or may not have more natural liking for the former type of beauty than the latter, but it is as probable as not that the affair was mainly or wholly due to a general amorousness of disposition. It is just the same with special pursuits. A gifted man is often capricious and fickle before he selects his occupation, but when it has been chosen, he devotes himself to it with a truly passionate ardour. After a man of genius has selected his hobby, and so adapted himself to it as to seem unfitted for any other occupation in life, and to be possessed of but one special aptitude, I often notice, with admiration, how well he bears himself when circumstances suddenly thrust him into a strange position. He will display an insight into new conditions, and a power of dealing with them, with which even his most intimate friends were unprepared to accredit him. Many a presumptuous fool has mistaken indifference and neglect for incapacity; and in trying to throw a man of genius on ground where he was unprepared for attack, has himself received a most severe and unexpected fall. I am sure that no one who has had the privilege of mixing in the society of the abler men of any great capital, or who is acquainted with the biographies of the heroes of history, can doubt the existence of grand human animals, of natures pre-eminently noble, of individuals born to be kings of men. I have been conscious of no slight misgiving that I was committing a kind of sacrilege whenever, in the preparation of materials for this book, I had occasion to take the measurement of modern intellects vastly superior to my own, or to criticise the genius of the most magnificent historical specimens of our race. It was a process that constantly recalled to me a once familiar sentiment in bygone days of African travel, when I used to take altitudes of the huge cliffs that domineered above me as I travelled along their bases, or to map the mountainous landmarks of unvisited tribes, that loomed in faint grandeur beyond my actual horizon.

I have not cared to occupy myself much with people whose gifts are

below the average, but they would be an interesting study. The number of idiots and imbeciles among the twenty million inhabitants of England and Wales is approximately estimated at 50,000, or as 1 in 400. Dr. Seguin, a great French authority on these matters, states that more than thirty per cent of idiots and imbeciles, put under suitable instruction, have been taught to conform to social and moral law, and rendered capable of order, of good feeling, and of working like *the third* of an average man. He says that more than forty per cent have become capable of the ordinary transactions of life, under friendly control; of understanding moral and social abstractions, and of working like *two-thirds* of a man. And, lastly, that from twenty-five to thirty per cent come nearer and nearer to the standard of manhood, till some of them will defy the scrutiny of good judges, when compared with ordinary young men and women. In the order next above idiots and imbeciles are a large number of milder cases scattered among private families and kept out of sight, the existence of whom is, however, well known to relatives and friends; they are too silly to take a part in general society, but are easily amused with some trivial, harmless occupation. Then comes a class of whom the Lord Dundreary of the famous play may be considered a representative; and so, proceeding through successive grades, we gradually ascend to mediocrity. I know two good instances of hereditary silliness short of imbecility, and have reason to believe I could easily obtain a large number of similar facts.

To conclude, the range of mental power between—I will not say the highest Caucasian and the lowest savage—but between the greatest and least of English intellects, is enormous. There is a continuity of natural ability reaching from one knows not what height, and descending to one can hardly say what depth. I propose in this chapter to range men according to their natural abilities, putting them into classes separated by equal degrees of merit, and to show the relative number of individuals included in the several classes. Perhaps some person might be inclined to make an offhand guess that the number of men included in the several classes would be pretty equal. If he thinks so, I can assure him he is most egregiously mistaken.

The method I shall employ for discovering all this is an application of the very curious theoretical law of "deviation from an average." First, I will explain the law, and then I will show that the production of natural intellectual gifts comes justly within its scope.

The law is an exceedingly general one. M. Quetelet, the Astronomer-Royal of Belgium, and the greatest authority on vital and social statistics,

has largely used it in his inquiries. He has also constructed numerical tables, by which the necessary calculations can be easily made, whenever it is desired to have recourse to the law. Those who wish to learn more than I have space to relate should consult his work, which is a very readable octavo volume, and deserves to be far better known to statisticians than it appears to be. Its title is *Letters on Probabilities,* translated by Downes. (Layton and Co., London, 1849.)

So much has been published in recent years about statistical deductions, that I am sure the reader will be prepared to assent freely to the following hypothetical case: Suppose a large island inhabited by a single race, who intermarried freely, and who had lived for many generations under constant conditions; then the average height of the male adults of that population would undoubtedly be the same year after year. Also— still arguing from the experience of modern statistics, which are found to give constant results in far less carefully-guarded examples—we should undoubtedly find, year after year, the same proportion maintained between the number of men of different heights. I mean, if the average stature was found to be sixty-six inches, and if it was also found in any one year that 100 per million exceeded seventy-eight inches, the same proportion of 100 per million would be closely maintained in all other years. An equal constancy of proportion would be maintained between any other limits of height we pleased to specify, as between seventy-one and seventy-two inches; between seventy-two and seventy-three inches; and so on. Statistical experiences are so invariably confirmatory of what I have stated would probably be the case, as to make it unnecessary to describe analogous instances. Now, at this point, the law of deviation from an average steps in. It shows that the number per million whose heights range between seventy-one and seventy-two inches (or between any other limits we please to name) can be *predicted* from the previous datum of the average, and of any one other fact, such as that of 100 per million exceeding seventy-eight inches.

The appended diagram will make this more intelligible. Suppose a million of the men to stand in turns, with their backs against a vertical board of sufficient height, and their heights to be dotted off upon it. The board would then present the appearance shown in the diagram. The line of average height is that which divides the dots into two equal parts, and stands, in the case we have assumed, at the height of sixty-six inches. The dots will be found to be ranged so symmetrically on either side of the line of average, that the lower half of the diagram will be almost a precise reflection of the upper. Next, let a hundred dots be

counted from above downwards, and let a line be drawn below them. According to the conditions, this line will stand at the height of seventy-eight inches. Using the data afforded by these two lines, it is possible, by the help of the law of deviation from an average, to reproduce, with extraordinary closeness, the entire system of dots on the board.

M. Quetelet gives tables in which the uppermost line, instead of cutting off 100 in a million, cuts off only one in a million. He divides the intervals between that line and the line of average, into eighty equal divisions, and gives the number of dots that fall within each of those divisions. It is easy, by the help of his tables, to calculate what would occur under any other system of classification we pleased to adopt.

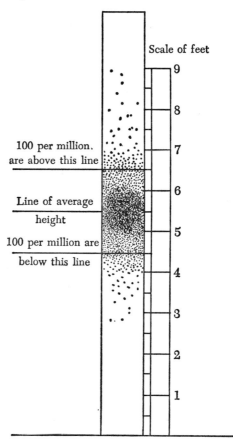

This law of deviation from an average is perfectly general in its application. Thus, if the marks had been made by bullets fired at a horizontal line stretched in front of the target, they would have been distributed according to the same law. Wherever there is a large number of similar events, each due to the resultant influences of the same variable conditions, two effects will follow. First, the average value of those events will be constant; and, secondly, the deviations of the several events from the average, will be governed by this law (which is, in principle, the same as that which governs runs of luck at a gaming-table).

The nature of the conditions affecting the several events must, I say, be the same. It clearly would not be proper to combine the heights of men belonging to two dissimilar races, in the expectation that the compound results would be governed by the same constants. A union of two dis-

similar systems of dots would produce the same kind of confusion as if half the bullets fired at a target had been directed to one mark, and the other half to another mark. Nay, an examination of the dots would show to a person, ignorant of what had occurred, that such had been the case, and it would be possible, by aid of the law, to disentangle two or any moderate number of superimposed series of marks. The law may, therefore, be used as a most trustworthy criterion, whether or no the events of which an average has been taken, are due to the same or to dissimilar classes of conditions.

I selected the hypothetical case of a race of men living on an island and freely intermarrying, to ensure the conditions under which they were all supposed to live, being uniform in character. It will now be my aim to show there is sufficient uniformity in the inhabitants of the British Isles to bring them fairly within the grasp of this law.

For this purpose, I first call attention to an example given in Quetelet's book. It is of the measurements of the circumferences of the chests of a large number of Scotch soldiers. The Scotch are by no means a strictly uniform race, nor are they exposed to identical conditions. They are a mixture of Celts, Danes, Anglo-Saxons, and others, in various proportions, the Highlanders being almost purely Celts. On the other hand,

Measures of the chest in inches.	Number of men per 1,000 by experience.	Number of men per 1,000 by calculation.	Measures of the chest in inches.	Number of men per 1,000 by experience.	Number of men per 1,000 by calculation.
33	5	7	41	1,628	1,675
34	31	29	42	1,148	1,096
35	141	110	43	645	560
36	322	323	44	160	221
37	732	732	45	87	69
38	1,305	1,333	46	38	16
39	1,867	1,838	47	7	3
40	1,882	1,987	48	2	1

these races, though diverse in origin, are not very dissimilar in character. Consequently, it will be found that their deviations from the average follow theoretical computations with remarkable accuracy. The instance is as [shown]. M. Quetelet obtained his facts from the thirteenth volume of the *Edinburgh Medical Journal,* where the measurements are given in respect to 5,738 soldiers, the results being grouped in order of

magnitude, proceeding by differences of one inch. Professor Quetelet compares these results with those that his tables give, and here is the result. The marvellous accordance between fact and theory must strike the most unpractised eye. I should say that, for the sake of convenience, both the measurements and calculations have been reduced to per thousandths.

I will now take a case where there is a greater dissimilarity in the elements of which the average has been taken. It is the height of 100,000 French conscripts. There is fully as much variety in the French as in the English, for it is not very many generations since France was divided into completely independent kingdoms. Among its peculiar races are those of Normandy, Brittany, Alsatia, Provence, Bearne, Auvergne—each with their special characteristics; yet the following table shows a most striking agreement between the results of experience compared with those derived by calculation, from a purely theoretical hypothesis:

Height of men in inches.	Number of men.	
	Measured.	Calculated.
Under 61.8	28,620	26,345
61.8 to 62.9	11,580	13,182
62.9 to 63.9	13,990	14,502
63.9 to 65.0	14,410	13,982
65.0 to 66.1	11,410	11,803
66.1 to 67.1	8,780	8,725
67.1 to 68.2	5,530	5,527
68.2 to 69.3	3,190	3,187
Above 69.3	2,490	2,645

The greatest differences are in the lowest ranks. They include the men who were rejected from being too short for the army. M. Quetelet boldly ascribes these differences to the effect of fraudulent returns. It certainly seems that men have been improperly taken out of the second rank and put into the first, in order to exempt them from service. Be this as it may, the coincidence of fact with theory is, in this instance also, quite close enough to serve my purpose.

I argue from the results obtained from Frenchmen and from Scotchmen, that, if we had measurements of the adult males in the British Isles, we should find those measurements to range in close accordance

with the law of deviation from an average, although our population is as much mingled as I described that of Scotland to have been, and although Ireland is mainly peopled with Celts. Now, if this be the case with stature, then it will be true as regards every other physical feature—as circumference of head, size of brain, weight of grey matter, number of brain fibres, etc.; and thence, by a step on which no physiologist will hesitate, as regards mental capacity.

This is what I am driving at—that analogy clearly shows there must be a fairly constant average mental capacity in the inhabitants of the British Isles, and that the deviations from that average—upwards towards genius, and downwards towards stupidity—must follow the law that governs deviations from all true averages.

I have, however, done somewhat more than rely on analogy, by discussing the results of those examinations in which the candidates had been derived from the same classes. Most persons have noticed the lists of successful competitors for various public appointments that are published from time to time in the newspapers, with the marks gained by each candidate attached to his name. These lists contain far too few names to fall into such beautiful accordance with theory, as was the case with the Scotch soldiers. There are rarely more than 100 names in any one of these examinations, while the chests of no less than 5,700 Scotchmen were measured. I cannot justly combine the marks of several independent examinations into one fagot, for I understand that different examiners are apt to have different figures of merit; so each examination was analysed separately. The following is a calculation I made on the examination last before me; it will do as well as any other. It was for admission into the Royal Military College at Sandhurst, December, 1868. The marks obtained were clustered most thickly about 3,000, so I take that number as representing the average ability of the candidates. From this datum, and from the fact that no candidate obtained more than 6,500 marks, I computed the column B in the following table, by the help of Quetelet's numbers. It will be seen that column B accords with column A quite as closely as the small number of persons examined could have led us to expect.

The symmetry of the descending branch has been rudely spoilt by the conditions stated at the foot of column A. There is, therefore, little room for doubt, if everybody in England had to work up some subject and then to pass before examiners who employed similar figures of merit, that their marks would be found to range, according to the law of

deviation from an average, just as rigorously as the heights of French conscripts, or the circumferences of the chests of Scotch soldiers.

Number of marks obtained by the Candidates.	Number of Candidates who obtained those marks.	
	A. According to fact.	B. According to theory.
6,500 and above 5,800 to 6,500 5,100 to 5,800 4,400 to 5,100 3,700 to 4,400 3,000 to 3,700 2,300 to 3,000 1,600 to 2,300	0 1 3 6 } 73 11 22 22 8	0 1 5 8 } 72 13 16 16 13
1,100 to 1,600 400 to 1,100 Below 400	Either did not venture to compete, or were plucked.	8 5 1

The number of grades into which we may divide ability is purely a matter of option. We may consult our convenience by sorting Englishmen into a few large classes, or into many small ones. I will select a system of classification that shall be easily comparable with the numbers of eminent men, as determined in the previous chapter. We have seen that 250 men per million become eminent; accordingly, I have so contrived the classes in the following table [p. 250] that the two highest, F and G, together with X (which includes all cases beyond G, and which are unclassed), shall amount to about that number—namely to 248 per million.

It will, I trust, be clearly understood that the numbers of men in the several classes in my table depend on no uncertain hypothesis. They are determined by the assured law of deviations from an average. It is an absolute fact that if we pick out of each million the one man who is naturally the ablest, and also the one man who is the most stupid, and divide the remaining 999,998 men into fourteen classes, the average ability in each being separated from that of its neighbours by *equal grades,* then the numbers in each of those classes will, on the average

Classification of Men According to Their Natural Gifts

Grades of natural ability, separated by equal intervals. (Below average / Above average)	Proportionate, viz. one in	In each million of the same age.	Numbers of men comprised in the several grades of natural ability, whether in respect to their general powers, or to special aptitudes. In total male population of the United Kingdom, say 15 millions, of the undermentioned ages:—					
			20-30	30-40	40-50	50-60	60-70	70-80
a — A	4	256,791	651,000	495,000	391,000	268,000	171,000	77,000
b — B	6	161,279	469,000	312,000	246,000	168,000	107,000	48,000
c — C	16	63,563	161,000	123,000	97,000	66,000	42,000	19,000
d — D	64	15,696	39,800	30,300	23,900	16,400	10,400	4,700
e — E	413	2,423	6,100	4,700	3,700	2,520	1,600	729
f — F	4,300	233	590	450	355	243	155	70
g — G	79,000	14	35	27	21	15	9	4
x all grades below g / X all grades above G	1,000,000	1	3	2	2	2	—	—
On either side of average............	500,000	1,268,000	964,000	761,000	521,000	332,000	149,000	
Total, both sides....................	1,000,000	2,536,000	1,928,000	1,522,000	1,042,000	664,000	298,000	

of many millions, be as is stated in the table. The table may be applied to special, just as truly as to general ability. It would be true for every examination that brought out natural gifts, whether held in painting, in music, or in statesmanship. The proportions between the different classes would be identical in all these cases, although the classes would be made up of different individuals, according as the examination differed in its purport.

It will be seen that more than half of each million is contained in the two mediocre classes a and A; the four mediocre classes a, b, A, B, contain more than four-fifths, and the six mediocre classes more than nineteen-twentieths of the entire population. Thus, the rarity of commanding ability, and the vast abundance of mediocrity, is no accident, but follows of necessity, from the very nature of these things.

The meaning of the word "mediocrity" admits of little doubt. It defines the standard of intellectual power found in most provincial gatherings, because the attractions of a more stirring life in the metropolis and elsewhere, are apt to draw away the abler classes of men, and the silly and the imbecile do not take a part in the gatherings. Hence, the residuum that forms the bulk of the general society of small provincial places, is commonly very pure in its mediocrity.

The class C possesses abilities a trifle higher than those commonly possessed by the foreman of an ordinary jury. D includes the mass of men who obtain the ordinary prizes of life. E is a stage higher. Then we reach F, the lowest of those yet superior classes of intellect, with which this volume is chiefly concerned.

On descending the scale, we find by the time we have reached f, that we are already among the idiots and imbeciles. We have seen . . . that there are 400 idiots and imbeciles to every million of persons living in this country; but that 30 per cent of their number appear to be light cases, to whom the name of idiot is inappropriate. There will remain 280 true idiots and imbeciles, to every million of our population. This ratio coincides very closely with the requirements of class f. No doubt a certain proportion of them are idiotic owing to some fortuitous cause, which may

[Left] *The proportions of men living at different ages are calculated from the proportions that are true for England and Wales. (Census 1861, Appendix, p. 107.)*

Example. *The class F contains 1 in every 4,300 men. In other words, there are 233 of that class in each million of men. The same is true of class f. In the whole United Kingdom there are 590 men of class F (and the same number of f) between the ages of 20 and 30; 450 between the ages of 30 and 40; and so on.*

interfere with the working of a naturally good brain, much as a bit of dirt may cause a first-rate chronometer to keep worse time than an ordinary watch. But I presume, from the usual smallness of head and absence of disease among these persons, that the proportion of accidental idiots cannot be very large.

Hence we arrive at the undeniable, but unexpected conclusion, that eminently gifted men are raised as much above mediocrity as idiots are depressed below it; a fact that is calculated to considerably enlarge our ideas of the enormous differences of intellectual gifts between man and man.

I presume the class F of dogs, and others of the more intelligent sort of animals, is nearly commensurate with the f of the human race, in respect to memory and powers of reason. Certainly the class G of such animals is far superior to the g of humankind.

COMPARISON OF THE TWO CLASSIFICATIONS

Is reputation a fair test of natural ability? It is the only one I can employ—am I justified in using it? How much of a man's success is due to his opportunities, how much to his natural power of intellect?

This is a very old question, on which a great many commonplaces have been uttered that need not be repeated here. I will confine myself to a few considerations, such as seem to me amply adequate to prove what is wanted for my argument.

Let it clearly be borne in mind, what I mean by reputation and ability. By reputation, I mean the opinion of contemporaries, revised by posterity—the favourable result of a critical analysis of each man's character, by many biographers. I do not mean high social or official position, nor such as is implied by being the mere lion of a London season; but I speak of the reputation of a leader of opinion, of an originator, of a man to whom the world deliberately acknowledges itself largely indebted.

By natural ability, I mean those qualities of intellect and disposition, which urge and qualify a man to perform acts that lead to reputation. I do not mean capacity without zeal, nor zeal without capacity, nor even a combination of both of them, without an adequate power of doing a great deal of very laborious work. But I mean a nature which, when left to itself, will, urged by an inherent stimulus, climb the path that leads to eminence, and has strength to reach the summit—one which, if hindered or thwarted, will fret and strive until the hindrance is overcome, and it is again free to follow its labour-loving instinct. It is almost

a contradiction in terms, to doubt that such men will generally become eminent. On the other hand, there is plenty of evidence in this volume to show that few have won high reputations without possessing these peculiar gifts. It follows that the men who achieve eminence, and those who are naturally capable, are, to a large extent, identical.

The particular meaning in which I employ the word ability, does not restrict my argument from a wider application; for, if I succeed in showing—as I undoubtedly shall do—that the concrete triple event, of ability combined with zeal and with capacity for hard labour, is inherited, much more will there be justification for believing that any one of its three elements, whether it be ability, or zeal, or capacity for labour, is similarly a gift of inheritance.

I believe, and shall do my best to show, that, if the "eminent" men of any period had been changelings when babies, a very fair proportion of those who survived and retained their health up to fifty years of age, would, notwithstanding their altered circumstances have equally risen to eminence. Thus—to take a strong case—it is incredible that any combination of circumstances, could have repressed Lord Brougham to the level of undistinguished mediocrity.

The arguments on which I rely are as follow. I will limit their application for the present to men of the pen and to artists. First, it is a fact that numbers of men rise, before they are middle-aged, from the humbler ranks of life to that worldly position, in which it is of no importance to their future career how their youth has been passed. They have overcome their hindrances, and thus start fair with others more fortunately reared, in the subsequent race of life. A boy who is to be carefully educated is sent to a good school, where he confessedly acquires little useful information, but where he is taught the art of learning. The man of whom I have been speaking has contrived to acquire the same art in a school of adversity. Both stand on equal terms, when they have reached mature life. They compete for the same prizes, measure their strength by efforts in the same direction, and their relative successes are thenceforward due to their relative natural gifts. There are many such men in the "eminent" class, as biographies abundantly show. Now, if the hindrances to success were very great, we should expect all who surmounted them to be prodigies of genius. The hindrances would form a system of natural selection, by repressing all whose gifts were below a certain very high level. But what is the case? We find very many who have risen from the ranks, who are by no means prodigies of genius; many who have no claim to "eminence," who have risen easily in spite of

all obstacles. The hindrances undoubtedly form a system of natural selec-
tion that represses mediocre men, and even men of pretty fair powers—
in short, the classes below D; but many of D succeed, a great many of E,
and I believe a very large majority of those above.

If a man is gifted with vast intellectual ability, eagerness to work, and
power of working, I cannot comprehend how such a man should be
repressed. The world is always tormented with difficulties waiting to be
solved—struggling with ideas and feelings, to which it can give no ade-
quate expression. If, then, there exists a man capable of solving those
difficulties, or of giving a voice to those pent-up feelings, he is sure to
be welcomed with universal acclamation. We may almost say that he has
only to put his pen to paper, and the thing is done. I am here speaking
of the very first-class men—prodigies—one in a million, or one in ten
millions, of whom numbers will be found described in this volume, as
specimens of hereditary genius.

Another argument to prove that the hindrances of English social life are
not effectual in repressing high ability is that the number of eminent
men in England is as great as in other countries where fewer hindrances
exist. Culture is far more widely spread in America, than with us, and the
education of their middle and lower classes far more advanced; but, for
all that, America most certainly does not beat us in first-class works of
literature, philosophy, or art. The higher kind of books, even of the most
modern date, read in America, are principally the work of English-
men. The Americans have an immense amount of the newspaper-article-
writer, or of the member-of-congress stamp of ability; but the number of
their really eminent authors is more limited even than with us. I argue
that, if the hindrances to the rise of genius, were removed from English
society as completely as they have been removed from that of America,
we should not become materially richer in highly eminent men.

People seem to have the idea that the way to eminence is one of great
self-denial, from which there are hourly temptations to diverge: in which
a man can be kept in his boyhood, only by a schoolmaster's severity or a
parent's incessant watchfulness, and in after-life by the attractions of
fortunate friendships and other favourable circumstances. This is true
enough of the great majority of men, but it is simply not true of the
generality of those who have gained great reputations. Such men, biog-
raphies show to be haunted and driven by an incessant instinctive crav-
ing for intellectual work. If forcibly withdrawn from the path that leads
towards eminence, they will find their way back to it, as surely as a lover
to his mistress. They do not work for the sake of eminence, but to satisfy

a natural craving for brain-work, just as athletes cannot endure repose on account of their muscular irritability, which insists upon exercise. It is very unlikely that any conjunction of circumstances, should supply a stimulus to brain work, commensurate with what these men carry in their own constitutions. The action of external stimuli must be uncertain and intermittent, owing to their very nature; the disposition abides. It keeps a man ever employed—now wrestling with his difficulties, now brooding over his immature ideas—and renders him a quick and eager listener to innumerable, almost inaudible teachings, that others less keenly on the watch, are sure to miss.

These considerations lead to my third argument. I have shown that social hindrances cannot impede men of high ability, from becoming eminent. I shall now maintain that social advantages are incompetent to give that status to a man of moderate ability. It would be easy to point out several men of fair capacity, who have been pushed forward by all kinds of help, who are ambitious, and exert themselves to the utmost, but who completely fail in attaining eminence. If great peers, they may be lord-lieutenants of counties; if they belong to great county families, they may become influential members of parliament and local notabilities. When they die, they leave a blank for a while in a large circle, but there is no Westminster Abbey and no public mourning for them—perhaps barely a biographical notice in the columns of the daily papers.

It is difficult to specify two large classes of men, with equal social advantages, in one of which they have high hereditary gifts, while in the other they have not. I must not compare the sons of eminent men with those of noneminent, because much which I should ascribe to breed, others might ascribe to parental encouragement and example. Therefore, I will compare the sons of eminent men with the adopted sons of popes and other dignitaries of the Roman Catholic Church. The practice of nepotism among ecclesiastics is universal. It consists in their giving those social helps to a nephew, or other more distant relative, that ordinary people give to their children. Now, I shall show abundantly in the course of this book, that the nephew of an eminent man has far less chance of becoming eminent than a son, and that a more remote kinsman has far less chance than a nephew. We may therefore make a very fair comparison, for the purposes of my argument, between the success of the sons of eminent men and that of the nephews or more distant relatives, who stand in the place of sons to the high unmarried ecclesiastics of the Romish Church. If social help is really of the highest importance, the nephews of the popes will attain eminence as frequently,

or nearly so, as the sons of other eminent men; otherwise, they will not.

Are, then, the nephews, etc., of the popes, on the whole, as highly distinguished as are the sons of other equally eminent men? I answer, decidedly not. There have been a few popes who were offshoots of illustrious races, such as that of the Medici, but in the enormous majority of cases the pope is the ablest member of his family. I do not profess to have worked up the kinships of the Italians with any especial care, but I have seen amply enough of them, to justify me in saying that the individuals whose advancement has been due to nepotism, are curiously undistinguished. The very common combination of an able son and an eminent parent, is not matched, in the case of high Romish ecclesiastics, by an eminent nephew and an eminent uncle. The social helps are the same, but hereditary gifts are wanting in the latter case.

To recapitulate: I have endeavoured to show in respect to literary and artistic eminence—

1. That men who are gifted with high abilities—even men of class E —easily rise through all the obstacles caused by inferiority of social rank.

2. Countries where there are fewer hindrances than in England to a poor man rising in life produce a much larger proportion of persons of culture, but not of what I call eminent men.

3. Men who are largely aided by social advantages, are unable to achieve eminence, unless they are endowed with high natural gifts.

It may be well to add a few supplementary remarks on the small effects of a good education on a mind of the highest order. A youth of abilities G and X, is almost independent of ordinary school education. He does not want a master continually at his elbow to explain difficulties and select suitable lessons. On the contrary, he is receptive at every pore. He learns from passing hints, with a quickness and thoroughness that others cannot comprehend. He is omnivorous of intellectual work, devouring a vast deal more than he can utilize, but extracting a small percentage of nutriment that makes, in the aggregate, an enormous supply. The best care that a master can take of such a boy is to leave him alone, just directing a little here and there, and checking desultory tendencies.

It is a mere accident if a man is placed in his youth in the profession for which he has the most special vocation. It will consequently be remarked in my short biographical notices that the most illustrious men have frequently broken loose from the life prescribed by their parents, and followed, careless of cost, the paramount dictation of their own natures: in short, they educate themselves. D'Alembert is a striking in-

stance of this kind of self-reliance. He was a foundling (afterwards shown to be well bred as respects ability), and put out to nurse as a pauper baby, to the wife of a poor glazier. The child's indomitable tendency to the higher studies, could not be repressed by his foster-mother's ridicule and dissuasion, nor by the taunts of his schoolfellows, nor by the discouragements of his schoolmaster, who was incapable of appreciating him, nor even by the reiterated deep disappointment of finding that his ideas, which he knew to be original, were not novel, but long previously discovered by others. Of course, we should expect a boy of this kind to undergo ten or more years of apparently hopeless strife, but we should equally expect him to succeed at last; and D'Alembert did succeed in attaining the first rank of celebrity, by the time he was twenty-four. The reader has only to turn over the pages of my book to find abundant instances of this emergence from obscurity, in spite of the utmost discouragement in early youth.

A prodigal nature commonly so prolongs the period when a man's receptive faculties are at their keenest that a faulty education in youth is readily repaired in after-life. The education of Watt, the great mechanician, was of a merely elementary character. During his youth and manhood he was engrossed with mechanical specialities. It was not till he became advanced in years, that he had leisure to educate himself, and yet by the time he was an old man, he had become singularly well-read and widely and accurately informed. The scholar who, in the eyes of his contemporaries and immediate successors, made one of the greatest reputations, as such, that any man has ever made, was Julius Caesar Scaliger. His youth was, I believe, entirely unlettered. He was in the army until he was twenty-nine, and then he led a vagrant professional life, trying everything and sticking to nothing. At length he fixed himself upon Greek. His first publications were at the age of forty-seven, and between that time and the period of a somewhat early death, he earned his remarkable reputation, only exceeded by that of his son. Boyhood and youth—the period between fifteen and twenty-two years of age, which afford to the vast majority of men, the only period for the acquirement of intellectual facts and habits—are just seven years—neither more nor less important than other years—in the lives of men of the highest order. People are too apt to complain of their imperfect education, insinuating that they would have done great things if they had been more fortunately circumstanced in youth. But if their power of learning is materially diminished by the time they have discovered their want of knowledge, it is very probable that their abilities are not of a

very high description, and that, however well they might have been educated, they would have succeeded but little better.

Even if a man be long unconscious of his powers, an opportunity is sure to occur—they occur over and over again to every man—that will discover them. He will then soon make up for past arrears, and outstrip competitors with very many years' start, in the race of life. There is an obvious analogy between the man of brains and the man of muscle, in the unmistakable way in which they may discover and assert their claims to superiority over less gifted, but far better educated, competitors. An average sailor climbs rigging, and an average Alpine guide scrambles along cliffs, with a facility that seems like magic to a man who has been reared away from ships and mountains. But if he have extraordinary gifts, a very little trial will reveal them, and he will rapidly make up for his arrears of education. A born gymnast would soon, in his turn, astonish the sailors by his feats. Before the voyage was half over, he would outrun them like an escaped monkey. I have witnessed an instance of this myself. Every summer, it happens that some young English tourist who had never previously planted his foot on crag or ice, succeeds in Alpine work to a marvellous degree.

Thus far, I have spoken only of literary men and artists, who, however, form the bulk of the 250 per million, that attain to eminence. The reasoning that is true for them, requires large qualifications when applied to statesmen and commanders. Unquestionably, the most illustrious statesmen and commanders belong, to say the least, to the classes F and G of ability; but it does not at all follow that an English cabinet minister, if he be a great territorial lord, should belong to those classes, or even to the two or three below them. Social advantages have enormous power in bringing a man into so prominent a position as a statesman, that it is impossible to refuse him the title of "eminent," though it may be more than probable that if he had been changed in his cradle, and reared in obscurity he would have lived and died without emerging from humble life. Again, we have seen that a union of three separate qualities—intellect, zeal, and power of work—are necessary to raise men from the ranks. Only two of these qualities, in a remarkable degree, namely intellect and power of work, are required by a man who is pushed into public life; because when he is once there, the interest is so absorbing, and the competition so keen, as to supply the necessary stimulus to an ordinary mind. Therefore, many men who have succeeded as statesmen, would have been nobodies had they been born in a lower rank of life: they would have needed zeal to rise. Talleyrand would have passed his life

in the same way as other grand seigneurs if he had not been ejected from his birthright by a family council on account of his deformity, and thrown into a vortex of the French Revolution. The furious excitement of the game overcame his inveterate indolence, and he developed into the foremost man of the period, after Napoleon and Mirabeau. As for sovereigns, they belong to a peculiar category. The qualities most suitable to the ruler of a great nation, are not such as lead to eminence in private life. Devotion to particular studies, obstinate perseverance, geniality and frankness in social relations, are important qualities to make a man rise in the world, but they are unsuitable to a sovereign. He has to view many interests and opinions with an equal eye, to know how to yield his favourite ideas to popular pressure, to be reserved in his friendships and able to stand alone. On the other hand, a sovereign does not greatly need the intellectual powers that are essential to the rise of a common man, because the best brains of the country are at his service. Consequently, I do not busy myself in this volume with the families of merely able sovereigns, only with those few whose military and administrative capacity is acknowledged to have been of the very highest order.

As regards commanders, the qualities that raise a man to a peerage may be of a peculiar kind, such as would not have raised him to eminence in ordinary times. Strategy is as much a speciality as chess-playing, and large practice is required to develop it. It is difficult to see how strategical gifts, combined with a hardy constitution, dashing courage, and a restless disposition, can achieve eminence in times of peace. These qualities are more likely to attract a man to the hunting-field, if he have enough money; or if not, to make him an unsuccessful speculator. It consequently happens that generals of high, but not the very highest order, such as Napoleon's marshals and Cromwell's generals, are rarely found to have eminent kinsfolk. Very different is the case with the most illustrious commanders. They are far more than strategists and men of restless dispositions; they would have distinguished themselves under any circumstances. Their kinships are most remarkable, as will be seen in my chapter on commanders, which includes the names of Alexander, Scipio, Hannibal, Caesar, Marlborough, Cromwell, the Princes of Nassau, Wellington, and Napoleon.

Precisely the same remarks are applicable to demagogues. Those who rise to the surface and play a prominent part in the transactions of a troubled period, must have courage and force of character, but they need not have high intellectual powers. Nay, it is more appropriate that the intellects of such men should be narrow and one-sided, and their dis-

positions moody and embittered. These are not qualities that lead to eminence in ordinary times. Consequently, the families of such men are mostly unknown to fame. But the kinships of popular leaders of the highest order, as of the two Gracchi, of the two Arteveldes, and of Mirabeau, are illustrious.

I may mention a class of cases that strikes me forcibly as a proof that a sufficient power of command to lead to eminence in troublous times is much less unusual than is commonly supposed, and that it lies neglected in the course of ordinary life. In beleaguered towns, as, for example, during the great Indian mutiny, a certain type of character very frequently made its appearance. People rose into notice who had never previously distinguished themselves, and subsided into their former way of life after the occasion for exertion was over; while during the continuance of danger and misery, they were the heroes of their situation. They were cool in danger, sensible in council, cheerful under prolonged suffering, humane to the wounded and sick, encouragers of the fainthearted. Such people were formed to shine only under exceptional circumstances. They had the advantage of possessing too tough a fibre to be crushed by anxiety and physical misery, and perhaps in consequence of that very toughness, they required a stimulus of the sharpest kind, to goad them to all the exertions of which they were capable.

The result of what I have said is to show that in statesmen and commanders mere "eminence" is by no means a satisfactory criterion of such natural gifts as would make a man distinguished under whatever circumstances he had been reared. On the other hand, statesmen of a high order, and commanders of the very highest, who overthrow all opponents, must be prodigiously gifted. The reader himself must judge the cases quoted in proof of hereditary gifts, by their several merits. I have endeavoured to speak of none but the most illustrious names. It would have led to false conclusions, had I taken a larger number, and thus descended to a lower level of merit.

In conclusion, I see no reason to be dissatisfied with the conditions of accepting high reputation as a very fair test of high ability. The nature of the test would not have been altered, if an attempt had been made to readjust each man's reputation according to his merits, because this is what every biographer does. If I had possessed the critical power of a Ste. Beuve, I should have merely thrown into literature another of those numerous expressions of opinion, by the aggregate of which all reputations are built.

To conclude: I feel convinced that no man can achieve a very high reputation without being gifted with very high abilities; and I trust that reason has been given for the belief that few who possess these very high abilities can fail in achieving eminence.

The foregoing consists of the Introductory Chapter
and Chapters I and II
from Galton's HEREDITARY GENIUS.

Claude Bernard

1813–1878

Claude Bernard's early ambitions were as nearly irrelevant to his later career as can be imagined. He was born near Villefranche, France, in 1813. He was first educated by the Jesuits and then proceeded to the college at Lyons, which he soon left to become a druggist's assistant. But his main effort was devoted to the composition of a musical farce, *The Rose of the Rhône*, which was produced and created a local stir. Encouraged, he attempted a prose drama in five acts, called *Arthur of Britain*. Armed with this work, he went, at the age of twenty-one, to Paris, carrying also an introduction to a famous literary critic. The latter convinced Bernard that he should study medicine instead of write plays!

Bernard became an interne at the Hôtel-Dieu, worked under the physiologist Magendie, became his deputy, and in 1855 succeeded him as professor of physiology. He was also named the first professor of physiology at the Sorbonne. There was, however, no laboratory in which he could work in the Sorbonne. Bernard acquainted Napoleon III of this deficiency in what must have been eloquent fashion, for the Emperor not only procured for the physiologist a laboratory at the Sorbonne but also built one for him in the Jardin des Plantes, and established a professorship which Bernard accepted in 1868. He was in the same year admitted to the Institut de

Notes from the artist: ". . . a linear study of Bernard enclosed by the left and right portions of a reflex arc, while above his head floats a facsimile of a drawing of the human nervous system by Andreas Vesalius, sixteenth-century Belgian, generally considered the founder of modern anatomy."

CLAUDE BERNARD

France. He died in Paris on February 10, 1878, and received a public funeral. He was the first scientist ever to be accorded this honor by France.

Bernard's most important work consisted of three great discoveries. The first involved the pancreas gland, which he proved to be of fundamental importance in digestion. The second involved the liver. He showed that this organ not only produces bile but also, by an "internal secretion," forms a starchlike substance named by him glycogen, the end product of which is dextrose—sugar. The third series of investigations resulted in the discovery of the so-called vasomotor nerves, which control the blood vessels.

Seventeen volumes of Bernard's lectures were published during his life and after his death. In 1865 he produced the *Introduction to Experimental Medicine,* from which the following selection is taken.

A long commentary would be necessary to present this splendid work to the reader," wrote Louis Pasteur of Bernard's *Introduction to Experimental Medicine;* "It is a monument raised to honor the method which has constituted Physical and Chemical Science since Galileo and Newton, and which M. Bernard is trying to introduce into physiology and pathology. Nothing so complete, so profound, so luminous has ever been written on the true principles of the difficult art of experimentation . . . This book will exert an immense influence on medical science, its teaching, its progress, its language even."

Concerning the method to which Pasteur refers, Bernard is perfectly clear. It consists in admitting that "the nature or very essence of phenomena, whether vital or mineral, will always remain unknown," that "we can learn only relations, and phenomena are merely the results of relations," and that "experience soon teaches us that we cannot get beyond the *how*" of things, "*i.e.,* beyond the immediate cause or the necessary conditions of phenomena." The introduction of this method into physiology involves the assertion that "a living organism is nothing but a wonderful machine endowed with the most marvellous properties and set going by means of the most complex and delicate mechanism." "Living machines are . . . created and constructed in such a way that, in perfecting themselves, they become freer and freer in the general cosmic environment. But the most absolute determinism still obtains, none the

less, in the inner environment which is separated more and more from the outer cosmic environment, by reason of the same organic development." And "determinism," according to Bernard, is "the foundation of all scientific progress and criticism."

Pasteur not only recognized the basic purpose of the book; the reader will also discover that his praise of it is merited. Even the selection included below can be said to be "complete," "profound" and "luminous." And Pasteur's predictions as to its effects were also accurate. The work has indeed had a profound influence on medical science. Bernard did much to create biochemistry: the science, that is, which treats—and with what wonderful results we know—the living organism as though it were a machine. It has been claimed that the theory of vitalism [1] had to be laid aside before man could understand life, and Bernard's work did much to bring about the demise of the old theory. And it is natural that the teaching of medicine should have reflected the progress produced in it by the ideas of Bernard and others.

Pasteur was even correct in his prediction that Bernard's book would exert an influence on the language of medicine. The terms "internal environment" and "external environment" became basic to the science. They reflected the important conception that is close to the heart of Bernard's idea of living things: that it is impossible, in his words, "to imagine a body wholly isolated in nature; it would no longer be real, because there would be no relation to manifest its existence."

Bernard was not only a great theorist; he was also a skillful experimenter. In another work, he expounds the principles that should underlie all experimentation. "Put off your imagination as you take off your overcoat when you enter the laboratory," he writes, "but put it on again, as you do the overcoat, when you leave the laboratory. Before the experiment and between whiles let your imagination wrap you around; put it right away from yourself during the experiment itself, lest it hinder your observing power." This is excellent advice—both parts of it. By the use of his metaphor of the overcoat, Bernard has neatly expressed the necessary interplay between experiment and hypothesis, between deduction and induction, between observation and thought. The student of any science can learn much from the physiologist Claude Bernard.

[1] For a discussion of vitalism, see the introductory note to Wöhler's "On the Artificial Production of Urea," Vol. 8, pp. 310–311.

Experimental Considerations Common to Living Things and Inorganic Bodies

The spontaneity enjoyed by beings endowed with life has been one of the principal objections urged against the use of experimentation in biological studies. Every living being indeed appears to us provided with a kind of inner force, which presides over manifestations of life more and more independent of general cosmic influence in proportion as the being rises higher in the scale of organization. In the higher animals and in man, for instance, this vital force seems to result in withdrawing the living being from general physico-chemical influences and thus making the experimental approach very difficult.

Inorganic bodies offer no parallel; whatever their nature, they are all devoid of spontaneity. As the manifestation of their properties is therefore absolutely bound up in the physico-chemical conditions surrounding them and forming their environment, it follows that the experimenter can reach them and alter them at will.

On the other hand, all the phenomena of a living body are in such reciprocal harmony one with another that it seems impossible to separate any part without at once disturbing the whole organism. Especially in higher animals, their more acute sensitiveness brings with it still more notable reactions and disturbances.

Many physicians and speculative physiologists, with certain anatomists and naturalists, employ these various arguments to attack experimentation on living beings. They assume a vital force in opposition to physico-chemical forces, dominating all the phenomena of life, subjecting them to entirely separate laws, and making the organism an organized whole which the experimenter may not touch without destroying the quality of life itself. They even go so far as to say that inorganic bodies

266

and living bodies differ radically from this point of view, so that experimentation is applicable to the former and not to the latter. Cuvier, who shares this opinion and thinks that physiology should be a science of observation and of deductive anatomy, expresses himself thus: "All parts of a living body are interrelated; they can act only in so far as they act all together; trying to separate one from the whole means transferring it to the realm of dead substances; it means entirely changing its essence."

If the above objections were well founded, we should either have to recognize that determinism is impossible in the phenomena of life, and this would be simply denying biological science; or else we should have to acknowledge that vital force must be studied by special methods, and that the science of life must rest on different principles from the science of inorganic bodies. These ideas, which were current in other times, are now gradually disappearing; but it is essential to extirpate their very last spawn, because the so-called vitalistic ideas still remaining in certain minds are really an obstacle to the progress of experimental science.

I propose, therefore, to prove that the science of vital phenomena must have the same foundations as the science of the phenomena of inorganic bodies, and that there is no difference in this respect between the principles of biological science and those of physico-chemical science. Indeed, as we have already said, the goal which the experimental method sets itself is everywhere the same; it consists in connecting natural phenomena with their necessary conditions or with their immediate causes. In biology, since these conditions are known, physiologists can guide the manifestation of vital phenomena as physicists guide the natural phenomena, the laws of which they have discovered; but in doing so, experimenters do not act on life.

Yet there is absolute determinism in all the sciences, because every phenomenon being necessarily linked with physico-chemical conditions, men of science can alter them to master the phenomenon, *i.e.*, to prevent or to promote its appearing. As to this, there is absolutely no question in the case of inorganic bodies. I mean to prove that it is the same with living bodies, and that for them also determinism exists.

The manifestation of properties of inorganic bodies is connected with surrounding conditions of temperature and moisture by means of which the experimenter can directly govern mineral phenomena. Living bodies at first sight do not seem capable of being thus influenced by neighbouring physico-chemical conditions; but that is merely a delusion depending

on the animal having and maintaining within himself the conditions of warmth and moisture necessary to the appearance of vital phenomena. The result is that an inert body, obedient to cosmic conditions, is linked with all their variations, while a living body on the contrary remains independent and free in its manifestations; it seems animated by an inner force that rules all its acts and liberates it from the influence of surrounding physico-chemical variations and disturbances. This quite different aspect of the manifestations of living bodies as compared with the behaviour of inorganic bodies has led the physiologists, called vitalists, to attribute to the former a vital force ceaselessly at war with physico-chemical forces and neutralizing their destructive action on the living organism. According to this view, the manifestations of life are determined by spontaneous action of this special vital force, instead of being, like the manifestations of inorganic bodies, the necessary results of conditions or of the physico-chemical influences of a surrounding environment. But if we consider it, we shall soon see that the spontaneity of living bodies is simply an appearance and the result of a certain mechanism in completely determined environments; so that it will be easy, after all, to prove that the behaviour of living bodies, as well as the behaviour of inorganic bodies, is dominated by a necessary determinism linking them with conditions of a purely physico-chemical order.

Let us note, first of all, that this kind of independence of living beings in the cosmic environment appears only in complex higher animals. Inferior beings, such as the Infusoria, reduced to an elementary organism, have no real independence. These creatures exhibit the vital properties with which they are endowed, only under the influence of external moisture, light or warmth, and as soon as one or more of these conditions happens to fail, the vital manifestation ceases, because the parallel physico-chemical phenomenon has stopped. In vegetables the manifestation of vital phenomena is linked in the same way with conditions of warmth, moisture and light in the surrounding environment. It is the same again with cold-blooded animals; the phenomena of life are benumbed or stimulated according to the same conditions. Now the influences producing or retarding vital manifestations in living beings are exactly the same as those which produce, accelerate or retard manifestations of physico-chemical phenomena in inorganic bodies, so that instead of following the example of the vitalists in seeing a kind of opposition or incompatibility between the conditions of vital manifestations and the conditions of physico-chemical manifestations, we must note, on the contrary, in these two orders of phenomena a complete parallelism

and a direct and necessary relation. Only in warm-blooded animals do the conditions of the organism and those of the surrounding environment seem to be independent; in these animals indeed the manifestation of vital phenomena no longer suffers the alternations and variations that the cosmic conditions display; and an inner force seems to join combat with these influences and in spite of them to maintain the vital forces in equilibrium. But fundamentally it is nothing of the sort; and the semblance depends simply on the fact that, by the more complete protective mechanism which we shall have occasion to study, the warm-blooded animal's internal environment comes less easily into equilibrium with the external cosmic environment. External influences, therefore, bring about changes and disturbances in the intensity of organic functions only in so far as the protective system of the organism's internal environment becomes insufficient in given conditions.

Thoroughly to understand the application of experimentation to living beings, it is of the first importance to reach a definite judgment on the ideas which we are now explaining. When we examine a higher, *i.e.*, a complex living organism, and see it fulfill its different functions in the general cosmic environment common to all the phenomena of nature, it seems to a certain extent independent of this environment. But this appearance results simply from our deluding ourselves about the simplicity of vital phenomena. The external phenomena which we perceive in the living being are fundamentally very complex; they are the resultant of a host of intimate properties of organic units whose manifestations are linked together with the physico-chemical conditions of the internal environment in which they are immersed. In our explanations we suppress this inner environment and see only the outer environment before our eyes. But the real explanation of vital phenomena rests on study and knowledge of the extremely tenuous and delicate particles which form the organic units of the body. This idea, long ago set forth in biology by great physiologists, seems more and more true in proportion as the science of the organization of living beings makes progress. We must, moreover, learn that the *intimate particles* of an organism exhibit their vital activity only through a necessary physico-chemical relation with immediate environments which we must also study and know. Otherwise, if we limit ourselves to the survey of total phenomena visible from without, we may falsely believe that a force in living beings violates the physico-chemical laws of the general cosmic environment, just as an untaught man might believe that some special force in a

machine, rising in the air or running along the ground, violated the laws of gravitation. Now, a living organism is nothing but a wonderful machine endowed with the most marvellous properties and set going by means of the most complex and delicate mechanism. There are no forces opposed and struggling one with another; in nature there can be only order and disorder, harmony or discord.

In experimentation on inorganic bodies, we need take account of only one environment, the external cosmic environment; while in the higher living animals, at least two environments must be considered, the external or extra-organic environment and the internal or intra-organic environment. In my course on physiology at the Faculty of Sciences, I explain each year these ideas on organic environment—new ideas which I regard as fundamental in general physiology; they are also necessarily fundamental in general pathology, and the same thoughts will guide us in adapting experimentation to living beings. For, as I have said elsewhere, the great difficulties that we meet in experimentally determining vital phenomena and in applying suitable means to altering them are caused by the complexity involved in the existence of an internal organic environment.

Physicists and chemists experimenting on inert bodies need consider only the external environment; by means of the thermometer, barometer and other instruments used in recording and measuring the properties of the external environment, they can always set themselves in equivalent conditions. For physiologists these instruments no longer suffice; and yet the internal environment is just the place where they should use them. Indeed, the internal environment of living beings is always in direct relation with the normal or pathological vital manifestations of organic units. In proportion as we ascend the scale of living beings, the organism grows more complex, the organic units become more delicate and require a more perfected internal environment. The circulating liquids, the blood serum and the intra-organic fluids all constitute the internal environment.

In living beings the internal environment, which is a true product of the organism, preserves the necessary relations of exchange and equilibrium with the external cosmic environment; but in proportion as the organism grows more perfect, the organic environment becomes specialized and more and more isolated, as it were, from the surrounding environment. In vegetables and in cold-blooded animals, as we have said, this isolation is less complete than in warm-blooded animals; in the latter the blood serum maintains an almost fixed and constant temperature and composition. But these differing conditions do not constitute differences of

nature in different living beings; they are merely improvements in the isolating and protecting mechanisms of their environment. Vital manifestations in animals vary only because the physico-chemical conditions of their internal environments vary; thus a mammal, whose blood has been chilled either by natural hibernation or by certain lesions of the nervous system, closely resembles a really cold-blooded animal in the properties of its tissues.

To sum up, from what has been said we can gain an idea of the enormous complexity of vital phenomena and of the almost insuperable difficulties which their accurate determination opposes to physiologists forced to carry on experimentation in the internal or organic environments. These obstacles, however, cannot terrify us if we are thoroughly convinced that we are on the right road. Absolute determinism exists indeed in every vital phenomenon; hence biological science exists also; and consequently the studies to which we are devoting ourselves will not all be useless. General physiology is the basic biological science toward which all others converge. Its problem is to determine the elementary condition of vital phenomena. Pathology and therapeutics also rest on this common foundation. By normal activity of its organic units, life exhibits a state of health; by abnormal manifestation of the same units, diseases are characterized; and finally through the organic environment modified by means of certain toxic or medicinal substances, therapeutics enables us to act on the organic units. To succeed in solving these various problems, we must, as it were, analyze the organism, as we take apart a machine to review and study all its works; that is to say, before succeeding in experimenting on smaller units we must first experiment on the machinery and on the organs. We must, therefore, have recourse to analytic study of the successive phenomena of life, and must make use of the same experimental method which physicists and chemists employ in analyzing the phenomena of inorganic bodies. The difficulties which result from the complexity of the phenomena of living bodies arise solely in applying experimentation; for fundamentally the object and principles of the method are always exactly the same.

If the physicist and the physiologist differ in this, that one busies himself with phenomena taking place in inorganic matter, and the other with phenomena occurring in living matter, still they do not differ in the object which they mean to attain. Indeed, they both set themselves a common object, viz., getting back to the immediate cause of the phenomena which they are studying.

Now, what we call the immediate cause of a phenomenon is nothing

but the physical and material condition in which it exists or appears. The object of the experimental method or the limit of every scientific research is therefore the same for living bodies as for inorganic bodies; it consists in finding the relations which connect any phenomenon with its immediate cause, or putting it differently, it consists in defining the conditions necessary to the appearance of the phenomenon. Indeed, when an experimenter succeeds in learning the necessary conditions of a phenomenon, he is, in some sense, its master; he can predict its course and its appearance, he can promote or prevent it at will. An experimenter's object, then, is reached; through science, he has extended his power over a natural phenomenon.

We shall therefore define physiology thus: the science whose object it is to study the phenomena of living beings and to *determine* the material conditions in which they appear. Only by the analytic or experimental method can we attain the determination of the conditions of phenomena, in living bodies as well as in inorganic bodies; for we reason in identically the same way in experimenting in all the sciences.

For physiological experimenters, neither spiritualism nor materialism can exist. These words belong to a philosophy which has grown old; they will fall into disuse through the progress of science. We shall never know either spirit or matter; and if this were the proper place I should easily show that on one side, as on the other, we quickly fall into scientific negations. The conclusion is that all such considerations are idle and useless. It is our sole concern to study phenomena, to learn their material conditions and manifestations, and to determine the laws of those manifestations.

First causes are outside the realm of science; they forever escape us in the sciences of living as well as in those of inorganic bodies. The experimental method necessarily turns aside from the chimerical search for a vital principle; vital force exists no more than mineral force exists, or, if you like, one exists quite as much as the other. The word force is merely an abstraction which we use for linguistic convenience. For mechanics, force is the relation of a movement to its cause. For physicists, chemists and physiologists, it is fundamentally the same. As the essence of things must always remain unknown, we can learn only relations, and phenomena are merely the results of relations. The properties of living bodies are revealed only through reciprocal organic relations. A salivary gland, for instance, exists only because it is in relation with the digestive system, and because its histological units are in certain relations one with another and with the blood. Destroy these relations by

isolating the units of the organism, one from another in thought, and the salivary gland simply ceases to be.

A scientific law gives us the numerical relation of an effect to its cause, and that is the goal at which science stops. When we have the law of a phenomenon, we not only know absolutely the conditions determining its existence, but we also have the relations applying to all its variations, so that we can predict modifications of the phenomenon in any given circumstances.

As a corollary to the above we must add that neither physiologists nor physicians need imagine it their task to seek the cause of life or the essence of disease. That would be entirely wasting one's time in pursuing a phantom. The words life, death, health, disease have no objective reality. We must imitate the physicists in this matter and say, as Newton said of gravitation: "Bodies fall with an accelerated motion whose law we know: that is a fact, that is reality. But the first cause which makes these bodies fall is utterly unknown. To picture the phenomenon to our minds, we may say that the bodies fall as if there were a force of attraction toward the centre of the earth, *quasi esset attractio*. But the force of attraction does not exist, we do not see it; it is merely a word used to abbreviate speech." When a physiologist calls in vital force or life, he does not see it; he merely pronounces a word; only the vital phenomenon exists, with its material conditions; that is the one thing that he can study and know.

To sum up, the object of science is everywhere the same: to learn the material conditions of phenomena. But though this goal is the same in the physico-chemical and in biological sciences, it is much harder to reach in the latter because of the mobility and complexity of the phenomena which we meet.

We must acknowledge as an experimental axiom that in living beings as well as in inorganic bodies the necessary conditions of every phenomenon are absolutely determined. That is to say, in other terms, that when once the conditions of a phenomenon are known and fulfilled, the phenomenon must always and necessarily be reproduced at the will of the experimenter. Negation of this proposition would be nothing less than negation of science itself. Indeed, as science is simply the determinate and the determinable, we must perforce accept as an axiom that, in identical conditions, all phenomena are identical and that, as soon as conditions are no longer the same, the phenomena cease to be identical. This principle is absolute in the phenomena of inorganic bodies as

well as in those of living beings, and the influence of life, whatever view
of it we take, can nowise alter it. As we have said, what we call vital
force is a first cause analogous to all other first causes, in this sense, that it
is utterly unknown. It matters little whether or not we admit that this
force differs essentially from the forces presiding over manifestations of
the phenomena of inorganic bodies, the vital phenomena which it governs
must still be determinable; for the force would otherwise be blind and
lawless, and that is impossible. The conclusion is that the phenomena
of life have their special law because there is rigorous determinism in
the various circumstances constituting conditions necessary to their exist-
ence or to their manifestations; and that is the same thing. Now in the
phenomena of living bodies as in those of inorganic bodies, it is only
through experimentation, as I have already often repeated, that we
can attain knowledge of the conditions which govern these phenomena
and so enable us to master them.

Everything so far said may seem elementary to men cultivating the
physico-chemical sciences. But among naturalists and especially among
physicians, we find men who, in the name of what they call vitalism,
express most erroneous ideas on the subject which concerns us. They be-
lieve that study of the phenomena of living matter can have no relation
to study of the phenomena of inorganic matter. They look on life as a
mysterious supernatural influence which acts arbitrarily by freeing itself
wholly from determinism, and they brand as materialists all who attempt
to reconcile vital phenomena with definite organic and physico-chemical
conditions. These false ideas are not easy to uproot when once estab-
lished in the mind; only the progress of science can dispel them. But
vitalistic ideas, taken in the sense which we have just indicated, are just
a kind of medical superstition—a belief in the supernatural. Now, in
medicine, belief in occult causes, whether it is called vitalism or is other-
wise named, encourages ignorance and gives birth to a sort of uninten-
tional quackery; that is to say, the belief in an inborn, indefinable science.
Confidence in absolute determinism in the phenomena of life leads, on
the contrary, to real science, and gives the modesty which comes from
the consciousness of our little learning and the difficulty of science. This
feeling incites us, in turn, to work toward knowledge; and to this feel-
ing alone, science in the end owes all its progress.

I should agree with the vitalists if they would simply recognize that liv-
ing beings exhibit phenomena peculiar to themselves and unknown in
inorganic nature. I admit, indeed, that manifestations of life cannot be
wholly elucidated by the physico-chemical phenomena known in in-

organic nature. I shall later explain my view of the part played in biology by physico-chemical sciences; I will here simply say that if vital phenomena differ from those of inorganic bodies in complexity and appearance, this difference obtains only by virtue of determined or determinable conditions proper to themselves. So if the sciences of life must differ from all others in explanation and in special laws, they are not set apart by scientific method. Biology must borrow the experimental method of physico-chemical sciences, but keep its special phenomena and its own laws.

In living bodies, as in inorganic bodies, laws are immutable, and the phenomena governed by these laws are bound to the conditions on which they exist, by a necessary and absolute determinism. I use the word determinism here as more appropriate than the word fatalism, which sometimes serves to express the same idea. Determinism in the conditions of vital phenomena should be one of the axioms of experimenting physicians. If they are thoroughly imbued with the truth of this principle, they will exclude all supernatural intervention from their explanations; they will have unshaken faith in the idea that fixed laws govern biological science; and at the same time they will have a reliable criterion for judging the often variable and contradictory appearance of vital phenomena. Indeed, starting with the principle that immutable laws exist, experimenters will be convinced that phenomena can never be mutually contradictory, if they are observed in the same conditions; and if they show variations, they will know that this is necessarily so because of the intervention or interference of other conditions which alter or mask phenomena. There will be occasion thenceforth to try to learn the conditions of these variations, for there can be no effect without a cause. Determinism thus becomes the foundation of all scientific progress and criticism. If we find disconcerting or even contradictory results in performing an experiment, we must never acknowledge exceptions or contradictions as real. That would be unscientific. We must simply and necessarily decide that conditions in the phenomena are different, whether or not we can explain them at the time.

I assert that the word exception is unscientific; and as soon as laws are known, no exception indeed can exist, and this expression, like so many others, merely enables us to speak of things whose causation we do not know. Every day we hear physicians use the words: ordinarily, more often, generally, or else express themselves numerically by saying, for instance: nine times out of ten, things happen in this way. I have heard old practitioners say that the words "always" and "never" should be

crossed out of medicine. I condemn neither these restrictions nor the use of these locutions if they are used as empirical approximations about the appearances of phenomena when we are still more or less ignorant of the exact conditions in which they exist. But certain physicians seem to reason as if exceptions were necessary; they seem to believe that a vital force exists which can arbitrarily prevent things from always happening alike; so that exceptions would result directly from the action of mysterious vital force. Now this cannot be the case; what we now call an exception is a phenomenon, one or more of whose conditions are unknown; if the conditions of the phenomena of which we speak were known and determined, there would be no further exceptions, medicine would be as free from them as is any other science. For instance, we might formerly say that sometimes the itch was cured and sometimes not; but now that we attack the cause of this disease, we cure it always. Formerly it might be said that a lesion of the nerves brought on paralysis, now of feeling, and again of motion; but now we know that cutting the anterior spinal nerve paralyzes motion only. Motor paralysis occurs consistently and always, because its condition has been accurately determined by experimenters.

The certainty with which phenomena are determined should also be, as we have said, the foundation of experimental criticism, whether applied to one's self or to others. A phenomenon, indeed, always appears in the same way if conditions are similar; the phenomenon never fails if the conditions are present, just as it does fail to appear if the conditions are absent. Thus an experimenter who has made an experiment, in conditions which he believes were determined, may happen not to get the same results in a new series of investigations as in his first observation; in repeating the experiment, with fresh precautions, it may happen again that, instead of his first result, he may encounter a wholly different one. In such a situation, what is to be done? Should we acknowledge that the facts are indeterminable? Certainly not, since that cannot be. We must simply acknowledge that experimental conditions, which we believed to be known, are not known. We must more closely study, search out and define the experimental conditions, for the facts cannot be contradictory one to another; they can only be indeterminate. Facts never exclude one another, they are simply explained by differences in the conditions in which they are born. So an experimenter can never deny a fact that he has seen and observed, merely because he cannot rediscover it. In the third part of this introduction, we shall cite instances in which

the principles of experimental criticism which we have just suggested are put in practice.

As a natural phenomenon is only the expression of ratios and relations and connections, at least two bodies are necessary to its appearance. So we must always consider, first, a body which reacts or which manifests the phenomenon; second, another body which acts and plays the part of environment in relation to the first. It is impossible to imagine a body wholly isolated in nature; it would no longer be real, because there would be no relation to manifest its existence.

In phenomenal relations, as nature presents them to us, more or less complexity always prevails. In this respect mineral phenomena are much less complex than vital phenomena; this is why the sciences dealing with inorganic bodies have succeeded in establishing themselves more quickly. In living bodies, the complexity of phenomena is immense, and what is more, the mobility accompanying vital characteristics makes them much harder to grasp and to define.

The properties of living matter can be learned only through their relation to the properties of inorganic matter; it follows that the biological sciences must have as their necessary foundation the physico-chemical sciences from which they borrow their means of analysis and their methods of investigation. Such are the necessary reasons for the secondary and backward evolution of the sciences concerned with the phenomena of life. But though the complexity of vital phenomena creates great obstacles, we must not be appalled, for, as we have already said, unless we deny the possibility of biological science, the principles of science are everywhere the same. So we may be sure that we are on the right road and that in time we shall reach the scientific result that we are seeking, that is to say, determinism in the phenomena of living beings.

We can reach knowledge of definite elementary conditions of phenomena only by one road, viz., by experimental analysis. Analysis dissociates all the complex phenomena successively into more and more simple phenomena, until they are reduced, if possible, to just two elementary conditions. Experimental science, in fact, considers in a phenomenon only the definite conditions necessary to produce it. Physicists try to picture these conditions to themselves, more or less ideally in mechanics or mathematical physics. Chemists successively analyze complex matters; and in thus reaching either elements or definite substances (individual compounds or chemical species), they attain the elementary

or irreducible conditions of phenomena. In the same way, biologists should analyze complex organisms and reduce the phenomena of life to conditions that cannot be analyzed in the present state of science.

Experimental physiology and medicine have no other goal. When faced by complex questions, physiologists and physicians, as well as physicists and chemists, should divide the total problem into simpler and simpler and more and more clearly defined partial problems. They will thus reduce phenomena to their simplest possible material conditions and make application of the experimental method easier and more certain. All the analytic sciences divide problems, in order to experiment better. By following this path, physicists and chemists have succeeded in reducing what seemed the most complex phenomena to simple properties connected with well-defined mineral species. By following the same analytic path, physiologists should succeed in reducing all the vital manifestations of a complex organism to the play of certain organs, and the action of these organs to the properties of well-defined tissues or organic units. Anatomico-physiological experimental analysis, which dates from Galen, has just this meaning, and histology, in pursuing the same problem to-day, is naturally coming closer and closer to the goal.

Though we can succeed in separating living tissues into chemical elements or bodies, still these elementary chemical bodies are not elements for physiologists. In this respect biologists are more like physicists than chemists, for they seek to determine the properties of bodies and are much less preoccupied with their elementary composition. In the present state of the science, it would be impossible to establish any relation between the vital properties of bodies and their chemical composition; because tissues and organs endowed with the most diverse properties are at times indistinguishable from the point of view of their elementary chemical composition. Chemistry is most useful to physiologists in giving them means of separating and studying individual compounds, true organic products which play important parts in the phenomena of life.

Organic individual compounds, though well defined in their properties, are still not active elements in physiological phenomena; like mineral matter, they are, as it were, only passive elements in the organism. For physiologists, the truly active elements are what we call anatomical or histological units. Like the organic individual compounds, these are not chemically simple; but physiologically considered, they are as simplified as possible in that their vital properties are the simplest that we know —vital properties which vanish when we happen to destroy this elementary organized part. However, all ideas of ours about these elements

are limited by the present state of our knowledge; for there can be no question that these histological units, in the condition of cells and fibres, are still complex. That is why certain naturalists refuse to give them the names of elements and propose to call them elementary organisms. This appellation is in fact more appropriate; we can perfectly well picture to ourselves a complex organism made up of a quantity of distinct elementary organisms, uniting, joining and grouping together in various ways, to give birth first to the different tissues of the body, then to its various organs; anatomical mechanisms are themselves only assemblages of organs which present endlessly varied combinations in living beings. When we come to analyze the complex manifestations of any organism, we should therefore separate the complex phenomena and reduce them to a certain number of simple properties belonging to elementary organisms; then synthetically reconstruct the total organism in thought, by reuniting and ordering the elementary organisms, considered at first separately, then in their reciprocal relations.

When physicians, chemists or physiologists, by successive experimental analyses, succeed in determining the irreducible element of a phenomenon in the present state of their science, the scientific problem is simplified, but its nature is not changed thereby; and men of science are no nearer to absolute knowledge of the essence of things. Nevertheless, they have gained what it is truly important to obtain, to wit, knowledge of the necessary conditions of the phenomenon and determination of the definite relation existing between a body manifesting its properties and the immediate cause of this manifestation. The object of analysis, in biological as in physico-chemical science, is, after all, to determine and, as far as possible, to isolate the conditions governing the occurrence of each phenomenon. We can act on the phenomena of nature only by reproducing the natural conditions in which they exist; and we act the more easily on these conditions in proportion as they have first been better analyzed and reduced to a greater state of simplicity. Real science exists, then, only from the moment when a phenomenon is accurately defined as to its nature and rigorously determined in relation to its material conditions, that is, when its law is known. Before that, we have only groping and empiricism.

The most superficial examination of what goes on around us shows that all natural phenomena result from the reaction of bodies one against another. There always come under consideration the *body*, in which the phenomenon takes place, and the outward circumstance or the

environment which determines or invites the body to exhibit its properties. The conjunction of these conditions is essential to the appearance of the phenomenon. If we suppress the environment, the phenomenon disappears, just as if the body had been taken away. The phenomena of life, as well as those of inorganic bodies, are thus doubly conditioned. On the one hand, we have the organism in which vital phenomena come to pass; on the other hand, the cosmic environment in which living bodies, like inorganic bodies, find the conditions essential to the appearance of their phenomena. The conditions necessary to life are found neither in the organism nor in the outer environment, but in both at once. Indeed, if we suppress or disturb the organism, life ceases, even though the environment remains intact; if, on the other hand, we take away or vitiate the environment, life just as completely disappears, even though the organism has not been destroyed.

Thus phenomena appear as results of contact or relation of a body with its environment. Indeed, if we absolutely isolate a body in our thought, we annihilate it in so doing; and if, on the contrary, we multiply its relations with the outer world, we multiply its properties.

Phenomena, then, are definite relations of bodies; we always conceive these relations as resulting from forces outside of matter, because we cannot absolutely localize them in a single body. For physicists, universal attraction is only an abstract idea; manifestation of this force requires the presence of two bodies; if only one body is present, we can no longer conceive of attraction. For example, electricity results from the action of copper and zinc in certain chemical conditions; but if we suppress the interrelation of bodies, electricity—an abstraction without existence in itself—ceases to appear. In the same way, life results from contact of the organism with its environment; we can no more understand it through the organism alone than through the environment alone. It is therefore a similar abstraction, that is to say, a force which appears as if it were outside of matter.

But however the mind conceives the forces of nature, that cannot alter an experimenter's conduct in any respect. For him the problem reduces itself solely to determining the material conditions in which a phenomenon appears. These conditions once known, he can then master the phenomenon; by supplying or not supplying them, he can make the phenomenon appear or disappear at will. Thus physicists and chemists exert their power over inorganic bodies; thus physiologists gain empire over vital phenomena. Living bodies, however, seem at first sight to elude the

experimenter's action. We see the higher organisms uniformly exhibit their vital phenomena, in spite of variations in the surrounding cosmic environment, and from another angle we see life extinguished in an organism after a certain length of time without being able to find reasons in the external environment for this extinction. But, as we have already said, there is an illusion here, resulting from incomplete and superficial analysis of the conditions of vital phenomena. Ancient science was able to conceive only the outer environment; but to establish the science of experimental biology, we must also conceive an inner environment. I believe I was the first to express this idea clearly and to insist on it, the better to explain the application of experimentation to living beings. Since the outer environment, on the other hand, infiltrates into the inner environment, knowing the latter teaches us the former's every influence. Only by passing into the inner, can the influence of the outer environment reach us, whence it follows that knowing the outer environment cannot teach us the actions born in, and proper to, the inner environment. The general cosmic environment is common to living and to inorganic bodies; but the inner environment created by an organism is special to each living being. Now, here is the true physiological environment; this it is which physiologists and physicians should study and know, for by its means they can act on the histological units which are the only effective agents in vital phenomena. Nevertheless, though so deeply seated, these units are in communication with the outer world; they still live in the conditions of the outer environment perfected and regulated by the play of the organism. The organism is merely a living machine so constructed that, on the one hand, the outer environment is in free communication with the inner organic environment, and, on the other hand, the organic units have protective functions, to place in reserve the materials of life and uninterruptedly to maintain the humidity, warmth and other conditions essential to vital activity. Sickness and death are merely a dislocation or disturbance of the mechanism which regulates the contact of vital stimulants with organic units. In a word, vital phenomena are the result of contact between the organic units of the body with the *inner physiological environment;* this is the pivot of all experimental medicine. Physiologists and physicians gain mastery over the phenomena of life by learning which conditions, in this inner environment, are normal and which abnormal, for the appearance of vital activity in the organic units; for apart from complexity of conditions, phenomena exhibiting life, like physico-chemical phenomena,

result from contact between an active body and the environment in which it acts.

To sum up, the study of life includes two things: (1) study of the properties of organized units; (2) study of the organic environment, *i.e.*, study of the conditions which this environment must fulfill to permit the appearance of vital activities. Physiology, pathology and therapeutics rest on this double knowledge; apart from this, neither medical science nor any truly scientific or effectual therapeutics exists.

In living organisms it is convenient to distinguish between three kinds of definite bodies: first, chemical elements; second, organic and inorganic individual compounds; third, organized anatomical units. Of about 70 elements known to chemistry to-day, only 16 are found in that most complex of organisms, the organism of man. But these 16 elements combine with one another to form the various liquid, solid and gaseous substances of the organism. Oxygen and nitrogen, however, are merely dissolved in the organic fluids; and in living beings, seem to act as elements. The inorganic individual compounds (earthy salts, phosphates, chlorides, sulphates, etc.) are essential constituents in the composition of living bodies, but are taken ready-made directly from the outer world. Organic individual compounds are also constituents of living bodies, but by no means borrowed from the outer world; they are made by the vegetable or animal organism; among such substances are starch, sugar, fat, albumen, etc., etc. When extracted from the body, they preserve their properties because they are not alive; they are organic products, but not organized. Anatomical units stand alone as organized living parts. These parts are irritable and, under the influence of various stimulants, exhibit properties exclusively characteristic of living beings. They live and nourish themselves, and their nourishment creates and preserves their properties, which means that they cannot be cut off from the organism without more or less rapidly losing their vitality.

Though very different from one another in respect to their functions in the organism, these three classes of bodies all show physico-chemical reactions under the influence of the outer stimuli—warmth, light, electricity; but living parts also have the power of being irritable, *i.e.*, reacting under the influence of certain stimuli in a way specially characteristic of living tissues, such as muscular contraction, nervous transmission, glandular secretion, etc. But whatever the variety presented by the three classes of phenomena, whether the reaction be physico-chemical or vital, it is never in any way spontaneous. The phenomenon always

results from the influence exerted on the reacting body by a physico-chemical stimulant outside itself.

Every definite substance, whether inorganic, organic or organized, is autonomous; that is to say, it has characteristic properties and exhibits independent action. Nevertheless, each one of these bodies is inert, that is, it is incapable of putting itself into action; to do this, it must always enter into relation with another body, from which it receives a stimulus. Thus every mineral body in the cosmic environment is stable; it changes its state only when the circumstances in which it is placed are rather seriously changed, either naturally or through experimental interference. In any organic environment, the substances created by animals and vegetables are much more changeable and less stable, but still they are inert and exhibit their properties only as they are influenced by agents outside themselves. Finally, anatomical units themselves, which are the most changeable and unstable of substances, are still inert, that is, they never break into vital activity unless some foreign influence invites them. A muscle-fibre, for instance, has the vital property peculiar to itself of contracting, but this living fibre is inert in the sense that if nothing changes in its environmental or its inner conditions, it cannot bring its functions into play, and it will not contract. For the musclar fibre to contract, a change must necessarily be produced in it, by its coming into relation with a stimulation from without, which may come either from the blood or from a nerve. We may say as much of all the histological units, nerve units, blood units, etc. Different living units thus play the part of stimuli, one in relation to another; and the functional manifestations of an organism are merely the expression of their harmonious reciprocal relations. The histological units react either separately or one against another by means of vital properties which are themselves in necessary connection with surrounding physico-chemical conditions; and this relation is so intimate that we may say the intensity of physico-chemical phenomena taking place in an organism may be used to measure the intensity of its vital phenomena. Therefore, as has already been said, we must not set up an antagonism between vital phenomena and physico-chemical phenomena, but, on the contrary, we must note the complete and necessary parallelism between the two classes of phenomena. To sum up, living matter is no more able than inorganic matter to get into activity or movement by itself. Every change in matter implies intervention of a new relation, i.e., an outside condition or influence. The role of men of science is to try to define and determine the material conditions producing the appearance of each phenomenon.

These conditions once known, experimenters master the phenomenon in this sense, that they can give movement to matter, or take it away, at pleasure.

What we have just said is equally true for the phenomena of living bodies and the phenomena of inorganic bodies. Only in the case of the complex higher organisms, physiologists and physicians must study the stimuli of vital phenomena, not in the relations of the whole organism with the general cosmic environment, but rather in the organic conditions of the inner environment. Considered in the general cosmic environment, the functions of man and of the higher animals seem to us, indeed, free and independent of the physico-chemical conditions of the environment, because its actual stimuli are found in an inner, organic, liquid environment. What we see from the outside is merely the result of physico-chemical stimuli from the inner environment; that is where physiologists must build up the real determinism of vital functions.

Living machines are therefore created and constructed in such a way that, in perfecting themselves, they become freer and freer in the general cosmic environment. But the most absolute determinism still obtains, none the less, in the inner environment which is separated more and more from the outer cosmic environment, by reason of the same organic development. A living machine keeps up its movement because the inner mechanism of the organism, by acts and forces ceaselessly renewed, repairs the losses involved in the exercise of its functions. Machines created by the intelligence of man, though infinitely coarser, are built in just this fashion. A steam engine's activity is independent of outer physico-chemical conditions, since the machine goes on working through cold, heat, dryness and moisture. But physicists going down into the inner environment of the machine find that this independence is only apparent, and that the movement of its every inner gear is determined by physical conditions whose law they know. As for physiologists, if they can go down into the inner environment of a living machine, they find likewise absolute determinism that must become the real foundation of the science of living bodies.

The nature of our mind leads us to seek the essence or the *why* of things. Thus we aim beyond the goal that it is given us to reach; for experience soon teaches us that we cannot get beyond the *how*, *i.e.*, beyond the immediate cause or the necessary conditions of phenomena. In this respect the limits of our knowledge are the same in biological as in physico-chemical sciences.

When, by successive analyses, we find the immediate cause determining the circumstances in which a phenomenon presents itself, we reach a scientific goal beyond which we cannot pass. When we know that water, with all its properties, results from combining oxygen and hydrogen in certain proportions, we know everything we can know about it; and that corresponds to the *how* and not to the *why* of things. We know how water can be made; but why does the combination of one volume of oxygen with two volumes of hydrogen produce water? We have no idea. In medicine it is equally absurd to concern one's self with the question "why." Yet physicians ask it often. It was probably to make fun of this tendency, which results from lack of the sense of limits to our learning, that Molière put the following answer into the mouth of his candidate for the medical degree. Asked why opium puts people to sleep, he answered: *"Quia est in eo virtus dormitiva, cujus est natura sensus assoupire* [Because it contains a soporific element, whose nature it is to put the senses to sleep]." This answer seems ludicrous and absurd; yet no other answer could be made. In the same way, if we wished to answer the question: "Why does hydrogen, in combining with oxygen, produce water?" we should have to answer: "Because hydrogen has the quality of being able to beget water." Only the question "why," then, is really absurd, because it necessarily involves a naïve or ridiculous answer. So we had better recognize that we do not know; and that the limits of our knowledge are precisely here.

In physiology, if we prove, for instance, that carbon monoxide is deadly when uniting more firmly than oxygen with the hemoglobin, we know all that we can know about the cause of death. Experience teaches us that a part of the mechanism of life is lacking; oxygen can no longer enter the organism, because it cannot displace the carbon monoxide in its union with the hemoglobin. But why has carbon monoxide more affinity than oxygen for this substance? Why is entrance of oxygen into the organism necessary to life? Here is the limit of our knowledge in our present state of learning; and even assuming that we succeed in further advancing our experimental analysis, we shall reach a blind cause at which we shall be forced to stop, without finding the primal reason for things.

Let us add that, when the relative determinism of a phenomenon is established, our scientific goal is reached. Experimental analysis of the conditions of the phenomenon, when pushed still further, gives us fresh information, but really teaches us nothing about the nature of the phenomenon originally determined. The conditions necessary to a phenome-

non teach us nothing about its nature. When we know that physical and chemical contact between the blood and the cerebral nerve cells is necessary to the production of intellectual phenomena, that points to conditions, but it cannot teach us anything about the primary nature of intelligence. Similarly, when we know that friction and that chemical action produce electricity, we are still ignorant of the primary nature of electricity.

We must therefore, in my opinion, stop differentiating the phenomena of living bodies from those of inorganic bodies, by a distinction based on our own ability to know the nature of the former and our inability to know that of the latter. The truth is that the nature or very essence of phenomena, whether vital or mineral, will always remain unknown. The essence of the simplest mineral phenomenon is as completely unknown to chemists and physicists to-day as is the essence of intellectual phenomena or of any other vital phenomenon to physiologists. That, moreover, is easy to apprehend; knowledge of the inmost nature or the absolute, in the simplest phenomenon, would demand knowledge of the whole universe; for every phenomenon of the universe is evidently a sort of radiation from that universe to whose harmony it contributes. In living bodies absolute truth would be still harder to attain; because, besides implying knowledge of the universe outside a living body, it would also demand complete knowledge of the organism which, as we have long been saying, is a little world (microcosm) in the great universe (macrocosm). Absolute knowledge could, therefore, leave nothing outside itself; and only on condition of knowing everything could man be granted its attainment. Man behaves as if he were destined to reach this absolute knowledge; and the incessant *why* which he puts to nature proves it. Indeed, this hope, constantly disappointed, constantly reborn, sustains and always will sustain successive generations in the passionate search for truth.

Our feelings lead us at first to believe that absolute truth must lie within our realm; but study takes from us, little by little, these chimerical conceits. Science has just the privilege of teaching us what we do not know, by replacing feeling with reason and experience and clearly showing us the present boundaries of our knowledge. But by a marvellous compensation, science, in humbling our pride, proportionately increases our power. Men of science who carry experimental analysis to the point of relatively determining a phenomenon doubtless see clearly their own ignorance of the phenomenon in its primary cause; but they have become its master; the instrument at work is unknown, but they can use it. This is true of all experimental sciences in which we can reach only relative

or partial truths and know phenomena only in their necessary conditions. But this knowledge is enough to broaden our power over nature. Though we do not know the essence of phenomena, we can produce or prevent their appearance, because we can regulate their physicochemical conditions. We do not know the essence of fire, of electricity, of light, and still we regulate their phenomena to our own advantage. We know absolutely nothing of the essence even of life; but we shall nevertheless regulate vital phenomena as soon as we know enough of their necessary conditions. Only in living bodies these conditions are much more complex and more difficult to grasp than in inorganic bodies; that is the whole difference.

To sum up, if our feeling constantly puts the question *why*, our reason shows us that only the question *how* is within our range; for the moment, then, only the question *how* concerns men of science and experimenters. If we cannot know *why* opium and its alkaloids put us to sleep, we can learn the mechanism of sleep and know *how* opium or its ingredients puts us to sleep; for sleep takes place only because an active substance enters into contact with certain organic substances which it changes. Learning these changes will give us the means of producing or preventing sleep, and we shall be able to act on the phenomenon and regulate it at pleasure.

In the knowledge that we acquire, we should distinguish between two sets of notions: the first corresponds to the *cause* of phenomena, the second to the *means* of producing them. By the cause of a phenomenon we mean the constant and definite condition necessary to existence; we call this the relative determinism or the *how* of things, *i.e.*, the immediate or determining cause. The means of obtaining phenomena are the varied processes by whose aid we may succeed in putting in action the single determining cause which produces the phenomenon. The necessary cause in the formation of water is the combination of two volumes of hydrogen with one of oxygen; this is the single cause which always determines the phenomenon. We cannot conceive of water apart from this essential condition. Subordinate conditions or processes in the formation of water may be extremely varied; only all these processes reach the same result, viz., combination of oxygen and hydrogen in invariable proportions. Let us take another example. I assume that we wish to transform starch into glucose; we have any number of means or processes for doing this, but fundamentally there will always be the identical cause, and a single determinism will beget the phenomenon. This cause is fixation of one more unit of water in the substance, to bring about its

transformation. Only we may produce this hydration in any number of conditions and by any number of methods: by means of acidulated water, of heat, of animal or vegetable enzymes; but all these processes finally come to a single condition, hydrolysis of the starch. The determinism, *i.e.*, the cause of the phenomenon, is therefore single, though the means for making it appear may be multiple and apparently very various. It is most important to establish this distinction especially in medicine, where the greatest confusion reigns, precisely because physicians recognize a multitude of causes for the same disease. To convince ourselves of what I am urging we have only to open a treatise on pathology. By no means all the circumstances enumerated are causes; at most they are means or processes by which a disease can be produced. But the real and effective cause of a disease must be *constant* and *determined,* that is unique; anything else would be a denial of science in medicine. It is true that determining causes are much harder to recognize and define in the phenomena of living beings; but they exist nevertheless, in spite of the seeming diversity of means employed. Thus in certain toxic phenomena we see different poisons lead to one cause and to a single determinism for the death of histological units, for example, the coagulation of muscular substance. In the same way, varied circumstances producing the same disease must all correspond to a single and determined pathogenic action. In a word, determinism which insists on identity of effect bound up with identity of cause is an axiom of science which can no more be transgressed in the sciences of life than in the sciences of inorganic matter.

We know the phenomena of nature only through their relations with the causes which produce them. Now the *law* of phenomena is nothing else than this relation numerically established, in such a way as to let us foresee the ratio of cause to effect in any given case. This ratio, established by observation, enables astronomers to predict celestial phenomena; this same ratio, established by observation and experiment, again enables physicists, chemists, physiologists not only to predict the phenomena of nature but even to modify them at pleasure and to a certainty, provided they do not swerve from the ratio which experience has pointed out, *i.e.*, the law. In other terms, we can guide natural phenomena only by submitting to laws that govern them.

Observers can only observe natural phenomena; experimenters can only modify them; it is not given them to create or to destroy them utterly, because they cannot change natural law. We have often repeated that

experimenters act, not on phenomena themselves, but on the physico-chemical conditions necessary to their appearance. Phenomena are just the actual expression of the ratio of these conditions; hence, when conditions are similar, the ratio is constant and the phenomenon identical, and when conditions change, there is another ratio, and a different phenomenon. In a word, to make a new phenomenon appear, experimenters merely bring new conditions to pass, but they create nothing, either in the way of force or of matter. At the end of the last century science proclaimed a great truth, to wit, that with respect to matter, nothing is lost, neither is anything created in nature; the bodies whose qualities ceaselessly vary under our eyes are all only transmutations of aggregations of matter of equal weight. In recent times science has proclaimed a second truth which it is still seeking to prove and which in some sense is truly complementary to the first, to wit, that with respect to forces nothing is lost and nothing created in nature; it follows that all the infinitely varied forms of phenomena in the universe are only equivalent transformation of forces, one into another. I reserve for treatment elsewhere the question whether differences separate the forces of living bodies from those of inert bodies; let it suffice for the moment to say that the two preceding truths are universal, and that they embrace the phenomena of living bodies as well as those of inert bodies.

All phenomena, to whatever order they belong, exist implicitly in the changeless laws of nature; and they show themselves only when their necessary conditions are actualized. The bodies and beings on the surface of our earth express the harmonious relation of the cosmic conditions of our planet and our atmosphere with the beings and phenomena whose existence they permit. Other cosmic conditions would necessarily make another world appear in which all the phenomena would occur which found in it their necessary conditions, and from which would disappear all that could not develop in it. But no matter what infinite varieties of phenomena we conceive on the earth, by placing ourselves in thought in all the cosmic conditions that our imagination can bring to birth, we are still forced to admit that this would all take place according to the laws of physics, chemistry and physiology, which have existed without our knowledge from all eternity; and that whatever happens, nothing is created by way either of force or of matter; that only different relations will be produced and through them creation of new beings and phenomena.

When a chemist makes a new body appear in nature, he cannot flatter himself with having created the laws which brought it to birth; he

produced only the conditions which the creative law demanded for its manifestation. The case of organic bodies is the same. Chemists and physiologists, in their experiments, can make new beings appear only by obeying the laws of nature which they cannot alter in any way.

It is not given to man to alter the cosmic phenomena of the whole universe nor even those of the earth; but the advances of science enable him to alter the phenomena within his reach. Thus man has already gained a power over mineral nature which is brilliantly revealed in the application of modern science, still at its dawn. The result of experimental science applied to living bodies must also be to alter vital phenomena, by acting solely on the conditions of these phenomena. But here our difficulties are greatly increased by the delicacy of the conditions of vital phenomena and the complexity and interrelation of all the parts grouped together to form an organized being. This is why man can probably never act as easily on animal or vegetable, as on mineral, species. His power over living beings will remain more limited, especially where they form higher, *i.e.*, more complicated, organisms. Nevertheless, the difficulties obstructing the power of physiologists do not pertain to the nature of vital phenomena, but merely to their complexity. Physiologists will first begin by getting at phenomena of vegetables and of animals in easier relations with the outer cosmic environment. It appears, at first sight, as if man and the higher animals must escape from its power to change, because they seem freed from the direct influence of the outer environment. But we know that vital phenomena in man, as in the animals nearest him, are connected with the physico-chemical conditions of an inner organic environment. This inner environment we must first seek to know, because this must become the real field of action for physiology and experimental medicine.

The foregoing is Chapter III from Bernard's
AN INTRODUCTION TO THE STUDY OF EXPERIMENTAL MEDICINE,
translated by Henry C. Greene.

Ivan Petrovich Pavlov

1849–1936

Pavlov was born in the district of Ryazan, in Russia, in 1849. He studied science and medicine at St. Petersburg and received a medical degree in 1883, but he chose to follow a career of research rather than practice medicine. In 1891, he was appointed director of the physiological department of the Institute of Experimental Medicine, in St. Petersburg; in 1895, he was made a professor at the Medical Academy. Later he was elected to the Russian Academy of Sciences and was made a foreign member of the British Royal Society. He won the Nobel Prize in 1904 for physiology and medicine and continued to accumulate fame and honors for the rest of his long life. He died on February 27, 1936.

Pavlov is best known for his work on conditioned, or modified, reflexes in experimental animals, but he did research in many areas of physiology. He worked on the problem of digestion, and he was much concerned, as the following selection shows, with the question of the activity of the central nervous system. He was a brilliant experimentalist, devising new and original methods of handling animals so that they could be observed under normal conditions. He was a meticulous scientist who took great care that his laboratory, as well as his reasoning, was uncluttered. He has had an important influence on the course which modern psychology has followed.

The first thing to consider in the following selection is the title of it. It is a "scientific study." And it is concerned with the "so-called psychical processes in the higher animals." The two phrases are both significant.

Pavlov himself emphasizes his use of the word "so-called." Psychi-

cal processes in higher animals are not directly observable. We cannot get into the mind of a dog and see how it works, or if it "works" at all. Since this is so, such processes can only be assumed.

"The naturalist must consider only one thing," Pavlov writes: "what is the relation of this or that external reaction of the animal to the phenomena of the external world?" This is what it means to him to be "scientific." In this sense, it is behavior alone that can be studied scientifically. It is the obligation of natural science "to ascertain completely how a living being maintains itself in constant equilibrium with its environment." Such equilibrium is a matter of give-and-take, but its psychological aspects are mysterious. Indeed, Pavlov says, the study of the "physiology of the highest parts of the central nervous system . . . has been cluttered with foreign ideas, borrowed from psychology." The implication would seem to be that psychology is not a natural science, and therefore not relevant to Pavlov's concern.

This position—that the scientist ought only to investigate the external behavior of organic as well as inorganic beings—is often taken by modern scientists. (It can be traced back at least as far as Claude Bernard.) Behavior can be *measured;* and measurement has been said to be the essence of science. What cannot be measured is illusory, it is sometimes contended. The supporters of the position can point to the great success of quantitative methods not only in physics and chemistry, but in the biological sciences as well.

Other modern scientists have wondered whether there is not something more to the science of man than Pavlov appears to allow. The argument cannot be ended by a few pages, written by exponents of either side. It is Pavlov's ultimate goal that "the human mind will contemplate itself not from within but from without." But it may be asked if such a view is sufficient. Is it really possible to understand man, or for that matter the outside world, without the view from within?

Notes from the artist: "Diagrammatic designs related to his work surround the portrait of Pavlov. Some of the recognizable elements are a dog, parotid glands, the sympathetic reflex, and taste buds at the back of the tongue, showing sensory impulses toward the brain."

Pavlov

Scientific Study of the So-called Psychical Processes in the Higher Animals[1]

The subject of today's address,[2] delivered in honor of Thomas Huxley, an eminent representative of natural science and a most energetic champion of that greatest biological principle (the doctrine of evolution), is the naturalistic investigation of the psychical processes in the higher animal.

I shall begin with an actual case which occurred in my laboratory a few years ago. Among my collaborators was a young doctor with an active mind capable of appreciating the joys and triumphs of investigation. Great was my astonishment when this loyal friend of science became profoundly disturbed on hearing of our plans to investigate the psychical activity of the dog in that same laboratory and by the same means which we had been using for the solution of physiological questions. All of our arguments were ineffective; he prophesied and hoped for only failure. The cause of this, as far as we could understand, was his idea that the psychical life of man and that of the higher animals was so individual and exalted that it not only did not lend itself to investigation, but would even be sullied by our rude physiological methods. Although this, gentlemen, may have been a somewhat exaggerated example, I believe it is characteristic and typical. In dealing with the highest vital

1. In the expression "the so-called psychical process" the reader will see that the author has taken a new position. Now he considers all of his results as purely physiological. And he rejects definitely the further possibility of investigating subjective states. He begins to bring out a mass of evidence in favor of the purely physiological nature of his data. The artificial conditioned reflex treated of in this chapter strengthened his view and gave new possibilities for thorough experimentation [Translator].
2. Read at the Charing Cross Medical School, London, October 1, 1906.

phenomena, the fact must not be overlooked that a systematic appreciation of natural science to the last limits of life will not be able to avoid misconception and opposition from those who are accustomed to regard these phenomena from another point of view and are convinced that this point of view is unassailable.

This is why I feel it obligatory first to explain exactly and clearly my point of view concerning the psychical activities of the higher animals, and secondly to pass from the preliminaries to the subject itself as soon as possible. I have referred intentionally to psychical activities as "so-called." If the naturalist hopes to make a complete analysis of the activity of the higher animals, he has not the right to speak of the psychical processes of these animals, and he can not so speak without deserting the principles of natural science. This is natural science—the work of the human mind applied to nature, and the investigation of nature without any kind of assumption or explanation from sources other than nature itself. Were the investigator to speak of the psychical faculties of the higher animals, he would be transferring ideas from his own inner world to nature, repeating the procedure of his predecessors who were accustomed, on observing nature, to apply to its inanimate phenomena their own thoughts, wishes and sensations. The naturalist must consider only one thing: what is the relation of this or that external reaction of the animal to the phenomena of the external world? This response may be extremely complicated in comparison with the reactions of lower animals, and infinitely complicated in comparison with the reaction of any inanimate object, but the principle involved remains the same.

Strictly speaking, natural science is under obligation to determine only the precise connection which exists between a given natural phenomenon and the response of the living organism to that phenomenon, or, in other words, to ascertain completely how a living being maintains itself in constant equilibrium with its environment. This assertion can hardly be contested, and is further supported by the fact that it receives daily more and more general acceptance in the investigation of the lower and intermediate stages of the zoological scale. The question is simply whether this rule is already applicable to the examination of the higher functions of the higher vertebrates. A serious endeavor to institute inquiries in that direction is, as it appears to me, the only reasonable answer to the question. I and my many collaborators began this work some years ago and we have recently devoted ourselves to it almost exclusively. I would now ask your attention to an account, first, of the

most important results of this inquiry, which seem to me to be very instructive; and secondly, to an account of the inferences which may be drawn from it.

Our experiments have been performed exclusively on the dog, in which the particular reaction used was an unimportant physiologic process—the secretion of saliva. The experimenter was always working with a perfectly normal animal; *i.e.*, an animal which was not subjected to abnormal influences during the experiment. Exact observations on the work of the salivary glands could be made at any moment by means of a simple method. Saliva flows, as we all know, when something is given the dog to eat or is introduced forcibly into his mouth. Both the quality and the quantity of the saliva, under these conditions, is strictly dependent upon the quality and quantity of the substances brought into the dog's mouth. In this well-known physiological process we have before us a reflex. The idea of reflex action as a special elementary function of the nervous system is an old and established truism of physiology. It is the reaction of the organism to the external world, effected through the nervous system, by which an external stimulus is transformed into a nervous process and transmitted along a circuitous route (from the peripheral endings of the centripetal nerve, along its fibers to the apparatus of the central nervous system, and out along the centrifugal path until, reaching one or another organ, it excites its activity). This reaction is specific and permanent. Its specificity is a manifestation of a close and peculiar relation of the external phenomenon to the physiological action, and is founded on the specific sensibility of the peripheral nerve endings in the given nervous chain. These specific reflex actions in normal life, or to state it much more accurately, in the absence of abnormal vital conditions, are constant and unchanging.

The responses of the salivary glands to external influences are, however, not limited by the above-mentioned ordinary reflex actions. We all know that the salivary glands begin to secrete not only when the stimulus of appropriate substances is impressed on the interior surface of the mouth but that they also often begin to secrete when other receptive surfaces, including the eye and the ear, are stimulated. The actions last mentioned are, however, generally considered apart from physiology and receive the name of psychical stimuli.

We shall take another course, and shall endeavor to restore to physiology what properly belongs to it. These exceptional manifestations unquestionably have much in common with ordinary reflex action. Every time that such a flow of saliva begins it is attributable to the occurrence

of some special stimulus among the external influences that may be recognized. On very careful exercise of his attention the observer perceives that the number of spontaneous flows of saliva forms a rapidly diminishing series, and it is in the highest degree probable that those extremely infrequent flows of saliva, for which no particular cause is at first sight apparent, are, in reality, the result of some stimulus invisible to the eye of the observer. From this it follows that the centripetal paths are always stimulated primarily, and the centrifugal paths secondarily, with the interposition, of course, of the central nervous system. Now these are actually all the elements of a reflex action, the only missing points being exact data as to the operation of the stimulus in the central nervous system. Are we familiar with this last mechanism in the ordinary reflexes? Speaking generally, then, our phenomena are reflexes, but the difference between these newly recognized reflexes and the long-known ones is certainly immense, for they have been assigned to quite different departments of science. Physiology has, therefore, before it the problem of evaluating this difference experimentally, and of establishing the essential properties of the reflexes which have been newly recognized.

In the first place they arise from all the body surfaces which are sensitive to stimulation, even from such regions as the eye and the ear, from which an ordinary reflex action affecting the salivary glands is never known to proceed. It must be mentioned that usual salivary reflexes may originate not only from the cavity of the mouth but also from the skin and the nasal cavity; the skin, however, produces this effect only when it is subjected to some destructive process such as cutting or erosion by caustics, while the nasal cavity produces this effect only through the contact of vapors or gases, such as ammonia, which cause local irritation, but never through the agency of usual odors. In the second place, a conspicuous feature of these reflexes is that they are in the highest degree inconstant. All stimuli applied to the mouth of the dog unfailingly give a positive result with reference to the secretion of saliva, but the same objects when presented to the eye, the ear, etc., may sometimes be efficient and sometimes not. In consequence only of the last-mentioned fact have we provisionally called the new reflexes "conditioned reflexes," and for the sake of distinction we have called the old ones "unconditioned."

The further question naturally arose whether the conditions which determine the occurrence of the "conditioned reflexes" could be investigated, and whether a complete knowledge of the conditions would make it possible to impart to these reflexes a character of constancy. This question

must be regarded, it seems to me, as answered in the affirmative. I will remind you of some well-established laws which have already been published from our laboratory. Every conditioned stimulus becomes totally ineffective on repetition. The shorter the interval between the separate repetitions of the conditioned reflex the more quickly is this reflex extinguished. The extinguishing of one conditioned reflex does not affect the operation of the others. Spontaneous restoration of extinguished conditioned reflexes does not occur until after the lapse of one, two, or more hours, but there is a way in which our reflex may be restored immediately. All that is necessary is to obtain a repetition of the *un-conditioned* reflex, as, for instance, by pouring a weak solution of acid into the dog's mouth and then either showing it to him or letting him smell it. The action of the last-mentioned stimulus, which was previously quite obliterated, is now restored in its full extent. The following fact can be regularly observed: If for a long time, such as days or weeks continuously, a certain kind of food is shown to the animal without it being given to him to eat, it loses its power of stimulating from a distance, that is, its power of acting from the eye, the nose, etc. These last-mentioned facts show plainly the close connection which exists between the stimulant effects of various properties of the substance—namely, the effects of the properties which excite secretion of saliva when the substance is in the mouth—and the effects of other properties of the same substance acting upon other receptive surfaces of the body. This material gives us the ground for assuming that the conditioned reflex in some way originates owing to the existence of the unconditioned reflex. And at the same time we may perceive the main features of the mechanism which gives rise to the conditioned reflex. When an object is placed in the mouth of the dog, some of its properties excite the simple reflex apparatus of the salivary glands; and for the production of our conditioned reflex that action must synchronize with the action of other properties of the same object influencing other receptive regions of the body whence the excitation is conveyed to other parts of the central nervous system. Just as the stimulant effects due to certain properties of an object placed in the mouth (unconditioned reflex) may coincide with a number of stimuli arising from other objects, so all these manifold stimuli may by frequent repetition be turned into conditioned stimuli for the salivary glands. Such stimuli may arise from the man who feeds the dog or who forcibly introduces certain articles into the dog's mouth, or they may owe their origin to the general environment in which this takes place. For this reason the above-mentioned experiments, by which the laws of the con-

ditioned reflexes must be determined, require for their performance a well-trained experimenter who can really investigate only the action of the given conditioned stimulus or a definite number of such stimuli, without unconsciously introducing new stimuli with each successive repetition. If this last condition is not realized the laws in question will naturally be obscured. It must be remembered that in feeding a dog or forcing something into his mouth, each separate movement and each variation of a movement may by itself represent a conditioned stimulus. If that is the case, and if our hypothesis as to the origin of the conditioned reflex is correct, it follows that any natural phenomenon chosen at will may be converted into a conditioned stimulus. This has, in effect, been proved to be true. Any visual stimulus, any desired sound, any odor, and the stimulation of any part of the skin, either by mechanical means or by the application of heat or cold, have never failed in our hands to stimulate the salivary glands, although before they were all ineffective for that purpose. This was accomplished by applying the stimuli simultaneously with the action of the salivary glands, their action having been evoked by the giving of certain kinds of food, or by forcing certain substances into the dog's mouth. These artificial conditioned reflexes,[3] the product of our training, showed exactly the same properties as the previously described natural conditioned reflexes. As regards their extinction and restoration they followed essentially the same laws as the natural conditioned reflexes.[4] Thus we have the right to say that our analysis of the origin of conditioned reflexes is proved by the facts.

———————

3. The possibility of establishing these artificial conditioned reflexes was of great importance. First of all it proved that the circumstances which give rise to the conditioned reflex . . . are adequately explained by the proposed theory. Besides this, the intentional formation of conditioned reflexes made possible a more thorough and conscious experimentation [Translator].

4. Professor Pavlov says (*Activity of the Cerebral Hemispheres*, p. 49):

Formerly we made a distinction between "natural" and "artificial" conditioned reflexes; "natural" reflexes being those which appeared to be formed spontaneously as a result of the natural association of, for example, the sight and smell of food with the eating of food itself, or of the procedure of introducing acid or some rejectable substances with the acid or the rejectable substance itself, while "artificial" reflexes were those which could be formed as a result of artificially associating with the food or rejectable substance, stimuli which in the ordinary course of events have nothing in common with food or the rejectable substance. At the present time, however, we know that there is not the slightest difference in properties between all these reflexes. I mention this fact here because the numerous experiments of the earlier period of our work were carried out with the "natural" conditioned reflexes, and it is from these that I shall draw many examples in the present lecture. All the numerous artificial stimuli which we now use every day in our experiments were important to us at the time of those experiments because they provided easily controlled, exact, and regularly reproducible

Now that so much has been adduced on the subject we may advance further than was possible at the outset in the understanding of conditioned reflexes. In the manifestations of nervous energy which have up to the present time been submitted to careful scientific examination (our old specific reflex), the stimuli with which we had to do were comparatively few in number, but very constant in their action, and there was abundant evidence of a constant connection existing between the external influences and definite physiological effects. Now, however, in another more complicated part of the nervous system we encounter a new phenomenon, namely, the conditioned stimulus. On the one hand, this nervous apparatus becomes responsible in the highest degree, *i.e.*, it is susceptible to the most varied external stimuli, but, on the other hand, these stimuli are not constant in their operation and are not definitely associated with certain physiological effects. At any given moment we find comparatively few circumstances favorable for these stimuli becoming active in the organism for a longer or shorter time and producing distinct physiological results.

The introduction of the idea of conditioned stimuli into physiology seems to me to be justified for many reasons. In the first place, it corresponds to the facts that have been adduced, since it represents a direct inference from them. In the second place, it is in agreement with the general mechanical hypotheses of natural science. In many kinds of apparatus and machinery, even of simple construction, certain forces can not develop their action unless at the proper time the necessary conditions are present. In the third place, it is completely covered by the ideas of facilitation (bahnung) and inhibition, ideas which have been sufficiently elaborated in recent physiological literature. Finally, in these conditioned stimuli, looked at from the point of view of general biology, we have a most perfect mechanism of adaptation, or, what amounts to the same thing, a very delicate mechanism for maintaining an equilibrium with the surrounding medium. The body has the capacity to react in a sensitive way to the phenomena of the outer world which are essential to it, because all other phenomena of the outer world, even the most insignificant, coinciding even temporarily with the essential become their indicators or, as they may be called, their signalling stimuli. The delicacy of the reaction shows itself both in the production of the con-

stimuli, and because they could be applied to check the correctness of our conception of the mechanism by which natural conditioned reflexes are formed. At present the artificial stimuli predominate in importance because of the vast field of research they have unfolded to us and because they came ultimately to provide the most important material for our investigation [Translator].

ditioned stimulus and in its disappearance when it ceases to be a proper signal. There must be assumed to exist at this point one of the chief mechanisms for further discrimination in the nervous system. In view of all this, it is permissible, I think, to regard the idea of conditioned stimuli as the fruit of previous labors of biologists, and to consider my present report as illustrating the result of this work on a most complicated subject. It would be unreasonable to attempt to determine at present the limits of the immense field thus opened and to partition it. The following must be regarded as, and nothing more than, a provisional arrangement of material that has been collected, giving only the points indispensable for purposes of explanation.

There are reasons for considering the process of the conditioned reflex to be elementary, namely, a process which consists only in the coincidence of any one of the innumerable indifferent external stimuli with a state of excitation of a point in a definite part of the central nervous system. Now a path is established between the former indifferent stimulus and this given point. The first argument in favor of this hypothesis is the repeated occurrence of this phenomenon: the conditioned reflex may be obtained in all dogs, and it may be produced by all imaginable stimuli. In the second place, there is the certainty of its occurrence; under definite conditions it is reproduced inevitably. We see, therefore, that the process is not complicated by any other (and unknown) conditions. It may here be mentioned that various conditioned stimuli which had been rendered effective were applied at a distance, as from another room; the experimenter, who for the purpose of obtaining the conditioned reflex usually either gave the dog something to eat or put a substance of some kind into the dog's mouth, was not now in close proximity to the animal, but the result of the stimuli was, nevertheless, the same.

It has already been stated that every imaginable phenomenon of the outer world affecting a specific receptive surface of the body may be converted into a conditioned stimulus. After conditioned reflexes had been obtained from the eye, the ear, the nose, and the skin, it was a matter of interest to know what relation the cavity of the mouth had to the general question, and whether a conditioned reflex originated in the mouth. The answer to the inquiry could not be a simple one, because in this case not only the receptive surfaces for the stimuli of the conditioned and of the unconditioned reflex, but also the stimuli themselves were all brought together. Careful observations, however, have made it possible to separate the conditioned stimulus from the unconditioned stimulus even in this instance. When inedible, irritant sub-

stances were many times in succession forcibly introduced into the dog's mouth, we could observe the following facts:

If, for instance, a certain amount of acid was poured into the dog's mouth many times in succession, on each fresh repetition of this procedure, there was regularly a greater flow of saliva; the same thing was repeated on a series of successive days until a certain maximum was attained, whereupon for a considerable time the secretion remained constant. If the experiments were stopped for some days the quantity of saliva secreted became much less. This fact could be very simply explained as follows. On the first administration of the acid solution the secretion of saliva depended principally, or even exclusively, on the unconditioned reflex which the acid caused, while the subsequently occurring increase in secretion pointed to a conditioned reflex gradually formed under the influence of the same acid, and having as its receptor surface also the mouth cavity.

We will now consider the conditions which determine the formation of conditioned reflexes. This question taken comprehensively is naturally a vast one. The following account will serve to give you only a slight idea of the full compass of this vast subject.

Although there are great differences in the time required for the establishing of a conditioned reflex, some relations have been seen to exist. From our experiments it is evident that the intensity of the stimulus is of essential importance. We have some dogs in which the cooling or warming of a definite place on the skin acted as a conditioned stimulus for the salivary glands. A temperature of zero or 1° C. in an experiment repeated 20 or 30 times caused saliva to flow, whilst a temperature of 4° or 5° C. in an experiment repeated 100 times gave no effect whatever. Exactly the same thing occurs with high temperatures. Heat of 45° C. applied as a conditioned stimulus showed similarly no action after even 100 applications; a temperature of 50°, on the other hand, caused a secretion of saliva after from 20 to 30 applications. In contradistinction to this we must state with regard to acoustic stimuli that very loud sounds such as the violent ringing of a bell did not, in comparison with weaker stimuli, quickly establish a conditioned reflex. It can be assumed that powerful acoustic stimuli call out some other important reaction in the body (*e.g.*, motor), which hinders the development of the salivary response.

There is another group of related phenomena which deserves mention. When an odor not naturally exciting the salivary reflex—that of camphor, for instance—is by means of a special apparatus diffused, this

diffusion of the odor must be made to coincide 10 or 20 times with the action of the unconditioned stimulus, such as acid poured into the dog's mouth. But if some of the odoriferous material is added to the acid, the new odor after one or two administrations acts as a conditioned stimulus. It should be asked whether the important circumstance in this experiment is the exact coincidence in time of the conditioned reflex or something else.

For the sake of brevity I will entirely omit the technical details, such as by what methods the conditioned reflexes are best obtained; whether with food or with nonfood substances; how many times the various stimuli may be applied in a day; with what length of intermissions, and so on. Next in order comes the important question, What are the stimuli that the nervous system of the dog recognizes as individual phenomena in the outer world? Or, in other words, What are the elements of a stimulus? With regard to this a good deal of evidence is in existence already. If the application of cold to a definite area of the skin (a circle having a diameter of from four to five centimeters) acts as a conditioned stimulus for the salivary glands, the application of cold to any other portion of the skin causes secretion of saliva on the very first occasion. This shows that the stimulation by cold is generalized over a considerable part of the skin, or perhaps even over the whole of it. But the application of cold to the skin is very clearly distinguished as such from the application of heat and from mechanical stimulation. Each of these stimuli must be elaborated separately in order to give a conditioned reflex. Just as in the case of cold, the application to the skin of heat as a conditioned stimulus also generalizes itself. This is equivalent to saying that if an application made to one place on the skin stimulates the salivary glands, an application made to another cutaneous area will also produce a secretion of saliva. Totally different results were yielded by mechanical stimulation of the skin, such as rubbing with a coarse brush (by means of a special apparatus). When this treatment applied to a certain area of the skin had become converted into a conditioned stimulus, the same treatment applied to another place on the skin remained completely ineffective. Other forms of mechanical stimulation, such as pressure with a sharp or a blunt object, proved themselves less effective. Apparently the first mechanical stimulus formed only a small part of the latter.

Stimulation by musical sounds or by noises is remarkably convenient for determining the discriminating or analytical faculty of the nervous system of the dog. In this respect the precision of our reaction is very great. If a certain note of an instrument is employed as a conditioned

stimulus, it often happens that not only all the notes adjoining it but even those differing from it by a quarter of a tone fail to produce any effect. Musical timbre (quality) is recognized with similar or even with much greater precision. An external agent acts as a conditioned stimulus not only when it comes on the scene but also when it disappears, so that either its beginning or its end may be made the stimulus. Of course, a separate analysis has to be undertaken in order to explain the nature of such stimuli.

We have hitherto spoken of the analytical ability of the nervous system as it presents itself to us in, so to say, a finished state. But we have now accumulated material which contains evidence of a continuous and great increase of this ability if the experimenter persists in sub-dividing and varying the conditioned stimuli. Here, again, is a new field of enormous extent.

In the material relating to the various conditioned stimuli, there are not a few cases in which can be seen an evident connection between the intensity of a stimulus and its effect. As soon as a temperature of 50° C. had begun to provoke a flow of saliva, it was found that even 30° C. had a similar but lesser effect. An analogous result may be observed in cases of mechanical stimulation. A diminished rate of rubbing with the brush (5 strokes instead of 25 to 30 strokes per minute) gives less saliva than the ordinary rate of rubbing, and accelerated rubbing (up to 60 strokes per minute) gives more saliva.

Furthermore, combinations consisting of stimuli of the same kind and also of stimuli of different kinds were tried. The simplest example is a combination of different musical tones, such as a chord consisting of three tones. When this is employed as a conditioned stimulus, the tones played in pairs and each separate tone of the chord produce an effect, but the pairs produce less saliva than the three together, and the notes played separately less than those played in pairs. The case becomes more complicated when we employ as a conditioned stimulus a combination of stimuli of different kinds, that is, of stimuli acting upon different receptive surfaces. Only a few of such combinations have been pro-visionally experimented with. In these cases, one of the stimuli generally became a conditioned stimulus. In a combination in which rubbing and cold were employed the former was preponderant as a conditioned stimulus, while the application of cold taken by itself produced an effect hardly perceptible. But if an attempt is made to convert the weaker stimulus separately into a conditioned stimulus it soon acts energetically. If we now apply the two stimuli together, we have be-fore us an increased effect resulting from the summation of stimuli.

The following problem had for its object the explanation of what happens to an active conditioned stimulus when a new stimulus is added to it. In the cases that we examined we saw that the action of the previously formed conditioned stimulus was disturbed when a new stimulus of like kind was added to it. A new similar odor inhibited the operation of another odor which was already a conditioned stimulus; a new musical note likewise impeded the action of a note employed as a conditioned stimulus, and just previously applied. It is not without interest, I think, to mention that we started with these experiments with another object in view. We were intending to form a new conditioned reflex with the aid of another conditioned reflex which had been previously formed. We accordingly experimented with combinations of dissimilar stimuli. Researches in this direction are well advanced. We have to discriminate between different cases. Some examples may be given. Scratching (or rubbing with a brush) may be a ready and effective conditioned stimulus. When we add to it the ticking of a metronome, applying both stimuli simultaneously, the scratching immediately loses its efficacy as a stimulant during the first applications (first phase); and this loss extends over some days but returns again, notwithstanding the addition of the metronome, and now our double stimulus has nearly the same effect as the scratching alone (second phase); later, scratching, when applied simultaneously with the metronome, ceases to act and the influence of this double stimulus now comes to an end altogether (third phase). When the glare of an ordinary electric lamp is added to scratching which is a conditioned stimulus, the scratching at first produces exactly the same effect as before when it was without the lamp, but afterwards the combination of scratching and the luminous stimulus ceases to act.[5] Apparently a phenomenon of the same kind was observed when the action of other mechanical stimuli was experimented with instead of the scratching which had been made to play the part of a conditioned stimulus. In the first place, secretion of saliva was caused by pressure with a sharp as well as with a blunt object, but to a less degree than by scratching; on repetition, however, the effect of the pressure stimulus became progressively less, until finally, it altogether disappeared.

We may assume that a part of the stimulation by the sharp and blunt

5. As in both these cases the action of the new agent which checks the activity of the conditioned agent, must be especially elaborated by coincidence of the conditioned stimuli with this new agent (in the cases cited, metronome or light) and with lack of activity, *i.e.*, elaborated in a direction opposite to that of the conditioned stimulus, this new agent was designated as a conditioned *inhibitor* and the corresponding process as conditioned inhibition. The building up of this conditioned inhibition [is discussed elsewhere by Pavlov]. [Translator.]

objects was identical with scratching, and that this component was re-
sponsible for the action of these objects during their first applications.
But a part of the action was special; it led in the course of time to a
destruction of the influence of the first. In these inhibitions we see the
following phenomenon which in all experiments of this kind is regularly
repeated. After a conditioned stimulus had been applied together with
another one which inhibited its action, the effect of the first one tried
alone was greatly weakened, and sometimes even arrested completely.
This is either an aftereffect of the inhibiting stimulus which was
added, or it is the extinguishing of the conditioned reflex because in the
experiment with the added stimulus the conditioned reflex had not been
strengthened by the unconditioned reflex.

The inhibition of the conditioned reflex is observed also in the con-
verse case. When you have a combination of agents acting as a condi-
tioned stimulus, in which, as has been already stated, one of the agents
by itself produces almost no effect, then frequent repetition of the power-
fully acting stimulus alone, without the other one, leads to a marked
inhibition of its action, almost to the point of its annihilation. The relative
magnitudes of all these manifestations of stimulation and inhibition are
closely dependent on the conditions under which they originate.

The following is an example. We assume that the stimulus of scratching
is acting as a conditioned reflex in the following manner: In the first place
nothing but scratching was employed for 15 seconds, then acid was
poured into the dog's mouth, scratching being continued up to the
end of one minute. If you now apply scratching for a full minute, you get
a copious secretion of saliva. Try to keep up this reflex, that is, continue
the scratching for a second minute, and only then pour acid into the
dog's mouth. If you do this several times in succession, the effect of the
scratching will quickly diminish during the first minute and will ulti-
mately cease altogether. In order that the scratching may regain its
efficiency during the first minute, it is only necessary to repeat the ex-
periment several times; indeed, its effect will be even greater than it was
in the previous experiments.

We have observed a similar course of events also in the exact measure-
ment of the inhibitory effect.

Finally, it may be mentioned that the attempt was made to form
conditioned reflexes from the traces [6] of the latest remnants or afteref-

6. Trace reflexes are the remnants of the excitations in the central nervous system.
 The traces of the excitation are supposed to function as signals for the setting in of
 the action. As stated in the text, these conditioned trace reflexes have quite peculiar

fects, both of a conditioned and of an unconditioned stimulus. This was accomplished by allowing a conditioned stimulus to act for one minute immediately before the unconditioned stimulus, or by even three minutes earlier. There was always an interval of a few seconds to several minutes between the stimuli. In all these cases the conditioned reflex developed. But in the cases in which the conditioned stimulus was applied three minutes before the unconditioned one, and was separated from the latter by an interval of two minutes, we obtained a result which, although quite unexpected and extremely peculiar, always occurred. When scratching, for example, was applied to a certain spot on the skin as a conditioned stimulus, after it became active we found that scratching of any other place also produced an effect; cold or heat applied to the skin, new musical sounds, optical stimuli, and odors—all these had the same effect as the conditioned stimulus. The unusually copious secretion of saliva and the extremely expressive movements of the animal attracted our attention. During the action of the conditioned stimulus the dog behaved exactly as if the acid which served as the unconditioned stimulus had been actually poured into its mouth.

It may appear that this phenomenon is of a different order from those with which we have hitherto been occupied. The fact is that in the earlier experiments at least one coincidence of the conditioned stimulus with the unconditioned one was necessary; but in these experiments, phenomena which had never occurred simultaneously with an unconditioned reflex were acting as conditioned stimuli. Here an unquestionable difference naturally comes to light, but at the same time there is seen an essential property of these phenomena which they have in common with the former ones, that is, the existence of an easily excitable point in the central nervous system, to which, as a result of its condition, are directed all the essential stimuli from the external world that affect the cells of the highest parts of the brain.

I now bring to a close my cursory and very incomplete summary of the data which have been obtained in this new field of research. Three characteristic features of this subject deeply impress the investigator. In the first place, these phenomena are easily accessible for exact investigation, being in this respect scarcely inferior to the ordinary physiological phenomena. I refer to the ease with which they may be repeated —beyond all expectation—to their uniformity under similar conditions

properties. The reader will meet with references to them at several places throughout the lectures. [Translator.]

of experimentation, and to the fact that they are suitable for experimental analysis. In the second place, there is the possibility of considering this subject objectively. The introduction of a few subjective considerations which we admitted now and again for purposes of comparison seemed on further reflection to be an act of violence or an affront to a serious intellectual endeavor. In the third place, the subject involves an unusual number of stimulating questions for the investigator.

Under what heading is the subject to be classified? To what part of physiology does it correspond? The reply to this question presents no difficulties. It corresponds partly to what was, in former days, the physiology of the special sense organs, and partly to the physiology of the central nervous system.

Up to the present time the physiology of the eye, ear, and other receptor organs has been regarded almost exclusively in its subjective aspect; this presented some advantages, but at the same time, of course, limited the range of inquiry. Investigation by the method of conditioned stimuli in higher animals avoids this limitation, and a number of important questions in this field of research can be at once examined with the aid of all the immense resources which experiments on animals place in the hand of the physiologist. Owing to the shortness of the time that remains it is impossible to give illustrations of such questions. The investigation of conditioned reflexes is even of greater importance for the physiology of the highest parts of the central nervous system. Hitherto this department of physiology, throughout most of its extent, has been cluttered with foreign ideas, borrowed from psychology, but now there is a possibility of its being liberated from such harmful dependence. The conditioned reflexes disclose before us the vast field of the relations and reactions of animals to nature; this is a subject of immense extent and one that must be treated objectively. The physiologist can and must examine these reactions, using in connection with them progressive and systematic removal of parts of the central nervous system in order that he may ultimately arrive at an exact knowledge of the mechanism involved. And here arise at once some urgent and practical questions.

Still one point remains. What relation is there between psychological data and the facts just described? What points of mutual correspondence are there? Who will occupy himself with these relations? and when? This relationship may be interesting even now, but it must be confessed that physiology has at present no serious reason for discussing it. Its immediate problem is to collect and to analyze the endless amount of objective

material which presents itself. But it is plain that the conquest which physiology has yet to make consists for the most part of the actual solution of those questions which hitherto have vexed and perplexed humanity. Mankind will possess incalculable advantages and extraordinary control over human behavior when the scientific investigator will be able to subject his fellow men to the same external analysis as he would employ for any natural object, and when the human mind will contemplate itself not from within but from without.

Must I say something about the relationship which exists between medicine and the subject of my address? Physiology and medicine are fundamentally inseparable. If the physician is in his actual practice, and even more important, in his ideals, a mechanic of the human organism, then inevitably every fresh discovery in physiology will sooner or later increase his power over this extraordinary machine, his power to conserve and repair this mechanism. It is extremely gratifying to me that in honoring the memory of a great naturalist and man of science I am able to make use of ideas and facts which from this single successful point of view promise to throw light upon the highest and most complicated part of the animal mechanism. I am fully persuaded of, and boldly express my confidence in, the ultimate triumph of this new method of research and I avow it the more fearlessly because Thomas Huxley, who is an example to all of us, fought with rare courage for the freedom and the rights of the scientific point of view.

The foregoing comprises Chapter IV
of LECTURES ON CONDITIONED REFLEXES.
Translated by W. Horsley Gantt.

Friedrich Wöhler

1800–1882

Friedrich Wöhler was born near Frankfurt am Main, Germany, in 1800. He studied at Heidelberg, where he worked in Gmelin's laboratory. Gmelin told him that he need not attend the chemistry lectures, as they would be, for him, a waste of time. He took a degree in medicine but was persuaded to devote himself to chemistry. He studied in Sweden and taught at Berlin and Cassel; in 1836 he was appointed professor of chemistry at Göttingen, in which position he remained until his death. He made Göttingen famous for its department of chemistry, and many prominent chemists were trained by him.

Wöhler's greatest single contribution to the science of chemistry was the synthesis of urea, his paper on which follows. This important work was done when he was only twenty-eight. He also, in company with the chemist Justus von Liebig, laid the foundations of organic chemistry—the chemistry of carbon compounds. He isolated, analyzed and studied many elements and compounds, the most notable among them being perhaps aluminum. His studies touched upon practically every known element. In his youth, chemistry was an open field of endeavor. Because of his work and that of others, the science of chemistry was divided into various special fields of investigation; now no man can do the kind of wide-ranging experimentation that Wöhler so much enjoyed.

Wöhler published more than 300 papers and memoirs on chemical subjects. He received many honors. He died in Göttingen on September 23, 1882.

Research gave the unexpected result," Wöhler writes, "that by the combination of cyanic acid with ammonia, urea is formed, a fact

that is noteworthy since it furnishes an example of the artificial production of an organic, indeed a so-called animal substance, from inorganic materials." The fact was indeed noteworthy. For with these few lines, and the short paper that supported them, a new epoch in thought was inaugurated. If an organic substance could be made in the laboratory out of inorganic materials, where was the essential dividing line between life and non-life?

Aristotle held that living things acted in a different way from non-living ones.[1] Each living thing had a principle of life, an entelechy, which naturally defined its form and function. This view was not seriously disputed until the seventeenth century, when Descartes suggested that animals, if not men, were machines subject to the basic mechanical laws that governed all natural things, living or non-living.[2] Descartes' idea was not a popular one. The theory of "vitalism" countered it. To vitalists, the word "machine" expressed exactly what the animal body was not. Living organisms were not governed by physical and chemical laws, but by laws of a completely different kind. Wöhler's three pages delivered an exacting challenge to vitalism.

Wöhler does not mention vitalism. Humbly, in true scientific fashion, he refrains "from the considerations which so naturally offer themselves as a consequence of these facts." He notes, however, with wonderful diffidence, that "from further experiments on these and similar cases, a general law might be deduced." He did not have to plunge into the controversy which continues to our day. He knew what he had done, and he knew also that other men would not refrain from consideration of the consequences of it.

What is life? Is there something mysteriously different about it, or is the difference between living and non-living things merely a matter, as some modern scientists say, of the relative size of molecules? An answer to this question—one which is completely satisfactory to everybody—may never be forthcoming. But the answer, whatever its form, will have to take into account this paper of Wöhler's, written by a twenty-eight-year-old chemist who did not have to attend class because he already knew so much.

[1] See *Great Books of the Western World*, Vol. 8, *On the Soul*, pp. 642–644.
[2] See *Great Books of the Western World*, Vol. 31, *Discourse on Method*, p. 59.

On the Artificial
Production of Urea

In a brief earlier communication, printed in Volume III of these
Annals, I stated that by the action of cyanogen on liquid ammonia, be-
sides several other products, there are formed oxalic acid and a
crystallizable white substance, which is certainly not ammonium cyanate,
but which one always obtains when one attempts to make ammonium
cyanate by combining cyanic acid with ammonia, *e.g.*, by so-called double
decomposition. The fact that in the union of these substances they appear
to change their nature, and give rise to a new body, drew my attention
anew to this subject, and research gave the unexpected result that by
the combination of cyanic acid with ammonia, urea is formed, a fact that
is noteworthy since it furnishes an example of the artificial production of
an organic, indeed a so-called animal substance, from inorganic materials.

I have already stated that the above-mentioned white crystalline sub-
stance is best obtained by breaking down silver cyanate with ammonium
chloride solution, or lead cyanate with liquid ammonia. In the latter way
I prepared for myself the not unimportant amounts employed in this
research. It was precipitated in colourless, transparent crystals, often
more than an inch long. . . .

With caustic soda or chalk this substance developed no trace of am-
monia; with acids it showed none of the breakdown phenomena of
cyanates which occur so easily, namely, the evolution of carbon dioxide
and cyanic acid; neither could the lead and silver salts be precipitated
from it, as from a true cyanate; it could thus contain neither cyanic acid
nor ammonia as such. Since I found that by the last named method of
preparation no other product was formed and the lead oxide was sepa-
rated in a pure form, I imagined that an organic substance might arise by
the union of cyanic acid with ammonia, possibly a substance like a
vegetable salifiable base. I therefore made some experiments from this

point of view on the behaviour of the crystalline substance to acids. But it was indifferent to them, nitric acid excepted; this, when added to a concentrated solution of the substance, produced at once a precipitate of glistening scales. After these had been purified by several recrystallizations, they showed very acid characters, and I was already inclined to take the compound for a real acid, when I found that after neutralization with bases it gave salts of nitric acid, from which the crystallizable substance could be extracted again with alcohol, with all the characters it had before the addition of nitric acid. This similarity to urea in behaviour induced me to make parallel experiments with perfectly pure urea separated from urine, from which I drew the conclusion that without doubt urea and this crystalline substance, or ammonium cyanate, if one can so call it, are absolutely identical compounds.

I will describe the behaviour of this artificial urea no further, since it coincides perfectly with that of urea from urine, according to the accounts of Proust, Prout and others, to be found in their writings, and I will mention only the fact, not specified by them, that both natural and artificial urea, on distillation, evolve first large amounts of ammonium carbonate, and then give off to a remarkable extent the stinging, acetic-acid-like smell of cyanic acid, exactly as I found in the distillation of mercuric cyanate or uric acid, and especially of the mercury salt of uric acid. In the distillation of urea, another white, apparently distinct substance also appears, with the examination of which I am still occupied.

But if the combination of cyanic acid and ammonia actually gives urea, it must have exactly the composition allotted to ammonium cyanate by calculation from my composition formula for the cyanates; and this is in fact the case if one atom of water is added to ammonium cyanate, as all ammonium salts contain water, and if Prout's analysis of urea is taken as the most correct. According to him, urea consists of

Nitrogen	46.650	4 atoms
Carbon	19.975	2 atoms
Hydrogen	6.670	8 atoms
Oxygen	26.650	2 atoms
	99.875	

But ammonium cyanate would consist of 56.92 cyanic acid, 28.14 ammonia, and 14.75 water, which for the separate elements gives

Nitrogen	46.78	4 atoms
Carbon	20.19	2 atoms
Hydrogen	6.59	8 atoms
Oxygen	26.24	2 atoms
	99.80	

One would have been able to reckon beforehand that ammonium cyanate with 1 atom of water has the same composition as urea, without having discovered by experiment the formation of urea from cyanic acid and ammonia. By the combustion of cyanic acid with copper oxide one obtains 2 volumes of carbon dioxide and 1 volume of nitrogen, but by the combustion of ammonium cyanate one must obtain equal volumes of these gases, which proportion also holds for urea, as Prout found.

I refrain from the considerations which so naturally offer themselves as a consequence of these facts, *e.g.*, with respect to the composition proportions of organic substances, and the similar elementary and quantitative composition of compounds of very different properties, as for example fulminic acid and cyanic acid, a liquid hydrocarbon and olefiant gas (ethylene). From further experiments on these and similar cases, a general law might be deduced.

Sir Charles Lyell

1797–1875

Charles Lyell was born in Scotland in 1797, the son of a botanist and translator of Dante. Like his father, he was for a time divided in his choice of a career. At Oxford he studied science, but to earn his bread he prepared for the law. He entered Lincoln's Inn and was called to the bar in 1825. But he had become progressively more drawn to science; and, after a conflict which lasted several years, he gave up the law and devoted himself entirely to geology. His major work, *The Principles of Geology*, was completed, in its first edition at least, by the time he was thirty-six years old.

A great theorist, Lyell was also a painstaking observer. He studied the marine remains of the Italian Tertiary strata and gave the names Eocene, Miocene, and Pliocene to the various ages of the earth. He traveled through Scandinavia and wrote a paper about Swedish mountains. He visited America twice, where he estimated the rate of recession of Niagara Falls, the average yearly increase of the Mississippi Delta, and the composition of the underlying vegetable matter of the Great Dismal Swamp, in Virginia. With another geologist, he discovered the earliest known land shell.

Unlike his friend Charles Darwin, Lyell was knighted by Queen Victoria, and later created a baronet. Though he accepted Darwin's theory—he had, indeed, helped to inspire it with his own work— Lyell was not attacked for his views. It may be that geology is less controversial than anthropology. He died, full of years and honors, on February 22, 1875, and was buried in Westminster Abbey.

Lyell's teacher at Oxford, Dr. Buckland, was a "catastrophist." Catastrophism maintained that the earth's present conformation was

the result of a series of geological crises, ending with the Biblical flood. This was an old idea, and it was still commonly believed in Lyell's youth.

In the centuries before Lyell, men looked at the earth and saw that it was changing, in its main characteristics, very slowly. There was, nevertheless, evidence that it had once been very different. The two facts would not have given trouble if devout Christians had not also believed that the earth was comparatively young. As late as 1800, it was widely held that the world had been created in 4004 B.C. Catastrophism seemed the only way out of the dilemma.

It was impossible to deny the slowness of geological change. Mountains do not rise overnight, and rivers wear away their valleys at a pace imperceptible even to generations. It was also impossible to deny the differences in the past. Marine fossils were discovered high above present sea level. Whole continents had apparently changed their shape. Thus, if catastrophism was unacceptable, something else had to give way.

What gave way was the view of the age of the earth. The effect of Copernicus had been immensely to increase the size of the universe. The effect of Lyell was immensely to increase its age. Lyell's *Principles of Geology* showed, beyond the possibility of reasonable doubt, that the earth was unimaginably old. His later studies, in which he supplied evidence of the antiquity of man, so useful to Darwin, were as nothing to his proofs of the antiquity of fossils like *Pupa vetusta,* the earliest known land shell. If that little shell was as old as he said it was, much that men believed in would have to be given up.

Darwin, for example, received from Lyell a fact essential to his theory of natural selection. Darwin had derived from Malthus the idea that the pressure of environment, the "struggle for existence," might be the cause of selection. But he could not see, as long as he believed that the world was only a few thousand years old, how the evolution of species could have occurred. When he read Lyell,

Notes from the artist: "Lyell's classic work on the nomenclature of geologic periods, which he developed largely through his study of sea-shell deposits, inspired the technique and form of this portrait."

Charles Lyell

his eyes were opened. Now there was plenty of time. Age after age stretched out behind the present, during which the slow, cumulative changes that his hypothesis called for could have taken place.

There may have been other effects of Lyell's work. The Copernican Revolution is said to have been one of the greatest shocks that mankind ever experienced. Infinite space "terrified" Pascal. Was it also disturbing to discover that a man's lifetime, once thought to be a significant portion of the total life of the earth, was no more than an infinitesimal part of it?

On the other hand, if the earth had great antiquity, was it not also reasonable to believe that its future might be equally vast in extent? Those who believed that the world had been created in 4004 B.C. also believed that it would end fairly soon. Was it possible now to envision an almost unlimited future, in which mankind could shape a better, a more just and satisfying, existence?

Geological Evolution
from *The Principles of Geology*

H aving considered, in the preceding volumes, the actual operation of the causes of change which affect the earth's surface and its inhabitants, we are now about to enter upon a new division of our inquiry, and shall therefore offer a few preliminary observations, to fix in the reader's mind the connection between two distinct parts of our work, and to explain in what manner the plan pursued by us differs from that more usually followed by preceding writers on geology.

All naturalists, who have carefully examined the arrangement of the mineral masses composing the earth's crust, and who have studied their internal structure and fossil contents, have recognized therein the signs of a great succession of former changes; and the causes of these changes have been the object of anxious inquiry. As the first theorists possessed but a scanty acquaintance with the present economy of the animate and inanimate world, and the vicissitudes to which these are subject, we find them in the situation of novices, who attempt to read a history written in a foreign language, doubting the meaning of the most ordinary terms; disputing, for example, whether a shell was really a shell, whether sand and pebbles were the result of aqueous trituration, whether stratification was the effect of successive deposition from water; and a thousand other elementary questions which now appear to us so easy and simple that we can hardly conceive them to have once afforded matter for warm and tedious controversy.

In the first volume we enumerated many prepossessions which biassed the minds of the earlier inquirers, and checked an impartial desire of arriving at truth. But of all the causes to which we alluded, no one contributed so powerfully to give rise to a false method of philosophizing as the entire unconsciousness of the first geologists of the extent of their own ignorance respecting the operations of the existing agents of change.

319

They imagined themselves sufficiently acquainted with the mutations now in progress in the animate and inanimate world, to entitle them at once to affirm, whether the solution of certain problems in geology, could ever be derived from the observation of the actual economy of nature, and having decided that they could not, they felt themselves at liberty to indulge their imaginations, in guessing what *might be*, rather than inquiring *what is;* in other words, they employed themselves in conjecturing what might have been the course of nature at a remote period, rather than in the investigation of what was the course of nature in their own times.

It appeared to them more philosophical to speculate on the possibilities of the past, than patiently to explore the realities of the present, and having invented theories under the influence of such maxims, they were consistently unwilling to test their validity by the criterion of their accordance with the ordinary operations of nature. On the contrary, the claims of each new hypothesis to credibility appeared enhanced by the great contrast of the causes or forces introduced to those now developed in our terrestrial system during a period, as it has been termed, of *repose.*

Never was there a dogma more calculated to foster indolence and to blunt the edge of curiosity, than this assumption of the discordance between the former and the existing causes of change. It produced a state of mind unfavourable in the highest conceivable degree to the candid reception of those minute, but incessant mutations, which every part of the earth's surface is undergoing, and by which the condition of its living inhabitants is continually made to vary. The student, instead of being encouraged with the hope of interpreting the enigmas presented to him in the earth's structure, instead of being prompted to undertake laborious inquiries into the natural history of the organic world, and the complicated effects of the igneous and aqueous causes now in operation, was taught to despond from the first. Geology, it was affirmed, could never rise to the rank of an exact science—the greater number of phenomena must for ever remain inexplicable, or only be partially elucidated by ingenious conjectures. Even the mystery which invested the subject was said to constitute one of its principal charms, affording, as it did, full scope to the fancy to indulge in a boundless field of speculation.

The course directly opposed to these theoretical views consists in an earnest and patient endeavour to reconcile the former indications of change with the evidence of gradual mutations now in progress; restricting us, in the first instance, to known causes, and then speculating on

those which may be in activity in regions inaccessible to us. It seeks an interpretation of geological monuments by comparing the changes of which they give evidence with the vicissitudes now in progress, or which may be in progress.

We shall give a few examples in illustration of the practical results already derived from the two distinct methods of theorizing, for we now have the advantage of being enabled to judge by experience of their respective merits, and by the respective value of the fruits which they have produced.

In our historical sketch of the progress of geology, the reader has seen that a controversy was maintained for more than a century, respecting the origin of fossil shells and bones—were they organic or inorganic substances? That the latter opinion should for a long time have prevailed, and that these bodies should have been supposed to be fashioned into their present form by a plastic virtue, or some other mysterious agency, may appear absurd; but it was, perhaps, as reasonable a conjecture as could be expected from those who did not appeal, in the first instance, to the analogy of the living creation, as affording the only source of authentic information. It was only by an accurate examination of living Testacea, and by a comparison of the osteology of the existing verte-brated animals with the remains found entombed in ancient strata, that this favourite dogma was exploded, and all were, at length, per-suaded that these substances were exclusively of organic origin.

In like manner, when a discussion had arisen as to the nature of basalt and other mineral masses, evidently constituting a particular class of rocks, the popular opinion inclined to a belief that they were of aqueous, not of igneous origin. These rocks, it was said, might have been precipitated from an aqueous solution, from a chaotic fluid, or an ocean which rose over the continents, charged with the requisite mineral in-gredients. All are now agreed that it would have been impossible for hu-man ingenuity to invent a theory more distant from the truth; yet we must cease to wonder, on that account, that it gained so many proselytes, when we remember that its claims to probability arose partly from its confirming the assumed want of all analogy between geological causes and those now in action. By what train of investigation were all theorists brought round at length to an opposite opinion, and induced to assent to the igneous origin of these formations? By an examination of the struc-ture of active volcanoes, the mineral composition of their lavas and ejec-tions, and by comparing the undoubted products of fire with the ancient rocks in question.

We shall conclude with one more example. When the organic origin of fossil shells had been conceded, their occurrence in strata forming some of the loftiest mountains in the world, was admitted as a proof of a great alteration of the relative level of sea and land, and doubts were then entertained whether this change might be accounted for by the partial drying-up of the ocean, or by the elevation of the solid land. The former hypothesis, although afterwards abandoned by general consent, was at first embraced by a vast majority. A multitude of ingenious speculations were hazarded to show how the level of the ocean might have been depressed, and when these theories had all failed, the inquiry, as to what vicissitudes of this nature might now be taking place, was, as usual, resorted to in the last instance. The question was agitated, whether any changes in the level of sea and land had occurred during the historical period, and, by patient research, it was soon discovered that considerable tracts of land had been permanently elevated and depressed, while the level of the ocean remained unaltered. It was therefore necessary to reverse the doctrine which had acquired so much popularity, and the un-expected solution of a problem at first regarded as so enigmatical, gave, perhaps, the strongest stimulus ever yet afforded to investigate the ordi-nary operations of nature. For it must have appeared almost as im-probable to the earlier geologists, that the laws of earthquakes should one day throw light on the origin of ·mountains, as it must to the first astronomers, that the fall of an apple should assist in explaining the motions of the moon.

Of late years the points of discussion in geology have been trans-ferred to new questions, and those, for the most part, of a higher and more general nature; but, notwithstanding the repeated warnings of experience, the ancient method of philosophizing has not been materially modified.

We are now, for the most part, agreed as to what rocks are of igneous, and what of aqueous origin, in what manner fossil shells, whether of the sea or of lakes, have been embedded in strata, how sand may have been converted into sandstone, and are unanimous as to other propositions which are not of a complicated nature; but when we ascend to those of a higher order, we find as little disposition, as formerly, to make a strenuous effort, in the first instance, to search out an explanation in the ordinary economy of Nature. If, for example, we seek for the causes why mineral masses are associated together in certain groups; why they are arranged in a certain order which is never inverted; why there are many breaks in the continuity of the series; why different organic re-

mains are found in distinct sets of strata; why there is often an abrupt passage from an assemblage of species contained in one formation to that in another immediately superimposed—when these and other topics of an equally extensive kind are discussed, we find the habit of indulging conjectures, respecting irregular and extraordinary causes, to be still in full force.

We hear of sudden and violent revolutions of the globe, of the instantaneous elevation of mountain chains, of paroxysms of volcanic energy, declining according to some, and according to others increasing in violence, from the earliest to the latest ages. We are also told of general catastrophes and a succession of deluges, of the alternation of periods of repose and disorder, of the refrigeration of the globe, of the sudden annihilation of whole races of animals and plants, and other hypotheses, in which we see the ancient spirit of speculation revived, and a desire manifested to cut, rather than patiently to untie, the Gordian knot.

In our attempt to unravel these difficult questions, we shall adopt a different course, restricting ourselves to the known or possible operations of existing causes; feeling assured that we have not yet exhausted the resources which the study of the present course of nature may provide, and therefore that we are not authorized, in the infancy of our science, to recur to extraordinary agents. We shall adhere to this plan, not only on the grounds explained in the first volume, but because, as we have above stated, history informs us that this method has always put geologists on the road that leads to truth, suggesting views which, although imperfect at first, have been found capable of improvement, until at last adopted by universal consent. On the other hand, the opposite method, that of speculating on a former distinct state of things, has led invariably to a multitude of contradictory systems, which have been overthrown one after the other, which have been found quite incapable of modification, and which are often required to be precisely reversed.

In regard to the subjects treated of in our first two volumes, if systematic treatises had been written on these topics, we should willingly have entered at once upon the description of geological monuments properly so called, referring to other authors for the elucidation of elementary and collateral questions, just as we shall appeal to the best authorities in conchology and comparative anatomy, in proof of many positions which, but for the labours of naturalists devoted to these departments, would have demanded long digressions. When we find it asserted, for example, that the bones of a fossil animal at Oeningen were those of man, and the fact adduced as a proof of the deluge, we are now able at once to

dismiss the argument as nugatory, and to affirm the skeleton to be that of a reptile, on the authority of an able anatomist; and when we find among ancient writers the opinion of the gigantic stature of the human race in times of old, grounded on the magnitude of certain fossil teeth and bones, we are able to affirm these remains to belong to the elephant and rhinoceros, on the same authority.

But since, in our attempt to solve geological problems, we shall be called upon to refer to the operation of aqueous and igneous causes, the geographical distribution of animals and plants, the real existence of species, their successive extinction, and so forth, we were under the necessity of collecting together a variety of facts, and of entering into long trains of reasoning, which could only be accomplished in preliminary treatises.

These topics we regard as constituting the alphabet and grammar of geology; not that we expect from such studies to obtain a key to the interpretation of all geological phenomena, but because they form the groundwork from which we must rise to the contemplation of more general questions relating to the complicated results to which, in an indefinite lapse of ages, the existing causes of change may give rise.

The foregoing consists of Chapter I
from Volume III
of Lyell's PRINCIPLES OF GEOLOGY.

Galileo Galilei

1564–1642

Galileo was born at Pisa, Italy, in 1564, the son of a musician. At a monastery near Florence he received his early education. In 1581, at his father's request, young Galileo began to study medicine at the University of Pisa, but when his passion for mathematics declared itself, he was allowed to follow his own scientific bent. In his first year at the university, he checked the time of the swings of a lamp by his pulse beats, noting that the time was always the same, whatever the amplitude of the swing. He had discovered the isochronism of the pendulum. When poverty obliged him to withdraw from the university in 1585, he gave lectures and published an account of his invention of the hydrostatic balance.

In 1589 he was made mathematical lecturer at the University of Pisa and spent the following two years conducting experiments on falling bodies, which laid the foundations for modern physical science. His results, directly contrary to the doctrine of Aristotle, angered the Aristotelian members of the faculty, and in 1591 he resigned to take the chair of mathematics at Padua. There he taught for eighteen years, established a European reputation as a scientist, and attracted many students.

In 1609, hearing that magnifying glasses were being made in Holland, he built his first telescope. Under this sudden magnification, which was gradually increased to thirty times, thousands of unknown stars were revealed in the Milky Way, and the huge moon and planets became new worlds to conquer. He described his discoveries in the *Starry Messenger* (1610), from which the following selection is taken.

Although Galileo had long since accepted the Copernican hypothesis, he prudently continued to teach the old Ptolemaic system

during his whole stay at Padua. By 1610, however, having just discovered the four satellites of Jupiter, and while regaling in the plaudits of scientists all over Europe, he at last took the bold step of announcing his belief in the Copernican theory. For a time all went well. He even received a lucrative post as court mathematician at Florence, under the Medicis.

Galileo demonstrated the telescope with great success to the ecclesiastical authorities at Rome. But his assertion that the Copernican hypothesis could be reconciled with Scripture brought him into conflict with the theologians. In defense of his position, he quoted the remark of Cardinal Baronius that the "Holy Spirit intended to teach us in the Bible how to go to Heaven, not how the heavens go." In 1615 he was warned by Maffeo Barberini (later Pope Urban VIII) not to defend or even to hold the heretical doctrine that the earth moves around the sun, and he agreed to keep silent on the subject henceforth.

He kept his word up to 1632, when his *Dialogue of the Two Principal Systems of the World* appeared. In this beautifully written dialogue, one speaker defends the Ptolemaic system, whereas the other two uphold the Copernican conception, but in very different ways. One is bold and imaginative, the other cautious—unwilling to go beyond the evidence. Galileo did not identify himself with any of the three characters, but it was clear that his sympathies were divided between the two Copernicans. There were two immediate developments. The book was a dazzling success and admired throughout Europe. Secondly, Galileo was summoned to Rome by the Inquisition. After a trial, he was forced to forswear on his knees "the false doctrine" that the earth moves around the sun and is not the center of the universe. He was placed under house arrest, in which relatively comfortable state he remained for the rest of his life. His real punishment was the compulsion to disavow a profound conviction that his own discoveries had gone far to confirm.

In December, 1633, he was permitted to return to Florence and

Notes from the artist: "Full length portrait of Galileo set in a background including the law of falling bodies, a quadrant, and Galileo's idea for a clock pendulum. The quotation, E pur si muove ('But it does move'), was attributed to Galileo after his recantation in 1632. The small portrait of Copernicus recalls Galileo's defense of the Copernican system."

live in his villa. There he completed his *Dialogues Concerning the Two New Sciences*[1] (1638), which treated of the physical investigations he had begun in his youth. He became blind in 1637 but continued to work on various problems in physics. He died on January 8, 1642, and was buried in the church of Santa Croce, in Florence. Isaac Newton was born on December 25 the same year.

Ancient peoples—the Indians, Egyptians, Assyrians, Persians, Greeks, and Romans—had followed the movements and patterns of the stars with passionate attention. The stars were the abode of the gods and the source of hope. They had guided travelers on sea and land, and the meaning of life and particular destinies had been seen in their constellations and conjunctions. Imagine the sensation caused by the first telescope, which suddenly transformed this immemorial steadfast sky, showing innumerable new stars, revealing satellites revolving about the familiar planets, and the moon scarred by rugged mountain chains and desolate valleys. The heavenly bodies could no longer be regarded as perfect and immutable. Old religions and long revered philosophical doctrines tottered at the spectacle.

Prior to Galileo and his telescope, the Copernican theory, in spite of its beautiful mathematical simplicity, was at a disadvantage. The followers of the old Ptolemaic system could point out that everyone *sees* the sun rise in the morning and set in the evening. Can we not trust our senses? Moreover, the world does *appear* to be the center of the universe. On all sides we see equal spaces. Copernican thinkers could reply that if space is infinite it has no center, and that if it is vast enough, any place you stand in will *appear* to be the center of the universe and will *seem* to be stationary, while the rest of creation moves. Space and motion are relative. If we take the sun to be the center, however, the scheme of the universe becomes far more economical and comprehensible.

But so far there was no *empirical* support for the heliocentric system. Galileo's telescopic discoveries began to turn the tide. His discovery that Jupiter has four satellites (the number has now been increased to twelve), which revolve about that planet, could be taken as a model of what goes on in the heavens. If these four satellites revolve about Jupiter, why may not Jupiter, Saturn, Uranus,

[1] See *Great Books of the Western World*, Vol. 28, pp. 129–260.

Mars, the Earth, Venus, and Mercury revolve about the sun? Would not Galileo's conclusions about the moon, and the shifting of light and shadow on its rugged surface, also favor the Copernican hypothesis?

Galileo's law of falling bodies, the reader will want to keep in mind, furnished in the end the strongest kind of support for the Copernican view, and for Kepler's system of elliptical planetary orbits, which was being evolved at the same time. The idea that the motion of bodies depends on their qualitative nature had been a serious handicap for centuries. Galileo's demonstration that the acceleration of falling bodies depends alone upon the time of fall led the way to Newton's laws of motion—to the modern science of mechanics, including celestial mechanics.

The larger spots on the moon had long been recognized. It was the smaller ones which Galileo discovered, and his measurement of these are renowned for their accuracy. They persuaded him that "the surface of the moon is not smooth, uniform and precisely spherical as a great number of philosophers believe it (and the other heavenly bodies) to be, but is uneven, rough, and full of cavities and prominences, being not unlike the face of the earth. . . ." The evidence offered for this conclusion is a model of careful induction and lucid exposition and takes on added interest today, when close-up lunar photographs have been taken and there is a near prospect of putting men on the moon.

The analogy drawn between the moon and the earth is of great assistance in understanding our "fickle" companion, but it can occasionally mislead. We find Galileo arguing, for example, that the reason we do not see the high mountains of the moon at its periphery may be that our line of vision here passes through a greater thickness of lunar atmosphere (see the diagram on p. 340). But why assume that the moon has an atmosphere? We know today that it has none. Galileo did not need this explanation, for he had just offered another: we may fail to see the peaks at the periphery, just as we fail to see the separate peaks of a mountain chain on earth, when we look at it from a distance.

Galileo's rapid account of his observations and deductions is flushed by the excitement of new and portentous discovery. The moon and Jupiter—the largest planet—are fascinating in themselves, but the *Starry Messenger* is also one of the finest examples of the scientific method in action.

The Starry Messenger

ASTRONOMICAL MESSAGE
*Which contains and explains recent observations
made with the aid of a new spyglass* [1]
*concerning the surface of the moon,
the Milky Way, nebulous stars, and
innumerable fixed stars,
as well as four planets never before seen, and
now named
The Medicean Stars*

Great indeed are the things which in this brief treatise I propose for observation and consideration by all students of nature. I say great, because of the excellence of the subject itself, the entirely unexpected and novel character of these things, and finally because of the instrument by means of which they have been revealed to our senses.

Surely it is a great thing to increase the numerous host of fixed stars previously visible to the unaided vision, adding countless more which have never before been seen, exposing these plainly to the eye in numbers ten times exceeding the old and familiar stars.

It is a very beautiful thing, and most gratifying to the sight, to behold the body of the moon, distant from us almost sixty earthly radii,[2] as if it

1. The word "telescope" was not coined until 1611. A detailed account of its origin is given by Edward Rosen in *The Naming of the Telescope* (New York, 1947). In the present translation the modern term has been introduced for the sake of dignity and ease of reading, but only after the passage in which Galileo describes the circumstances which led him to construct the instrument.
2. The original text reads "diameters" here and in another place. That this error was Galileo's and not the printer's has been convincingly shown by Edward Rosen (*Isis*, 1952, pp. 344 ff.). The slip was a curious one, as astronomers of all schools

were no farther away than two such measures—so that its diameter appears almost thirty times larger, its surface nearly nine hundred times, and its volume twenty-seven thousand times as large as when viewed with the naked eye. In this way one may learn with all the certainty of sense evidence that the moon is not robed in a smooth and polished surface but is in fact rough and uneven, covered everywhere, just like the earth's surface, with huge prominences, deep valleys, and chasms.

Again, it seems to me a matter of no small importance to have ended the dispute about the Milky Way by making its nature manifest to the very senses as well as to the intellect. Similarly it will be a pleasant and elegant thing to demonstrate that the nature of those stars which astronomers have previously called "nebulous" is far different from what has been believed hitherto. But what surpasses all wonders by far, and what particularly moves us to seek the attention of all astronomers and philosophers, is the discovery of four wandering stars not known or observed by any man before us. Like Venus and Mercury, which have their own periods about the sun, these have theirs about a certain star that is conspicuous among those already known, which they sometimes precede and sometimes follow, without ever departing from it beyond certain limits. All these facts were discovered and observed by me not many days ago with the aid of a spyglass which I devised, after first being illuminated by divine grace. Perhaps other things, still more remarkable, will in time be discovered by me or by other observers with the aid of such an instrument, the form and construction of which I shall first briefly explain, as well as the occasion of its having been devised. Afterwards I shall relate the story of the observations I have made.

About ten months ago a report reached my ears that a certain Fleming[3] had constructed a spyglass by means of which visible objects, though very distant from the eye of the observer, were distinctly seen as if nearby. Of this truly remarkable effect several experiences were related, to which some persons gave credence while others denied them. A few days later the report was confirmed to me in a letter from a noble Frenchman at Paris, Jacques Badovere,[4] which caused me to apply my-

had long agreed that the maximum distance of the moon was approximately sixty terrestrial radii. Still more curious is the fact that neither Kepler nor any other correspondent appears to have called Galileo's attention to this error; not even a friend who ventured to criticize the calculations in this very passage.

3. Credit for the original invention is generally assigned to Hans Lippershey, a lens grinder in Holland who chanced upon this property of combined lenses and applied for a patent on it in 1608.

4. Badovere studied in Italy toward the close of the sixteenth century and is said to have been a pupil of Galileo's about 1598. When he wrote concerning the new

self wholeheartedly to inquire into the means by which I might arrive at the invention of a similar instrument. This I did shortly afterwards, my basis being the theory of refraction. First I prepared a tube of lead, at the ends of which I fitted two glass lenses, both plane on one side while on the other side one was spherically convex and the other concave. Then placing my eye near the concave lens I perceived objects satisfactorily large and near, for they appeared three times closer and nine times larger than when seen with the naked eye alone. Next I constructed another one, more accurate, which represented objects as enlarged more than sixty times. Finally, sparing neither labor nor expense, I succeeded in constructing for myself so excellent an instrument that objects seen by means of it appeared nearly one thousand times larger and over thirty times closer than when regarded with our natural vision.

It would be superfluous to enumerate the number and importance of the advantages of such an instrument at sea as well as on land. But forsaking terrestrial observations, I turned to celestial ones, and first I saw the moon from as near at hand as if it were scarcely two terrestrial radii away. After that I observed often with wondering delight both the planets and the fixed stars, and since I saw these latter to be very crowded, I began to seek (and eventually found) a method by which I might measure their distances apart.

Here it is appropriate to convey certain cautions to all who intend to undertake observations of this sort, for in the first place it is necessary to prepare quite a perfect telescope, which will show all objects bright, distinct, and free from any haziness, while magnifying them at least four hundred times and thus showing them twenty times closer. Unless the instrument is of this kind it will be vain to attempt to observe all the things which I have seen in the heavens, and which will presently be set forth. Now in order to determine without much trouble the magnifying power of an instrument, trace on paper the contour of two circles or two squares of which one is four hundred times as large as the other, as it will be when the diameter of one is twenty times that of the other. Then, with both these figures attached to the same wall, observe them simultaneously from a distance, looking at the smaller one through the telescope and at the larger one with the other eye unaided. This may be done without inconvenience while holding both eyes open at the same time; the two figures will appear to be of the same size if the instrument magnifies objects in the desired proportion.

instrument in 1609 he was in the French diplomatic service at Paris, where he died in 1620.

Such an instrument having been prepared, we seek a method of measuring distances apart. This we shall accomplish by the following contrivance.

Let ABCD be the tube and E be the eye of the observer. Then if there were no lenses in the tube, the rays would reach the object FG along the straight lines ECF and EDG. But when the lenses have been inserted, the rays go along the refracted lines ECH and EDI; thus they are brought closer together, and those which were previously directed freely to the object FG now include only the portion of it HI. The ratio of the distance EH to the line HI then being found, one may by means of a table of sines determine the size of the angle formed at the eye by the object HI, which we shall find to be but a few minutes of arc. Now, if to the lens CD we fit thin plates, some pierced with larger and some with smaller apertures, putting now one plate and now another over the lens as required, we may form at pleasure different angles subtending more or fewer minutes of arc, and by this means we may easily measure the intervals between stars which are but a few minutes apart, with no greater error than one or two minutes. And for the present let it suffice that we have touched lightly on these matters and scarcely more than mentioned them, as on some other occasion we shall explain the entire theory of this instrument.

Now let us review the observations made during the past two months, once more inviting the attention of all who are eager for true philosophy to the first steps of such important contemplations. Let us speak first of that surface of the moon which faces us. For greater clarity I distinguish two parts of this surface, a lighter and a darker; the lighter part seems to surround and to pervade the whole hemisphere, while the darker part discolors the moon's surface like a kind of cloud, and makes it appear covered with spots. Now those spots which are fairly dark and rather large are plain to everyone and have been seen throughout the ages; these I shall call the "large" or "ancient" spots, distinguishing them from others that are smaller in size but so numerous as to occur all over the lunar surface, and especially the lighter part. The latter spots had never been seen by anyone before me. From observations of these spots repeated many times I have been led to the opinion and conviction

that the surface of the moon is not smooth, uniform, and precisely spherical as a great number of philosophers believe it (and the other heavenly bodies) to be, but is uneven, rough, and full of cavities and prominences, being not unlike the face of the earth, relieved by chains of mountains and deep valleys. The things I have seen by which I was enabled to draw this conclusion are as follows.

On the fourth or fifth day after new moon, when the moon is seen with brilliant horns, the boundary which divides the dark part from the light does not extend uniformly in an oval line as would happen on a perfectly spherical solid, but traces out an uneven, rough, and very wavy line as shown in the figure below. Indeed, many luminous excrescences extend beyond the boundary into the darker portion, while on the other hand some dark patches invade the illuminated part. Moreover a great quantity of small blackish spots, entirely separated from the dark region, are scattered almost all over the area illuminated by the sun with the exception only of that part which is occupied by the large and ancient spots. Let us note, however, that the said small spots always agree in having their blackened parts directed toward the sun, while on the side opposite the sun they are crowned with bright contours, like shining summits. There is a similar sight on earth about sunrise, when we behold the valleys not yet flooded with light though the mountains surrounding them are already ablaze with glowing splendor on the side opposite the sun. And just as the shadows in the hollows on earth diminish in size as the sun rises higher, so these spots on the moon lose their blackness as the illuminated region grows larger and larger.

Again, not only are the boundaries of shadow and light in the moon seen to be uneven and wavy, but still more astonishingly many bright points appear within the darkened portion of the moon, completely divided and separated from the illuminated part and at a considerable

distance from it. After a time these gradually increase in size and bright-
ness, and an hour or two later they become joined with the rest of the
lighted part which has now increased in size. Meanwhile more and more
peaks shoot up as if sprouting now here, now there, lighting up within the
shadowed portion; these become larger, and finally they too are united
with that same luminous surface which extends ever further. An illustra-
tion of this is to be seen in the figure above. And on the earth,
before the rising of the sun, are not the highest peaks of the mountains
illuminated by the sun's rays while the plains remain in shadow? Does
not the light go on spreading while the larger central parts of those
mountains are becoming illuminated? And when the sun has finally risen,
does not the illumination of plains and hills finally become one? But on
the moon the variety of elevations and depressions appears to surpass in
every way the roughness of the terrestrial surface, as we shall demon-
strate further on.

At present I cannot pass over in silence something worthy of considera-
tion which I observed when the moon was approaching first quarter, as
shown in the previous figure. Into the luminous part there extended a
great dark gulf in the neighborhood of the lower cusp. When I had ob-
served it for a long time and had seen it completely dark, a bright peak
began to emerge, a little below its center, after about two hours. Grad-
ually growing, this presented itself in a triangular shape, remaining com-
pletely detached and separated from the lighted surface. Around it three
other small points soon began to shine, and finally, when the moon
was about to set, this triangular shape (which had meanwhile become
more widely extended) joined with the rest of the illuminated region and
suddenly burst into the gulf of shadow like a vast promontory of light,
surrounded still by the three bright peaks already mentioned. Beyond
the ends of the cusps, both above and below, certain bright points
emerged which were quite detached from the remaining lighted part, as
may be seen depicted in the same figure. There were also a great number
of dark spots in both the horns, especially in the lower one; those nearest
the boundary of light and shadow appeared larger and darker, while
those more distant from the boundary were not so dark and distinct.
But in all cases, as we have mentioned earlier, the blackish portion of each
spot is turned toward the source of the sun's radiance, while a bright
rim surrounds the spot on the side away from the sun in the direction
of the shadowy region of the moon. This part of the moon's surface,
where it is spotted as the tail of a peacock is sprinkled with azure eyes,
resembles those glass vases which have been plunged while still hot into

cold water and have thus acquired a crackled and wavy surface, from which they receive their common name of "ice-cups."

As to the large lunar spots, these are not seen to be broken in the above manner and full of cavities and prominences; rather, they are even and uniform, and brighter patches crop up only here and there. Hence if anyone wished to revive the old Pythagorean [5] opinion that the moon is like another earth, its brighter part might very fitly represent the surface of the land and its darker region that of the water. I have never doubted that if our globe were seen from afar when flooded with sunlight, the land regions would appear brighter and the watery regions darker.[6] The large spots in the moon are also seen to be less elevated than the brighter tracts, for whether the moon is waxing or waning there are always seen, here and there along its boundary of light and shadow, certain ridges of brighter hue around the large spots (and we have attended to this in preparing the diagrams); the edges of these spots are not only lower, but also more uniform, being uninterrupted by peaks or ruggedness.

Near the large spots the brighter part stands out particularly in such a way that before first quarter and toward last quarter, in the vicinity of a certain spot in the upper (or northern) region of the moon, some vast prominences arise both above and below as shown in the figures reproduced below. Before last quarter this same spot is seen to be walled about with certain blacker contours which, like the loftiest mountain-

5. Pythagoras was a mathematician and philosopher of the sixth century B.C., a semilegendary figure whose followers were credited at Galileo's time with having anticipated the Copernican system. This tradition was based upon a misunderstanding. The Pythagoreans made the earth revolve about a "central fire" whose light and heat were reflected to the earth by the sun.

6. Leonardo da Vinci had previously suggested that the dark and light regions of the moon were bodies of land and water, though Galileo probably did not know this. Da Vinci, however, had mistakenly supposed that the water would appear brighter than the land.

tops, appear darker on the side away from the sun and brighter on that which faces the sun. (This is the opposite of what happens in the cavities, for there the part away from the sun appears brilliant, while that which is turned toward the sun is dark and in shadow.) After a time, when the lighted portion of the moon's surface has diminished in size and when all (or nearly all) the said spot is covered with shadow, the brighter ridges of the mountains gradually emerge from the shade. This double aspect of the spot is illustrated in the ensuing figures.

There is another thing which I must not omit, for I beheld it not without a certain wonder; this is that almost in the center of the moon there is a cavity larger than all the rest, and perfectly round in shape. I have observed it near both first and last quarters, and have tried to represent it as correctly as possible in the second of the above figures. As to light and shade, it offers the same appearance as would a region like Bohemia [7] if that were enclosed on all sides by very lofty mountains arranged exactly in a circle. Indeed, this area on the moon is surrounded by such enormous peaks that the bounding edge adjacent to the dark portion of the moon is seen to be bathed in sunlight before the boundary of light and shadow reaches halfway across the same space. As in other spots, its shaded portion faces the sun while its lighted part is toward the dark side of the moon; and for a third time I draw attention to this as a very cogent proof of the ruggedness and unevenness that pervades all the bright region of the moon. Of these spots, moreover, those are always darkest which touch the boundary line between light and shadow, while those farther off appear both smaller and less dark, so that when

7. This casual comparison between a part of the moon and a specific region on earth was later the basis of much trouble for Galileo. Even in antiquity the idea that the moon (or any other heavenly body) was of the same nature as the earth had been dangerous to hold. The Athenians banished the philosopher Anaxagoras for teaching such notions, and charged Socrates with blasphemy for repeating them.

the moon ultimately becomes full (at opposition [8] to the sun), the shade
of the cavities is distinguished from the light of the places in relief by a
subdued and very tenuous separation.

The things we have reviewed are to be seen in the brighter region of
the moon. In the large spots, no such contrast of depressions and promi-
nences is perceived as that which we are compelled to recognize in
the brighter parts by the changes of aspect that occur under varying il-
lumination by the sun's rays throughout the multiplicity of positions
from which the latter reach the moon. In the large spots there exist some
holes rather darker than the rest, as we have shown in the illustrations.
Yet these present always the same appearance, and their darkness is
neither intensified nor diminished, although with some minute differ-
ence they appear sometimes a little more shaded and sometimes a little
lighter according as the rays of the sun fall on them more or less obliquely.
Moreover, they join with the neighboring regions of the spots in a gentle
linkage, the boundaries mixing and mingling. It is quite different with the
spots which occupy the brighter surface of the moon; these, like precipi-
tous crags having rough and jagged peaks, stand out starkly in sharp
contrasts of light and shade. And inside the large spots there are ob-
served certain other zones that are brighter, some of them very bright
indeed. Still, both these and the darker parts present always the same
appearance; there is no change either of shape or of light and shadow;
hence one may affirm beyond any doubt that they owe their appearance
to some real dissimilarity of parts. They cannot be attributed merely to
irregularity of shape, wherein shadows move in consequence of varied
illuminations from the sun, as indeed is the case with the other, smaller,
spots which occupy the brighter part of the moon and which change,
grow, shrink, or disappear from one day to the next, as owing their origin
only to shadows of prominences.

But here I foresee that many persons will be assailed by uncertainty and
drawn into a grave difficulty, feeling constrained to doubt a conclusion
already explained and confirmed by many phenomena. If that part of the
lunar surface which reflects sunlight more brightly is full of chasms (that
is, of countless prominences and hollows), why is it that the western edge
of the waxing moon, the eastern edge of the waning moon, and the entire
periphery of the full moon are not seen to be uneven, rough, and wavy?
On the contrary they look as precisely round as if they were drawn

8. Opposition of the sun and moon occurs when they are in line with the earth be-
tween them (full moon, or lunar eclipse); conjunction, when they are in line on the
same side of the earth (new moon, or eclipse of the sun).

with a compass; and yet the whole periphery consists of that brighter lunar substance which we have declared to be filled with heights and chasms. In fact not a single one of the great spots extends to the extreme periphery of the moon, but all are grouped together at a distance from the edge.

Now let me explain the twofold reason for this troublesome fact, and in turn give a double solution to the difficulty. In the first place, if the protuberances and cavities in the lunar body existed only along the extreme edge of the circular periphery bounding the visible hemisphere, the moon might (indeed, would necessarily) look to us almost like a toothed wheel, terminated by a warty or wavy edge. Imagine, however, that there is not a single series of prominences arranged only along the very circumference, but a great many ranges of mountains together with their valleys and canyons disposed in ranks near the edge of the moon, and not only in the hemisphere visible to us but everywhere near the boundary line of the two hemispheres. Then an eye viewing them from afar will not be able to detect the separation of prominences by cavities, because the intervals between the mountains located in a given circle or a given chain will be hidden by the interposition of other heights situated in yet other ranges. This will be especially true if the eye of the observer is placed in the same straight line with the summits of these elevations. Thus on earth the summits of several mountains close together appear to be situated in one plane if the spectator is a long way off and is placed at an equal elevation. Similarly in a rough sea the tops of the waves seem to lie in one plane, though between one high crest and another there are many gulfs and chasms of such depth as not only to hide the hulls but even the bulwarks, masts, and rigging of stately ships. Now since there are many chains of mountains and chasms on the moon in addition to those around its periphery, and since the eye, regarding these from a great distance, lies nearly in the plane of their summits, no one need wonder that they appear as arranged in a regular and unbroken line.

To the above explanation another may be added; namely, that there exists around the body of the moon, just as around the earth, a globe of some substance denser than the rest of the aether.[9] This may serve to receive and reflect the sun's radiations without being sufficiently opaque to prevent our seeing through it, especially when it is not illuminated.

9. The aether, or "ever-moving," was the special substance of which the sky and all the heavenly bodies were supposed to be made, a substance essentially different from all the earthly "elements." In later years Galileo abandoned his suggestion here that the moon has a vaporous atmosphere.

Such a globe, lighted by the sun's rays, makes the body of the moon appear larger than it really is, and if it were thicker it would be able to prevent our seeing the actual body of the moon. And it actually is thicker near the circumference of the moon; I do not mean in an absolute sense, but relatively to the rays of our vision, which cut it obliquely there. Thus it may obstruct our vision, especially when it is lighted, and cloak the lunar periphery that is exposed to the sun. This may be more clearly understood from the figure below, in which the body of the moon, ABC, is surrounded by the vaporous globe DEG.

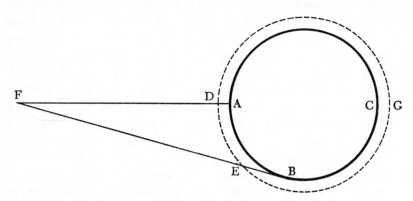

The eyesight from F reaches the moon in the central region, at A for example, through a lesser thickness of the vapors DA, while toward the extreme edges a deeper stratum of vapors, EB, limits and shuts out our sight. One indication of this is that the illuminated portion of the moon appears to be larger in circumference than the rest of the orb, which lies in shadow. And perhaps this same cause will appeal to some as reasonably explaining why the larger spots on the moon are nowhere seen to reach the very edge, probable though it is that some should occur there. Possibly they are invisible by being hidden under a thicker and more luminous mass of vapors.

That the lighter surface of the moon is everywhere dotted with protuberances and gaps has, I think, been made sufficiently clear from the appearances already explained. It remains for me to speak of their dimensions, and to show that the earth's irregularities are far less than those of the moon. I mean that they are absolutely less, and not merely in relation to the sizes of the respective globes. This is plainly demonstrated as follows.

I had often observed, in various situations of the moon with respect to the sun, that some summits within the shadowy portion appeared lighted,

though lying some distance from the boundary of the light. By comparing this separation to the whole diameter of the moon, I found that it sometimes exceeded one-twentieth of the diameter. Accordingly, let CAF be a great circle of the lunar body, E its center, and CF a diameter, which is to the diameter of the earth as two is to seven.

Since according to very precise observations the diameter of the earth is seven thousand miles, CF will be two thousand, CE one thousand, and one-twentieth of CF will be one hundred miles. Now let CF be the diameter of the great circle which divides the light part of the moon from the dark part (for because of the very great distance of the

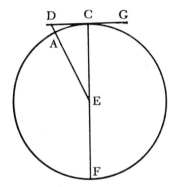

sun from the moon, this does not differ appreciably from a great circle), and let A be distant from C by one-twentieth of this. Draw the radius EA, which, when produced, cuts the tangent line GCD (representing the illuminating ray) in the point D. Then the arc CA, or rather the straight line CD, will consist of one hundred units whereof CE contains one thousand, and the sum of the squares of DC and CE will be 1,010,000. This is equal to the square of DE; hence ED will exceed 1,004, and AD will be more than four of those units of which CE contains one thousand. Therefore the altitude AD on the moon, which represents a summit reaching up to the solar ray GCD and standing at the distance CD from C, exceeds four miles. But on the earth we have no mountains which reach to a perpendicular height of even one mile.[10] Hence it is quite clear that the prominences on the moon are loftier than those on the earth.

10. Galileo's estimate of four miles for the height of some lunar mountains was a very good one. His remark about the maximum height of mountains on the earth was, however, quite mistaken. An English propagandist for his views, John Wilkins, took pains to correct this error in his anonymous *Discovery of a New World* . . . *in the Moon* (London, 1638), Prop. ix.

Here I wish to assign the cause of another lunar phenomenon well worthy of notice. I observed this not just recently, but many years ago, and pointed it out to some of my friends and pupils, explaining it to them and giving its true cause. Yet since it is rendered more evident and easier to observe with the aid of the telescope, I think it not unsuitable for introduction in this place, especially as it shows more clearly the connection between the moon and the earth.

When the moon is not far from the sun, just before or after new moon, its globe offers itself to view not only on the side where it is adorned with shining horns, but a certain faint light is also seen to mark out the periphery of the dark part which faces away from the sun, separating this from the darker background of the aether. Now if we examine the matter more closely, we shall see that not only does the extreme limb of the shaded side glow with this uncertain light, but the entire face of the moon (including the side which does not receive the glare of the sun) is whitened by a not inconsiderable gleam. At first glance only a thin luminous circumference appears, contrasting with the darker sky coterminous with it; the rest of the surface appears darker from its contact with the shining horns which distract our vision. But if we place ourselves so as to interpose a roof or chimney or some other object at a considerable distance from the eye, the shining horns may be hidden while the rest of the lunar globe remains exposed to view. It is then found that this region of the moon, though deprived of sunlight, also shines not a little. The effect is heightened if the gloom of night has already deepened through departure of the sun, for in a darker field a given light appears brighter.

Moreover, it is found that this secondary light of the moon (so to speak) is greater according as the moon is closer to the sun. It diminishes more and more as the moon recedes from that body until, after the first quarter and before the last, it is seen very weakly and uncertainly even when observed in the darkest sky. But when the moon is within sixty degrees of the sun it shines remarkably, even in twilight; so brightly indeed that with the aid of a good telescope one may distinguish the large spots. This remarkable gleam has afforded no small perplexity to philosophers, and in order to assign a cause for it some have offered one idea and some another. Some would say it is an inherent and natural light of the moon's own; others, that it is imparted by Venus; others yet, by all the stars together; and still others derive it from the sun, whose rays they would have permeate the thick solidity of the moon. But statements of this sort are refuted and their falsity evinced with little difficulty.

For if this kind of light were the moon's own, or were contributed by the stars, the moon would retain it and would display it particularly during eclipses, when it is left in an unusually dark sky. This is contradicted by experience, for the brightness which is seen on the moon during eclipses is much fainter and is ruddy, almost copper-colored, while this is brighter and whitish. Moreover the other light is variable and movable, for it covers the face of the moon in such a way that the place near the edge of the earth's shadow is always seen to be brighter than the rest of the moon; this undoubtedly results from contact of the tangent solar rays with some denser zone which girds the moon about.[11] By this contact a sort of twilight is diffused over the neighboring regions of the moon, just as on earth a sort of crepuscular light is spread both morning and evening; but with this I shall deal more fully in my book on the system of the world.[12]

To assert that the moon's secondary light is imparted by Venus is so childish as to deserve no reply. Who is so ignorant as not to understand that from new moon to a separation of sixty degrees between moon and sun, no part of the moon which is averted from the sun can possibly be seen from Venus? And it is likewise unthinkable that this light should depend upon the sun's rays penetrating the thick solid mass of the moon, for then this light would never dwindle, inasmuch as one hemisphere of the moon is always illuminated except during lunar eclipses. And the light does diminish as the moon approaches first quarter, becoming completely obscured after that is passed.

Now since the secondary light does not inherently belong to the moon, and is not received from any star or from the sun, and since in the whole universe there is no other body left but the earth, what must we conclude? What is to be proposed? Surely we must assert that the lunar body (or any other dark and sunless orb) is illuminated by the earth. Yet what is there so remarkable about this? The earth, in fair and grateful exchange, pays back to the moon an illumination similar to that which it receives from her throughout nearly all the darkest gloom of night.

Let us explain this matter more fully. At conjunction the moon occu-

11. Kepler had correctly accounted for the existence of this light and its ruddy color. It is caused by refraction of sunlight in the earth's atmosphere, and does not require a lunar atmosphere as supposed by Galileo.

12. The book thus promised was destined not to appear for more than two decades. Events which will presently be recounted prevented its publication for many years, and then it had to be modified to present the arguments for both the Ptolemaic and Copernican systems instead of just the latter as Galileo here planned. Even then it was suppressed, and the author was condemned to life imprisonment.

pies a position between the sun and the earth; it is then illuminated by the sun's rays on the side which is turned away from the earth. The other hemisphere, which faces the earth, is covered with darkness; hence the moon does not illuminate the surface of the earth at all. Next, departing gradually from the sun, the moon comes to be lighted partly upon the side it turns toward us, and its whitish horns, still very thin, illuminate the earth with a faint light. The sun's illumination of the moon increasing now as the moon approaches first quarter, a reflection of that light to the earth also increases. Soon the splendor on the moon extends into a semicircle, and our nights grow brighter; at length the entire visible face of the moon is irradiated by the sun's resplendent rays, and at full moon the whole surface of the earth shines in a flood of moonlight. Now the moon, waning, sends us her beams more weakly, and the earth is less strongly lighted; at length the moon returns to conjunction with the sun, and black night covers the earth.

In this monthly period, then, the moonlight gives us alternations of brighter and fainter illumination; and the benefit is repaid by the earth in equal measure. For while the moon is between us and the sun (at new moon), there lies before it the entire surface of that hemisphere of the earth which is exposed to the sun and illuminated by vivid rays. The moon receives the light which this reflects, and thus the nearer hemisphere of the moon—that is, the one deprived of sunlight—appears by virtue of this illumination to be not a little luminous. When the moon is ninety degrees away from the sun it sees but half the earth illuminated (the western half), for the other (the eastern half) is enveloped in night. Hence the moon itself is illuminated less brightly from the earth, and as a result its secondary light appears fainter to us. When the moon is in opposition to the sun, it faces a hemisphere of the earth that is steeped in the gloom of night, and if this position occurs in the plane of the ecliptic the moon will receive no light at all, being deprived of both the solar and the terrestrial rays. In its various other positions with respect to the earth and sun, the moon receives more or less light according as it faces a greater or smaller portion of the illuminated hemisphere of the earth. And between these two globes a relation is maintained such that whenever the earth is most brightly lighted by the moon, the moon is least lighted by the earth, and vice versa.

Let these few remarks suffice us here concerning this matter, which will be more fully treated in our *System of the World*. In that book, by a multitude of arguments and experiences, the solar reflection from the

earth will be shown to be quite real—against those who argue that the earth must be excluded from the dancing whirl of stars for the specific reason that it is devoid of motion and of light. We shall prove the earth to be a wandering body surpassing the moon in splendor, and not the sink of all dull refuse of the universe; this we shall support by an infinitude of arguments drawn from nature.

Thus far we have spoken of our observations concerning the body of the moon. Let us now set forth briefly what has thus far been observed regarding the fixed stars. And first of all, the following fact deserves consideration: The stars, whether fixed or wandering,[13] appear not to be enlarged by the telescope in the same proportion as that in which it magnifies other objects, and even the moon itself. In the stars this enlargement seems to be so much less that a telescope which is sufficiently powerful to magnify other objects a hundredfold is scarcely able to enlarge the stars four or five times. The reason for this is as follows.

When stars are viewed by means of unaided natural vision, they present themselves to us not as of their simple (and, so to speak, their physical) size, but as irradiated by a certain fulgor and as fringed with sparkling rays, especially when the night is far advanced. From this they appear larger than they would if stripped of those adventitious hairs of light, for the angle at the eye is determined not by the primary body of the star but by the brightness which extends so widely about it. This appears quite clearly from the fact that when stars first emerge from twilight at sunset they look very small, even if they are of the first magnitude; Venus itself, when visible in broad daylight, is so small as scarcely to appear equal to a star of the sixth magnitude. Things fall out differently with other objects, and even with the moon itself; these, whether seen in daylight or the deepest night, appear always of the same bulk. Therefore the stars are seen crowned among shadows, while daylight is able to remove their headgear; and not daylight alone, but any thin cloud that interposes itself between a star and the eye of the observer. The same effect is produced by black veils or colored glasses, through the interposition of which obstacles the stars are abandoned by their surrounding brilliance. A telescope similarly accomplishes the same result. It removes from the stars their adventitious and accidental rays, and then it enlarges their simple globes (if indeed the stars are naturally globular) so that they seem to be magnified in a lesser ratio than other objects.

13. That is, planets. Among these bodies Galileo counted his newly discovered satellites of Jupiter. The term "satellites" was introduced somewhat later by Kepler.

In fact a star of the fifth or sixth magnitude when seen through a telescope presents itself as one of the first magnitude.

Deserving of notice also is the difference between the appearances of the planets and of the fixed stars.[14] The planets show their globes perfectly round and definitely bounded, looking like little moons, spherical and flooded all over with light; the fixed stars are never seen to be bounded by a circular periphery, but have rather the aspect of blazes whose rays vibrate about them and scintillate a great deal. Viewed with a telescope they appear of a shape similar to that which they present to the naked eye, but sufficiently enlarged so that a star of the fifth or sixth magnitude seems to equal the Dog Star, largest of all the fixed stars. Now, in addition to stars of the sixth magnitude, a host of other stars are perceived through the telescope which escape the naked eye; these are so numerous as almost to surpass belief. One may, in fact, see more of them than all the stars included among the first six magnitudes. The largest of these, which we may call stars of the seventh magnitude, or the first magnitude of invisible stars, appear through the telescope as larger and brighter than stars of the second magnitude when the latter are viewed with the naked eye. In order to give one or two proofs of their almost inconceivable number, I have adjoined pictures of two constellations. With these as samples, you may judge of all the others.

In the first I had intended to depict the entire constellation of Orion, but I was overwhelmed by the vast quantity of stars and by limitations of time, so I have deferred this to another occasion. There are more than five hundred new stars distributed among the old ones within limits of one or two degrees of arc. Hence to the three stars in the Belt of Orion and the six in the Sword which were previously known, I have added eighty adjacent stars discovered recently, preserving the intervals between them as exactly as I could. To distinguish the known or ancient stars, I have depicted them larger and have outlined them doubly; the other (invisible) stars I have drawn smaller and without the extra line. I have also preserved differences of magnitude as well as possible.

In the second example I have depicted the six stars of Taurus known as the Pleiades (I say six, inasmuch as the seventh is hardly ever visible) which lie within very narrow limits in the sky. Near them are more than

14. Fixed stars are so distant that their light reaches the earth as from dimensionless points. Hence their images are not enlarged by even the best telescopes, which serve only to gather more of their light and in that way increase their visibility. Galileo was never entirely clear about this distinction. Nevertheless, by applying his knowledge of the effects described here, he greatly reduced the prevailing overestimation of visual dimensions of stars and planets.

forty others, invisible, no one of which is much more than half a degree away from the original six. I have shown thirty-six of these in the diagram [p. 348]; as in the case of Orion I have preserved their intervals and magnitudes, as well as the distinction between old stars and new.

Third, I have observed the nature and the material of the Milky Way. With the aid of the telescope this has been scrutinized so directly and

The Belt and Sword of Orion

with such ocular certainty that all the disputes which have vexed philosophers through so many ages have been resolved, and we are at last freed from wordy debates about it. The galaxy is, in fact, nothing but a congeries of innumerable stars grouped together in clusters. Upon whatever part of it the telescope is directed, a vast crowd of stars is immediately presented to view. Many of them are rather large and quite bright, while the number of smaller ones is quite beyond calculation.

But it is not only in the Milky Way that whitish clouds are seen; several

patches of similar aspect shine with faint light here and there throughout
the aether, and if the telescope is turned upon any of these it confronts
us with a tight mass of stars. And what is even more remarkable, the
stars which have been called "nebulous" by every astronomer up to this
time turn out to be groups of very small stars arranged in a wonderful
manner. Although each star separately escapes our sight on account of
its smallness or the immense distance from us, the mingling of their
rays gives rise to that gleam which was formerly believed to be some
denser part of the aether that was capable of reflecting rays from stars or
from the sun. I have observed some of these constellations and have
decided to depict two of them [see opposite page].

The Pleiades

In the first you have the nebula called the Head of Orion, in which I
have counted twenty-one stars. The second contains the nebula called
Praesepe,[15] which is not a single star but a mass of more than forty
starlets. Of these I have shown thirty-six, in addition to the Aselli, ar-
ranged in the order shown.

We have now briefly recounted the observations made thus far with
regard to the moon, the fixed stars, and the Milky Way. There remains
the matter which in my opinion deserves to be considered the most im-
portant of all—the disclosure of four Planets never seen from the creation
of the world up to our own time, together with the occasion of my hav-
ing discovered and studied them, their arrangements, and the observa-

15. Praesepe, "the Manger," is a small whitish cluster of stars lying between the two
 Aselli (ass-colts) which are imagined as feeding from it. It lies in the constellation
 Cancer.

tions made of their movements and alterations during the past two months. I invite all astronomers to apply themselves to examine them and determine their periodic times, something which has so far been quite impossible to complete, owing to the shortness of the time. Once more, however, warning is given that it will be necessary to have a very accurate telescope such as we have described at the beginning of this discourse.

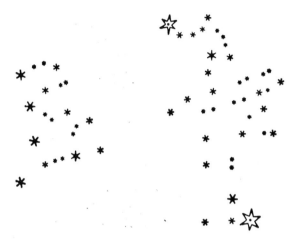

Nebula of Orion *Nebula of Praesepe*

On the seventh day of January in this present year 1610, at the first hour of night, when I was viewing the heavenly bodies with a telescope, Jupiter presented itself to me; and because I had prepared a very excellent instrument for myself, I perceived (as I had not before, on account of the weakness of my previous instrument) that beside the planet there were three starlets, small indeed, but very bright. Though I believed them to be among the host of fixed stars, they aroused my curiosity somewhat by appearing to lie in an exact straight line parallel to the ecliptic, and by their being more splendid than others of their size. Their arrangement with respect to Jupiter and each other was the following:

that is, there were two stars on the eastern side and one to the west. The most easterly star and the western one appeared larger than the other. I paid no attention to the distances between them and Jupiter, for at the

outset I thought them to be fixed stars, as I have said.[16] But returning to
the same investigation on January eighth—led by what, I do not know—I
found a very different arrangement. The three starlets were now all to the
west of Jupiter, closer together, and at equal intervals from one another
as shown in the following sketch:

East ● ✳ ✳ ✳ *West*

At this time, though I did not yet turn my attention to the way the
stars had come together, I began to concern myself with the question
how Jupiter could be east of all these stars when on the previous day it
had been west of two of them. I commenced to wonder whether Jupiter
was not moving eastward at that time, contrary to the computations
of the astronomers, and had got in front of them by that motion.[17]
Hence it was with great interest that I awaited the next night. But I was
disappointed in my hopes, for the sky was then covered with clouds
everywhere.

On the tenth of January, however, the stars appeared in this position
with respect to Jupiter:

East ✳ ✳ ● *West*

that is, there were but two of them, both easterly, the third (as I sup-
posed) being hidden behind Jupiter. As at first, they were in the same
straight line with Jupiter and were arranged precisely in the line of the
zodiac. Noticing this, and knowing that there was no way in which
such alterations could be attributed to Jupiter's motion, yet being certain
that these were still the same stars I had observed (in fact no other was to
be found along the line of the zodiac for a long way on either side of
Jupiter), my perplexity was now transformed into amazement. I was sure
that the apparent changes belonged not to Jupiter but to the observed
stars, and I resolved to pursue this investigation with greater care and
attention.

And thus, on the eleventh of January, I saw the following disposition:

16. The reader should remember that the telescope was nightly revealing to Galileo
hundreds of fixed stars never previously observed. His unusual gifts for astronom-
ical observation are illustrated by his having noticed and remembered these three
merely by reason of their alignment, and recalling them so well that when by
chance he happened to see them the following night he was certain that they had
changed their positions. No such plausible and candid account of the discovery was
given by the rival astronomer Simon Mayr, who four years later claimed priority.
17. Jupiter was at this time in "retrograde" motion; that is, the earth's motion made
the planet appear to be moving westward among the fixed stars.

East ✷ ✶ ⬤ *West*

There were two stars, both to the east, the central one being three times as far from Jupiter as from the one farther east. The latter star was nearly double the size of the former, whereas on the night before they had appeared approximately equal.

I had now decided beyond all question that there existed in the heavens three stars wandering about Jupiter as do Venus and Mercury about the sun, and this became plainer than daylight from observations on similar occasions which followed. Nor were there just three such stars; four wanderers complete their revolutions about Jupiter, and of their alterations as observed more precisely later on we shall give a description here. Also I measured the distances between them by means of the telescope, using the method explained before. Moreover I recorded the times of the observations, especially when more than one was made during the same night—for the revolutions of these planets are so speedily completed that it is usually possible to take even their hourly variations.

Thus on the twelfth of January at the first hour of night I saw the stars arranged in this way:

East ✷ ✶⬤ ✷ *West*

The most easterly star was larger than the western one, though both were easily visible and quite bright. Each was about two minutes of arc distant from Jupiter. The third star was invisible at first, but commenced to appear after two hours; it almost touched Jupiter on the east, and was quite small. All were on the same straight line directed along the ecliptic.

On the thirteenth of January four stars were seen by me for the first time, in this situation relative to Jupiter:

East ✷ ⬤✷✷✷ *West*

Three were westerly and one was to the east; they formed a straight line except that the middle western star departed slightly toward the north. The eastern star was two minutes of arc away from Jupiter, and the intervals of the rest from one another and from Jupiter were about one minute. All the stars appeared to be of the same magnitude, and though small were very bright, much brighter than fixed stars of the same size.[18]

18. Galileo's day-by-day journal of observations continued in unbroken sequence until ten days before publication of the book, which he remained in Venice to supervise. The observations omitted here contained nothing of a novel character.

On the twenty-sixth of February, midway in the first hour of night, there were only two stars:

East * ● * West

One was to the east, ten minutes from Jupiter; the other to the west, six minutes away. The eastern one was somewhat smaller than the western. But at the fifth hour three stars were seen:

East * ●* * West

In addition to the two already noticed, a third was discovered to the west near Jupiter; it had at first been hidden behind Jupiter and was now one minute away. The eastern one appeared farther away than before, being eleven minutes from Jupiter.

This night for the first time I wanted to observe the progress of Jupiter and its accompanying planets along the line of the zodiac in relation to some fixed star, and such a star was seen to the east, eleven minutes distant from the easterly starlet and a little removed toward the south, in the following manner:

East * ●* * West

 ★

On the twenty-seventh of February, four minutes after the first hour, the stars appeared in this configuration:

East * *● ** West

 ★

The most easterly was ten minutes from Jupiter; the next, thirty seconds; the next to the west was two minutes thirty seconds from Jupiter, and the most westerly was one minute from that. Those nearest Jupiter appeared very small, while the end ones were plainly visible, especially the westernmost. They marked out an exactly straight line along the course of the ecliptic. The progress of these planets toward the east is seen quite clearly by reference to the fixed star mentioned, since Jupiter and its accompanying planets were closer to it, as may be seen in the figure above. At the fifth hour, the eastern star closer to Jupiter was one minute away.

At the first hour on February twenty-eighth, two stars only were seen; one easterly, distant nine minutes from Jupiter, and one to the west, two minutes away. They were easily visible and on the same

straight line. The fixed star, perpendicular to this line, now fell under
the eastern planet as in this figure:

East ✱ ⬤ ✱ *West*

★

At the fifth hour a third star, two minutes east of Jupiter, was seen in
this position:

East ✱ ✱ ⬤ ✱ *West*

On the first of March, forty minutes after sunset, four stars all to the
east were seen, of which the nearest to Jupiter was two minutes away,
the next was one minute from this, the third two seconds from that and
brighter than any of the others; from this in turn the most easterly was
four minutes distant, and it was smaller than the rest. They marked
out almost a straight line, but the third one counting from Jupiter was a
little to the north. The fixed star formed an equilateral triangle with
Jupiter and the most easterly star, as in this figure:

East ✱ ✴✱✱ ⬤ *West*

★

On March second, half an hour after sunset, there were three planets,
two to the east and one to the west, in this configuration:

East ✴✱ ⬤ ✱ *West*

★

The most easterly was seven minutes from Jupiter and thirty seconds
from its neighbor; the western one was two minutes away from Jupiter.
The end stars were very bright and were larger than that in the middle,
which appeared very small. The most easterly star appeared a little
elevated toward the north from the straight line through the other
planets and Jupiter. The fixed star previously mentioned was eight min-
utes from the western planet along the line drawn from it perpen-
dicularly to the straight line through all the planets, as shown above.

I have reported these relations of Jupiter and its companions with the fixed star so that anyone may comprehend that the progress of those planets, both in longitude and latitude, agrees exactly with the movements derived from planetary tables.

Such are the observations concerning the four Medicean planets recently first discovered by me, and although from these data their periods have not yet been reconstructed in numerical form, it is legitimate at least to put in evidence some facts worthy of note. Above all, since they sometimes follow and sometimes precede Jupiter by the same intervals, and they remain within very limited distances either to east or west of Jupiter, accompanying that planet in both its retrograde and direct movements in a constant manner, no one can doubt that they complete their revolutions about Jupiter and at the same time effect all together a twelve-year period about the center of the universe. That they also revolve in unequal circles is manifestly deduced from the fact that at the greatest elongation [19] from Jupiter it is never possible to see two of these planets in conjunction, whereas in the vicinity of Jupiter they are found united two, three, and sometimes all four together. It is also observed that the revolutions are swifter in those planets which describe smaller circles about Jupiter, since the stars closest to Jupiter are usually seen to the east when on the previous day they appeared to the west, and vice versa, while the planet which traces the largest orbit appears upon accurate observation of its returns to have a semimonthly period.

Here we have a fine and elegant argument for quieting the doubts of those who, while accepting with tranquil mind the revolutions of the planets about the sun in the Copernican system, are mightily disturbed to have the moon alone revolve about the earth and accompany it in an annual rotation about the sun. Some have believed that this structure of the universe should be rejected as impossible. But now we have not just one planet rotating about another while both run through a great orbit around the sun; our own eyes show us four stars which wander around Jupiter as does the moon around the earth, while all together trace out a grand revolution about the sun in the space of twelve years.

And finally we should not omit the reason for which the Medicean stars appear sometimes to be twice as large as at other times, though their orbits about Jupiter are very restricted. We certainly cannot seek the cause in terrestrial vapors, as Jupiter and its neighboring fixed stars are not seen to change size in the least while this increase and diminution are tak-

19. By this is meant the greatest angular separation from Jupiter attained by any of the satellites.

ing place. It is quite unthinkable that the cause of variation should be their change of distance from the earth at perigee and apogee, since a small circular rotation could by no means produce this effect, and an oval motion (which in this case would have to be nearly straight) seems unthinkable and quite inconsistent with the appearances.[20] But I shall gladly explain what occurs to me on this matter, offering it freely to the judgment and criticism of thoughtful men. It is known that the interposition of terrestrial vapors makes the sun and moon appear large, while the fixed stars and planets are made to appear smaller. Thus the two great luminaries are seen larger when close to the horizon, while the stars appear smaller and for the most part hardly visible. Hence the stars appear very feeble by day and in twilight, though the moon does not, as we have said. Now from what has been said above, and even more from what we shall say at greater length in our *System*, it follows that not only the earth but also the moon is surrounded by an envelope of vapors, and we may apply precisely the same judgment to the rest of the planets. Hence it does not appear entirely impossible to assume that around Jupiter also there exists an envelope denser than the rest of the aether, about which the Medicean planets revolve as does the moon about the elemental sphere. Through the interposition of this envelope they appear larger when they are in perigee by the removal, or at least the attenuation, of this envelope.

Time prevents my proceeding further, but the gentle reader may expect more soon.

20. The marked variation in brightness of the satellites which Galileo observed may be attributed mainly to markings upon their surfaces, though this was not determined until two centuries later. The mention here of a possible oval shape of the orbits is the closest Galileo ever came to accepting Kepler's great discovery of the previous year. Even here, however, he was probably not thinking of Kepler's work but of an idea proposed by earlier astronomers for the moon and the planet Venus.

Translated by Stillman Drake.

Tommaso Campanella

1568–1639

Campanella, Italian philosopher, was born at Stilo, Calabria, in 1568. He became a member of the Dominican Order in 1582. The chance reading of a work of natural philosophy called *De Rerum Natura* by one Telesio is said to have changed his view of the world. Telesio's work appealed to nature rather than to authority, and Campanella defended its author in a book titled *Philosophy Demonstrated According to the Senses* (1591). This book, and his own opposition to the authorities, required his departure from Naples for Rome and other Italian cities in the following years. He returned to Naples in 1598 and was implicated, perhaps unjustly, in a plot to free the city from Spanish rule. He was convicted, sentenced to prison, and remained there for twenty-eight years. During this time he composed a sonnet series and most of his philosophical works, including the *Defense of Galileo,* from which the following selection is taken.

Campanella never denied—indeed he always supported—the temporal power of the pope. On his release from prison, he found favor with Pope Urban VIII. The latter persuaded Campanella to go to Paris upon the outbreak of a new conspiracy. There he was well received by Cardinal Richelieu. Campanella died in Paris, while engaged in preparing a complete edition of his works, on May 21, 1639.

Campanella was widely read in the scientific literature of his day. He rejected Aristotelianism in the study of man and nature, preferring instead direct recourse to the subject of inquiry. He accepted the authority of faith in matters of revealed theology, but he maintained that philosophy should be based on experience. In what is probably his most famous work, *The City of the Sun* (1623),

he describes an ideal state, much influenced by Plato's *Republic,* which is ruled by philosopher-priests.

I s the philosophy which Galileo has made famous and important in harmony with or opposed to the Holy Scriptures?" asks Campanella in the Foreword to the *Defense of Galileo.* That is the prime question which concerns him in the following selection, and it should not surprise us, therefore, that he does not defend Galileo by asserting the "truth" of Galileo's discoveries, in which Campanella probably believed. The question is, after all, not whether Galileo's theories are true, but whether their truth, even if it exists, runs counter to what even Campanella would have insisted was a higher truth. For any Christian of the seventeenth century, Galileo not excepted, the assertion of propositions obviously or demonstrably contrary to Scripture would have been unthinkable.

The question whether Galileo's philosophy was in fact contrary to Scripture was, however, susceptible to argument, and Campanella discusses that question here. Though it is clear enough where his sympathies lie, it is noteworthy that he is careful to do full justice to the arguments of his opponents. And he counters them on their own terms. If they cite authority against Galileo, he cites authority for Copernicus, which is in effect authority for Galileo himself. If they cite Scripture, he cites Scripture in return. If they cite tradition, then he cites tradition in return. The argument is thus a proper one; the issue is truly joined. The same cannot be said of some of the controversies, however hotly waged, of our own day.

Simply stated, the position of those who opposed Galileo was as follows: that Galileo asserted the truth, and not merely the hypothetical possibility, of the Copernican system; that this assertion involved the denial of Holy Writ; that this denial involved the denial of God; and that the denial of God involved the eternal damnation of the denier and, possibly, of the entire human race. The fact that the last three propositions are no longer held to follow from the first should not lead us to ignore the deadly seriousness of the matter. Indeed, within the last generation the question whether scientific advances involve the possible destruction of the entire human race has once again been raised. There are many persons of so-called liberal persuasion—persons, that is, who would have defended Galileo's

right to speak—who now advocate the control of science because of what it can and may do to man and the world. At the same time, modern states feel morally obliged, as the church did in Galileo's time, to set limits on the freedom of scientific inquiry and on the communication of scientific knowledge.

Though it is stated in an outmoded way, the question that Campanella asks is a perennial one. Should science be in the service of man? If so, and if it is allowed free reign, then its results may lead to the disservice of man. However, the restriction of science might also lead to the disservice of man. On the other hand, it is sometimes claimed that science is an end in itself, and that it is wrong to demand that it be in the service of anything else. It is not at all too much to say that Campanella's arguments are capable of helping us to understand this great dilemma.

Arguments for and against Galileo
from *The Defense of Galileo*

I

FOREWORD

FOREWORD

t is now essential to discuss two questions: first, should the new philosophy be permitted to search for truth, and secondly, is it desirable or allowable to suppress both the Aristotelian sect and the authority of heathen philosophers, and for our Christian schools to teach the new philosophy in harmony with Sacred Doctrine? A third fundamental controversy has been precipitated by those who condemn the exalted philosophy of Galileo the Florentine because they believe it opposed to the dogmas of Holy Scripture. I shall reply as the truth appears to me.

I ask therefore: Is the philosophy which Galileo has made famous and important in harmony with or opposed to the Holy Scriptures? Five chapters will complete this inquiry. In the first I shall set forth the arguments and contentions which oppose Galileo; in the second, those which support him. I shall develop in the following chapter three hypotheses which lead to a double conclusion, and answer in the fourth the arguments brought against Galileo. In the fifth and last I shall discuss [and in part refute] the arguments which favor him.

THE ARGUMENTS BROUGHT AGAINST GALILEO

1. He has completely overturned theological dogmas, and attempts to introduce new theories opposed to the science and metaphysics of Aristotle upon which St. Thomas and all scholastics have based theological doctrine.

2. He promulgates opinions which contradict those of all the Fathers and scholastics. Indeed, he teaches that the sun and sphere of the stars

remain fixed, that the earth moves, and is placed beyond the center of the world. The Fathers, the scholastics, and our senses inform us differently.

3. Galileo openly contradicts Sacred Scripture. It is said in Psalm 92, "For he hath established the world which shall not be moved," and in Psalm 103, "Who hast founded the earth upon its own bases; it shall not be moved for ever and ever." And Solomon states in Ecclesiastes 1, "But the earth standeth for ever."

4. Scripture clearly describes the motion of the sun, and says in Ecclesiastes 1, "The earth standeth for ever; the sun riseth and goeth down, and returneth to his place, and there rising again, maketh his round by the south, and turneth again to the north; the spirit goeth forward surveying all places round about, and returneth to his circuits."

5. It is called in Joshua 10 a great miracle that Joshua restrained the motion of the sun by his command, "Move not, O sun, toward Gabaon, nor thou, O moon, toward the valley of Ajalon. . . . So the sun stood still in the midst of heaven, and hasted not to go down for the space of one day." This miracle again is described in Ecclesiasticus 46.

6. In Isaiah 38, God gave Hezekiah a portent in the sundial of Ahaz, as a sign that he would recover his health, "And the sun returned ten lines by the degrees by which it had gone down." As we know from 2 Paralipomenon 32 [2 Chronicles], the King of the Chaldeans questioned Hezekiah regarding this portent, and believing that it resulted from natural causes, denied that the sun had moved backward. If God did not stop the motion of the sun [it is declared], there was no miracle. Therefore Galileo shows that Scripture is false, for Scripture describes as true miracles the standing and the returning of the sun.

7. The moving stars of heaven are praised in Holy Scripture. Deborah sings in her song, Judges 5, "The stars remaining in their order and courses fought against Sisra." Therefore the stars move, and necessarily the heaven, for they are believed placed within it as knots within a board. Moreover, the Apostle Judas speaks of "wandering stars," [13] and 3 Esdras 4, "Great is the earth, high is the heaven, swift is the sun in his course, for he compasseth the heavens round about, and returneth again to his own place in one day." Since Galileo makes the starry heaven immobile, he openly contradicts the Scripture of God.

8. Galileo also says that water exists on the moon and the planets, which cannot be. These bodies are incorruptible, for do not all scholastics contend with Aristotle that they endure without change throughout all time? He describes lands and mountains in the moon and other celestial globes,

and not only vilifies immeasurably the homes of the angels, but lessens our hope regarding heaven.

9. If the four elements which form our world exist in the stars, it follows from the doctrine of Galileo that, as Mohammed declared, there are many worlds with lands and seas, and with human inhabitants. However, Scripture speaks of only one world and of one created man, so that this belief is opposed to Scripture. I pass without comment the opinion that Galileo has revived the heresy that Christ must make atonement for the men who inhabit the stars, and die there again; just as formerly it was said that Christ must be crucified a second time in the antipodes, if the men living there were to be saved as we have been saved. The heretic Paracelsus, whom the Jesuit Martin Delrio attacked in his *Discourse on Magic,* placed men, who rightly should participate in heavenly bliss, under the earth, in the air, and within the water, and questioned their redemption.

10. It is believed that nothing except the derogatory and the scandalous can be contributed by Galileo. Our schools now have and teach a theory of heaven and earth which supports scholastic theology. Whatever conflicting theory others present is therefore believed to degrade this theology and to prepare the way for its destruction.

11. Holy Scripture counsels us to "seek nothing higher, nor attempt to know more than it is necessary to know"; that we "leap not over the bounds which the Fathers set"; and that "the diligent searcher of majesty is overcome by vainglory." Galileo disregards this counsel, subjects the heavens to his invention, and constructs the whole fabric of the world according to his pleasure. Cato rightly taught us to "leave secret things to God, and to permit heaven to inquire concerning them; for he who is mortal should concern himself with mortal things."

THE ARGUMENTS WHICH SUPPORT GALILEO

1. I mention first that *De Revolutionibus Orbium Caelestium Libri VI,* which Copernicus grounded upon observations of the heavens made in 1525, was presented for publication by respected and reputable theologians. By this act they expressed a judgment that the book contains nothing inimical to Catholic faith, despite the fact that it argues for the motion of the earth, the immobility of the firmament, and places the sun in the center of the starry heaven. Galileo has made no additions to the system advanced by Copernicus, and if the *Revolutions* does not adversely affect Catholic faith, neither does the work of Galileo.

2. Pope Paul III, to whom Copernicus dedicated the *Revolutions,* approved the book. Likewise did the Cardinal [Schonberg], who, as the prefatory epistle shows, begged to have the unprinted manuscript transcribed at his own expense. At the time of Paul III distinguished genius flourished within the church, and the Pontiff summoned from afar men of ability, spirit, and noble mind, and supported and adorned them with honor. It indeed would be strange if such able men had imitated blind moles by rejecting Copernicus. Our contemporaries who oppose his theory are not so great in reputation. I add that Galileo, who seeks always more precise observations, has [with the telescope] sharper eyes than Argus.

3. After Copernicus had published the *Revolutions,* Erasmus Reinhold, John Stadius, Michael Maestlin, Christopher Rothmann and many others accepted his theory. Later astronomers thought themselves unable to prepare accurate ephemerides unless they employed the calculations of Copernicus. They also found themselves wholly at a loss to explain celestial motions without violation of mathematical principles and in harmony with the judgment of reason and of all people, unless they employed the Copernican hypothesis. Nor is the heliocentric theory as recent as Copernicus. As the result of his observations of celestial phenomena, Francesco [Domenico] Maria of Ferrara previously had taught that a new system of astronomy should be constructed. His disciple Copernicus built this system.

4. The learned Cardinal Cusanus accepted the hypothesis, and acknowledged that other suns and planets move in orbits in the starry heaven. Nolanus [Bruno], whose errors cannot be named, also supported the theory, as did other philosophers. (Nor were the heretics so much condemned for upholding the hypothesis; rather, Catholics were forbidden to read their books.) Outstanding among Copernican advocates is John Kepler, mathematician to the Emperor, who defends the theory in his prefatory dissertation to the *Starry Messenger* of Galileo. I also may add to them William Gilbert, in his *On the Magnet,* and innumerable other Englishmen. Giovanni Antonio Magini, mathematician of Padua, declared in his *Ephemerides* from 1581 to the present year of 1616 that he accepted the calculations and positions set forth by Copernicus and Reinhold. He boldly criticized other cosmological theories in many of his letters.

5. For more than thirty years the Jesuit and Aristotelian, Reverend Father Clavius, supported the Ptolemaic hypothesis. When he observed however that the planets Mercury and Venus revolve about the sun, he

advised astronomers in the final edition of his *Works* that some system other than the Ptolemaic must be sought. One recent astronomer, Fictus Apelles, gave serious consideration to this admonition, and as a result of both the warning and his observation of spots on the sun, looked with favor upon the hypothesis of Galileo and Copernicus.

6. Galileo's theory of the motion of the earth, of a central sun, and of the systems of stars with waters and earthly elements is indeed an ancient conception. It comes from the mouth of Moses himself, and from Pythagoras. Saint Ambrose tells us that although Pythagoras was born in a Grecian city, he was a Jew with Moses. He taught disciples in Greece, and after going into Italy, in Crotona of Calabria. His beliefs [later] were attacked by Aristotle, not with mathematical demonstrations, but with inane reasons and moralistic, rustic conjectures. According to the statements of Giovanni Pico della Mirandola and Saint Ambrose, Aristotle condemned Pythagoras in the same fashion as he condemned the *Books* of Moses. He was unable by syllogistic logic to understand their divine mystery, recondite thought, and sublime majesty. Such an attack upon Moses vindicates our great Galileo from similar insults cast by the Greeks.

As not only Ovid, but as many historians declare, Numa Pompilius, disciple of Pythagoras and the wisest emperor of Rome, supported the hypothesis. Pliny truthfully states, despite the denial of some writers, that having been commanded by the oracle of Delphos to erect and dedicate a statue to the wisest of the Greeks, the Roman Senate dedicated a statue to Pythagoras and named him the most learned of the philosophers. Those who blacken the doctrine and scientific method of Galileo defame Moses, Rome, and Italy. They set Aristotle above Pythagoras at a time when long-buried truth is gleaming forth. But this is not our greatest sin; this sin is that we have neither made known the new earths, the new systems in the heavens, and the new celestial phenomena, nor have declared abroad the harmony of Scripture and Copernican philosophy.

7. From the time of Caselli and Francesco Maria of Ferrara until the present, theologians did not condemn Copernican astronomy. Moreover, reputable men ordered that the *Revolutions* be printed. Such theologians are not fewer today. The traducers of Galileo have fomented insurrection, not because of their zeal for the teaching of Christ, but from ignorance and jealousy.

8. Because heaven is immobile, Holy Scripture names it the firmament. The earth therefore must rotate, and the sun stand in the center of

the world. As Copernicus and his followers prove and the followers of Ptolemy now admit, this system explains all phenomena and accords with all principles of mathematics.

9. The spots on the sun, the new stars in the heavens, and comets above the moon demonstrate clearly that the stars are worlds constructed of material substance.

10. It is not possible to explain correctly and satisfactorily the text of Moses unless the stars are so constructed. We prove this below from the most saintly Fathers.

11. In his *Answers to the Orthodox*, St. Justin teaches us that when controversy regarding the shape and movement of heaven arose between Christians and heathen, the heathen declared heaven was spherical and mobile, and the Christians that it was a vault which stood immobile. Many Fathers of the Church describe heaven as the firmament because it is unmoved.

Translated by G. McColley.

Michael Faraday [1]

1791–1867

The Royal Institution in London, of which Michael Faraday was the director for more than forty years, was not a school. It was supported by endowments and was a pure research establishment. But there were paying members who were allowed to come to the lectures given by associates of the Institution. The audience of these lectures consisted at first only of adults. But Faraday liked to talk to young people about scientific subjects, and he knew that young people liked to hear him. In December, 1826, he began a series of lectures for the sons and daughters of members of the Institution. These became known as the Christmas Lectures, since they were given during the Christmas holidays.

The Christmas Lectures were highly successful from the very beginning. In all, Faraday gave them nineteen times, choosing as his subject matter, on different occasions, aspects of chemistry, electricity and magnetism, gravitation, the various forces of nature, and other scientific fields. In December, 1860, Faraday gave the last of his Christmas Lectures. The title was *The Chemical History of a Candle.*

Faraday did not write down his lectures. We owe our knowledge of them to a young scientist named William Crookes, who had a stenographer take down a complete word-for-word record. Crookes published the lectures, and it is this version that we reprint here. In his introduction, Crookes bemoaned "the impossibility, alas! of conveying the manner as well as the matter of the Lecturer." Faraday was sixty-nine years old when he gave the lectures on *The Chemical History of a Candle,* but he was still alert and as enthusiastic about

[1] For a biography of Faraday, see Vol. 7, pp. 204–206, in this set.

science as he ever had been. His slender fingers handled the pieces of equipment with the same wonderful skill for which he was famous throughout the scientific world. What we have here in print is perhaps a pale copy of the reality. It would have been a fine thing to be one of those young people in the great lecture hall of the Royal Institution, listening to its celebrated director talking about candles, light, and the beauty of scientific truth. Yet it may be that some of the magic of that occasion comes through in the printed text. At least, generations of readers have found it to be so.

"You have the glittering beauty of gold and silver," says Faraday, "and the still higher lustre of jewels, like the ruby and diamond; but none of these rival the brilliancy and beauty of flame." Perhaps the greatest scientist who ever lived was that forgotten Stone Age man who discovered fire. He gave mankind something to use and to worship. In our enlightened age we still maintain some "sacred" flames to remind us how much we owe to fire.

Fire is sacred not only because it gives us power to control nature. Fire, a flame, is also symbolical of understanding; it gives light. Faraday, in these lectures, sees not only the pure light of the candle as beautiful. What the burning candle represents is also beautiful, and he succeeds in making us see this. For "there is not a law under which any part of this universe is governed which does not come into play, and is touched upon in these phenomena" of the candle flame. Everything fits together. The universe is understandable. Facts have meaning; they are not just so many puzzles. It is Faraday's delight in the scientific laws which he did so much to discover that shines through these pages.

The candle flame represents for him even more than the meaningfulness of the physical world. The study of fire shows us the interdependence of all living things. Flame itself has a kind of life; "it breaks out with a power of life which is quite wonderful." What is more, our breathing is a kind of fire. The air acts upon the blood in our lungs, "producing precisely the same results in kind as we have seen in the case of the candle." Finally, the product of our breathing is carbonic acid (we call it carbon dioxide); this goes up into the air and "is the very life and support of plants and vegetables that grow upon the surface of the earth." These in turn produce oxygen, and "so are we made dependent, not merely upon our fellow-creatures, but upon our fellow-existers, all Nature being tied to-

gether by the laws that make one part conduce to the good of another."

"Life is a pure flame; we live by an invisible fire within us," wrote Sir Thomas Browne. Though Sir Thomas was a physician, he lived before the Age of Science, and he probably meant something more mysterious by that famous sentence than Faraday would have liked. Nevertheless, Faraday does seem to be saying that there is something mysterious, as well as beautiful, about a candle flame. "The candle alone shines by itself, and for itself," he says, and he ends his last lecture by wishing "that you may, in your generation, be fit to compare to a candle; that you may, like it, shine as light to those about you."

The Chemical History
of a Candle

I purpose, in return for the honour you do us by coming to see what are our proceedings here, to bring before you, in the course of these lectures, the chemical history of a candle. I have taken this subject on a former occasion; and were it left to my own will, I should prefer to repeat it almost every year—so abundant is the interest that attaches itself to the subject, so wonderful are the varieties of outlet which it offers into the various departments of philosophy. There is not a law under which any part of this universe is governed which does not come into play, and is touched upon in these phenomena. There is no better, there is no more open door by which you can enter into the study of natural philosophy, than by considering the physical phenomena of a candle. I trust, therefore, I shall not disappoint you in choosing this for my subject rather than any newer topic, which could not be better, were it even so good.

And before proceeding, let me say this also—that though our subject be so great, and our intention that of treating it honestly, seriously, and philosophically, yet I mean to pass away from all those who are seniors amongst us. I claim the privilege of speaking to juveniles as a juvenile myself. I have done so on former occasions—and, if you please, I shall do so again. And though I stand here with the knowledge of having the words I utter given to the world, yet that shall not deter me from speaking in the same familiar way to those whom I esteem nearest to me on this occasion.

And now, my boys and girls, I must first tell you of what candles are made. Some are great curiosities. I have here some bits of timber, branches of trees particularly famous for their burning. And here you see a piece of that very curious substance taken out of some of the bogs in

Ireland, called *candle-wood*—a hard, strong, excellent wood, evidently fitted for good work as a resister of force, and yet withal burning so well that where it is found they make splinters of it, and torches, since it burns like a candle, and gives a very good light indeed. And in this wood we have one of the most beautiful illustrations of the general nature of a candle that I can possibly give. The fuel provided, the means of bringing that fuel to the place of chemical action, the regular and gradual supply of air to that place of action, heat and light—all produced by a little piece of wood of this kind, forming, in fact, a natural candle.

But we must speak of candles as they are in commerce. Here are a couple of candles commonly called dips. They are made of lengths of cotton cut off, hung up by a loop, dipped into melted tallow, taken out again and cooled, then re-dipped until there is an accumulation of tallow round the cotton. In order that you may have an idea of the various characters of these candles, you see these which I hold in my hand—they are very small, and very curious. They are, or were, the candles used by the miners in coal mines. In olden times the miner had to find his own candles; and it was supposed that a small candle would not so soon set fire to the fire-damp in the coal mines as a large one; and for that reason, as well as for economy's sake, he had candles made of this sort— twenty, thirty, forty, or sixty to the pound. They have been replaced since then by the steel mill, and then by the Davy lamp, and other safety-lamps of various kinds. I have here a candle that was taken out of the *Royal George*,[1] it is said, by Colonel Pasley. It has been sunk in the sea for many years, subject to the action of salt water. It shows you how well candles may be preserved; for though it is cracked about and broken a good deal, yet, when lighted, it goes on burning regularly, and the tallow resumes its natural condition as soon as it is fused.

Mr. Field, of Lambeth, has supplied me abundantly with beautiful illustrations of the candle and its materials. I shall therefore now refer to them. And, first, there is the suet—the fat of the ox—Russian tallow, I believe, employed in the manufacture of these dips, which Gay-Lussac, or some one who entrusted him with his knowledge, converted into that beautiful substance, stearin, which you see lying beside it. A candle, you know, is not now a greasy thing like an ordinary tallow candle, but a clean thing, and you may almost scrape off and pulverize the drops which

1. The *Royal George* sunk at Spithead on the 29th of August, 1782. Colonel Pasley commenced operations for the removal of the wreck by the explosion of gunpowder, in August, 1839. The candle which Professor Faraday exhibited must therefore have been exposed to the action of salt water for upwards of fifty-seven years.— William Crookes.

fall from it without soiling anything. This is the process he adopted.[2] The fat or tallow is first boiled with quicklime, and made into a soap, and then the soap is decomposed by sulphuric acid, which takes away the lime, and leaves the fat re-arranged as stearic acid, while a quantity of glycerine is produced at the same time. Glycerine—absolutely a sugar, or a substance similar to sugar—comes out of the tallow in this chemical change. The oil is then pressed out of it; and you see here this series of pressed cakes, showing how beautifully the impurities are carried out by the oily part as the pressure goes on increasing, and at last you have left that substance which is melted, and cast into candles as here represented. The candle I have in my hand is a stearin candle, made of stearin from tallow in the way I have told you. Then here is a sperm candle, which comes from the purified oil of the spermaceti whale. Here also are yellow bees-wax and refined bees-wax, from which candles are made. Here, too, is that curious substance called paraffin, and some paraffin candles made of paraffin obtained from the bogs of Ireland. I have here also a substance brought from Japan, since we have forced an entrance into that out-of-the-way place—a sort of wax which a kind friend has sent me, and which forms a new material for the manufacture of candles.

And how are these candles made? I have told you about dips, and I will show you how moulds are made. Let us imagine any of these candles to be made of materials which can be cast. "Cast!" you say. "Why, a candle is a thing that melts; and surely if you can melt it, you can cast it." Not so. It is wonderful, in the progress of manufacture, and in the consideration of the means best fitted to produce the required result, how things turn up which one would not expect beforehand. Candles cannot always be cast. A wax candle can never be cast. It is made by a particular process, which I can illustrate in a minute or two; but I must not spend much time on it. Wax is a thing which, burning so well, and melting so easily in a candle, cannot be cast. However, let us take a material that can be cast. Here is a frame, with a number of moulds fastened in it. The first thing to be done is to put a wick through them. Here is one—a

2. The fat or tallow consists of a chemical combination of fatty acids with glycerine. The lime unites with the palmitic, oleic, and stearic acids, and separates the glycerine. After washing, the insoluble lime soap is decomposed with hot dilute sulphuric acid. The melted fatty acids thus rise as an oil to the surface, when they are decanted. They are again washed and cast into thin plates, which, when cold, are placed between layers of cocoa-nut matting, and submitted to intense hydraulic pressure. In this way the soft oleic acid is squeezed out, while the hard palmitic and stearic acids remain. These are further purified by pressure at a higher temperature, and washing in warm dilute sulphuric acid, when they are ready to be made into candles. These acids are harder and whiter than the fats from which they were obtained, while at the same time they are cleaner and more combustible.

plaited wick, which does not require snuffing [3]—supported by a little wire. It goes to the bottom, where it is pegged in—the little peg holding the cotton tight, and stopping the aperture, so that nothing fluid shall run out. At the upper part there is a little bar placed across, which stretches the cotton and holds it in the mould. The tallow is then melted, and the moulds are filled. After a certain time, when the moulds are cool, the excess of tallow is poured off at one corner, and then cleaned off altogether, and the ends of the wick cut away. The candles alone then remain in the mould, and you have only to upset them, as I am doing, when out they tumble, for the candles are made in the form of cones, being narrower at the top than at the bottom; so that what with their form and their own shrinking, they only need a little shaking, and out they fall. In the same way are made these candles of stearin and of paraffin. It is a curious thing to see how wax candles are made. A lot of cottons are hung upon frames, as you see here, and covered with metal tags at the ends to keep the wax from covering the cotton in those places. These are carried to a heater, where the wax is melted. As you see, the frames can turn round; and as they turn, a man takes a vessel of wax and pours it first down one, and then the next, and the next, and so on. When he has gone once round, if it is sufficiently cool, he gives the first a second coat, and so on until they are all of the required thickness. When they have been thus clothed, or fed, or made up to that thickness, they are taken off, and placed elsewhere. I have here, by the kindness of Mr. Field, several specimens of these candles. Here is one only half-finished. They are then taken down, and well rolled upon a fine stone slab, and the conical top is moulded by properly shaped tubes, and the bottoms cut off and trimmed. This is done so beautifully that they can make candles in this way weighing exactly four, or six, to the pound, or any number they please.

We must not, however, take up more time about the mere manufacture, but go a little further into the matter. I have not yet referred you to luxuries in candles (for there is such a thing as luxury in candles). See how beautifully these are coloured: you see here mauve, magenta, and all the chemical colours recently introduced, applied to candles. You observe, also, different forms employed. Here is a fluted pillar most beautifully shaped; and I have also here some candles sent me by Mr. Pearsall, which are ornamented with designs upon them, so that as they burn you have as it were a glowing sun above, and a bouquet of flowers beneath.

3. A little borax or phosphorus salt is sometimes added, in order to make the ash fusible.

All, however, that is fine and beautiful is not useful. These fluted candles, pretty as they are, are bad candles; they are bad because of their external shape. Nevertheless, I show you these specimens sent to me from kind friends on all sides, that you may see what is done, and what may be done in this or that direction; although, as I have said, when we come to these refinements, we are obliged to sacrifice a little in utility.

Now, as to the light of the candle. We will light one or two, and set them at work in the performance of their proper functions. You observe a candle is a very different thing from a lamp. With a lamp you take a little oil, fill your vessel, put in a little moss or some cotton prepared by artificial means, and then light the top of the wick. When the flame runs down the cotton to the oil, it gets extinguished, but it goes on burning in the part above. Now I have no doubt you will ask, how is it that the oil, which will not burn of itself, gets up to the top of the cotton, where it will burn? We shall presently examine that; but there is a much more wonderful thing about the burning of a candle than this. You have here a solid substance with no vessel to contain it; and how is it that this solid substance can get up to the place where the flame is? How is it that this solid gets there, it not being a fluid? or, when it is made a fluid, then how is it that it keeps together? This is a wonderful thing about a candle.

We have here a good deal of wind, which will help us in some of our illustrations, but tease us in others; for the sake, therefore, of a little regularity, and to simplify the matter, I shall make a quiet flame—for who can study a subject when there are difficulties in the way not belonging to it? Here is a clever invention of some costermonger or street stander in the market-place for the shading of their candles on Saturday nights, when they are selling their greens, or potatoes, or fish. I have very often admired it. They put a lamp-glass round the candle, supported on a kind of gallery, which clasps it, and it can be slipped up and down as required. By the use of this lamp-glass, employed in the same way, you have a steady flame, which you can look at, and carefully examine, as I hope you will do, at home.

You see, then, in the first instance, that a beautiful cup is formed. As the air comes to the candle it moves upwards by the force of the current which the heat of the candle produces, and it so cools all the sides of the wax, tallow, or fuel, as to keep the edge much cooler than the part within; the part within melts by the flame that runs down the wick as far as it can go before it is extinguished, but the part on the outside does not melt. If I made a current in one direction, my cup would be lop-sided, and the fluid would consequently run over—for the same force of gravity

which holds worlds together holds this fluid in a horizontal position, and if the cup be not horizontal, of course the fluid will run away in guttering. You see, therefore, that the cup is formed by this beautifully regular ascending current of air playing upon all sides, which keeps the exterior of the candle cool. No fuel would serve for a candle which has not the property of giving this cup, except such fuel as the Irish bogwood, where the material itself is like a sponge, and holds its own fuel. You see now why you would have had such a bad result if you were to burn these beautiful candles that I have shown you, which are irregular, intermittent in their shape, and cannot therefore have that nicely formed edge to the cup which is the great beauty in a candle. I hope you will now see that the perfection of a process—that is, its utility—is the better point of beauty about it. It is not the best-looking thing, but the best-acting thing, which is the most advantageous to us. This good-looking candle is a bad burning one. There will be a guttering round about it because of the irregularity of the stream of air and the badness of the cup which is formed thereby. You may see some pretty examples (and I trust you will notice these instances) of the action of the ascending current when you have a little gutter run down the side of a candle, making it thicker there than it is elsewhere. As the candle goes on burning, that keeps its place and forms a little pillar sticking up by the side, because, as it rises higher above the rest of the wax or fuel, the air gets better round it, and it is more cooled and better able to resist the action of the heat at a little distance. Now, the greatest mistakes and faults with regard to candles, as in many other things, often bring with them instruction which we should not receive if they had not occurred. We come here to be philosophers; and I hope you will always remember that whenever a result happens, especially if it be new, you should say, "What is the cause? Why does it occur?" and you will in the course of time find out the reason.

Then, there is another point about these candles which will answer a question—that is, as to the way in which this fluid gets out of the cup, up the wick, and into the place of combustion. You know that the flames on these burning wicks in candles made of bees-wax, stearin, or spermaceti do not run down to the wax or other matter, and melt it all away, but keep to their own right place. They are fenced off from the fluid below, and do not encroach on the cup at the sides. I cannot imagine a more beautiful example than the condition of adjustment under which a candle makes one part subserve to the other to the very end of its action. A combustible thing like that, burning away gradually, never being intruded upon by the flame, is a very beautiful sight; especially when

you come to learn what a vigorous thing flame is—what power it has of destroying the wax itself when it gets hold of it, and of disturbing its proper form if it come only too near.

But how does the flame get hold of the fuel? There is a beautiful point about that—*capillary attraction.*[4] "Capillary attraction!" you say. "The attraction of hairs!" Well, never mind the name: it was given in old times, before we had a good understanding of what the real power was. It is by what is called capillary attraction that the fuel is conveyed to the part where combustion goes on, and is deposited there, not in a careless way, but very beautifully in the very midst of the centre of action which takes place around it. Now, I am going to give you one or two instances of capillary attraction. It is that kind of action or attraction which makes two things that do not dissolve in each other still hold together. When you wash your hands, you wet them thoroughly; you take a little soap to make the adhesion better, and you find your hand remains wet. This is by that kind of attraction of which I am about to speak. And, what is more, if your hands are not soiled (as they almost always are by the usages of life), if you put your finger into a little warm water, the water will creep a little way up the finger, though you may not stop to examine it. I have here a substance which is rather porous—a column of salt—and I will pour into the plate at the bottom, not water, as it appears, but a saturated solution of salt which cannot absorb more; so that the action which you see will not be due to its dissolving anything. We may consider the plate to be the candle, and the salt the wick, and this solution the melted tallow. (I have coloured the fluid, that you may see the action better.) You observe that, now I pour in the fluid, it rises and gradually creeps up the salt higher

4. Capillary attraction or repulsion is the cause which determines the ascent or descent of a fluid in a capillary tube. If a piece of thermometer tubing, open at each end, be plunged into water, the latter will instantly rise in the tube considerably above its external level. If, on the other hand, the tube be plunged into mercury, repulsion instead of attraction will be exhibited, and the level of the mercury will be lower in the tube than it is outside.

and higher; and provided the column does not tumble over, it will go to the top. If this blue solution were combustible, and we were to place a wick at the top of the salt, it would burn as it entered into the wick. It is a most curious thing to see this kind of action taking place, and to observe how singular some of the circumstances are about it. When you wash your hands, you take a towel to wipe off the water; and it is by that kind of wetting, or that kind of attraction which makes the towel become wet with water, that the wick is made wet with the tallow. I have known some careless boys and girls (indeed, I have known it happen to careful people as well) who, having washed their hands and wiped them with a towel, have thrown the towel over the side of the basin, and before long it has drawn all the water out of the basin and conveyed it to the floor, because it happened to be thrown over the side in such a way as to serve the purpose of a siphon.[5] That you may the better see the way in which the substances act one upon another, I have here a vessel made of wire gauze filled with water, and you may compare it in its action to the cotton in one respect, or to a piece of calico in the other. In fact, wicks are sometimes made of a kind of wire gauze. You will observe that this vessel is a porous thing; for if I pour a little water on to the top, it will run out at the bottom. You would be puzzled for a good while if I asked you what the state of this vessel is, what is inside it, and why it is there? The vessel is full of water, and yet you see the water goes in and runs out as if it were empty. In order to prove this to you, I have only to empty it. The reason is this: the wire, being once wetted, remains wet; the meshes are so small that the fluid is attracted so strongly from the one side to the other, as to remain in the vessel although it is porous. In like manner the particles of melted tallow ascend the cotton and get to the top; other particles then follow by their mutual attraction for each other, and as they reach the flame they are gradually burned.

Here is another application of the same principle. You see this bit of cane. I have seen boys about the streets, who are very anxious to appear like men, take a piece of cane, and light it and smoke it, as an imitation of a cigar. They are enabled to do so by the permeability of the cane in one direction, and by its capillarity. If I place this piece of cane on a plate containing some camphine (which is very much like paraffin in its

5. The late Duke of Sussex was, we believe, the first to show that a prawn might be washed upon this principle. If the tail, after pulling off the fan part, be placed in a tumbler of water, and the head be allowed to hang over the outside, the water will be sucked up the tail by capillary attraction, and will continue to run out through the head until the water in the glass has sunk so low that the tail ceases to dip into it.

general character), exactly in the same manner as the blue fluid rose through the salt will this fluid rise through the piece of cane. There being no pores at the side, the fluid cannot go in that direction, but must pass through its length. Already the fluid is at the top of the cane:

now I can light it and make it serve as a candle. The fluid has risen by the capillary attraction of the piece of cane, just as it does through the cotton in the candle.

Now, the only reason why the candle does not burn all down the side of the wick is that the melted tallow extinguishes the flame. You know that a candle, if turned upside down so as to allow the fuel to run upon the wick, will be put out. The reason is that the flame has not had time to make the fuel hot enough to burn, as it does above, where it is carried in small quantities into the wick, and has all the effect of the heat exercised upon it.

There is another condition which you must learn as regards the candle, without which you would not be able fully to understand the philosophy of it, and that is the vaporous condition of the fuel. In order that you may understand that, let me show you a very pretty but very commonplace experiment. If you blow a candle out cleverly, you will see the vapour rise from it. You have, I know, often smelt the vapour of a blown-out candle—and a very bad smell it is; but if you blow it out cleverly, you will be able to see pretty well the vapour into which this solid matter is transformed. I will blow out one of these candles in such a way as not to disturb the air around it, by the continuing action of my breath; and now, if I hold a lighted taper two or three inches from the wick, you will observe a train of fire going through the air till it reaches the candle. I am obliged to be quick and ready, because, if I allow the vapour time to cool, it becomes condensed into a liquid or solid, or the stream of combustible matter gets disturbed [illustration above].

Now, as to the shape or form of the flame. It concerns us much to know about the condition which the matter of the candle finally assumes at the top of the wick—where you have such beauty and brightness as nothing but combustion or flame can produce. You have the glittering beauty of gold and silver, and the still higher lustre of jewels, like the ruby and diamond; but none of these rival the brilliancy and beauty of

flame. What diamond can shine like flame? It owes its lustre at night-time to the very flame shining upon it. The flame shines in darkness, but the light which the diamond has is as nothing until the flame shine upon it, when it is brilliant again. The candle alone shines by itself, and for itself, or for those who have arranged the materials. Now, let us look a little at the form of the flame as you see it under the glass shade. It is steady and equal; and its general form is that which is represented in the diagram, varying with atmospheric disturbances, and also varying according to the size of the candle. It is a bright oblong—brighter at the top than towards the bottom—with the wick in the middle, and besides the wick in the middle, certain darker parts towards the bottom, where the ignition is not so perfect as in the part above. I have a drawing here, sketched many years ago by Hooker, when he made his investigations. It is the drawing of the flame of a lamp, but it will apply to the flame of a candle. The cup of the candle is the vessel or lamp, the melted spermaceti is the oil, and the wick is common to both. Upon that he sets this little flame, and then he represents what is true—a certain quantity of matter rising about it which you do not see, and which, if you have not been here before, or are not familiar with the subject, you will not know of. He has here represented the parts of the surrounding atmosphere that are very essential to the flame, and that are always present with it. There is a current formed, which draws the flame out—for the flame which you see is really drawn out by the current, and drawn upward to a great height—just as Hooker has here shown you by that prolongation of the current in the diagram. You may see this by taking a lighted candle, and putting it in the sun so as to get its shadow thrown on a piece of paper. How remarkable it is that that thing which is light enough to produce shadows of other objects can be made to throw its own shadow on a piece of white paper or card, so that you can actually see streaming round the flame something which is not part of the flame, but is ascending and drawing the flame upwards. Now, I am going to imitate the sunlight, by applying the voltaic battery to the electric lamp. You now see our sun, and its great luminosity; and by placing a candle between it and the screen, we get the shadow of the flame. You observe the shadow of the candle and of the wick; then there is a darkish part, as represented in the diagram, and then a part which is

more distinct. Curiously enough, however, what we see in the shadow as the darkest part of the flame is, in reality, the brightest part; and here you see streaming upwards the ascending current of hot air, as shown by Hooker, which draws out the flame, supplies it with air, and cools the sides of the cup of melted fuel [illustration below].

I can give you here a little further illustration, for the purpose of showing you how flame goes up or down, according to the current. I have here a flame—it is not a candle flame—but you can, no doubt, by this time, generalize enough to be able to compare one thing with another. What I am about to do is to change the ascending current that takes the flame upwards into a descending current. This I can easily do by the little apparatus you see before me. The flame, as I have said, is not a candle flame, but it is produced by alcohol, so that it shall not smoke too much. I will also colour the flame with another substance,[6] so that you may trace its course; for with the spirit alone you could hardly see well enough to have the opportunity of tracing its direction. By lighting this spirit-of-wine, we have then a flame produced; and you observe that when held in the air, it naturally goes upwards. You understand now easily enough why flames go up under ordinary circumstances—it is because of the draught of air by which the combustion is formed. But now, by blowing the flame down, you see I am enabled to make it go downwards into this little chimney—the direction of the current being changed [illustration p. 379]. Before we have concluded this course of lectures, we shall show you a lamp in which the flame goes up and the smoke goes down, or the flame goes down and the smoke goes up. You see, then, that we have the power in this way of varying the flame in different directions.

There are now some other points that I must bring before you. Many of the flames you see here vary very much in their shape by the currents of air blowing around them in different directions; but we can, if we like, make flames so that they will look like fixtures, and we can photograph them—indeed, we have to photograph them, so that they become fixed to us, if we wish to find out everything concerning them. That, however, is not the only thing I wish to mention. If I take a flame sufficiently large, it does not keep that homogeneous, that uniform condition of shape, but it breaks out with a power of life which is quite won-

6. The alcohol had chloride of copper dissolved in it: this produces a beautiful green flame.

derful. I am about to use another kind of fuel, but one which is truly and fairly a representative of the wax or tallow of a candle. I have here a large ball of cotton, which will serve as a wick. And, now that I have immersed it in spirit and applied a light to it, in what way does it differ from an ordinary candle? Why, it differs very much in one respect, that we have a vivacity and power about it, a beauty and a life entirely different from the light presented by a candle. You see those fine tongues of flame rising up. You have the same general disposition of the mass of the flame from below upwards; but, in addition to that, you have this remarkable breaking out into tongues which you do not perceive in the case of a candle. Now, why is this? I must explain it to you, because

when you understand that perfectly, you will be able to follow me better in what I have to say hereafter. I suppose some here will have made for themselves the experiment I am going to show you. Am I right in supposing that anybody here has played at snapdragon? I do not know a more beautiful illustration of the philosophy of flame, as to a certain part of its history, than the game of snapdragon. First, here is the dish; and let me say, that when you play snapdragon properly, you ought to have the dish well warmed; you ought also to have warm plums and warm brandy, which, however, I have not got. When you have put the spirit into the dish, you have the cup and the fuel; and are not the raisins acting like the wicks? I now throw the plums into the dish, and light the spirit, and you see those beautiful tongues of flame that I refer to. You have the air creeping in over the edge of the dish forming these tongues. Why? Because, through the force of the current and the irregularity of the action of the flame, it cannot flow in one uniform stream. The air flows in so irregularly that you have what would otherwise be a single image, broken up into a variety of forms, and each of these little tongues has an independent existence of its own. Indeed, I might say, you have here a multitude of independent candles. You must not imagine, because you see these tongues all at once, that the flame is of this particular shape. A flame of that shape is never so at any one time. Never is a body of flame, like that which you just saw rising from the ball, of the shape it appears to you. It consists of a multitude of dif-

ferent shapes, succeeding each other so fast that the eye is only able to take cognizance of them all at once. In former times, I purposely analysed a flame of that general character, and the diagram shows you the different parts of which it is composed. They do not occur all at once: it is only because we see these shapes in such rapid succession, that they seem to us to exist all at one time.

It is too bad that we have not got further than my game of snap-dragon; but we must not, under any circumstances, keep you beyond your time. It will be a lesson to me in future to hold you more strictly to the philosophy of the thing, than to take up your time so much with these illustrations.

LECTURE II

We were occupied the last time we met in considering the general character and arrangement as regards the fluid portion of a candle, and the way in which that fluid got into the place of combustion. You see, when we have a candle burning fairly in a regular, steady atmosphere, it will have a shape something like the one shown in the diagram, and will look pretty uniform, although very curious in its character. And now, I have to ask your attention to the means by which we are enabled to ascertain what happens in any particular part of the flame—why it happens, what it does in happening, and where, after all, the whole candle goes to: because, as you know very well, a candle being brought before us and burned, disappears, if burned properly, without the least trace of dirt in the candlestick—and this is a very curious circumstance. In order, then, to examine this candle carefully, I have arranged certain apparatus, the use of which you will see as I go on. Here is a candle: I am about to put the end of this glass tube into the middle of the flame —into that part which old Hooker has represented in the diagram as being rather dark, and which you can see at any time, if you will look at a candle carefully, without blowing it about. We will examine this dark part first.

Now, I take this bent glass tube, and introduce one end into that part of the flame, and you see at once that something is coming from the flame, out at the other end of the tube; and if I put a flask there, and leave it for a little while, you will see that something from the middle part of the flame is grad-ually drawn out, and goes through the tube and into that flask, and there be-haves very differently from what it does in the open air. It not only escapes from the end of the tube, but falls down to the bot-tom of the flask like a heavy substance, as indeed it is. We find that this is

the wax of the candle made into a vaporous fluid—not a gas. (You must learn the difference between a gas and a vapour: a gas remains permanent, a vapour is something that will condense.) If you blow out a candle, you perceive a very nasty smell, resulting from the condensation of this vapour. That is very different from what you have outside the flame; and, in order to make that more clear to you, I am about to produce and set fire to a larger portion of this vapour—for what we have in the small way in a candle, to understand thoroughly, we must, as philosophers, produce in a larger way, if needful, that we may examine the different parts. And now Mr. Anderson will give me a source of heat, and I am about to show you what that vapour is. Here is some wax in a glass flask, and I am going to make it hot, as the inside of that candle-flame is hot, and the matter about the wick is hot. [*The Lecturer placed some wax in a glass flask, and heated it over a lamp.*] Now, I dare say that is hot enough for me. You see that the wax I put in it has become fluid, and there is a little smoke coming from it. We shall very soon have the vapour rising up. I will make it still hotter, and now we get more of it, so that I can actually pour the vapour out of the flask into that basin, and set it on fire there. This, then, is exactly the same kind of vapour as we have in the middle of the candle; and that you may be sure this is the case, let us try whether we have not got here, in this flask, a real combustible vapour out of the middle of the candle [*taking the flask into which the tube from the candle proceeded, and introducing a lighted taper*]. See how it burns. Now, this is the vapour from the middle of the candle, produced by its own heat; and

that is one of the first things you have to consider with respect to the progress of the wax in the course of its combustion, and as regards the changes it undergoes. I will arrange another tube carefully in the flame,

and I should not wonder if we were able, by a little care, to get that vapour to pass through the tube to the other extremity, where we will light it, and obtain absolutely the flame of the candle at a place distant from it. Now, look at that. Is not that a very pretty experiment? Talk about laying on gas—why, we can actually lay on a candle! And you see from this that there are clearly two different kinds of action—one the *production* of the vapour, and the other the *combustion* of it—both of which take place in particular parts of the candle.

I shall get no vapour from that part which is already burnt. If I raise the tube [see fig. on p. 381] to the upper part of the flame, so soon as the vapour has been swept out, what comes away will be no longer combustible; it is already burned. How burned? Why, burned thus: in the middle of the flame, where the wick is, there is this combustible vapour; on the outside of the flame is the air which we shall find necessary for the burning of the candle; between the two, intense chemical action takes place, whereby the air and the fuel act upon each other, and at the very same time that we obtain light the vapour inside is destroyed. If you examine where the heat of a candle is, you will find it very curiously arranged. Suppose I take this candle, and hold a piece of paper close upon the flame, where is the heat of that flame? Do you not see that it is *not* in the inside? It is in a ring, exactly in the place where I told you the chemical action was; and even in my irregular mode of making the experiment, if there is not too much disturbance, there will always be a ring. This is a good experiment for you to make at home. Take a strip of paper, have the air in the room quiet, and put the piece of paper right across the middle of the flame (I must not talk while I make the experiment), and you will find that it is burnt in two places, and that it is not burnt, or very little so, in the middle; and when you have tried the experiment once or twice, so as to make it nicely, you will be very in-

terested to see where the heat is, and to find that it is where the air and the fuel come together.

This is most important for us as we proceed with our subject. Air is absolutely necessary for combustion; and, what is more, I must have you understand that *fresh* air is necessary, or else we should be imperfect in our reasoning and our experiments. Here is a jar of air. I place it over a candle, and it burns very nicely in it at first, showing that what I have said about it is true; but there will soon be a change. See how the flame is drawing upwards, presently fading, and at last going out. And going out, why? Not because it wants air merely, for the jar is as full now as it was before; but it wants pure, fresh air. The jar is full of air, partly changed, partly not changed; but it does not contain sufficient of the fresh air which is necessary for the combustion of a candle. These are all points which we, as young chemists, have to gather up; and if we look a little more closely into this kind of action, we shall find certain steps of reasoning extremely interesting. For instance, here is the oil-lamp I showed you—an excellent lamp for our experiments—the old Argand lamp. I now make it like a candle [*obstructing the passage of air into the centre of the flame*]; there is the cotton; there is the oil rising up it; and there is the conical flame. It burns poorly, because there is a partial restraint of air. I have allowed no air to get to it, save round the outside of the flame, and it does not burn well. I cannot admit more air from the outside, because the wick is large; but if, as Argand did so cleverly, I open a passage to the middle of the flame, and so let air come in there, you will see how much more beautifully it burns. If I shut the air off, look how it smokes; and why? We have now some very interesting points to study. We have the case of the combustion of a candle; we have the case of a candle being put out by the want of air; and we have now the case of imperfect combustion; and this is to us so interesting, that I want you to understand it as thoroughly as you do the case of a candle burning in its best possible manner. I will now make a great flame, because we need the largest possible illustrations. Here is a larger wick [*burning turpentine on a ball of cotton*]. All these things are the same as candles, after all. If we have larger wicks, we must have a larger supply of air, or we shall have less perfect combustion. Look now at this black substance going up into the atmosphere; there is a regular stream of it. I have provided means to carry off the imperfectly burned part, lest it should annoy you. Look at the soots that fly off from the flame: see what an imperfect combustion it is, because it cannot get enough air. What, then, is happening? Why, certain things which are necessary to the com-

bustion of a candle are absent, and very bad results are accordingly produced; but we see what happens to a candle when it is burnt in a pure and proper state of air. At the time when I showed you this charring by the ring of flame on the one side of the paper, I might have also shown you, by turning to the other side, that the burning of a candle produces the same kind of soot—charcoal or carbon.

But, before I show that, let me explain to you—as it is quite necessary for our purpose—that, though I take a candle and give you, as the general result, its combustion in the form of a flame, we must see whether combustion is always in this condition, or whether there are other conditions of flame; and we shall soon discover that there are, and that they are most important to us. I think, perhaps, the best illustration of such a point to us, as juveniles, is to show the result of strong contrast. Here is a little gunpowder. You know that gunpowder burns with flame—we may fairly call it flame. It contains carbon and other materials, which altogether cause it to burn with a flame. And here is some pulverized iron, or iron filings. Now, I purpose burning these two things together. I have a little mortar in which I will mix them. (Before I go into these experiments, let me hope that none of you, by trying to repeat them, for fun's sake, will do any harm. These things may all be very properly used if you take care; but without that, much mischief will be done.) Well, then, here is a little gunpowder, which I put at the bottom of that little wooden vessel, and mix the iron filings up with it, my object being to make the gunpowder set fire to the filings and burn them in the air, and thereby show the difference between substances burning with flame and not with flame. Here is the mixture; and when I set fire to it, you must watch the combustion, and you will see that it is of two kinds. You will see the gunpowder burning with a flame, and the filings thrown up. You will see them burning too, but without the production of flame. They will each burn separately. [*The Lecturer then ignited the mixture.*] There is the gunpowder, which burns with a flame; and there are the filings—they burn with a different kind of combustion. You see, then, these two great distinctions; and upon these differences depend all the utility and all the beauty of flame which we use for the purpose of giving out light. When we use oil, or gas, or candle, for the purpose of illumination, their fitness all depends upon these different kinds of combustion.

There are such curious conditions of flame, that it requires some cleverness and nicety of discrimination to distinguish the kinds of combustion one from another. For instance, here is a powder which is very

combustible, consisting, as you see, of separate little particles. It is called *lycopodium*,[7] and each of these particles can produce a vapour, and produce its own flame; but, to see them burning, you would imagine it was all one flame. I will now set fire to a quantity, and you will see the effect. We saw a cloud of flame, apparently in one body; but that rushing noise [*referring to the sound produced by the burning*] was a proof that the combustion was not a continuous or regular one. This is the lightning of the pantomimes, and a very good imitation. [*The experiment was twice repeated by blowing lycopodium from a glass tube through a spirit-flame.*] This is not an example of combustion like that of the filings I have been speaking of, to which we must now return.

Suppose I take a candle, and examine that part of it which appears brightest to our eyes. Why, there I get these black particles, which already you have seen many times evolved from the flame, and which I am now about to evolve in a different way. I will take this candle and clear away the gutterage, which occurs by reason of the currents of air; and if I now arrange a glass tube so as just to dip into this luminous part, as in our first experiment, only higher, you see the result. In place of having the same white vapour that you had before, you will now have a black vapour. There it goes, as black as ink. It is certainly very different from the white vapour; and when we put a light to it, we shall find that it does not burn, but that it puts the light out. Well, these particles, as I said before, are just the smoke of the candle; and this brings to mind that old employment which Dean Swift recommended to servants for their amusement, namely, writing on the ceiling of a room with a candle. But what is that black substance? Why, it is the same carbon which exists in the candle. How comes it out of the candle? It evidently existed in the candle, or else we should not have had it here. And now I want you to follow me in this explanation. You would hardly think that all those substances which fly about London, in the form of soots and blacks, are the very beauty and life of the flame, and which are burned in it as those iron filings were burned here. Here is a piece of wire gauze, which will not let the flame go through it; and I think you will see, almost immediately, that when I bring it low enough to touch that part of the flame which is otherwise so bright, that it quells and quenches it at once, and allows a volume of smoke to rise up.

I want you now to follow me in this point—that whenever a substance burns, as the iron filings burnt in the flame of gunpowder, without assum-

7. Lycopodium is a yellowish powder found in the fruit of the club moss (*Lycopodium clavatum*). It is used in fireworks.

ing the vaporous state (whether it becomes liquid or remains solid), it becomes exceedingly luminous. I have here taken three or four examples apart from the candle, on purpose to illustrate this point to you; because what I have to say is applicable to all substances, whether they burn or whether they do not burn—that they are exceedingly bright if they retain their solid state, and that it is to this presence of solid particles in the candle-flame that it owes its brilliancy.

Here is a platinum-wire, a body which does not change by heat. If I heat it in this flame, see how exceedingly luminous it becomes. I will make the flame dim, for the purpose of giving a little light only, and yet you will see that the heat which it can give to that platinum-wire, though far less than the heat it has itself, is able to raise the platinum-wire to a far higher state of effulgence. This flame has carbon in it; but I will take one that has no carbon in it. There is a material, a kind of fuel—a vapour, or gas, whichever you like to call it—in that vessel, and it has no solid particles in it; so I take that because it is an example of flame itself burning without any solid matter whatever; and if I now put this solid substance in it, you see what an intense heat it has and how brightly it causes the solid body to glow. This is the pipe through which we convey this particular gas, which we call hydrogen, and which you shall know all about next time we meet. And here is a substance called oxygen, by means of which this hydrogen can burn; and although we produce, by their mixture, far greater heat [8] than you can obtain from the candle, yet there is very little light. If, however, I take a solid substance, and put that into it, we produce an intense light. If I take a piece of lime, a substance which will not burn, and which will not vaporize by the heat (and because it does not vaporize, remains solid, and remains heated), you will soon observe what happens as to its glowing. I have here a most intense heat, produced by the burning of hydrogen in contact with the oxygen; but there is as yet very little light—not for want of heat, but for want of particles which can retain their solid state; but when I hold this piece of lime in the flame of the hydrogen as it burns in the oxygen, see how it glows! This is the glorious lime-light, which rivals the voltaic-light, and which is almost equal to sunlight. I have here a piece of carbon or charcoal, which will burn and give us light exactly in the same manner as if it were burnt as part of a candle. The heat that is in the flame of a candle decomposes the vapour of the wax, and sets

8. Bunsen has calculated that the temperature of the oxyhydrogen blowpipe is 8,061° C. Hydrogen burning in air has a temperature of 3,259 C., and coal-gas in air, 2,350 C.

free the carbon particles—they rise up heated and glowing as this now glows, and then enter into the air. But the particles when burnt never pass off from a candle in the form of carbon. They go off into the air as a perfectly invisible substance, about which we shall know hereafter.

Is it not beautiful to think that such a process is going on, and that such a dirty thing as charcoal can become so incandescent? You see it comes to this—that all bright flames contain these solid particles; all things that burn and produce solid particles, either during the time they are burning, as in the candle, or immediately after being burnt, as in the case of the gunpowder and iron-filings—all these things give us this glorious and beautiful light.

I will give you a few illustrations. Here is a piece of phosphorus, which burns with a bright flame. Very well; we may now conclude that phosphorus will produce, either at the moment that it is burning or afterwards, these solid particles. Here is the phosphorus lighted, and I cover it over with this glass for the purpose of keeping in what is produced. What is all that smoke? That smoke consists of those very particles which are produced by the combustion of the phosphorus. Here, again, are two substances. This is chlorate of potassa, and this other sulphuret of antimony. I shall mix these together a little, and then they may be burnt in many ways. I shall touch them with a drop of sulphuric acid, for the purpose of giving you an illustration of chemical action, and they will instantly burn.[9] [*The Lecturer then ignited the mixture by means of sulphuric acid.*] Now, from the appearance of things, you can judge for yourselves whether they produce solid matter in burning. I have given you the train of reasoning which will enable you to say whether they do or do not; for what is this bright flame but the solid particles passing off? [See illustration on p. 388.]

Mr. Anderson has in the furnace a very hot crucible—I am about to throw into it some zinc filings, and they will burn with a flame like gunpowder. I make this experiment because you can make it well at home. Now, I want you to see what will be the result of the combustion of this zinc. Here it is burning—burning beautifully like a candle, I may say. But what is all that smoke, and what are those little clouds of wool which will come to you if you cannot come to them, and make themselves sensible to you in the form of the old philosophic wool, as it was called? We

9. The following is the action of the sulphuric acid in inflaming the mixture of sulphuret of antimony and chlorate of potassa. A portion of the latter is decomposed by the sulphuric acid into oxide of chlorine, bisulphate of potassa, and perchlorate of potassa. The oxide of chlorine inflames the sulphuret of antimony, which is a combustible body, and the whole mass instantly bursts into flame.

shall have left in that crucible, also, a quantity of this woolly matter. But I will take a piece of this same zinc and make an experiment a little more closely at home, as it were. You will have here the same thing happening. Here is the piece of zinc, there [*pointing to a jet of hydrogen*] is the

furnace, and we will set to work and try and burn the metal. It glows, you see: there is the combustion, and there is the white substance into which it burns. And so, if I take that flame of hydrogen as the representative of a candle, and show you a substance like zinc burning in the flame, you will see that it was merely during the action of combustion that this substance glowed—while it was kept hot; and if I take a flame of hydrogen, and put this white substance from the zinc into it, look how beautifully it glows, and just because it is a solid substance.

I will now take such a flame as I had a moment since, and set free from it the particles of carbon. Here is some camphine, which will burn with a smoke; but if I send these particles of smoke through this pipe into the hydrogen flame, you will see they will burn and become luminous, because we heat them a second time. There they are. Those are the particles of carbon re-ignited a second time. They are those particles which you can easily see by holding a piece of paper behind them, and which, while they are in the flame, are ignited by the heat produced, and, when so ignited, produce this brightness. When the particles are not separated, you get no brightness. The flame of coal-gas owes its brightness to the separation, during combustion, of these particles of carbon, which are equally in that as in a candle. I can very quickly alter that arrangement. Here, for instance, is a bright flame of gas. Supposing I add so much air to the flame as to cause it all to burn before those particles are set free, I shall not have this brightness; and I can do that in this way: if I place over the jet this wire-gauze cap, as you see, and then light the gas over it, it burns with a nonluminous flame, owing to its having plenty of air mixed with it before it burns; and if I raise the gauze, you see it does not burn below.[10] There is plenty of carbon in the gas; but, because

10. The "air-burner," which is of such value in the laboratory, owes its advantage to this principle. It consists of a cylindrical metal chimney, covered at the top with a piece of rather coarse iron-wire gauze. This is supported over an Argand burner, in such a manner that the gas may mix in the chimney with an amount of air sufficient to burn the carbon and hydrogen simultaneously, so that there may be no separation of carbon in the flame with consequent deposition of soot. The flame, being unable to pass through the wire gauze, burns in a steady, nearly invisible manner above.

the atmosphere can get to it, and mix with it before it burns, you see how pale and blue the flame is. And if I blow upon a bright gas-flame, so as to consume all this carbon before it gets heated to the glowing point, it will also burn blue. [*The Lecturer illustrated his remarks by blowing on the gas-light.*] The only reason why I have not the same bright light when I thus blow upon the flame is that the carbon meets with sufficient air to burn it before it gets separated in the flame in a free state. The difference is solely due to the solid particles not being separated before the gas is burnt.

You observe that there are certain products as the result of the combustion of a candle, and that of these products one portion may be considered as charcoal, or soot; that charcoal, when afterwards burnt, produces some other product; and it concerns us very much now to ascertain what that other product is. We showed that something was going away; and I want you now to understand how much is going up into the air; and for that purpose we will have combustion on a little larger scale. From that candle ascends heated air, and two or three experiments will show you the ascending current; but, in order to give you a notion of the quantity of matter which ascends in this way, I will make an experiment by which I shall try to imprison some of the products of this combustion. For this purpose I have here what boys call a fire-balloon. I use this fire-balloon merely as a sort of measure of the result of the combustion we are considering; and I am about to make a flame in such an easy and simple manner as shall best serve my present purpose. This plate shall be the "cup," we will so say, of the candle; this spirit shall be our fuel; and I am about to place this chimney over it, because it is better for me to do so than to let things proceed at random. Mr. Anderson will now light the fuel, and here at the top we shall get the results of the combustion. What we get at the top of that tube is exactly the same, generally speaking, as you get from the combustion of a candle; but we do not get a luminous flame here, because we use a substance which is feeble in carbon. I am about to put this balloon— not into action, because that is not my object—but to show you the effect which results from the action of those products which arise from the candle, as they arise here from the furnace. [*The balloon was held over the chimney, when it immediately commenced to fill.*] You see how

it is disposed to ascend; but we must not let it up, because it might come in contact with those upper gas-lights, and that would be very incon- venient. [*The upper gas-lights were turned out, at the request of the Lecturer, and the balloon was allowed to ascend.*] Does not that show you what a large bulk of matter is being evolved? Now, there are going through this tube [*placing a large glass tube over a candle*] all the prod- ucts of that candle, and you will presently see that the tube will become quite opaque. Suppose I take another candle, and place it under a jar, and then put a light on the other side, just to show you what is going on. You see that the sides of the jar become cloudy, and the light begins to burn feebly. It is the products, you see, which make the light so dim, and this is the same thing which makes the sides of the jar so opaque. If you go home and take a spoon that has been in the cold air, and hold it over a candle—not so as to soot it—you will find that it becomes dim, just as that jar is dim. If you can get a silver dish, or something of that kind, you will make the experiment still better. And now, just to carry your thoughts forward to the time we shall next meet, let me tell you that it is *water* which causes the dimness; and when we next meet, I will show you that we can make it, without difficulty, assume the form of a liquid.

LECTURE III

I dare say you will remember that when we parted we had just men- tioned the word "products" from the candle. For when a candle burns we found we were able, by nice adjustment, to get various products from it. There was one substance which was not obtained when the candle was burning properly, which was charcoal or smoke; and there was some other substance that went upwards from the flame, which did not ap- pear as smoke, but took some other form, and made part of that general current which, ascending from the candle upwards, becomes invisible, and escapes. There were also other products to mention. You remem- ber that in that rising current having its origin at the candle, we found that one part was condensable against a cold spoon, or against a clean plate, or any other cold thing, and another part was incondensable.

We will first take the condensable part, and examine it; and, strange to say, we find that that part of the product is just water—nothing but water. On the last occasion I spoke of it incidentally, merely saying that water was produced among the condensable products of the candle; but today I wish to draw your attention to water, that we may examine it carefully,

especially in relation to this subject, and also with respect to its general existence on the surface of the globe.

Now, having previously arranged an experiment for the purpose of condensing water from the products of the candle, my next point will be to show you this water; and perhaps one of the best means that I can adopt for showing its presence to so many at once is to exhibit a very visible action of water, and then to apply that test to what is collected as a drop at the bottom of that vessel. I have here a chemical substance, discovered by Sir Humphry Davy, which has a very energetic action upon water, which I shall use as a test of the presence of water. If I take a little piece of it— it is called potassium, as coming from potash—if I take a little piece of it, and throw it into that basin, you see how it shows the presence of water by

lighting up and floating about, burning with a violent flame. I am now going to take away the candle which has been burning beneath the vessel containing ice and salt, and you see a drop of water—a condensed product of the candle—hanging from under the surface of the dish. I will show you that potassium has the same action upon it as upon the water in that basin in the experiment we have just tried. See, it takes fire, and burns in just the same manner. I will take another drop upon this glass slab, and when I put the potassium onto it, you see at once, from its taking fire, that there is water present. Now, that water was produced by the candle. In the same manner, if I put this spirit-lamp under that jar, you will soon see the latter become damp, from the dew which is deposited upon it—that dew being the result of combustion; and I have no doubt you will shortly see by the drops of water which fall upon the paper below, that there is a good deal of water produced from the combustion of the lamp. I will let it remain, and you can afterwards see how much water has been collected. So, if I take a gas-lamp, and put any cooling arrangement over it, I shall get water—water being likewise produced from the combustion of gas. Here, in this bottle, is a quantity of water—perfectly pure, distilled water—produced from the combustion of a gas-lamp, in no point different from the water that you distil from the river, or ocean, or spring, but exactly the same thing. Water is one individual thing—it never changes. We can add to it by careful adjustment, for a little while, or we can take it apart, and get other things from it; but water, as water, remains always the same,

either in a solid, liquid, or fluid state. Here, again [*holding another bottle*], is some water produced by the combustion of an oil-lamp. A pint of oil, when burnt fairly and properly, produces rather more than a pint of water. Here, again, is some water, produced by a rather long experiment from a wax candle. And so we can go on with almost all combustible substances, and find that if they burn with a flame, as a candle, they produce water. You may make these experiments yourselves. The head of a poker is a very good thing to try with, and if it remains cold long enough over the candle, you may get water condensed in drops on it; or a spoon or ladle, or anything else may be used, provided it be clean, and can carry off the heat, and so condense the water.

And now—to go into the history of this wonderful production of water from combustibles, and by combustion—I must first of all tell you that this water may exist in different conditions; and although you may now be acquainted with all its forms, they still require us to give a little attention to them for the present, so that we may perceive how the water, while it goes through its protean changes, is entirely and absolutely the same thing, whether it is produced from a candle, by combustion, or from the rivers or ocean.

First of all, water, when at the coldest, is ice. Now, we philosophers—I hope that I may class you and myself together in this case—speak of water as water; whether it be in its solid, or liquid, or gaseous state, we speak of it chemically as water. Water is a thing compounded of two substances, one of which we have derived from the candle, and the other we shall find elsewhere. Water may occur as ice; and you have had most excellent opportunities lately of seeing this. Ice changes back into water—for we had on our last Sabbath a strong instance of this change, by the sad catastrophe which occurred in our own house, as well as in the houses of many of our friends—ice changes back into water when the temperature is raised: water also changes into steam when it is warmed enough. The water which we have here before us is in its densest state,[11] and although it changes in weight, in condition, in form, and in many other qualities, it still is water; and whether we alter it into ice by cooling, or whether we change it into steam by heat, it increases in volume—in the one case very strangely and powerfully, and in the other case very largely and wonderfully. For instance, I will now take this tin cylinder, and pour a little water into it; and seeing how much water I pour in, you may easily estimate for yourselves how high it will rise in

11. Water is in its densest state at a temperature of 39.1° F.

the vessel: it will cover the bottom about two inches. I am now about to convert the water into steam, for the purpose of showing to you the different volumes which water occupies in its different states of water and steam.

Let us now take the case of water changing into ice: we can effect that by cooling it in a mixture of salt and pounded ice;[12] and *I* shall do so to show you the expansion of water into a thing of larger bulk when it is so changed. These bottles [*holding one*] are made of strong cast iron, very strong and very thick—I suppose they are the third of an inch in thickness; they are very carefully filled with water, so as to exclude all air, and then they are screwed down tight. We shall see that when we freeze the water in these iron vessels, they will not be able to hold the ice, and the expansion within them will break them in pieces as these [*pointing to some fragments*] are broken, which have been bottles of exactly the same kind. I am about to put these two bottles into that mixture of ice and salt, for the purpose of showing that when water becomes ice, it changes in volume in this extraordinary way.

In the mean time, look at the change which has taken place in the water to which we have applied heat—it is losing its fluid state. You may tell this by two or three circumstances. I have covered the mouth of this glass flask, in which water is boiling, with a watch-glass. Do you see what happens? It rattles away like a valve chattering, because the steam rising from the boiling water sends the valve up and down, and forces itself out, and so makes it clatter. You can very easily perceive that the flask is quite full of steam, or else it would not force its way out. You see, also, that the flask contains a substance very much larger than the water, for it fills the whole of the flask over and over again, and there it is blowing away into the air; and yet you cannot observe any great diminution in the bulk of the water, which shows you that its change of bulk is very great when it becomes steam.

I have put our iron bottles containing water into this freezing mixture, that you may see what happens. No communication will take place, you observe, between the water in the bottles and the ice in the outer vessel. But there will be a conveyance of heat from the one to the other; and if we are successful—we are making our experiment in very great haste—I expect you will by and by, so soon as the cold has taken possession of the bottles and their contents, hear a pop on the occasion of the bursting of the one bottle or the other; and, when we come to

12. A mixture of salt and pounded ice reduces the temperature from 32° F. to zero— the ice at the same time becoming fluid.

examine the bottles, we shall find their contents masses of ice, partly en-
closed by the covering of iron which is too small for them, because the ice
is larger in bulk than the water. You know very well that ice floats upon
water: if a boy falls through a hole into the water, he tries to get on
the ice again to float him up. Why does the ice float? Think of that, and
philosophize. Because the ice is larger than the quantity of water which
can produce it; and therefore the ice weighs the lighter, and the water
is the heavier.

To return now to the action of heat on water. See what a stream of
vapour is issuing from this tin vessel! You observe, we must have made it
quite full of steam to have it sent out in that great quantity. And now, as
we can convert the water into steam by heat, we convert it back into
liquid water by the application of cold. And if we take a glass, or any
other cold thing, and hold it over this steam, see how soon it gets damp
with water; it will condense it until the glass is warm—it condenses the
water which is now running down the sides of it. I have here another
experiment to show the condensation of water from a vaporous state back
into a liquid state, in the same way as the vapour, one of the products of
the candle, was condensed against the bottom of the dish, and obtained
in the form of water; and to show you how truly and thoroughly these

changes take place, I will take this tin flask, which is now full of steam,
and close the top. We shall see what takes place when we cause this
water or steam to return back to the fluid state by pouring some cold
water on the outside. [*The Lecturer poured the cold water over the ves-*

sel, when it immediately collapsed.] You see what has happened. If I had closed the stopper, and still kept the heat applied to it, it would have burst the vessel; yet, when the steam returns to the state of water, the vessel collapses, there being a vacuum produced inside by the condensation of the steam. I show you these experiments for the purpose of pointing out that in all these occurrences there is nothing that changes the water into any other thing—it still remains water; and so the vessel is obliged to give way, and is crushed inwards, as in the other case, by the further application of heat, it would have been blown outwards.

And what do you think the bulk of that water is when it assumes the vaporous condition? You see that cube [*pointing to a cubic foot*]. There, by its side, is a cubic inch, exactly the same shape as the cubic foot, and that bulk of water [*the cubic inch*] is sufficient to expand into that bulk [*the cubic foot*] of steam; and, on the contrary, the application of cold will contract that large quantity of steam into this small quantity of water. [*One of the iron bottles burst at that moment.*] Ah! There is one of our bottles burst, and here you see is a crack down one side an eighth of an inch in width. [*The other now exploded, sending the freezing mixture in all directions.*] This other bottle is also broken; although the iron was nearly half an inch thick, the ice has burst it asunder. These changes always take place in water: they do not require to be always produced by artificial means—we only use them here because we want to produce a small winter round that little bottle, instead of a long and severe one. But if you go to Canada, or to the North, you will find the temperature there out-of-doors will do the same thing as has been done here by the freezing mixture.

To return to our quiet philosophy. We shall not in future be deceived, therefore, by any changes that are produced in water. Water is the same everywhere, whether produced from the ocean or from the flame of the candle. Where, then, is this water which we get from a candle? I must anticipate a little, and tell you. It evidently comes, as to part of it, from the candle; but is it within the candle beforehand? No. It is not in the candle; and it is not in the air round about the candle which is necessary for its combustion. It is neither in one nor the other, but it comes from their conjoint action, a part from the candle, a part from the air; and this we have now to trace, so that we may understand thoroughly

what is the chemical history of a candle when we have it burning on our table. How shall we get at this? I myself know plenty of ways, but I want *you* to get at it from the association in your own minds of what I have already told you.

I think you can see a little in this way. We had just now the case of a substance which acted upon the water in the way that Sir Humphry Davy showed us,[13] and which I am now going to recall to your minds by making again an experiment upon that dish. It is a thing which we have to handle very carefully, for you see, if I allow a little splash of water to come upon this mass, it sets fire to part of it; and if there were free access of air, it would quickly set fire to the whole. Now, this is a metal—a beautiful and bright metal—which rapidly changes in the air, and, as you know, rapidly changes in water. I will put a piece on the water, and you see it burns beautifully, making a floating lamp, using the water in the place of air. Again, if we take a few iron filings or turnings, and put them in water, we find that they likewise undergo an alteration. They do not change so much as this potassium does, but they change somewhat in the same way; they become rusty, and show an action upon the water, though in a different degree of intensity to what this beautiful metal does: but they act upon the water in the same manner generally as this potassium. I want you to put these different facts together in your minds. I have another metal here [*zinc*], and when we examined it with regard to the solid substance produced by its combustion, we had an opportunity of seeing that it burned; and I suppose, if I take a little strip of this zinc and put it over the candle, you will see something half-way, as it were, between the combustion of potassium on the water and the action of iron—you see there is a sort of combustion. It has burned, leaving a white ash or residuum, and here also we find that the metal has a certain amount of action upon water.

By degrees we have learned how to modify the action of these different substances, and to make them tell us what we want to know. And now, first of all, I take iron. It is a common thing in all chemical reactions, where we get any result of this kind, to find that it is increased by the action of heat; and if we want to examine minutely and carefully the action of bodies one upon another, we often have to refer to the action of heat. You are aware, I believe, that iron filings burn beauti-

13. Potassium, the metallic basis of potash, was discovered by Sir Humphry Davy in 1807, who succeeded in separating it from potash by means of a powerful voltaic battery. Its great affinity for oxygen causes it to decompose water with evolution of hydrogen, which takes fire with the heat produced.

fully in the air; but I am about to show you an experiment of this kind, because it will impress upon you what I am going to say about iron in its action on water. If I take a flame and make it hollow—you know why, because I want to get air to it and into it, and therefore I make it hollow —and then take a few iron filings and drop them into the flame, you see how well they burn. That combustion results from the chemical action which is going on when we ignite those particles. And so we proceed to consider these different effects, and ascertain what iron will do when it meets with water. It will tell us the story so beautifully, so gradually and regularly, that I think it will please you very much.

I have here a furnace with a pipe going through it like an iron gun barrel, and I have stuffed that barrel full of bright iron turnings, and placed it across the fire, to be made red-hot. We can either send air through the barrel to come in contact with the iron, or we can send steam from this little boiler at the end of the barrel. Here is a stopcock which shuts off the steam from the barrel until we wish to admit it. There is some water in these glass jars, which I have coloured blue, so that you may see what happens. Now, you know very well that any steam I might send through that barrel, if it went through into the water, would be condensed; for you have seen that steam cannot retain its gaseous form if it be cooled down. You saw it here [*pointing to the tin flask*], crushing itself into a small bulk, and causing the flask holding it to collapse; so that if I were to send steam through that barrel, it would be condensed—supposing the barrel were cold: it is, therefore, heated to

perform the experiment I am now about to show you. I am going to send the steam through the barrel in small quantities; and you shall judge for yourselves, when you see it issue from the other end, whether it still remains steam. Steam is condensable into water, and when you lower the temperature of steam, you convert it back into fluid water; but I have lowered the temperature of the gas which I have collected

in this jar, by passing it through water after it has traversed the iron barrel, and still it does not change back into water. I will take another test and apply to this gas. (I hold the jar in an inverted position, or my substance would escape.) If I now apply a light to the mouth of the jar, it ignites with a slight noise. That tells you that it is not steam. Steam puts out a fire—it does not burn; but you saw that what I had in that jar burnt. We may obtain this substance equally from water produced from the candle-flame as from any other source. When it is obtained by the action of the iron upon the aqueous vapour, it leaves the iron in a state very similar to that in which these filings were after they were burnt. It makes the iron heavier than it was before. So long as the iron remains in the tube and is heated, and is cooled again without the access of air or water, it does not change in its weight; but after having had this current of steam passed over it, it then comes out heavier than it was before, having taken something out of the steam, and having allowed something else to pass forth, which we see here. And now, as we have another jar full, I will show you something most interesting. It is a combustible gas; and I might at once take this jar and set fire to the contents, and show you that it is combustible; but I intend to show you more if I can. It is also

a very light substance. Steam will condense; this body will rise in the air, and not condense. Suppose I take another glass jar, empty of all but air: if I examine it with a taper, I shall find that it contains nothing but air. I will now take this jar full of the gas that I am speaking of, and deal with it as though it were

a light body. I will hold both upside down, and turn the one up under the other; and that which did contain the gas procured from the

steam, what does it contain now? You will find it now only contains air. But look! Here is the combustible substance [*taking the other jar*] which I have poured out of the one jar into the other. It still preserves its quality, and condition, and independence, and therefore is the more worthy of our consideration, as belonging to the products of a candle.

Now, this substance which we have just prepared by the action of iron on the steam or water, we can also get by means of those other things which you have already seen act so well upon the water. If I take a piece of potassium, and make the necessary arrangements, it will produce this gas; and if, instead, a piece of zinc, I find, when I come to examine it very carefully, that the main reason why this zinc cannot act upon the water continuously as the other metal does is because the result of the action of the water envelops the zinc in a kind of protecting coat. We have learned, in consequence, that if we put into our vessel only the zinc and water, they by themselves do not give rise to much action, and we get no result. But suppose I proceed to dissolve off this varnish—this encumbering substance—which I can do by a little acid; the moment I do this, I find the zinc acting upon the water exactly as the iron did, but at the common temperature. The acid in no way is altered, except in its combination with the oxide of zinc, which is produced. I have now poured the acid into the glass, and the effect is as though I were applying heat to cause this boiling up. There is something coming off from the zinc very abundantly, which is not steam. There is a jar full of it; and you will find that I have exactly the same combustible substance remaining in the vessel, when I hold it upside down, that I produced during the experiment with the iron barrel. This is what we get from water—the same substance which is contained in the candle.

Let us now trace distinctly the connection between these two points. This is hydrogen—a body classed among those things which in chemistry we call elements, because we can get nothing else out of them. A candle is not an elementary body, because we can get carbon out of it; we can get this hydrogen out of it, or at least out of the water which it supplies. And this gas has been so named hydrogen, because it is that element which, in association with another, generates water. Mr. Anderson having now been able to get two or three jars of gas, we shall have a few experiments to make, and I want to show you the best way of making these experiments. I am not afraid to show you, for I wish you to make experiments, if you will only make them with care and attention, and the assent of those around you. As we advance in chemistry, we are obliged to deal with substances which are rather injurious, if in their wrong

places—the acids, and heat, and combustible things we use might do harm if carelessly employed. If you want to make hydrogen, you can make it easily from bits of zinc, and sulphuric or muriatic acid. Here is what in former times was called the "philosopher's candle." It is a little phial with a cork, and a tube or pipe passing through it. And I am now putting a few little pieces of zinc into it. This little instrument I am going to apply to a useful purpose in our demonstrations—for I want to show you that you can prepare hydrogen, and make some experiments with it as you please at your own homes. Let me here tell you why I am so careful to fill this phial nearly, and yet not quite full. I do it because the evolved gas, which, as you have seen, is very combustible, is explosive to a considerable extent when mixed with air, and might lead to harm, if you were to apply a light to the end of that pipe before all the air had been swept out of the space above the water. I am now about to pour in the sulphuric acid. I have used very little zinc, and more sulphuric acid and water, because I want to keep it at work for some time. I therefore take care in this way to modify the proportions of the ingredients, so that I may have a regular supply—not too quick, and not too slow. Supposing I now take a glass and put it upside down over the end of the tube; because the hydrogen is light I expect that it will remain in that vessel a little while. We will now test the contents of our glass to see if there be hydrogen in it. I think I am safe in saying we have caught some [*applying a light*]. There it is, you see. I will now apply a light to the

top of the tube. There is the hydrogen burning. There is our philosophical candle. It is a foolish feeble sort of a flame, you may say; but it is so hot that scarcely any common flame gives out so much heat. It goes on burning regularly, and I am now about to put that flame to burn under a certain arrangement, in order that we may examine its results and make use of the information which we may thereby acquire. Inasmuch as the candle produces water, and this gas comes out of the water, let us see what this gives us by the same process of combustion that the candle went through when it burnt in the atmosphere; and for that purpose I am going to put the lamp under this apparatus, in order to condense whatever may arise from the combustion within it. In the course of a short time you will see moisture appearing in the cylinder [p. 401], and you will get the water running down the side; and the water from this hydrogen flame

will have absolutely the same effect upon all our tests, being obtained by the same general process as in the former case. This hydrogen is a very beautiful substance. It is so light that it carries things up: it is far lighter than the atmosphere; and I dare say I can show you this by an experiment which, if you are very clever, some of you may even have skill enough to repeat. Here is our generator of hydrogen, and here are some soap-suds. I have an india-rubber tube connected with the hydrogen generator, and at the end of the tube is a tobacco-pipe. I can thus put the pipe into the suds, and blow bubbles by means of the hydrogen. You observe how the bubbles fall downwards when I blow them with my warm breath; but notice the difference when I blow them with hydrogen. [*The Lecturer here blew bubbles with hydrogen, which rose to the roof of the theatre.*] It shows you how light this gas must be in order to carry with it not merely the ordinary soap-bubble, but the larger portion of a drop hanging to the bottom of it. I can show its lightness in a better way than this; larger bubbles than these may be so lifted up; indeed, in former times balloons used to be filled with this gas. Mr. Anderson will fasten this tube on to our generator, and we shall have a stream of hydrogen here with which we can charge this balloon made of collodion. I need not even be very careful to get all the air out, for I know the power of this gas to carry it up. [*Two collodion balloons were inflated and sent up, one being held by a string.*] Here is another larger one made of thin membrane, which we will fill and allow to ascend. You will see they will all remain floating about until the gas escapes.

What, then, are the comparative weights of these substances? I have a table here which will show you the proportion which their weights bear to each other. I have taken a pint and a cubic foot as the measures, and have placed opposite to them the respective figures. A pint measure of this hydrogen weighs three quarters of our smallest weight (a grain), and a cubic foot weighs one-twelfth of an ounce; whereas a pint of water weighs 8,750 grains, and a cubic foot of water weighs almost 1,000 ounces. You see, therefore, what a vast difference there is between the weight of a cubic foot of water and a cubic foot of hydrogen.

Hydrogen gives rise to no substance that can become solid, either

during combustion or afterwards as a product of its combustion. But when it burns, it produces water only; and if we take a cold glass and put it over the flame, it becomes damp, and you have water produced immediately in appreciable quantity; and nothing is produced by its combustion but the same water which you have seen the flame of the candle produce. It is important to remember that this hydrogen is the only thing in nature which furnishes water as the sole product of combustion.

And now we must endeavour to find some additional proof of the general character and composition of water; and for this purpose I will keep you a little longer, so that at our next meeting we may be better prepared for the subject. We have the power of arranging the zinc, which you have seen acting upon the water by the assistance of an acid, in such a manner as to cause all the power to be evolved in the place where we require it. I have behind me a voltaic pile, and I am just about to show you, at the end of this lecture, its character and power, that you may see what we shall have to deal with when next we meet. I hold here the extremities of the wires which transport the power from behind me, and which I shall cause to act on the water.

We have previously seen what a power of combustion is possessed by the potassium, or the zinc, or the iron filings; but none of them show such energy as this. [*The Lecturer here made contact between the two terminal wires of the battery, when a brilliant flash of light was produced.*] This light is, in fact, produced by a forty-zinc power of burning; it is a power that I can carry about in my hands, through these wires, at pleasure—although, if I applied it wrongly to myself, it would destroy me in an instant, for it is a most intense thing, and the power you see here put forth while you count five [*bringing the poles in contact, and exhibiting the electric light*] is equivalent to the power of several thunder-storms, so great is its force.[14] And that you may see what intense energy it has, I will take the ends of the wires which convey the power from the battery, and with it I dare say I can burn this iron file. Now, this is a chemical power, and one which, when we next meet, I shall apply to water, and show you what results we are able to produce.

LECTURE IV

I see you are not tired of the candle yet, or I am sure you would not be interested in the subject in the way you are. When our candle was burn-

14. Professor Faraday has calculated that there is as much electricity required to decompose one grain of water as there is in a very powerful flash of lightning.

ing, we found it produced water exactly like the water we have around us; and by further examination of this water we found in it that curious body, hydrogen—that light substance of which there is some in this jar. We afterwards saw the burning powers of that hydrogen, and that it produced water. And I think I introduced to your notice an apparatus which I very briefly said was an arrangement of chemical force, or power, or energy, so adjusted as to convey its power to us in these wires; and I said I should use that force to pull the water to pieces, to see what else there was in the water besides hydrogen; because, you remember, when we passed the water through the iron tube, we by no means got the weight of water back which we put in, in the form of steam, though we had a very large quantity of gas evolved. We have now to see what is the other substance present. That you may understand the character and use of this instrument, let us make an experiment or two. Let us put together, first of all, some substances, knowing what they are, and then see what that instrument does to them. There is some copper (observe the various changes which it can undergo), and here is some nitric acid, and you will find that this, being a strong chemical agent, will act very power-fully when I add it to the copper. It is now sending forth a beautiful red vapour; but as we do not want that vapour, Mr. Anderson will hold it near the chimney for a short time, that we may have the use and beauty of the experiment without the annoyance. The copper which I have put into the flask will dissolve: it will change the acid and the water into a blue fluid, containing copper and other things; and I propose then show-ing you how this voltaic battery deals with it; and in the mean time we will arrange another kind of experiment for you to see what power it has. This is a substance which is to us like water—that is to say, it contains bodies which we do not know of as yet, as water contains a body which we do not know as yet. Now, this solution of a salt [15] I will put upon paper, and spread about, and apply the power of the battery to it, and observe what will happen. Three or four important things will happen which we shall take advantage of. I place this wetted paper upon a sheet of tinfoil, which is convenient for keeping all clean, and also for the advantageous application of the power; and this solution, you see, is not at all affected by being put upon the paper or tinfoil, nor by anything else I have brought in contact with it yet, and therefore is free to us to use as

15. A solution of acetate of lead, submitted to the action of the voltaic current, yields lead at the negative pole, and brown peroxide of lead at the positive pole. A solution of nitrate of silver, under the same circumstances, yields silver at the negative pole, and peroxide of silver at the positive pole.

regards that instrument. But first let us see that our instrument is in order. Here are our wires. Let us see whether it is in the state in which it was last time. We can soon tell. As yet, when I bring them together, we have no power, because the conveyors—what we call the electrodes, the passages or ways for the electricity—are stopped; but now Mr. Anderson by that [*referring to a sudden flash at the ends of the wires*] has given me a telegram to say that it is ready. Before I begin our experiment I will get Mr. Anderson to break contact again at the battery behind me, and we will put a platinum-wire across to connect the poles, and then if I find I can ignite a pretty good length of this wire, we shall be safe in our experiment. Now you will see the power. [*The connection was established, and the intermediate wire became red-hot.*] There is the power running beautifully through the wire, which I have made thin on purpose to show you that we have those powerful forces; and now, having that power, we will proceed with it to the examination of water.

I have here two pieces of platinum, and if I lay them down upon this piece of paper [*the moistened paper on the tinfoil*], you will see no action; and if I take them up, there is no change that you can see, but the arrangement remains just as it was before. But, now, see what happens: if I take these two poles and put either one or the other of them down separately on the platinum-plates, they do nothing for me; both are perfectly without action; but if I let them both be in contact at the same moment, see what happens. [*A brown spot appeared under each pole of the battery.*] Look here at the effect that takes place, and see how I have pulled something apart from the white—something brown; and I have no doubt, if I were to arrange it thus, and were to put one of the poles to the tinfoil on the other side of the paper—why, I get such a beautiful action upon the paper, that I am going to see whether I cannot write with it—a telegram, if you please. [*The Lecturer here traced the word "juvenile" on the paper with one of the terminal wires.*] See there how beautifully we can get our results!

You see we have here drawn something, which we have not known about before, out of this solution. Let us now take that flask from Mr. Anderson's hands, and see what we can draw out of that. This, you know, is a liquid which we have just made up from copper and nitric acid, while our other experiments were in hand; and though I am making this experiment very hastily, and may bungle a little, yet I prefer to let you see what I do rather than prepare it beforehand.

Now, see what happens. These two platinum-plates are the two ends (or I will make them so immediately) of this apparatus; and I am about

to put them in contact with that solution just as we did a moment ago on the paper. It does not matter to us whether the solution be on the paper or whether it be in the jar, so long as we bring the ends of the apparatus to it. If I put the two platinums in by themselves, they come out as clean and as white as they go in [*inserting them into the fluid without connecting them with the battery*]; but when we take the power and lay that on [*the platinums were connected with the battery and again dipped into the solution*], this, you see [*exhibiting one of the platinums*], is at once turned into copper, as it were: it has become like a plate of copper; and that [*exhibiting the other piece of platinum*] has come out quite clean. If I take this coppered piece and change sides, the copper will leave the right-hand side and come over to the left side; what was before the coppered plate comes out clean, and the plate which was clean comes out coated with copper; and thus you see that the same copper we put into this solution we can also take out of it by means of this instrument.

Putting that solution aside, let us now see what effect this instrument [see drawing below] will have upon water. Here are two little platinum-plates which I intend to make the ends of the battery, and this [c] is a little vessel so shaped as to enable me to take it to pieces, and show you its construction. Into these two cups [A *and* B] I pour mercury, which touches the ends of the wires connected with the platinum-plates. In the vessel [c] I pour some water containing a little acid (but which is put only for the purpose of facilitating the action; it undergoes no change in the process), and connected with the top of the vessel is a bent glass tube [D], which may remind you of the pipe which was connected with the gun barrel in our furnace experiment, and which now passes under the

jar [F]. I have now adjusted this apparatus, and we will proceed to affect the water in some way or other. In the other case, I sent the water through a tube which was made red-hot; I am now going to pass the electricity through the contents of this vessel. Perhaps I may boil the water; if I do boil the water, I shall get steam; and you know that steam condenses when it gets cold, and you will therefore see by that whether I do boil the water or not. Perhaps, however, I shall not boil the water, but produce some other effect. You shall have the experiment and see. There is one wire which I will put to this side [A], and here is the other wire which I will put to the other side [B], and you will soon see whether any disturbance takes place. Here it is seeming to boil up famously; but does it boil? Let us see whether that which goes out is steam or not. I think you will soon see the jar [F] will be filled with vapour, if that which rises from the water is steam. But can it be steam? Why, certainly not; because there it remains, you see, unchanged. There it is standing over the water, and it cannot therefore be steam, but must be a permanent gas of some sort. What is it? Is it hydrogen? Is it anything else? Well, we will examine it. If it is hydrogen, it will burn. [*The Lecturer then ignited a portion of the gas collected, which burnt with an explosion.*] It is certainly something combustible, but not combustible in the way that hydrogen is. Hydrogen would not have given you that noise; but the colour of that light, when the thing did burn, was like that of hydrogen: it will, however, burn without contact with the air. That is why I have chosen this other form of apparatus, for the purpose of pointing out to you what are the particular circumstances of this experiment. In place of an open vessel I have taken one that is closed (our battery is so beautifully active that we are even boiling the mercury, and getting all things right—not wrong, but vigorously right); and I am going to show you that that gas, whatever it may be, can burn without air, and in that respect differs from a candle, which cannot burn without the air. And our manner of doing this is as follows: I have here a glass vessel [G] which is fitted with two platinum-wires [I *and* K], through which I can apply electricity; and we can put the vessel on the air-pump and exhaust the air, and when we have taken the air out we can bring it here and fasten it on to this jar [F], and let into the vessel that gas which was formed by the action of the voltaic battery upon the water, and which we have produced by changing the water into it—for I may go as far as this, and say we have really, by that experiment, changed the water into that gas. We have not only altered its condition, but we have changed it really and truly into that gaseous substance, and all the water is there

which was decomposed by the experiment. As I screw this vessel [G H] on here [H], and make the tubes well connected, and when I open the stopcocks [H, H, H], if you watch the level of the water [in F], you will see that the gas will rise. I will now close the stopcocks, as I have drawn up as much as the vessel can hold, and being safely conveyed into that chamber, I will pass into it an electric spark from this Leyden jar [L], when the vessel, which is now quite clear and bright, will become dim. There will be no sound, for the vessel is strong enough to confine the explosion. [*A spark was then passed through the jar, when the explosive mixture was ignited.*] Did you see that brilliant light? If I again screw the vessel on to the jar, and open these stopcocks, you will see that the gas will rise a second time. [*The stopcocks were then opened.*] Those gases [*referring to the gases first collected in the jar, and which had just been ignited by the electric spark*] have disappeared, as you see: their place is vacant, and fresh gas has gone in. Water has been formed from them; and if we repeat our operation [*repeating the last experiment*], I shall have another vacancy, as you will see by the water rising. I always have an empty vessel after the explosion, because the vapour or gas into which that water has been resolved by the battery explodes under the influence of the spark, and changes into water; and by and by you will see in this upper vessel some drops of water trickling down the sides and collecting at the bottom.

We are here dealing with water entirely, without reference to the atmosphere. The water of the candle had the atmosphere helping to produce it; but in this way it can be produced independently of the air. Water, therefore, ought to contain that other substance which the candle takes from the air, and which, combining with the hydrogen, produces water.

Just now you saw that one end of this battery took hold of the copper, extracting it from the vessel which contained the blue solution. It was effected by this wire; and surely we may say, if the battery has such power with a metallic solution which we made and unmade, may we not find that it is possible to split asunder the component parts of the water, and put them into this place and that place? Suppose I take the poles—the metallic ends of this battery—and see what will happen with the water in this apparatus [see fig. on p. 408], where we have separated the two ends far apart. I place one here [at A], and the other there [at B], and I have little shelves with holes which I can put upon each pole, and so arrange them that whatever escapes from the two ends of the battery will appear as separate gases; for you saw that the water

did not become vaporous, but gaseous. The wires are now in perfect and proper connection with the vessel containing the water; and you see the bubbles rising: let us collect these bubbles and see what they are. Here is a glass cylinder [o]; I fill it with water and put it over one end [A] of

the pile; and I will take another [H] and put it over the other end [B] of the pile. And so now we have a double apparatus, with both places delivering gas. Both these jars will fill with gas. There they go, that to the right [H] filling very rapidly; the one to the left [o] filling not so rapidly; and though I have allowed some bubbles to escape, yet still the action is going on pretty regularly;

and were it not that one is rather smaller than the other, you would see that I should have twice as much in this [H] as I have in that [o]. Both these gases are colourless; they stand over the water without condensing; they are alike in all things—I mean in all *apparent* things; and we have here an opportunity of examining these bodies and ascertaining what they are. Their bulk is large, and we can easily apply experiments to them. I will take this jar [H] first, and will ask you to be prepared to recognize hydrogen.

Think of all its qualities—the light gas which stood well in inverted vessels, burning with a pale flame at the mouth of the jar—and see whether this gas does not satisfy all these conditions. If it be hydrogen, it will remain here while I hold this jar inverted. [*A light was then applied, when the hydrogen burnt.*] What is there now in the other jar? You know that the two together made an explosive mixture. But what can this be which we find as the other constituent in water, and which must therefore be that substance which made the hydrogen burn? We know that the water we put into the vessel consisted of the two things together. We find one of these is hydrogen; what must that other be which was in the water before the experiment, and which we now have by itself? I am about to put this lighted splinter of wood into the gas. The gas itself will not burn, but it will make the splinter of wood burn. [*The Lecturer ignited the end of the wood, and introduced it into the*

jar of gas.] See how it invigorates the combustion of the wood, and how it makes it burn far better than the air would make it burn; and now you see by itself that very other substance which is contained in the water, and which, when the water was formed by the burning of the candle, must have been taken from the atmosphere. What shall we call it, A, B, or C? Let us call it O—call it "Oxygen": it is a very good distinct-sounding name. This, then, is the oxygen which was present in the water, forming so large a part of it.

We shall now begin to understand more clearly our experiments and researches; because, when we have examined these things once or twice, we shall soon see why a candle burns in the air. When we have in this way analysed the water—that is to say, separated, or electrolyzed, its parts out of it—we get two volumes of hydrogen, and one of the body that burns it. And these two are represented to us on the following diagram, with their weights also stated; and we shall find that the oxygen is a very heavy body by comparison with the hydrogen. It is the other element in water.

VOLUME

			WEIGHT
	8 Oxygen	Oxygen	88.9
1 Hydrogen		Hydrogen	11.1
	9	Water	100.0

I had better, perhaps, tell you now how we get this oxygen abundantly, having shown you how we can separate it from the water. Oxygen, as you will immediately imagine, exists in the atmosphere; for how should the candle burn to produce water without it? Such a thing would be absolutely impossible, and chemically impossible, without oxygen. Can we get it from the air? Well, there are some very complicated and difficult processes by which we can get it from the air; but we have better processes. There is a substance called the black oxide of manganese: it is a very black-looking mineral, but very useful, and when made red-hot gives out oxygen. Here is an iron bottle which has had some of this substance put into it, and there is a tube fixed to it, and a fire ready made, and Mr. Anderson will put that retort into the fire, for it is made of iron, and can stand the heat. Here is a salt called chlorate of potassa, which is now made in large quantities for bleaching, and chemical and medical uses, and for pyrotechnic and other purposes. I will take some and

mix it with some of the oxide of manganese (oxide of copper, or oxide of iron would do as well); and if I put these together in a retort, far less than a red heat is sufficient to evolve this oxygen from the mixture. I am not preparing to make much, because we only want sufficient for our experi-

ments; only, as you will see immediately, if I use too small a charge, the first portion of the gas will be mixed with the air already in the retort, and I should be obliged to sacrifice the first portion of the gas, because it would be so much diluted with air; the first portion must therefore be thrown away. You will find, in this case, that a common spirit-lamp is quite sufficient for me to get the oxygen, and so we shall have two proc-esses going on for its preparation. See how freely the gas is coming over from that small portion of the mixture. We will examine it, and see what are its properties. Now, in this way we are producing, as you will observe, a gas just like the one we had in the experiment with the battery—transparent, undissolved by water, and presenting the ordinary visible properties of the atmosphere. (As this first jar contains the air, together with the first portions of the oxygen set free during the preparation, we will carry it out of the way, and be prepared to make our experiments in a regular, dignified man-ner.) And, inasmuch as that power of making wood, wax, or other things burn, was so marked in the oxygen we obtained by means of the voltaic battery from water, we may expect to find the same property here. We will try it. You see there is the combustion of a lighted taper in air, and here is its combustion in this gas [*lowering the taper into the jar*]. See how brightly and how beautifully it burns! You can also see more than this—you will perceive it is a heavy gas, while the hydrogen would go up like a balloon, or even faster than a balloon, when not encumbered with the weight of the envelope. You may easily see that although we obtained from water twice as much in volume of the hydrogen as of oxy-gen, it does not follow that we have twice as much in weight—because one is heavy, and the other a very light gas. We have means of weighing gases or air; but without stopping to explain that, let me just tell you what their respective weights are. The weight of a pint of hydrogen is three-quarters of a grain; the weight of the same quantity of oxygen is nearly twelve grains. This

is a very great difference. The weight of a cubic foot of hydrogen is one-twelfth of an ounce; and the weight of a cubic foot of oxygen is one ounce and a third. And so on we might come to masses of matter which may be weighed in the balance, and which we can take account of as to hundredweights and as to tons, as you will see almost immediately.

Hydrogen

Oxygen

Now, as regards this very property of oxygen supporting combustion, which we may compare to air, I will take a piece of candle to show it you in a rough way, and the result will be rough. There is our candle burning in the air: how will it burn in oxygen? I have here a jar of this gas, and I am about to put it over the candle for you to compare the action of this gas with that of the air. Why, look at it: it looks something like the light you saw at the poles of the voltaic battery. Think how vigorous that action must be! And yet, during all that action, nothing more is produced than what is produced by the burning of the candle in air. We have the same production of water, and the same phenomena exactly, when we use this gas instead of air, as we have when the candle is burnt in air.

But now we have got a knowledge of this new substance, we can look

at it a little more distinctly, in order to satisfy ourselves that we have got a good general understanding of this part of the product of a candle. It is wonderful how great the supporting powers of this substance are as regards combustion. For instance, here is a lamp which, simple though it be, is the original, I may say, of a great variety of lamps which are constructed for divers purposes—for lighthouses, microscopic illuminations, and other uses; and if it were proposed to make it burn very brightly, you would say, "If a candle burnt better in oxygen, will not a lamp do the same?" Why, it will do so. Mr. Anderson will give me a tube coming from our oxygen reservoir, and I am about to apply it to this flame, which I will previously make burn

badly on purpose. There comes the oxygen: what a combustion that makes! But if I shut it off, what becomes of the lamp? [*The flow of oxygen was stopped, and the lamp relapsed to its former dimness.*] It is wonderful how, by means of oxygen, we get combustion accelerated. But it does not affect merely the combustion of hydrogen, or carbon, or the candle; but it exalts all combustions of the common kind. We will take one which relates to iron, for instance, as you have already seen iron burn

a little in the atmosphere. Here is a jar of oxygen, and this is a piece of iron wire; but if it were a bar as thick as my wrist, it would burn the same. I first attach a little piece of wood to the iron, I then set the wood on fire, and let them both down together into the jar. The wood is now alight, and there it burns as wood should burn in oxygen; but it will soon communicate its combustion to the iron. The iron is now burning brilliantly, and will continue so for a long time. As long as we supply oxygen, so long can we carry on the combustion of the iron, until the latter is consumed.

We will now put that on one side, and take some other substance; but we must limit our experiments, for we have not time to spare for all the illustrations you would have a right to if we had more time. We will take a piece of sulphur—you know how sulphur burns in the air—well, we put it into the oxygen, and you will see that whatever can burn in air can burn with a far greater intensity in oxygen, leading you to think that perhaps the atmosphere itself owes all its power of combustion to this gas. The sulphur is now burning very quietly in the oxygen; but you cannot for a moment mistake the very high and increased action which takes place when it is so burnt, instead of being burnt merely in common air.

I am now about to show you the combustion of another substance—phosphorus. I can do it better for you here than you can do it at home. This is a very combustible substance; and if it be so combustible in air, what might you expect it would be in oxygen? I am about to show it to you, not in its fullest intensity, for if I did so we should almost blow the apparatus up—I may even now crack the jar, though I do not want to break things carelessly. You see how it burns in the air. But what a glorious light it gives out when I introduce it into oxygen! [*Introducing*

the lighted phosphorus into the jar of oxygen] There you see the solid particles going off which cause that combustion to be so brilliantly luminous.

Thus far we have tested this power of oxygen, and the high combustion it produces, by means of other substances. We must now, for a little while longer, look at it as respects the hydrogen. You know, when we allowed the oxygen and the hydrogen derived from the water to mix and burn together, we had a little explosion. You remember, also, that when I burnt the oxygen and the hydrogen in a jet together, we got very little light, but great heat. I am now about to set fire to oxygen and hydrogen, mixed in the proportion in which they occur in water. Here is a vessel containing one volume of oxygen and two volumes of hydrogen. This mixture is exactly of the same nature as the gas we just now obtained from the voltaic battery: it would be far too much to burn at once; I have therefore arranged to blow soap-bubbles with it, and burn those bubbles, that we may see by a general experiment or two how this oxygen supports the combustion of the hydrogen. First of all, we will see whether we can blow a bubble. Well, there goes the gas [*causing it to issue through a tobacco-pipe into some soap-suds*]. Here I have a bubble. I am receiving them on my hand: and you will perhaps think I am acting oddly in this experiment; but it is to show you that we must not always trust to noise and sounds, but rather to real facts [*exploding a bubble on the palm of his hand*]. I am afraid to fire a bubble from the end of the pipe, because the explosion would pass up into the jar and blow it to pieces. This oxygen then will unite with the hydrogen, as you see by the phenomena, and hear by the sound, with the utmost readiness of action, and all its powers are then taken up in its neutralization of the qualities of the hydrogen.

So now I think you will perceive the whole history of water with reference to oxygen and the air, from what we have before said. Why does a piece of potassium decompose water? Because it finds oxygen in the water. What is set free when I put it in the water, as I am about to do again? It sets free hydrogen, and the hydrogen burns; but the potassium itself combines with oxygen; and this piece of potassium, in taking the water apart—the water, you may say, derived from the combustion of the candle—takes away the oxygen which the candle took from the air, and so sets the hydrogen free; and even if I take a piece of ice, and put a piece of potassium upon it, the beautiful affinities by which the oxygen and the hydrogen are related are such that the ice will absolutely set fire to the potassium. I show this to you today, in order to enlarge your

ideas of these things, and that you may see how greatly results are modified by circumstances. There is the potassium on the ice, producing a sort of volcanic action.

It will be my place, when next we meet, having pointed out these anomalous actions, to show you that none of these extra and strange effects are met with by us—that none of these strange and injurious actions take place when we are burning, not merely a candle, but gas in our streets, or fuel in our fire places—so long as we confine ourselves within the laws that Nature has made for our guidance.

LECTURE V

We have now seen that we can produce hydrogen and oxygen from the water that we obtained from the candle. Hydrogen, you know, comes from the candle, and oxygen, you believe, comes from the air. But then you have a right to ask me, "How is it that the air and the oxygen do not equally well burn the candle?" If you remember what happened when I put a jar of oxygen over a piece of candle, you recollect there was a very different kind of combustion to that which took place in the air. Now, why is this? It is a very important question, and one I shall endeavour to make you understand: it relates most intimately to the nature of the atmosphere, and is most important to us.

We have several tests for oxygen besides the mere burning of bodies. You have seen a candle burnt in oxygen, or in the air; you have seen phosphorus burnt in the air, or in oxygen; and you have seen iron filings burnt in oxygen. But we have other tests besides these, and I am about to refer to one or two of them for the purpose of carrying your conviction and your experience further. Here we have a vessel of oxygen. I will show its presence to you: if I take a little spark and put it into that oxygen, you know, by the experience you gained the last time we met, what will happen; if I put that spark into the jar, it will tell you whether we have oxygen here or not. Yes! We have proved it by combustion; and now here is another test for oxygen, which is a very curious and useful one. I have here two jars full of gas, with a plate between them to prevent their mixing; I take the plate away, and the gases are creeping one into the other. "What happens?" say you. "They together produce no such combustion as was seen in the case of the candle." But see how the presence of oxygen is told by its association with this other substance.[16] What a beautifully coloured gas I have obtained in this way, showing me

16. The gas which is thus employed as a test for the presence of oxygen is the binoxide of nitrogen, or nitrous oxide. It is a colourless gas, which, when brought in contact with oxygen, unites with it, forming hyponitric acid, the red gas referred to.

the presence of the oxygen! In the same way we can try this experiment by mixing common air with this test gas. Here is a jar containing air—such air as the candle would burn in—and here is a jar or bottle containing the test gas. I let them come together over water, and you see the result: the contents of the test bottle are flowing into the jar of air, and you see I obtain exactly the same kind of action as before, and that shows me that there is oxygen in the air—the very same substance that has been already obtained by us from the water produced by the candle. But then, beyond that, how is it that the candle does not burn in air as well as in oxygen? We will come to that point at once. I have here two jars; they are filled to the same height with gas, and the appearance to the eye is alike in both, and I really do not know at present which of these jars contains oxygen and which contains air, although I know they have previously been filled with these gases. But here is our test gas, and I am going to work with the two jars, in order to examine whether there is any difference between them in the quality of reddening this gas. I am now going to turn this test gas into one of the jars, and observe what happens. There is reddening, you see; there is then oxygen present. We will now test the other jar; but you see this is not so distinctly red as the first: and, further, this curious thing happens—if I take these two gases and shake them well together with water, we shall absorb the red gas; and then, if I put in more of this test gas and shake again, we shall absorb more; and I can go on as long as there be any oxygen present to produce that effect. If I let in air, it will not matter; but the moment I introduce water, the red gas disappears; and I may go on in this way, putting in more and more of the test gas, until I come to something left behind which will not redden any longer by the use of that particular body that rendered the air and the oxygen red. Why is that? You see in a moment it is because there is, besides oxygen, something else present which is left behind. I will let a little more air into the jar, and if it turns red you will know that some of that reddening gas is still present, and that consequently it was not for the want of this producing body that the air was left behind.

Now, you will begin to understand what I am about to say. You saw that when I burnt phosphorus in a jar, as the smoke produced by the phosphorus and the oxygen of the air condensed, it left a good deal of gas unburnt, just as this red gas left something untouched—there was, in fact, this gas left behind, which the phosphorus cannot touch, which the reddening gas cannot touch, and this something is not oxygen, and yet is part of the atmosphere.

So that is one way of opening out air into the two things of which it is

composed—oxygen, which burns our candles, our phosphorus, or anything else; and this other substance—nitrogen—which will not burn them. This other part of the air is by far the larger proportion, and it is a very curious body, when we come to examine it; it is remarkably curious, and yet you say, perhaps, that it is very uninteresting. It is uninteresting in some respects because of this—that it shows no brilliant effects of combustion. If I test it with a taper as I do oxygen and hydrogen, it does not burn like hydrogen, nor does it make the taper burn like oxygen. Try it in any way I will, it does neither the one thing nor the other: it will not take fire; it will not let the taper burn; it puts out the combustion of everything. There is nothing that will burn in it in common circumstances. It has no smell; it is not sour; it does not dissolve in water; it is neither an acid nor an alkali; it is as indifferent to all our organs as it is possible for a thing to be. And you might say, "It is nothing; it is not worth chemical attention; what does it do in the air?" Ah! then come our beautiful and fine results shown us by an observant philosophy. Suppose, in place of having nitrogen, or nitrogen and oxygen, we had pure oxygen as our atmosphere; what would become of us? You know very well that a piece of iron lit in a jar of oxygen goes on burning to the end. When you see a fire in an iron grate, imagine where the grate would go to if the whole of the atmosphere were oxygen. The grate would burn up more powerfully than the coals—for the iron of the grate itself is even more combustible than the coals which we burn in it. A fire put into the middle of a locomotive would be a fire in a magazine of fuel, if the atmosphere were oxygen. The nitrogen lowers it down and makes it moderate and useful for us, and then, with all that, it takes away with it the fumes that you have seen produced from the candle, disperses them throughout the whole of the atmosphere, and carries them away to places where they are wanted to perform a great and glorious purpose of good to man, for the sustenance of vegetation; and thus does a most wonderful work, although you say, on examining it, "Why, it is a perfectly indifferent thing." This nitrogen in its ordinary state is an inactive element; no action short of the most intense electric force, and then in the most infinitely small degree, can cause the nitrogen to combine directly with the other element of the atmosphere, or with other things round about it; it is a perfectly indifferent, and therefore to say, a safe substance.

But before I take you to that result, I must tell you about the atmosphere itself. I have written on this diagram the composition of one hundred parts of atmospheric air:

	Bulk	Weight
Oxygen	20	22.3
Nitrogen	80	77.7
	100	100.0

It is a true analysis of the atmosphere, so far as regards the quantity of oxygen and the quantity of nitrogen present. By our analysis, we find that 5 pints of the atmosphere contain only 1 pint of oxygen, and 4 pints, or 4 parts, of nitrogen by bulk. That is our analysis of the atmosphere. It requires all that quantity of nitrogen to reduce the oxygen down, so as to be able to supply the candle properly with fuel, so as to supply us with an atmosphere which our lungs can healthily and safely breathe; for it is just as important to make the oxygen right for us to breathe, as it is to make the atmosphere right for the burning of the fire and the candle.

But now for this atmosphere. First of all, let me tell you the weight of these gases. A pint of nitrogen weighs $10\frac{4}{10}$ grains, or a cubic foot weighs $1\frac{1}{6}$ ounce. That is the weight of the nitrogen. The oxygen is heavier: a pint of it weighs $11\frac{9}{10}$ grains, and a cubic foot weighs $1\frac{1}{3}$ ounce. A pint of air weighs about $10\frac{7}{10}$ grains, and a cubic foot $1\frac{1}{5}$ ounce.

You have asked me several times, and I am very glad you have, "How do you weigh gases?" I will show you; it is very simple, and easily done. Here is a balance, and here a copper bottle, made as light as we can consistent with due strength, turned very nicely in the lathe, and made perfectly air-tight, with a stopcock, which we can open and shut, which at present is open, and therefore allows the bottle to be full of air. I have here a nicely adjusted balance, in which I think the bottle, in its present condition, will be balanced by the weight on the other side. And here is a pump by which we can force the air into this bottle, and with it we will force in a certain number of volumes of air, as measured by the pump. [*Twenty measures were pumped in.*] We will shut that in and put it in the balance. See how it sinks: it is much heavier than it was. By what? By the air that we have forced into it by the pump. There is not a greater *bulk* of air, but there is the same bulk of *heavier* air, because we have forced in air upon it. And that you may have a fair notion in your mind as to how much this air measures, here is a jar full of water. We will open that copper vessel into this jar, and let the air

return to its former state. All I have to do now is to screw them tightly together, and to turn the taps, when there, you see, is the bulk of the twenty pumps of air which I forced into the bottle; and to make sure *t*hat we have been quite correct in what we have been doing, we will

take the bottle again to the balance, and, if it is now counterpoised by the original weight, we shall be quite sure we have made our experiment correctly. It is balanced; so, you see, we can find out the weight of the extra volumes of air forced in, in that way, and by that means we are able to ascertain that a cubic foot of air weighs 1⅕ ounce. But that small experiment will by no means convey to your mind the whole literal truth of this matter. It is wonderful how it accumulates when you come to larger volumes. This

bulk of air [*a cubic foot*] weighs 1⅕ ounce. What do you think of the contents of that box above there, which I have had made for the purpose? The air which is within that box weighs one pound—a full pound; and I have calculated the weight of the air in this room—you would hardly imagine it, but it is above a ton. So rapidly do the weights rise up, and so important is the presence of the atmosphere, and of the oxygen and the nitrogen in it, and the use it performs in conveying things to and fro from place to place, and carrying bad vapours to places where they will do good instead of harm.

Having given you that little illustration with respect to the weight of the air, let me show you certain consequences of it. You have a right to them, because you would not understand so much without it. Do you remember this kind of experiment? Have you ever seen it? Suppose I take a pump somewhat similar to the one I had a little while ago to force air into the bottle, and suppose I place it in such a manner that by certain arrangements I can apply my hand to it: my hand moves about in the air so easily that it seems to feel nothing, and I can hardly get velocity enough by any motion of my own in the atmosphere to make sure that there is much resistance to it. But, when I put my hand here [*on the air-pump receiver, which was afterwards exhausted*], you see what happens. Why is my hand fastened to this place, and why am I

able to pull this pump about? And see! how is it that I can hardly get my hand away? Why is this? It is the weight of the air—the weight of the air that is above. I have another experiment here, which I think will explain to you more about it. When the air is pumped from underneath the bladder which is stretched over this glass, you will see the effect in another shape: the top is quite flat at present, but I will make a very little motion with the pump, and now look at it—see how it has gone down, see how it is bent in. You will see the bladder go in more and more, until at last I expect it will be driven in and broken by the force

of the atmosphere pressing upon it. [*The bladder at last broke with a loud report.*] Now, that was done entirely by the weight of the air pressing on it, and you can easily understand how that is. The particles that are piled up in the atmosphere stand upon each other, as these five cubes do [p. 420]. You can easily conceive that four of these five cubes are resting upon the bottom one, and if I take that away, the others will all sink down. So it is with the atmosphere: the air that is above is sustained by the air that is beneath; and when the air is pumped away from beneath them, the change occurs which you saw when I placed my hand on the air-pump, and which you saw in the case of the bladder, and which you shall see better here. I have tied over this jar a piece of sheet india-rubber, and I am now about to take away the air from the inside of the jar; and if you will watch the india-rubber—which acts as a partition between the air below and the air above—you will see, when I pump, how the pressure shows itself. See where it is going to—I can actually put my hand into the jar; and yet this result is only caused by the great and powerful action of the air above. How beautifully it shows this curious circumstance!

Here is something that you can have a pull at, when I have finished to-day. It is a little apparatus of two hollow brass hemispheres, closely fitted together, and having connected with it a pipe and a cock, through which we can exhaust the air from the inside; and although the two

halves are so easily taken apart, while the air is left within, yet you will see, when we exhaust it by and by, no power of any two of you will be able to pull them apart. Every square inch of surface that is contained in

the area of that vessel sustains fifteen pounds by weight, or nearly so, when the air is taken out; and you may try your strength presently in seeing whether you can overcome that pressure of the atmosphere.

Here is another very pretty thing—the boys' sucker, only refined by the philosopher. We young ones have a perfect right to take toys, and make them into philosophy, inasmuch as now-a-days we are turning philosophy into toys. Here is a sucker, only it is made of india-rubber: if I clap it upon the table, you see at once it holds. Why does it hold? I can slip it about, and yet if I try to pull it up, it seems as if it would pull the table with it. I can easily make it slip about from place to place; but only when I bring it to the edge of the table can I get it off. It is only kept down by the pressure of the atmosphere above. We have a couple of them; and if you take these two and press them together, you will see how firmly they stick. And, indeed, we may use them as they are proposed to be used, to stick against windows, or against walls, where they will adhere for an evening, and serve to hang anything on that you want. I think, however, that you boys ought to be shown experiments that you can make at home; and so here is a very pretty experiment in illustration of the pressure of the atmosphere. Here is a tumbler of water. Suppose I were to ask you to turn that tumbler upside down, so that the water should not fall out, and yet not be kept in by your hand, but merely by using the pressure of the atmosphere. Could you do that? Take a wine-glass, either quite full or half full of water, and put a flat card on the top, turn it upside down, and then see what becomes of the card and of the water. The air cannot get in because the water by its capillary attraction round the edge keeps it out.

I think this will give you a correct notion of what you may call the materiality of the air; and when I tell you that the box holds a pound of it, and this room more than a ton, you will begin to think that air is

something very serious. I will make another experiment, to convince you of this positive resistance. There is that beautiful experiment of the pop-gun, made so well and so easily, you know, out of a quill, or a tube or anything of that kind, where we take a slice of potato, for instance, or an apple, and take the tube and cut out a pellet, as I have now done, and push it to one end. I have made that end tight; and now I take another piece and put it in: it will confine the air that is within the tube perfectly and completely for our purpose; and I shall now find it absolutely impossible by any force of mine to drive that little pellet close up to the other. It cannot be done. I may press the air to a certain extent, but if I go on pressing, long before it comes to the second, the confined air will drive the front one out with a force something like that of gunpowder; for gunpowder is in part dependent upon the same action that you see here exemplified.

I saw the other day an experiment which pleased me much, as I thought it would serve our purpose here. (I ought to have held my tongue for four or five minutes before beginning this experiment, because it depends upon my lungs for success.) By the proper application of air I expect to be able to drive this egg out of one cup into the other by the force of my breath; but if I fail, it is in a good cause; and I do not promise success, because I have been talking more than I ought to do to make the experiment succeed.

[*The Lecturer here tried the experiment, and succeeded in blowing the egg from one egg-cup to the other.*]

You see that the air which I blow goes downwards between the egg and the cup, and makes a blast under the egg, and is thus able to lift a heavy thing—for a full egg is a very heavy thing for air to lift. If you want to make the experiment, you had better boil the egg quite hard first, and then you may very safely try to blow it from one cup to the other, with a little care.

I have now kept you long enough upon this property of the weight of the air, but there is another thing I should like to mention. You saw the way in which, in this pop-gun, I was able to drive the second piece of potato half or two-thirds of an inch before the first piece started, by virtue of the elasticity of the air—just as I pressed into the copper bottle the particles of air by means of the pump. Now, this depends upon a wonderful property in the air, namely, its elasticity; and I should like to give you a good illustration of this. If I take anything that confines the air properly, as this membrane, which also is able to contract and expand so as to give us a measure of the elasticity of the air, and confine in

this bladder a certain portion of air; and then, if we take the atmosphere off from the outside of it, just as in these cases we put the pressure on —if we take the pressure off, you will see how it will then go on expanding and expanding, larger and larger, until it will fill the whole of this bell-jar, showing you that wonderful property of the air, its elasticity, its compressibility, and expansibility, to an exceedingly large extent, and which is very essential for the purposes and services it performs in the economy of creation.

We will now turn to another very important part of our subject, remembering that we have examined the candle in its burning, and have found that it gives rise to various products. We have the products, you know, of soot, of water, and of something else which you have not yet examined. We have collected the water, but have allowed the other things to go into the air. Let us now examine some of these other products.

Here is an experiment which I think will help you in part in this way. We will put our candle there, and place over it a chimney, thus. I think my candle will go on burning, because the air-passage is open at the bottom and the top. In the first place, you see the moisture appearing— that you know about. It is water produced from the candle by the action of the air upon its hydrogen. But, besides that, something is going out at the top: it is not moisture—it is not water—it is not condensable; and yet, after all, it has very singular properties. You will find that the air coming out of the top of our chimney is nearly sufficient to blow out

the light I am holding to it; and if I put the light fairly opposed to the current, it will blow it quite out. You will say that is as it should be; and I am supposing that you think it ought to do so, because the nitrogen does not support combustion, and ought to put the candle out, since the candle will not burn in nitrogen. But is there nothing else there than nitrogen? I must now anticipate—that is to say, I must use my own knowledge to supply you with the means that we adopt for the purpose of ascertaining these things, and examining such gases as these. I will take an empty bottle—here is one—and if I hold it over this chimney, I shall get the combustion of the candle below sending its results into the bottle above; and we shall soon find that this bottle con-

tains, not merely an air that is bad as regards the combustion of a taper put into it, but having other properties.

Let me take a little quicklime and pour some common water on to it —the commonest water will do. I will stir it a moment, then pour it upon a piece of filtering paper in a funnel, and we shall very quickly have a clear water proceeding to the bottle below, as I have here. I have plenty of this water in another bottle; but, nevertheless, I should like to use the lime-water that was prepared before you, so that you may see what its uses are. If I take some of this beautiful clear lime-water, and pour it into this jar, which has collected the air from the candle, you will see a change coming about. Do you see that the water has become quite milky? Observe, that will not happen with air merely. Here is a bottle filled with air; and if I put a little lime-water into it, neither the oxygen nor the nitrogen, nor anything else that is in that quantity of air, will make any change in the lime-water. It remains perfectly clear, and no shaking of that quantity of lime-water with that quantity of air in its common state will cause any change; but if I take this bottle with the lime-water, and hold it so as to get the general products of the candle in contact with it, in a very short time we shall have it milky. There is the chalk, consisting of the lime which we used in making the lime-water, combined with something that came from the candle—that other product which we are in search of, and which I want to tell you about to-day. This is a substance made visible to us by its action, which is not the action of the lime-water either upon the oxygen or upon the nitrogen, nor upon the water itself, but it is something new to us from the candle. And then we find this white powder, produced by the lime-water and the vapour from the candle, appears to us very much like whitening or chalk, and, when examined, it does prove to be exactly the same substance as whitening or chalk. So we are led, or have been led, to observe upon the various circumstances of this experiment, and to trace this production of chalk to its various causes, to give us the true knowledge of the nature of this combustion of the candle—to find that this substance, issuing from the candle, is exactly the same as that substance which would issue from a retort, if I were to put some chalk into it with a little moisture, and make it red-hot: you would then find that exactly the same substance would issue from it as from the candle.

But we have a better means of getting this substance, and in greater quantity, so as to ascertain what its general characters are. We find this substance in very great abundance in a multitude of cases where you would least expect it. All limestones contain a great deal of this gas

which issues from the candle, and which we call *carbonic acid.* All chalks, all shells, all corals contain a great quantity of this curious air. We find it fixed in these stones; for which reason Dr. Black called it "fixed air"—finding it in these fixed things like marble and chalk. He called it fixed air, because it lost its quality of air, and assumed the condition of a solid body. We can easily get this air from marble. Here is a jar containing a little muriatic acid, and here is a taper which, if I put it into that jar, will show only the presence of common air. There is, you see, pure air down to the bottom; the jar is full of it. Here is a substance— marble,[17] a very beautiful and superior marble—and if I put these pieces of marble into the jar, a great boiling apparently goes on. That, however, is not steam—it is a gas that is rising up; and if I now search the jar by a candle, I shall have exactly the same effect produced upon the taper as I had from the air which issued from the end of the chimney over the burning candle. It is exactly the same action, and caused by the very same substance that issued from the candle; and in this way we can get carbonic acid in great abundance—we have already nearly filled the jar. We also find that this gas is not merely contained in marble. Here is a vessel in which I have put some common whitening— chalk, which has been washed in water and deprived of its coarser particles, and so supplied to the plasterer as whitening. Here is a large jar containing this whitening and water, and I have here some strong sulphuric acid, which is the acid you might have to use if you were to make these experiments (only, in using this acid with limestone, the body that is produced is an insoluble substance, whereas the muriatic acid produces a soluble substance that does not so much thicken the water). And you will seek out a reason why I take this kind of apparatus for the purpose of showing this experiment. I do it because you may repeat in a small way what I am about to do in a large one. You will have here just the same kind of action; and I am evolving in this large jar carbonic acid, exactly the same in its nature and properties as the gas which we obtained from the combustion of the candle in the atmosphere. And no matter how different the two methods by which we prepare this carbonic acid, you will see, when we get to the end of our subject, that it is all exactly the same, whether prepared in the one way or in the other.

We will now proceed to the next experiment with regard to this gas.

17. Marble is a compound of carbonic acid and lime. The muriatic acid, being the stronger of the two, takes the place of the carbonic acid, which escapes as a gas, the residue forming muriate of lime or chloride of calcium.

What is its nature? Here is one of the vessels full, and we will try it, as we have done so many other gases, by combustion. You see it is not combustible, nor does it support combustion. Neither, as we know, does it dissolve much in water, because we collect it over water very easily. Then, you know that it has an effect, and becomes white in contact with lime-water; and when it does become white in that way, it becomes one of the constituents to make carbonate of lime or limestone.

The next thing I must show you is, that it really does dissolve a little in water, and therefore that it is unlike oxygen and hydrogen in that respect. I have here an apparatus by which we can produce this solution. In the lower part of this apparatus is marble and acid, and in the upper part cold water. The valves are so arranged that the gas can get from one to the other. I will set it in action now, and you can see the gas bubbling up through the water, as it has been doing all night long, and by this time we shall find that we have this substance dissolved in the water. If I take a glass and draw off some of the water, I find that it tastes a little acid to the mouth: it is impregnated with carbonic acid; and if I now apply a little lime-water to it, that will give us a test of its presence. This water will make the lime-water turbid and white, which is proof of the presence of carbonic acid.

Then it is a very weighty gas—it is heavier than the atmosphere. I have put their respective weights at the lower part of this table, along with, for comparison, the weights of the other gases we have been examining:

	Pint (Grains)	Cubic Foot (Ounces)
Hydrogen	¾	$\frac{1}{12}$
Oxygen	11$\frac{9}{10}$	1$\frac{1}{3}$
Nitrogen	10$\frac{4}{10}$	1$\frac{1}{6}$
Air	10$\frac{7}{10}$	1$\frac{1}{5}$
Carbonic acid	16$\frac{1}{3}$	1$\frac{9}{10}$

A pint of it weighs 16$\frac{1}{3}$ grains, and a cubic foot weighs 1$\frac{9}{10}$ ounce, almost two ounces. You can see by many experiments that this is a heavy gas. Suppose I take a glass containing nothing else but air, and from this vessel containing the carbonic acid I attempt to pour a little of this gas into that glass; I wonder whether any has gone in or not. I cannot tell by the appearance, but I can in this way [*introducing the taper*]. Yes, there it is, you see; and if I were to examine it by lime-water, I should find it by that test also. I will take this little bucket, and put it down into the

well of carbonic acid—indeed, we too often have real wells of carbonic acid—and now, if there is any carbonic acid, I must have got to it by this time, and it will be in this bucket, which we will examine with a taper. There it is, you see; it is full of carbonic acid.

There is another experiment by which I will show you its weight. I have here a jar suspended at one end of a balance—it is now equipoised; but when I pour this carbonic acid into the jar on the one side which now contains air, you will see it sink down at once, because of the carbonic acid that I pour into it. And now, if I examine this jar with the lighted taper, I shall find that the carbonic acid has fallen into it, and it no longer has any power of supporting the combustion. If I blow a soap-bubble, which of course will be filled with air, and let it fall into this jar of carbonic acid, it will float. But I shall first of all take one of these little balloons filled with air. I am not quite sure where the carbonic acid is; we will just try the depth, and see whereabouts is its level. There, you see, we have this bladder floating on the carbonic acid; and if I evolve some more of the carbonic acid, the bladder will be lifted up higher. There it goes—the jar is nearly full; and now I will see whether I can blow a soap-bubble on that, and float it in the same way. [*The Lecturer here blew a soap-bubble, and allowed it to fall into the jar of carbonic acid, when it floated in it midway.*] It is floating, as the balloon floated, by virtue of the greater weight of the carbonic acid than of the air. And now, having so far given you the history of the carbonic acid—as to its sources in the candle, as to its physical properties and weight—when we next meet I shall show you of what it is composed, and where it gets its elements from.

LECTURE VI

A lady who honours me by her presence at these lectures has conferred a still further obligation by sending me these two candles, which are from Japan, and, I presume, are made of that substance to which I referred in a former lecture. You see that they are even far more highly ornamented than the French candles; and, I suppose, are candles of luxury, judging from their appearance. They have a remarkable peculiarity about them, namely, a hollow wick—that beautiful peculiarity which Argand introduced into the lamp, and made so valuable. To those who receive such presents from the East, I may just say that this and such like materials gradually undergo a change which gives them on the surface a dull and dead appearance; but they may easily be restored to their original beauty, if the surface be rubbed with a clean cloth or silk handkerchief, so as to polish the little rugosity or roughness: this will restore the beauty of the colours. I have so rubbed one of these candles, and you see the difference between it and the other which has not been polished, but which may be restored by the same process. Observe, also, that these moulded candles from Japan are made more conical than the moulded candles in this part of the world.

I told you, when we last met, a good deal about carbonic acid. We found, by the lime-water test, that when the vapour from the top of the candle or lamp was received into bottles, and tested by this solution of lime-water (the composition of which I explained to you, and which you can make for yourselves), we had that white opacity which was in fact calcareous matter, like shells and corals, and many of the rocks and minerals in the earth. But I have not yet told you fully and clearly the chemical history of this substance—carbonic acid—as we have it from the candle, and I must now resume that subject. We have seen the products, and the nature of them, as they issue from the candle. We have traced the water to its elements, and now we have to see where are the elements of the carbonic acid supplied by the candle. A few experiments will show this. You remember that when a candle burns badly, it produces smoke; but if it is burning well, there is no smoke. And you know that the brightness of the candle is due to this smoke, which becomes ignited. Here is an experiment to prove this: so long as the smoke remains in the flame of the candle and becomes ignited, it gives a beautiful light, and never appears to us in the form of black particles. I will light some fuel which is extravagant in its burning. This will serve our purpose—a

little turpentine on a sponge. You see the smoke rising from it, and floating into the air in large quantities; and, remember now, the carbonic acid that we have from the candle is from such smoke as that. To make that evident to you, I will introduce this turpentine burning on the sponge into a flask where I have plenty of oxygen, the rich part of the atmosphere, and you now see that the smoke is all consumed. This is the first part of our experiment; and now, what follows? The carbon which you saw flying off from the turpentine flame in the air is now entirely burned in this oxygen, and we shall find that it will, by this rough and temporary experiment, give us exactly the same conclusion and result as we had from the combustion of the candle. The reason why I make the experiment in this manner is solely that I may cause the steps of our demonstration to be so simple that you can never for a moment lose the train of reasoning, if you only pay attention. All the carbon which is burned in oxygen, or air, comes out as carbonic acid, while those particles which are not so burned show you the second substance in the carbonic acid—namely, the carbon—that body which made the flame so bright while there was plenty of air, but which was thrown off in excess when there was not oxygen enough to burn it.

I have also to show you a little more distinctly the history of carbon and oxygen, in their union to make carbonic acid. You are now better able to understand this than before, and I have prepared three or four experiments by way of illustration. This jar is filled with oxygen, and here is some carbon which has been placed in a crucible, for the purpose of being made red-hot. I keep my jar dry, and venture to give you a result imperfect in some degree, in order that I may make the experiment brighter. I am about to put the oxygen and the carbon together. That this is carbon (common charcoal pulverized), you will see by the way in which it burns in the air [*letting some of the red-hot charcoal fall out of the crucible*]. I am now about to burn it in oxygen gas, and look at the difference. It may appear to you at a distance as if it were burning with a flame; but it is not so. Every little piece of charcoal is burning as a spark, and while it so burns it is producing carbonic acid. I specially want these two or three experiments to point out what I shall dwell upon more distinctly by and by—that carbon burns in this way, and not as a flame.

Instead of taking many particles of carbon to burn, I will take a rather large piece, which will enable you to see the form and size, and to trace the effects very decidedly. Here is the jar of oxygen, and here is the piece of charcoal, to which I have fastened a little piece of wood,

which I can set fire to, and so commence the combustion, which I could not conveniently do without. You now see the charcoal burning, but not as a flame (or if there be a flame, it is the smallest possible one, which I know the cause of—namely, the formation of a little carbonic oxide close upon the surface of the carbon). It goes on burning, you see, slowly producing carbonic acid by the union of this carbon or charcoal (they are equivalent terms) with the oxygen. I have here another piece of charcoal, a piece of bark, which has the quality of being blown to pieces—exploding as it burns. By the effect of the heat, we shall reduce the lump of carbon into particles that will fly off; still every particle, equally with the whole mass, burns in this peculiar way: it burns as a coal, and not like a flame. You observe a multitude of little combustions going on, but no flame. I do not know a finer experiment than this to show that carbon burns with a spark.

Here, then, is carbonic acid formed from its elements. It is produced at once; and if we examined it by lime-water, you will see that we have the same substance which I have previously described to you. By putting together 6 parts of carbon by weight (whether it comes from the flame of a candle or from powdered charcoal) and 16 parts of oxygen by weight, we have 22 parts of carbonic acid; and, as we saw last time, the 22 parts of carbonic acid, combined with 28 parts of lime, produced common carbonate of lime. If you were to examine an oyster-shell, and weigh the component parts, you would find that every 50 parts would give 6 of carbon and 16 of oxygen, combined with 28 of lime. However, I do not want to trouble you with these minutiae—it is only the general philosophy of the matter that we can now go into. See how finely the carbon is dissolving away [*pointing to the lump of charcoal burning quietly in the jar of oxygen*]. You may say that the charcoal is actually dissolving in the air round about; and if that were perfectly pure charcoal, which we can easily prepare, there would be no residue whatever. When we have a perfectly cleansed and purified piece of carbon, there is no ash left. The carbon burns as a solid dense body, that heat alone cannot change as to its solidity, and yet it passes away into vapour that never condenses into solid or liquid under ordinary circumstances; and what is more curious still is the fact that the oxygen does not change in its bulk by the solution of the carbon in it. Just as the bulk is at first, so it is at last, only it has become carbonic acid.

There is another experiment which I must give you before you are fully acquainted with the general nature of carbonic acid. Being a compound body, consisting of carbon and oxygen, carbonic acid is a body that

we ought to be able to take asunder. And so we can. As we did with water, so we can with carbonic acid—take the two parts asunder. The simplest and quickest way is to act upon the carbonic acid by a substance that can attract the oxygen from it, and leave the carbon behind. You recollect that I took potassium and put it upon water or ice, and you saw that it could take the oxygen from the hydrogen. Now, suppose we do something of the same kind here with this carbonic acid. You know carbonic acid to be a heavy gas. I will not test it with lime-water, as that will interfere with our subsequent experiments; but I think the heaviness of the gas and the power of extinguishing flame will be sufficient for our purpose. I introduce a flame into the gas, and you will see whether it will be put out. You see the light is extinguished. Indeed, the gas may, perhaps, put out phosphorus, which, you know, has a pretty strong combustion. Here is a piece of phosphorus heated to a high degree. I introduce it into the gas, and you observe the light is put out; but it will take fire again in the air, because there it re-enters into combustion. Now, let me take a piece of potassium, a substance which, even at common temperatures, can act upon carbonic acid, though not sufficiently for our present purpose, because it soon gets covered with a protecting coat; but if we warm it up to the burning point in air, as we have a fair right to do, and as we have done with phosphorus, you will see that it can burn in carbonic acid; and if it burns, it will burn by taking oxygen, so that you will see what is left behind. I am going, then, to burn this potassium in the carbonic acid, as a proof of the existence of oxygen in the carbonic acid. [*In the preliminary process of heating, the potassium exploded.*] Sometimes we get an awkward piece of potassium that explodes, or something like it, when it burns. I will take another piece; and now that it is heated, I introduce it into the jar, and you perceive that it burns in the carbonic acid—not so well as in the air, because the carbonic acid contains the oxygen combined; but it does burn, and takes away the oxygen. If I now put this potassium into water, I find that, besides the potash formed (which you need not trouble about), there is a quantity of carbon produced. I have here made the experiment in a very rough way; but I assure you that if I were to make it carefully, devoting a day to it, instead of five minutes, we should get all the proper amount of charcoal left in the spoon, or in the place where the potassium was burned, so that there could be no doubt as to the result. Here, then, is the carbon obtained from the carbonic acid, as a common black substance; so that you have the entire proof of the nature of carbonic acid as consisting of carbon and oxygen. And now, I may tell you, that

whenever carbon burns under common circumstances, it produces carbonic acid.

Suppose I take this piece of wood, and put it into a bottle with lime-water. I might shake that lime-water up with wood and the atmosphere as long as I pleased, it would still remain clear as you see it; but suppose I burn the piece of wood in the air of that bottle. You, of course, know I get water. Do I get carbonic acid? [*The experiment was performed.*] There it is, you see—that is to say, the carbonate of lime, which results from carbonic acid, and that carbonic acid must be formed from the carbon which comes from the wood, from the candle, or any other thing. Indeed, you have yourselves frequently tried a very pretty experiment, by which you may see the carbon in wood. If you take a piece of wood, and partly burn it, and then blow it out, you have carbon left. There are things that do not show carbon in this way. A candle does not show it, but it contains carbon. Here also is a jar of coal-gas, which produces carbonic acid abundantly. You do not see the carbon, but we can soon show it to you. I will light it, and as long as there is any gas in this cylinder it will go on burning. You see no carbon, but you see a flame; and because that is bright, it will lead you to guess that there is carbon in the flame. But I will show it to you by another process. I have some of the same gas in another vessel, mixed with a body that will burn the hydrogen of the gas, but will not burn the carbon. I will light them with a burning taper, and you perceive the hydrogen is consumed, but not the carbon, which is left behind as a dense black smoke. I hope that by these three or four experiments you will learn to see when carbon is present, and understand what are the products of combustion, when gas or other bodies are thoroughly burned in the air.

Before we leave the subject of carbon, let us make a few experiments and remarks upon its wonderful condition as respects ordinary combustion. I have shown you that the carbon in burning burns only as a solid body, and yet you perceive that, after it is burned, it ceases to be a solid. There are very few fuels that act like this. It is, in fact, only that great source of fuel, the carbonaceous series, the coals, charcoals, and woods, that can do it. I do not know that there is any other elementary substance besides carbon that burns with these conditions; and if it had not been so, what would happen to us? Suppose all fuel had been like iron, which, when it burns, burns into a solid substance. We could not then have such a combustion as you have in this fire-place. Here also is another kind of fuel which burns very well—as well as, if not better, than carbon—so well, indeed, as to take fire of itself when it is in the air, as you see

[*breaking a tube full of lead pyrophorus*]. This substance is lead, and you see how wonderfully combustible it is. It is very much divided, and is like a heap of coals in the fire-place; the air can get to its surface and inside, and so it burns. But why does it not burn in that way now, when it is lying in a mass? [*emptying the contents of the tube in a heap on to a plate of iron*]. Simply because the air cannot get to it. Though it can produce a great heat, the great heat which we want in our furnaces and under our boilers, still that which is produced cannot get away from the portion which remains unburned underneath, and that portion, therefore, is prevented from coming in contact with the atmosphere, and cannot be consumed. How different is that from carbon. Carbon burns just in the same way as this lead does, and so gives an intense fire in the furnace, or wherever you choose to burn it; but then the body produced by its combustion passes away, and the remaining carbon is left clear. I showed you how carbon went on dissolving in the oxygen, leaving no ash; whereas here [*pointing to the heap of pyrophorus*] we have actually more ash than fuel, for it is heavier by the amount of the oxygen which has united with it. Thus you see the difference between carbon and lead or iron: if we choose iron, which gives so wonderful a result in our application of this fuel, either as light or heat. If, when the carbon burnt, the product went off as a solid body, you would have had the room filled with an opaque substance, as in the case of the phosphorus; but when carbon burns, everything passes up into the atmosphere. It is in a fixed, almost unchangeable condition before the combustion; but afterwards it is in the form of gas, which it is very difficult (though we have succeeded) to produce in a solid or a liquid state.

Now, I must take you to a very interesting part of our subject—to the relation between the combustion of a candle and that living kind of combustion which goes on within us. In every one of us there is a living process of combustion going on very similar to that of a candle; and I must try to make that plain to you. For it is not merely true in a poetical sense—the relation of the life of man to a taper; and if you will follow, I think I can make this clear. In order to make the relation very plain, I have devised a little apparatus which we can soon build up before you. Here is a board and a groove cut in it, and I can close the groove at the top part by a little cover. I can then continue the groove as a channel by a glass tube at each end, there being a free passage through the whole. Suppose I take a taper or candle (we can now be liberal in our use of the word "candle," since we understand what it means), and place it in one of the tubes; it will go on, you see, burning very well. You observe

that the air which feeds the flame passes down the tube at one end, then goes along the horizontal tube, and ascends the tube at the other end in which the taper is placed. If I stop the aperture through which the air enters, I stop combustion, as you perceive. I stop the supply of air, and consequently the candle goes out. But, now, what will you think of this fact? In a former experiment I showed you the air going from one burning candle to a second candle. If I took the air proceeding from another candle, and sent it down by a complicated arrangement into this tube, I should put this burning candle out. But what will you

say when I tell you that my breath will put out that candle? I do not mean by blowing at all, but simply that the nature of my breath is such that a candle cannot burn in it. I will now hold my mouth over the aperture, and without blowing the flame in any way, let no air enter the tube but what comes from my mouth. You see the result. I did not blow the candle out. I merely let the air which I expired pass into the aperture, and the result was that the light went out for want of oxygen, and for no other reason. Something or other—namely, my lungs—had taken away the oxygen from the air, and there was no more to supply the combustion of the candle. It is, I think, very pretty to see the time it takes before the bad air which I throw into this part of the apparatus has reached

the candle. The candle at first goes on burning, but so soon as the air has had time to reach it, it goes out. And, now, I will show you another experiment, because this is an important part of our philosophy. Here is a jar which contains fresh air, as you can see by the circumstance of a candle or gas-light burning it. I make it close for a little time, and by means of a pipe I get my mouth over it so that I can inhale the air. By putting it over water, in the way that you see, I am able to draw up this air (supposing the cork to be quite tight), take it into my lungs, and throw it back into the jar. We can then examine it, and see the result. You observe, I first take up the air, and

then throw it back, as is evident from the ascent and descent of the water; and now, by putting a taper into the air, you will see the state in which it is, by the light being extinguished. Even one inspiration, you see, has completely spoiled this air, so that it is no use my trying to

breathe it a second time. Now, you understand the ground of the impropriety of many of the arrangements among the houses of the poorer classes, by which the air is breathed over and over again, for the want of a supply, by means of proper ventilation, sufficient to produce a good result. You see how bad the air becomes by a single breathing; so that you can easily understand how essential fresh air is to us.

To pursue this a little further, let us see what will happen with lime-water. Here is a globe which contains a little lime-water, and it is so arranged as regards the pipes, as to give access to the air within, so that we can ascertain the effect of respired or unrespired air upon it. Of course, I can either draw in air [*through* A], and so make the air that feeds my lungs go through the lime-water, or I can force the air out of my lungs through the tube [B], which goes to the bottom, and so show its effect upon the lime-water. You will observe that, however long I draw the external air into the lime-water, and then through it to my lungs, I shall produce no effect upon the water—it will not make the lime-water turbid; but if I throw the air *from* my lungs through the lime-water, several times in succession, you see how white and milky the water is getting, showing the effect which expired air has had upon it; and now you begin to know that the atmosphere which we have spoiled by respiration is spoiled by carbonic acid, for you see it here in contact with the lime-water.

I have here two bottles, one containing lime-water and the other common water, and tubes which pass into the bottles and connect them. The apparatus is very rough, but it is useful notwithstanding. If I take these two bottles, inhaling here and exhaling there, the arrangement of the tubes will prevent the air going backwards. The air coming in will go to my mouth and lungs, and in going out, will pass through the lime-water, so that I can go on breathing and making an experiment, very refined in its nature, and very good in its results. You will ob-

serve that the good air has done nothing to the lime-water; in the other case nothing has come to the lime-water but my respiration, and you see the difference in the two cases.

Let us now go a little further. What is all this process going on within us which we cannot do without, either day or night, which is so provided for by the author of all things that He has arranged that it shall be independent of all will? If we restrain our respiration, as we can to a certain extent, we should destroy ourselves. When we are asleep, the organs of respiration, and the parts that are associated with them, still go on with their action—so necessary is this process of respiration to us, this contact of the air with the lungs. I must tell you, in the briefest possible manner, what this process is. We consume food; the food goes through that strange set of vessels and organs within us, and is brought into various parts of the system, into the digestive parts especially; and alternately the portion which is so changed is carried through our lungs by one set of vessels, while the air that we inhale and exhale is drawn into and thrown out of the lungs by another set of vessels, so that the air and the food come close together, separated only by an exceedingly thin surface: the air can thus act upon the blood by this process, producing precisely the same results in kind as we have seen in the case of the candle. The candle combines with parts of the air, forming carbonic acid, and evolves heat; so in the lungs there is this curious, wonderful change taking place. The air entering, combines with the carbon (not carbon in a free state, but, as in this case, placed ready for action at the moment), and makes carbonic acid, and is so thrown out into the atmosphere, and thus this singular result takes place: we may thus look upon the food as fuel. Let me take that piece of sugar, which will serve my purpose. It is a compound of carbon, hydrogen, and oxygen, similar to a candle, as containing the same elements, though not in the same proportion—the proportions being as shown in this table:

Sugar

Carbon	72	
Hydrogen	11	} 99
Oxygen	88	

This is, indeed, a very curious thing, which you can well remember, for

the oxygen and hydrogen are in exactly the proportions which form water, so that sugar may be said to be compounded of 72 parts of carbon and 99 parts of water; and it is the carbon in the sugar that combines with the oxygen carried in by the air in the process of respiration—so making us like candles—producing these actions, warmth, and far more wonderful results besides, for the sustenance of the system, by a most beautiful and simple process. To make this still more striking, I will take a little sugar; or, to hasten the experiment, I will use some syrup, which contains about three-fourths of sugar and a little water. If I put a little oil of vitriol on it, it takes away the water, and leaves the carbon in a black mass. [*The Lecturer mixed the two together.*] You see how the carbon is coming out, and before long we shall have a solid mass of charcoal, all of which has come out of sugar. Sugar, as you know, is food, and here we have absolutely a solid lump of carbon where you would not have expected it. And if I make arrangements so as to oxidize the carbon of sugar, we shall have a much more striking result. Here is sugar, and I have here an oxidizer—a quicker one than the atmosphere; and so we shall oxidize this fuel by a process different from respiration in its form, though not different in its kind. It is the combustion of the carbon by the contact of oxygen which the body has supplied to it. If I set this into action at once, you will see combustion produced. Just what occurs in my lungs—taking in oxygen from another source, namely, the atmosphere—takes place here by a more rapid process.

You will be astonished when I tell you what this curious play of carbon amounts to. A candle will burn some four, five, six, or seven hours. What, then, must be the daily amount of carbon going up into the air in the way of carbonic acid! What a quantity of carbon must go from each of us in respiration! What a wonderful change of carbon must take place under these circumstances of combustion or respiration! A man in twenty-four hours converts as much as seven ounces of carbon into carbonic acid; a milch-cow will convert seventy ounces, and a horse seventy-nine ounces, solely by the act of respiration. That is, the horse in twenty-four hours burns seventy-nine ounces of charcoal, or carbon, in his organs of respiration, to supply his natural warmth in that time. All the warm-blooded animals get their warmth in this way, by the conversion of carbon, not in a free state, but in a state of combination. And what an extraordinary notion this gives us of the alterations going on in our atmosphere. As much as 5,000,000 pounds, or 548 tons, of carbonic acid is formed by respiration in London alone in twenty-four hours. And where does all this go? Up into the air. If the carbon had been like

the lead which I showed you, or the iron which, in burning, produces a solid substance, what would happen? Combustion could not go on. As charcoal burns, it becomes a vapour and passes off into the atmosphere, which is the great vehicle, the great carrier for conveying it away to other places. Then, what becomes of it? Wonderful is it to find that the change produced by respiration, which seems so injurious to us (for we cannot breathe air twice over), is the very life and support of plants and vegetables that grow upon the surface of the earth. It is the same also under the surface, in the great bodies of water; for fishes and other animals respire upon the same principle, though not exactly by contact with the open air.

Such fish as I have here [*pointing to a globe of gold-fish*] respire by the oxygen which is dissolved from the air by the water, and from carbonic acid; and they all move about to produce the one great work of making the animal and vegetable kingdoms subservient to each other. And all the plants growing upon the surface of the earth, like that which I have brought here to serve as an illustration, absorb carbon. These leaves are taking up their carbon from the atmosphere, to which we have given it in the form of carbonic acid, and they are growing and prospering. Give them a pure air like ours, and they could not live in it; give them carbon with other matters, and they live and rejoice. This piece of wood gets all its carbon, as the trees and plants get theirs, from the atmosphere, which, as we have seen, carries away what is bad for us and at the same time good for them—what is disease to the one being health to the other. So are we made dependent, not merely upon our fellow-creatures, but upon our fellow-existers, all Nature being tied together by the laws that make one part conduce to the good of another.

There is another little point which I must mention before we draw to a close—a point which concerns the whole of these operations, and most curious and beautiful it is to see it clustering upon and associated with the bodies that concern us—oxygen, hydrogen, and carbon, in different states of their existence. I showed you just now some powdered lead, which I set burning; [18] and you saw that the moment the fuel was brought to the air, it acted, even before it got out of the bottle—the moment the air crept in, it acted. Now, there is a case of chemical affinity by which all our operations proceed. When we breathe, the same operation is go-

18. Lead pyrophorus is made by heating dry tartrate of lead in a glass tube (closed at one end, and drawn out to a fine point at the other) until no more vapours are evolved. The open end of the tube is then to be sealed before the blow-pipe. When the tube is broken and the contents shaken out into the air, they burn with a red flash.

ing on within us. When we burn a candle, the attraction of the different parts one to the other is going on. Here it is going on in this case of the lead; and it is a beautiful instance of chemical affinity. If the products of combustion rose off from the surface, the lead would take fire, and go on burning to the end; but you remember that we have this difference between charcoal and lead—that, while the lead can start into action at once, if there be access of air to it, the carbon will remain days, weeks, months, or years. The manuscripts of Herculaneum were written with carbonaceous ink, and there they have been for 1,800 years or more, not having been at all changed by the atmosphere, though coming in contact with it under various circumstances. Now, what is the circumstance which makes the lead and carbon differ in this respect? It is a striking thing to see that the matter which is appointed to serve the purpose of fuel *waits* in its action: it does not start off burning, like the lead and many other things that I could show you, but which I have not encumbered the table with; but it waits for action. This waiting is a curious and wonderful thing. Candles—those Japanese candles, for instance—do not start into action at once, like the lead or iron (for iron finely divided does the same thing as lead), but there they wait for years, perhaps for ages, without undergoing any alteration. I have here a supply of coal-gas. The jet is giving forth the gas, but you see it does not take fire—it comes out into the air, but it waits till it is hot enough before it burns. If I make it hot enough, it takes fire. If I blow it out, the gas that is issuing forth waits till the light is applied to it again. It is curious to see how different substances wait—how some will wait till the temperature is raised a little, and others till it is raised a good deal. I have here a little gunpowder and some gun-cotton; even these things differ in the conditions under which they will burn. The gunpowder is composed of carbon and other substances, making it highly combustible; and the gun-cotton is another combustible preparation. They are both waiting, but they will start into activity at different degrees of heat, or under different conditions. By applying a heated wire to them, we shall see which will start first [*touching the gun-cotton with the hot iron*]. You see the gun-cotton has gone off, but not even the hottest part of the wire is now hot enough to fire the gunpowder. How beautifully that shows you the difference in the degree in which bodies act in this way! In the one case the substance will wait any time until the associated bodies are made active by heat; but in the other, as in the process of respiration, it waits no time. In the lungs, as soon as the air enters, it unites with the carbon; even in the lowest temperature which the body can bear short of being frozen, the action

begins at once, producing the carbonic acid of respiration: and so all things go on fitly and properly. Thus you see the analogy between respiration and combustion is rendered still more beautiful and striking. Indeed, all I can say to you at the end of these lectures (for we must come to an end at one time or other) is to express a wish that you may, in your generation, be fit to compare to a candle; that you may, like it, shine as light to those about you; that, in all your actions, you may justify the beauty of the taper by making your deeds honourable and effectual in the discharge of your duty to your fellow-men.

Dmitri Mendeleev

1834–1907

D mitri Ivanovich Mendeleev (or Mendeleyev) was the youngest of seventeen children. He was born at Tobolsk, Siberia, in 1834. He studied science at St. Petersburg, where he graduated in chemistry. He studied further abroad with Regnault and Bunsen, inventor of the famous burner. He was made professor of chemistry at the University of St. Petersburg, but in 1890 he resigned the position to become Director of the Bureau of Weights and Measures. There he remained until his death.

His best known work was on the periodic law of the elements, but he did important research in many branches of chemistry. He studied the nature of solutions and investigated the expansion of liquids when heated. He studied the origins of petroleum, and he speculated on the nature of the ether, that will-o'-the-wisp of nineteenth-century physics. He wrote *The Principles of Chemistry* in 1868–70. It is a standard work which has gone through many editions in a number of languages. The following selection is often printed as an appendix.

Mendeleev was also one of the great teachers of his time. His lecture room was always crowded. Many of his auditors found it difficult to keep up with him. The subject was difficult, his reasoning tight; he wasted no words. These are characteristics of the selection that follows. Yet it was said that all of his listeners gained from him "a lesson in scientific thinking." He died in St. Petersburg in 1907.

T he atomic theory was first proposed by such ancient writers as Democritus and Lucretius. Dalton, the English chemist, revived it in the 18th century to explain chemical reactions. In the beginning of

the 19th century, the distinction between chemical elements—that is, substances which could not be broken down into components—and compounds became clear. But the atomic hypothesis was not enough in itself. Given a group of apparently unrelated chemical elements, it was desirable to put them in some sort of order. Many men tried to do this, but Mendeleev was the first to suggest an adequate arrangement.

He describes the "three series of data without the knowledge of which the periodic law could not have been discovered." None of these was gathered by Mendeleev. His effort was synthetic rather than analytical. The periodic law was, he says, "a direct outcome of the stock of generalizations and established facts which had accumulated by . . . 1870." Still, the law was a very great discovery. Why was this so? And why was Mendeleev's formulation of the relation between the elements preferred to those that had gone before?

Mendeleev lists eight considerations which led him to propose the law. The sixth is the most important. He was able to predict that elements of a certain weight would be found, though they were not yet known. On his hypothesis, he predicted the existence, and a number of the properties, of elements which he called eka-boron, eka-aluminum, eka-silicon, eka-manganese, dvi-manganese and eka-tantalum. ("Eka" means "one," "dvi" means "two." Thus the words are in effect like mathematical subscripts.) These hypothetical elements were soon discovered: they are now called, respectively, scandium, gallium, germanium, technetium, rhenium, and protactinium. Mendeleev's hypothesis was thus triumphantly validated.

It was recognized after Mendeleev's death, due to the work of such men as Planck, Einstein, Bohr, and others, that the order of elements in the periodic table corresponds to their atomic numbers, and that these in turn depend on the number of protons in the atomic nuclei. But this new knowledge has not contradicted the old law; in fact, it has increased its value. The periodic law, the genesis of which is described in this selection, is one of the fundamentals of modern science.

The Genesis of a Law of Nature

from *The Periodic Law*
of the Chemical Elements

Before one of the oldest and most powerful of (scientific socie-
ties) I am about to take the liberty of passing in review the 20 years' life
of a generalization which is known under the name of the Periodic Law.
It was in March, 1869, that I ventured to lay before the then youthful Rus-
sian Chemical Society the ideas upon the same subject which I had ex-
pressed in my just written *Principles of Chemistry*.

Without entering into details, I will give the conclusions I then arrived
at in the very words I used:

1. The elements, if arranged according to their atomic weights, ex-
hibit an evident *periodicity* of properties.

2. Elements which are similar as regards their chemical properties
have atomic weights which are either of nearly the same value (*e.g.* plat-
inum, iridium, osmium) or which increase regularly (*e.g.* potassium, ru-
bidium, caesium).

3. The arrangement of the elements, or of groups of elements, in
the order of their atomic weights, corresponds to their so-called
valencies as well as, to some extent, to their distinctive chemical prop-
erties—as is apparent, among other series, in that of lithium, beryllium,
barium, carbon, nitrogen, oxygen, and iron.

4. The elements which are the most widely diffused have small
atomic weights.

5. The *magnitude* of the atomic weight determines the character of
the element, just as the magnitude of the molecule determines the char-
acter of a compound.

6. We must expect the discovery of many yet *unknown* elements—

for example, elements analogous to aluminium and silicon, whose atomic weight would be between 65 and 75.

7. The atomic weight of an element may sometimes be amended by a knowledge of those of the contiguous elements. Thus, the atomic weight of tellurium must lie between 123 and 126, and cannot be 128.

8. Certain characteristic properties of the elements can be foretold from their atomic weights.

The aim of this communication will be fully attained if I succeed in drawing the attention of investigators to those relations which exist between the atomic weights of dissimilar elements, which, as far as I know, have hitherto been almost completely neglected. I believe that the solution of some of the most important problems of our science lies in researches of this kind.

To-day, twenty years after the above conclusions were formulated, they may still be considered as expressing the essence of the now well-known periodic law.

Reverting to the epoch terminating with the sixties, it is proper to indicate three series of data without the knowledge of which the periodic law could not have been discovered, and which rendered its appearance natural and intelligible.

In the first place, it was at that time that the numerical value of atomic weights became definitely known. Ten years earlier such knowledge did not exist, as may be gathered from the fact that in 1860 chemists from all parts of the world met at Karlsruhe in order to come to some agreement, if not with respect to views relating to atoms, at any rate as regards their definite representation. Many of those present probably remember how vain were the hopes of coming to an understanding, and how much ground was gained at that congress by the followers of the unitary theory so brilliantly represented by Cannizzaro. I vividly remember the impression produced by his speeches, which admitted of no compromise, and seemed to advocate truth itself, based on the conceptions of Avogadro, Gerhardt, and Regnault, which at that time were far from being generally recognized. And though no understanding could be arrived at, yet the objects of the meeting were attained, for the ideas of Cannizzaro proved, after a few years, to be the only ones which could stand criticism, and which represented an atom as—"the smallest portion of an element which enters into a molecule of its compound." Only such real atomic weights—not conventional ones—could af-

ford a basis for generalization. It is sufficient, by way of example, to indicate the following cases in which the relation is seen at once and is perfectly clear:

$$K = 39 \qquad Rb = 85 \qquad Cs = 133$$
$$Ca = 40 \qquad Sr = 87 \qquad Ba = 137$$

whereas with the equivalents then in use—

$$K = 39 \qquad Rb = 85 \qquad Cs = 133$$
$$Ca = 20 \qquad Sr = 43.5 \qquad Ba = 68.5$$

the consecutiveness of change in atomic weights, which with the true values is so evident, completely disappears.

Secondly, it had become evident during the period 1860–70, and even during the preceding decade, that the relations between the atomic weights of analogous elements were governed by some general and simple laws. Cooke, Cremers, Gladstone, Gmelin, Lenssen, Pettenkofer, and especially Dumas, had already established many facts bearing on that view. Thus Dumas compared the following groups of analogous elements with organic radicals:

Diff.		Diff.		Diff.		Diff.
	Mg = 12 ⎱ 8		P = 31 ⎱ 44		O = 8 ⎱ 8	
Li = 7 ⎱ 16	Ca = 20 ⎰	As = 75 ⎰	S = 16 ⎰			
Na = 23 ⎰	Sr = 44 ⎱ 3 × 8	Sb = 119 ⎱ 44	Se = 40 ⎱ 3 × 8			
K = 39 ⎰ 16	Ba = 68 ⎰ 3 × 8	Bi = 207 ⎰ 2 × 44	Te = 64 ⎰ 3 × 8			

Distribution of the Elements

Group	I		II		III		IV	
Series								
1	Hydrogen	1	—		—		—	
2	Lithium	7	Beryllium	9	Boron	11	Carbon	12
3	Sodium	23	Magnesium	24	Aluminum	27	Silicon	28
4	Potassium	39	Calcium	40	Scandium	44	Titanium	48
5	Copper	63	Zinc	65	Gallium	70	Germanium	72
6	Rubidium	85	Strontium	87	Yttrium	89	Zirconium	91
7	Silver	108	Cadmium	112	Indium	113	Tin	118
8	Caesium	133	Barium	137	Lanthanum	138	Cerium	140
9	—		—		—		—	
10	—		—		Ytterbium	173	—	
11	Gold	198	Mercury	200	Thallium	204	Lead	206
12	—		—		—		Thorium	232

and pointed out some really striking relationships, such as the following:

$$F = 19$$
$$Cl = 35.5 = 19 + 16.5$$
$$Br = 80 = 19 + (2 \times 16.5) + 28$$
$$I = 127 = (2 \times 19) + (2 \times 16.5) + (2 \times 28).$$

A. Strecker, in his work *Theorien und Experimente zur Bestimmung der Atomgewichte der Elemente* (Braunschweig, 1859), after summarizing the data relating to the subject, and pointing out the remarkable series of equivalents—$Cr = 26.2$ $Mn = 27.6$ $Fe = 28$ $Ni = 29$ $Co = 30$ $Cu = 31.7$ $Zn = 32.5$

remarks that: "It is hardly probable that all the above-mentioned relations between the atomic weights (or equivalents) of chemically analogous elements are merely accidental. We must, however, leave to the future the discovery of the *law* of the relations which appear in these figures."

In such attempts at arrangement and in such views are to be recognized the real forerunners of the periodic law; the ground was prepared for it between 1860 and 1870, and that it was not expressed in a determinate form before the end of the decade may, I suppose, be ascribed to the fact that only analogous elements had been compared. The idea of seeking for a relation between the atomic weights of all elements was foreign to the ideas then current, so that neither the *vis tellurique* [telluric screw] of De Chancourtois, nor the *law of octaves* of Newlands, could secure anybody's attention. And yet both De Chancourtois and Newlands, like Dumas and Strecker, more than Lenssen and Petten-

in Groups and Series

V		VI		VII		VIII		
—		—		—		—		
Nitrogen	14	Oxygen	16	Fluorine	19			
Phosphorus	31	Sulphur	32	Chlorine	35			
Vanadium	51	Chromium	52	Manganese	55	Iron	Cobalt	Nickel
						56	58	59
Arsenic	75	Selenium	79	Bromine	80			
Niobium	94	Molybdenum	96	—		Ruthen-	Rhodium	Pallad-
						ium 103	104	ium 106
Antimony	120	Tellurium	125	Iodine	127	—	—	—
Didymium ?		—		—				
—		—		—				
Tantalum	182	Tungsten	185	—		Osmium	Iridium	Platinum
						191	193	196
Bismuth	208	—		—				
—		Uranium	240	—				

kofer, had made an approach to the periodic law and had discovered its germs. The solution of the problem advanced but slowly, because the facts, and not the law, stood foremost in all attempts; and the law could not awaken a general interest so long as elements, having no apparent connection with each other, were included in the same octave, as for example:

1st octave of Newlands	H	F	Cl	Co and Ni	Br	Pd	I	Pt & Ir
7th ditto	O	S	Fe	Se	Rh & Ru	Te	Au	Os or Th

Analogies of the above order seemed quite accidental, and the more so as the octave contained occasionally ten elements instead of eight, and when two such elements as Ba and V, Co and Ni, or Rh and Ru, occupied one place in the octave. Nevertheless, the fruit was ripening, and I now see clearly that Strecker, De Chancourtois, and Newlands stood foremost in the way towards the discovery of the periodic law, and that they merely wanted the boldness necessary to place the whole question at such a height that its reflection on the facts could be clearly seen.

A third circumstance which revealed the periodicity of chemical elements was the accumulation, by the end of the sixties, of new information respecting the rare elements, disclosing their many-sided relations to the other elements and to each other. The researches of Marignac on niobium, and those of Roscoe on vanadium, were of special moment. The striking analogies between vanadium and phosphorus on the one hand, and between vanadium and chromium on the other, which became so apparent in the investigations connected with that element, naturally induced the comparison of $V = 51$ with $Cr = 52$, $Nb = 94$ with $Mo = 96$, and $Ta = 192$ with $W = 194$; while, on the other hand, $P = 31$ could be compared with $S = 32$, $As = 75$ with $Se = 79$, and $Sb = 120$ with $Te = 125$. From such approximations there remained but one step to the discovery of the law of periodicity.

The law of periodicity was thus a direct outcome of the stock of generalizations and established facts which had accumulated by the end of the decade 1860–1870: it is the embodiment of those data in a more or less systematic expression.

The foregoing is a selection from the Faraday Lecture delivered before the Fellows of the Chemical Society at the Royal Institution, June 4, 1889.

H. L. F. von Helmholtz

1821–1894

Hermann Ludwig Ferdinand von Helmholtz was born at Potsdam, Germany, in 1821. He studied at Berlin and held various professorships at Potsdam, Königsberg (in physiology), Bonn (in anatomy and physiology), Heidelberg (in physiology), and Berlin (in physics). He was named director of the Physicotechnical Institute at Charlottenburg, near Berlin, 1887, and held this position as well as his Berlin professorship until his death.

Helmholtz did work in most areas of nineteenth-century science. In this respect, he was remarkable even in an age when many scientists ranged much more widely in their researches than they now do. His most important early paper was on the conservation of energy; the essay that follows is a popular exposition of some of the conclusions described therein. In 1851 he invented the ophthalmoscope, and with it investigated the mechanism of sight. He collected his researches in a book, *Physiological Optics* (1856–66), which was the most important work on the physics of vision to have appeared until that time. He then turned his attention to acoustics. He explained the mechanism of the ear and attempted to account for our sensations of tone. He showed that these depend on the order, number and intensity of the overtones, or harmonics, which constitute a part of the structure of musical notes. His book *The Sensations of Tone* (1862) is said to be the principia of physiological acoustics.

In his later years, Helmholtz did work on the conservation of energy, hydrodynamics, electrodynamics, meteorology, optics, and the abstract principles of dynamics. He also wrote and lectured on philosophical and aesthetic problems. He died on September 8, 1894.

The mathematician W. K. Clifford paid tribute to Helmholtz for his remarkable ability to make important contributions in fields far

removed from that of his own special competence. Helmholtz was, Clifford wrote, "the physiologist who learned physics for the sake of his physiology, and mathematics for the sake of his physics, and is now in the first rank of all three."

The title of the following very famous essay is a little misleading. Helmholtz is here not writing primarily of force but of energy, or work. Work is the product of a force times the distance over which the force acts. The modern term for this quantity is kinetic energy, and the modern title of the essay would be "The Conservation of Energy."

"The total quantity of all the forces capable of work in the whole universe remains eternal and unchanged throughout all their changes," writes Helmholtz. This is the famous law of the conservation of energy, the so-called first law of thermodynamics. The relation of this law to the second law of thermodynamics, and entropy, is discussed in *The Running-down of the Universe*, by A. S. Eddington.

Helmholtz' researches into the nature of energy conversion were of prime importance. When he was a young doctor, the prevailing biological theory was vitalism.[1] Helmholtz came to the conclusion that vitalism must violate natural laws, because the vital force did not require any energy, and its operation seemed to him to imply perpetual motion. He decided that the question consisted in whether the force—the sum of the mechanical energy plus heat— produced by an organism was or was not solely the result of the digestion of foods by the organism. He concluded that the question must be answered in the affirmative. He collected his researches in

[1] For a discussion of vitalism see the Introductory note to Wöhler's *On the Artificial Production of Urea*, Vol. 8, pp. 310–311, in this set, and Claude Bernard, *Experimental Considerations Common to Living Things and to Inorganic Bodies*, Vol. 8, pp. 266–290, in this set.

the early paper, *On the Conservation of Force* (1847), which is the source of the following essay.

Helmholtz' work was not entirely original. Eighteenth-century physicists such as Bernoulli, Euler, d'Alembert, and La Grange had extended the principle of the conservation of energy from simple machines to the actions of all mechanical systems in the universe. Helmholtz gives credit to Rumford and Davy, and especially to Robert Mayer and Joule, for their extension of it to living beings. But Helmholtz' paper had a great influence. After its publication, the principle gained wider and wider acceptance. In particular, it went far toward convincing physicists that perpetual motion was impossible. And the popular essays which Helmholtz subsequently wrote on this subject helped laymen and scientists alike to understand the change to the new mechanical theory of heat from the older caloric theory—the idea that heat was a substance. This change in theories is discussed by Einstein and Infeld in "The Rise and Decline of Classical Physics." [2]

Max Planck in his *Scientific Autobiography* recalled that Helmholtz was a disappointing classroom lecturer. To others, however, and later even to Planck, who became his colleague at Berlin, he was a superior teacher. And Helmholtz took seriously the task of interpreting science to the general public, for he was disturbed by the split, which has perhaps grown even wider since his time, between scientists and what are now called humanists. He was a clear and patient writer, and he searched his mind for interesting and illuminating examples which would be meaningful to his readers. These virtues, which are by no means shared by all writers of popular scientific exposition, are much in evidence in the following selection.

[2] See Vol. 8, pp. 490–560, in this set.

On the Conservation
of Force

As I have undertaken to deliver here a series of lectures, I think the best way in which I can discharge that duty will be to bring before you, by means of a suitable example, some view of the special character of those sciences to the study of which I have devoted myself. The natural sciences, partly in consequence of their practical applications, and partly from their intellectual influence on the last four centuries, have so profoundly, and with such increasing rapidity, transformed all the relations of the life of civilized nations; they have given these nations such increase of riches, of enjoyment of life, of the preservation of health, of means of industrial and of social intercourse, and even such increase of political power, that every educated man who tries to understand the forces at work in the world in which he is living, even if he does not wish to enter upon the study of a special science, must have some interest in that peculiar kind of mental labor, which works and acts in the sciences in question.

On a former occasion I have already discussed the characteristic differences which exist between the natural and the mental sciences as regards the kind of scientific work. I then endeavored to show that it is more especially in the thorough conformity with law which natural phenomena and natural products exhibit, and in the comparative ease with which laws can be stated, that this difference exists. Not that I wish by any means to deny, that the mental life of individuals and peoples is also in conformity with law, as is the object of philosophical, philological, historical, moral, and social sciences to establish. But in mental life, the influences are so interwoven, that any definite sequence can but seldom be demonstrated. In nature the converse is the case. It has been possible to discover the law of the origin and progress of many enormously extended series of natural phenomena with such ac-

curacy and completeness that we can predict their future occurrence
with the greatest certainty; or in cases in which we have power over the
conditions under which they occur, we can direct them just according to
our will. The greatest of all instances of what the human mind can effect
by means of a well-recognized law of natural phenomena is that afforded
by modern astronomy. The one simple law of gravitation regulates the
motions of the heavenly bodies not only of our own planetary system,
but also of the far more distant double stars; from which, even the ray of
light, the quickest of all messengers, needs years to reach our eye; and,
just on account of this simple conformity with law, the motions of the
bodies in question can be accurately predicted and determined both for
the past and for future years and centuries to a fraction of a minute.

On this exact conformity with law depends also the certainty with
which we know how to tame the impetuous force of steam, and to make
it the obedient servant of our wants. On this conformity depends, more-
over, the intellectual fascination which chains the physicist to his sub-
jects. It is an interest of quite a different kind to that which mental and
moral sciences afford. In the latter it is man in the various phases of
his intellectual activity who chains us. Every great deed of which his-
tory tells us, every mighty passion which art can represent, every pic-
ture of manners, of civic arrangements, of the culture of peoples of
distant lands or of remote times, seizes and interests us, even if there is
no exact scientific connection among them. We continually find points
of contact and comparison in our conceptions and feelings; we get to
know the hidden capacities and desires of the mind, which in the ordi-
nary peaceful course of civilized life remain unawakened.

It is not to be denied that, in the natural sciences, this kind of in-
terest is wanting. Each individual fact, taken by itself, can indeed
arouse our curiosity or our astonishment, or be useful to us in its practi-
cal applications. But intellectual satisfaction we obtain only from a
connection of the whole, just from its conformity with law. *Reason* we
call that faculty innate in us of discovering laws and applying them with
thought. For the unfolding of the peculiar forces of pure reason in their
entire certainty and in their entire bearing, there is no more suitable
arena than inquiry into nature in the wider sense, the mathematics in-
cluded. And it is not only the pleasure at the successful activity of one
of our most essential mental powers; and the victorious subjections to
the power of our thought and will of an external world, partly un-
familiar, and partly hostile, which is the reward of this labor; but there is
a kind, I might almost say, of artistic satisfaction, when we are able to

survey the enormous wealth of nature as a regularly ordered whole—a cosmos, an image of the logical thought of our own mind.

The last decades of scientific development have led us to the recognition of a new universal law of all natural phenomena, which, from its extraordinarily extended range, and from the connection which it constitutes between natural phenomena of all kinds, even of the remotest times and the most distant places, is especially fitted to give us an idea of what I have described as the character of the natural sciences, which I have chosen as the subject of this lecture.

This law is *the law of the conservation of force,* a term the meaning of which I must first explain. It is not absolutely new; for individual domains of natural phenomena it was enunciated by Newton and Daniel Bernoulli; and Rumford and Humphry Davy have recognized distinct features of its presence in the laws of heat.

The possibility that it was of universal application was first stated by Dr. Julius Robert Mayer, a Schwabian physician (now living in Heilbronn), in the year 1842, while almost simultaneously with, and independently of him, James Prescott Joule, an English manufacturer, made a series of important and difficult experiments on the relation of heat to mechanical force, which supplied the chief points in which the comparison of the new theory with experience was still wanting.

The law in question asserts that the *quantity of force which can be brought into action in the whole of nature is unchangeable,* and can neither be increased nor diminished. My first object will be to explain to you what is understood by *quantity of force;* or, as the same idea is more popularly expressed with reference to its technical application, what we call *amount of work* in the mechanical sense of the word.

The idea of work for machines, or natural processes, is taken from comparison with the working power of man; and we can therefore best illustrate from human labor the most important features of the question with which we are concerned. In speaking of the work of machines and of natural forces we must, of course, in this comparison eliminate anything in which activity of intelligence comes into play. The latter is also capable of the hard and intense work of thinking, which tries a man just as muscular exertion does. But whatever of the actions of intelligence is met with in the work of machines, of course is due to the mind of the constructor and cannot be assigned to the instrument at work.

Now, the external work of man is of the most varied kind as regards the force or ease, the form and rapidity, of the motions used on it, and the kind of work produced. But both the arm of the blacksmith who

delivers his powerful blows with the heavy hammer, and that of the violinist who produces the most delicate variations in sound, and the hand of the lace-maker who works with threads so fine that they are on the verge of the invisible, all these acquire the force which moves them in the same manner and by the same organs, namely, the muscles of the arms. An arm the muscles of which are lamed is incapable of doing any work; the moving force of the muscle must be at work in it, and these must obey the nerves, which bring to them orders from the brain. That member is then capable of the greatest variety of motions; it can compel the most varied instruments to execute the most diverse tasks.

Just so it is with machines: they are used for the most diversified arrangements. We produce by their agency an infinite variety of movements, with the most various degrees of force and rapidity, from powerful steam hammers and rolling mills, where gigantic masses of iron are cut and shaped like butter, to spinning and weaving frames, the work of which rivals that of the spider. Modern mechanism has the richest choice of means of transferring the motion of one set of rolling wheels to another with greater or less velocity; of changing the rotating motion of wheels into the up-and-down motion of the piston rod, of the shuttle, of falling hammers and stamps; or, conversely, of changing the latter into the former; or it can, on the other hand, change movements of uniform into those of varying velocity, and so forth. Hence this extraordinarily rich utility of machines for so extremely varied branches of industry. But one thing is common to all these differences; they all need a *moving force*, which sets and keeps them in motion, just as the works of the human hand all need the moving force of the muscles.

Now, the work of the smith requires a far greater and more intense exertion of the muscles than that of the violin player; and there are in machines corresponding differences in the power and duration of the moving force required. These differences, which correspond to the different degree of exertion of the muscles in human labor, are alone what we have to think of when we speak of the *amount of work* of a machine. We have nothing to do here with the manifold character of the actions and arrangements which the machines produce; we are only concerned with an expenditure of force.

This very expression which we use so fluently, "expenditure of force," which indicates that the force applied has been expended and lost, leads us to a further characteristic analogy between the effects of the human arm and those of machines. The greater the exertion, and the longer it lasts, the more is the arm *tired*, and the more *is the store of its*

moving force for the time exhausted. We shall see that this peculiarity of becoming exhausted by work is also met with in the moving forces of inorganic nature; indeed, that this capacity of the human arm of being tired is only one of the consequences of the law with which we are now concerned. When fatigue sets in, recovery is needed, and this can only be effected by rest and nourishment. We shall find that also in the inorganic moving forces, when their capacity for work is spent, there is a possibility of reproduction, although in general other means must be used to this end than in the case of the human arm.

From the feeling of exertion and fatigue in our muscles, we can form a general idea of what we understand by amount of work; but we must endeavor, instead of the indefinite estimate afforded by this comparison, to form a clear and precise idea of the standard by which we have to measure the amount of work. This we can do better by the simplest inorganic moving forces than by the actions of our muscles, which are a very complicated apparatus, acting in an extremely intricate manner.

Let us now consider that moving force which we know best, and which is simplest—gravity. It acts, for example, as such in those clocks which are driven by a weight. This weight, fastened to a string, which is wound round a pulley connected with the first toothed wheel of the clock, cannot obey the pull of gravity without setting the whole clockwork in motion. Now I must beg you to pay special attention to the following points: the weight cannot put the clock in motion without itself sinking; did the weight not move, it could not move the clock, and its motion can only be such a one as obeys the action of gravity. Hence, if the clock is to go, the weight must continually sink lower and lower, and must at length sink so far that the string which supports it is run out. The clock then stops. The usual effect of its weight is for the present exhausted. Its gravity is not lost or diminished; it is attracted by the earth as before, but the capacity of this gravity to produce the motion of the clockwork is lost. It can only keep the weight at rest in the lowest point of its path, it cannot farther put it in motion.

But we can wind up the clock by the power of the arm, by which the weight is again raised. When this has been done, it has regained its former capacity, and can again set the clock in motion.

We learn from this that a raised weight possesses a *moving force*, but that it must necessarily sink if this force is to act; that by sinking, this moving force is exhausted, but by using another extraneous moving force—that of the arm—its activity can be restored.

The work which the weight has to perform in driving the clock is not indeed great. It has continually to overcome the small resistances which the friction of the axles and teeth, as well as the resistance of the air, oppose to the motion of the wheels, and it has to furnish the force for the small impulses and sounds which the pendulum produces at each oscillation. If the weight is detached from the clock, the pendulum swings for a while before coming to a rest, but its motion becomes each moment feebler, and ultimately ceases entirely, being gradually used up by the small hindrances I have mentioned. Hence, to keep the clock going, there must be a moving force, which, though small, must be continually at work. Such a one is the weight.

We get, moreover, from this example, a measure for the amount of work. Let us assume that a clock is driven by a weight of a pound, which falls five feet in twenty-four hours. If we fix ten such clocks, each with a weight of one pound, then ten clocks will be driven twenty-four hours; hence, as each has to overcome the same resistances in the same time as the others, ten times as much work is performed for ten pounds fall through five feet. Hence, we conclude that the height of the fall being the same, the work increases directly as the weight.

Now, if we increase the length of the string so that the weight runs down ten feet, the clock will go two days instead of one; and, with double the height of fall, the weight will overcome on the second day the same resistances as on the first, and will therefore do twice as much work as when it can only run down five feet. The weight being the same, the work increases as the height of fall. Hence, we may take the product of the weight into the height of fall as a measure of work, at any rate, in the present case. The application of this measure is, in fact, not limited to the individual case, but the universal standard adopted in manufactures for measuring magnitude of work is a *foot-pound*—that is, the amount of work which a pound raised through a foot can produce.[1]

We may apply this measure of work to all kinds of machines, for we should be able to set them all in motion by means of a weight sufficient to turn a pulley. We could thus always express the magnitude of any driving force, for any given machine, by the magnitude and height of fall of such a weight as would be necessary to keep the machine going with its arrangements until it had performed a certain work. Hence it is that the measurement of work by foot-pounds is universally applica-

1. This is the *technical* measure of work; to convert it into scientific measure it must be multiplied by the intensity of gravity.

ble. The use of such a weight as a driving force would not indeed be practically advantageous in those cases in which we were compelled to raise it by the power of our own arm; it would in that case be simpler to work the machine by the direct action of the arm. In the clock we use a weight so that we need not stand the whole day at the clock-work, as we should have to do to move it directly. By winding up the clock we accumulate a store of working capacity in it, which is sufficient for the expenditure of the next twenty-four hours.

Fig. 1

The case is somewhat different when nature herself raises the weight, which then works for us. She does not do this with solid bodies, at least not with such regularity as to be utilized; but she does it abundantly with water, which, being raised to the tops of mountains by meteorological processes, returns in streams from them. The gravity of water we use as moving force, the most direct application being in what are called *overshot* wheels, one of which is represented in Fig. 1. Along the circumference of such a wheel are a series of buckets, which act as receptacles for the water, and, on the side turned to the observer, have the tops uppermost; on the opposite side the tops of the buckets are upside down. The water flows at M into the buckets of the front of the wheel,

and at F, where the mouth begins to incline downwards, it flows out. The buckets on the circumference are filled on the side turned to the observer, and empty on the other side. Thus the former are weighted by the water contained in them, the latter not; the weight of the water acts continuously on only one side of the wheel, draws this down, and thereby turns the wheel; the other side of the wheel offers no resistance, for it contains no water. It is thus the weight of the falling water which turns the wheel, and furnishes the motive power. But you will at once see that the mass of water which turns the wheel must necessarily fall in order to do so, and that though, when it has reached the bottom, it has lost none of its gravity, it is no longer in a position to drive the wheel, if it is not restored to its original position, either by the power of the human arm or by means of some other natural force. If it can flow from the mill stream to still lower levels, it may be used to work other wheels. But when it has reached its lowest level, the sea, the last remainder of the moving force is used up, which is due to gravity—that is, to the attraction of the earth, and it cannot act by its weight until it has been again raised to a high level. As this is actually effected by meteorological processes, you will at once observe that these are to be considered as sources of moving force.

Water power was the first inorganic force which man learned to use instead of his own labor or of that of domestic animals. According to Strabo, it was known to King Mithridates of Pontus, who was also otherwise celebrated for his knowledge of nature; near his palace there was a water wheel. Its use was first introduced among the Romans in the time of the first emperors. Even now we find water mills in all mountains, valleys, or wherever there are rapidly flowing regularly filled brooks and streams. We find water power used for all purposes which can possibly be effected by machines. It drives mills which grind corn, sawmills, hammers and oil presses, spinning frames and looms, and so forth. It is the cheapest of all motive powers, it flows spontaneously from the inexhaustible stores of nature; but it is restricted to a particular place, and only in mountainous countries is it present in any quantity; in level countries extensive reservoirs are necessary for damming the rivers to produce any amount of water power.

Before passing to the discussion of other motive forces I must answer an objection which may readily suggest itself. We all know that there are numerous machines, systems of pulleys, levers and cranes, by the aid of which heavy burdens may be lifted by a comparatively small expenditure of force. We have all of us often seen one or two workmen

hoist heavy masses of stones to great heights, which they would be quite unable to do directly; in like manner, one or two men, by means of a crane, can transfer the largest and heaviest chests from a ship to the quay. Now, it may be asked, If a large, heavy weight had been used for driving a machine, would it not be very easy, by means of a crane or a system of pulleys, to raise it anew, so that it could again be used as a motor, and thus acquire motive power, without being compelled to use a corresponding exertion in raising the weight?

The answer to this is, that all these machines, in that degree in which for the moment they facilitate the exertion, also prolong it, so that by their help no motive power is ultimately gained. Let us assume that four laborers have to raise a load of four hundredweight by means of a rope passing over a single pulley. Every time the rope is pulled down through four feet, the load is also raised through four feet. But now, for the sake of comparison, let us suppose the same load hung to a block of four pulleys, as represented in Fig. 2. A single laborer would now be able to raise the load by the same exertion of force as each one of the four put forth. But when he pulls the rope through four feet, the load only rises one foot, for the length through which he pulls the rope, at a, is uniformly distributed in the block over four ropes, so that each of these is only shortened by a foot. To raise the load, therefore, to the same height, the one man must necessarily work four times as long as the four together did. But the total expenditure of work is the same, whether four laborers work for a quarter of an hour or one works for an hour.

Fig. 2

If, instead of human labor, we introduce the work of a weight, and hang to the block a load of 400, and at a, where otherwise the laborer works, a weight of 100 pounds, the block is then in equilibrium, and, without any appreciable exertion of the arm, may be set in motion. The weight of 100 pounds sinks, that of 400 rises. Without any measurable expenditure of force, the heavy weight has been raised by the sinking of the smaller one. But observe that the smaller weight will have sunk through four times the distance that the greater one has risen. But a fall of 100 pounds through four feet is just as much 400 foot-pounds as a fall of 400 pounds through one foot.

The action of levers in all their various modifications is precisely simi-

lar. Let *a b*, Fig. 3, be a simple lever, supported at *c*, the arm *c b* being four times as long as the other arm *a c*. Let a weight of one pound be hung at *b*, and a weight of four pounds at *a*, the lever is then in equilibrium, and the least pressure of the finger is sufficient, without any ap-

Fig. 3

preciable exertion of force, to place it in the position *a′ b′*, in which the heavy weight of four pounds has been raised, while the one-pound weight has sunk. But here, also, you will observe no work has been gained, for while the heavy weight has been raised through one inch, the lighter one has fallen through four inches; and four pounds through one inch is, as work, equivalent to the product of one pound through four inches.

Most other fixed parts of machines may be regarded as modified and compound levers; a toothed-wheel, for instance as a series of levers, the ends of which are represented by the individual teeth, and one after the other of which is put in activity in the degree in which the tooth in question seizes or is seized by the adjacent pinion. Take, for instance, the crabwinch, represented in Fig. 4. Suppose the pinion, G, on the axis of the barrel of the winch has twelve teeth, and the toothed-wheel, H, seventy-two teeth, that is, six times as many as the former. The winch must now be turned round six times before the toothed-wheel, H, and the barrel, D, have made one turn, and before the rope which raises the load has been lifted by a length equal to the circumference of the barrel. The workman thus requires six times the time, though to be sure only one-sixth of the exertion, which he would have to use if the handle

were directly applied to the barrel, D. In all these machines, and parts of machines, we find it confirmed that in proportion as the velocity of the motion increases its power diminishes, and that when the power increases the velocity diminishes, but that the amount of work is never thereby increased.

Fig. 4

In the overshot mill wheel, described above, water acts by its weight. But there is another form of mill wheel, what is called the *undershot wheel*, in which it only acts by its impact, as represented in Fig. 5 [p. 462]. These are used where the height from which the water comes is not great enough to flow on the upper part of the wheel. The lower part of undershot wheels dips in the flowing water which strikes against their float-boards and carries them along. Such wheels are used in swift-flowing streams which have a scarcely perceptible fall, as, for instance, on the Rhine. In the immediate neighborhood of such a wheel, the water need not necessarily have a great fall if it only strikes with considerable velocity. It is the velocity of the water, exerting an impact against the float-boards, which acts in this case, and which produces the motive power.

Windmills, which are used in the great plains of Holland and North Germany to supply the want of falling water, afford another instance of the action of velocity. The sails are driven by air in motion—by wind.

Air at rest could just as little drive a windmill as water at rest a water wheel. The driving force depends here on the velocity of moving masses.

A bullet resting in the hand is the most harmless thing in the world; by its gravity it can exert no great effect; but when fired and endowed with great velocity it drives through all obstacles with the most tremendous force.

Fig. 5

If I lay the head of a hammer gently on a nail, neither its small weight nor the pressure of my arm is quite sufficient to drive the nail into the wood; but if I swing the hammer and allow it to fall with great velocity, it acquires a new force, which can overcome far greater hindrances.

These examples teach us that the velocity of a moving mass can act as motive force. In mechanics, velocity in so far as it is motive force, and can produce work, is called *vis viva*. The name is not well chosen; it is too apt to suggest to us the force of living beings. Also in this case you will see, from the instances of the hammer and of the bullet, that velocity is lost, as such, when it produces working power. In the case of the water mill, or of the windmill, a more careful investigation of the moving masses of water and air is necessary to prove that part of their velocity has been lost by the work which they have performed.

The relation of velocity to working power is most simply and clearly seen in a simple pendulum, such as can be constructed by any weight which we suspend to a cord. Let M, Fig. 6, be such a weight, of a spherical form; A B, a horizontal line drawn through the center of the sphere;

P the point at which the cord is fastened. If now I draw the weight M on one side towards A, it moves in the arc *m a*, the end of which, *a*, is somewhat higher than the point A in the horizontal line. The weight is thereby raised to the height A *a*. Hence my arm must exert a certain force to bring the weight to *a*. Gravity resists this motion, and endeavors to bring back the weight to M, the lowest point which it can reach.

Now, if after I have brought the weight to *a* I let it go, it obeys this force of gravity and returns to *m*, arrives there with a certain velocity, and no longer remains quietly hanging at *m* as it did before, but swings

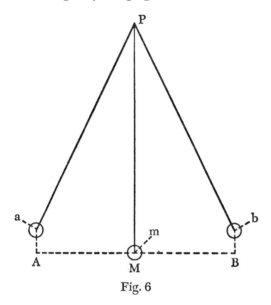

Fig. 6

beyond *m* towards *b*, where its motion stops as soon as it has traversed on the side of B an arc equal in length to that on the side of A, and after it has risen to a distance B *b* above the horizontal line, which is equal to the height A *a*, to which my arm had previously raised it. In *b* the pendulum returns, swings the same way back through *m* towards *a*, and so on, until its oscillations are gradually diminished, and ultimately annulled by the resistance of the air and by friction.

You see here that the reason why the weight, when it comes from *a* to *m*, and does not stop there, but ascends to *b*, in opposition to the action of gravity, is only to be sought in its velocity. The velocity which it has acquired in moving from the height A *a* is capable of again raising it to an equal height, B *b*. The velocity of the moving mass, M, is thus capable

of raising this mass; that is to say, in the language of mechanics, of performing work. This would also be the case if we had imparted such a velocity to the suspended weight by a blow.

From this we learn further how to measure the working power of velocity—or, what is the same thing, the *vis viva* of the *moving mass*. It is equal to the work, expressed in foot-pounds, which the same mass can exert after its velocity has been used to raise it, under the most favorable circumstances, to as great a height as possible.[2] This does not depend on the direction of the velocity; for if we swing a weight attached to a thread in a circle, we can even change a downward motion into an upward one.

The motion of the pendulum shows us very distinctly how the forms of working power hitherto considered—that of a raised weight and that of a moving mass—may merge into one another. In the points *a* and *b*, Fig. 6, the mass has no velocity; at the point *m* it has fallen as far as possible, but possesses velocity. As the weight goes from *a* to *m* the work of the raised weight is changed into *vis viva;* as the weight goes further from *m* to *b* the *vis viva* is changed into the work of a raised weight. Thus the work which the arm originally imparted to the pendulum is not lost in these oscillations provided we may leave out of consideration the influence of the resistance of the air and of friction. Neither does it increase, but it continually changes the form of its manifestation.

Let us now pass to other mechanical forces, those of elastic bodies. Instead of the weights which drive our clocks, we find in timepieces and in watches, steel springs which are coiled in winding up the clock, and are uncoiled by the working of the clock. To coil up the spring we consume the force of the arm; this has to overcome the resisting elastic force of the spring as we wind it up, just as in the clock we have to overcome the force of gravity which the weight exerts. The coiled spring can, however, perform work; it gradually expends this acquired capability in driving the clockwork.

If I stretch a crossbow and afterwards let it go, the stretched string moves the arrow; it imparts to it force in the form of velocity. To stretch the cord my arm must work for a few seconds; this work is imparted to the arrow at the moment it is shot off. Thus the crossbow concentrates into an extremely short time the entire work which the

2. The measure of *vis viva* in theoretical mechanics is half the product of the weight into the square of the velocity. To reduce it to the technical measure of the work we must divide it by the intensity of gravity; that is, by the velocity at the end of the first second of a freely falling body.

arm had communicated in the operation of stretching; the clock, on the contrary, spreads it over one or several days. In both cases no work is produced which my arm did not originally impart to the instrument; it is only expended more conveniently.

The case is somewhat different if by any other natural process I can place an elastic body in a state of tension without having to exert my arm. This is possible and is most easily observed in the case of gases.

If, for instance, I discharge a firearm loaded with gunpowder, the greater part of the mass of the powder is converted into gases at a very high temperature, which have a powerful tendency to expand, and can only be retained in the narrow space in which they are formed, by the exercise of the most powerful pressure. In expanding with enormous force they propel the bullet, and impart to it a great velocity, which we have already seen is a form of work.

In this case, then, I have gained work which my arm has not performed. Something, however, has been lost—the gunpowder, that is to say, whose constituents have changed into other chemical compounds, from which they cannot, without further ado, be restored to their original condition. Here, then, a chemical change has taken place, under the influence of which work has been gained.

Elastic forces are produced in gases by the aid of heat, on a far greater scale.

Let us take, as the most simple instance, atmospheric air. In Fig. 7 an apparatus is represented such as Regnault used for measuring the expansive force of heated gases. If no great accuracy is required in the measurement, the apparatus may be arranged more simply. At C is a glass globe filled with dry air, which is placed in a metal vessel, in which it can be heated by steam. It is connected with the U-shaped tube, S s, which contains a liquid, and the limbs of which communicate with each other when the stopcock R is closed. If the liquid is in equilibrium in the tube S s when the globe is cold, it rises in the leg s, and ultimately overflows when the globe is heated. If, on the contrary, when the globe is heated, equilibrium be restored by allowing some of the liquid to flow out at R, as the globe cools it will be drawn up towards n. In both cases liquid is raised, and work thereby produced.

The same experiment is continuously repeated on the largest scale in steam engines, though, in order to keep up a continual disengagement of compressed gases from the boiler, the air in the globe in Fig. 7, which would soon reach the maximum of its expansion, is replaced by water, which is gradually changed into steam by the application of heat.

But steam, so long as it remains as such, is an elastic gas which endeavors to expand exactly like atmospheric air. And instead of the column of liquid which was raised in our last experiment, the machine is caused to drive a solid piston which imparts its motion to other parts of the machine. Fig. 8 represents a front view of the working parts of a high-pressure engine, and Fig. 9 [p. 468] a section. The boiler in which steam is generated is not represented; the steam passes through the tube z z, Fig. 9, to the cylinder A A, in which moves a tightly fitting piston C.

Fig. 7

The parts between the tube z z and the cylinder A A, that is the slide valve in the valve-chest K K, and the two tubes d and e allow the steam to pass first below and then above the piston, while at the same time the steam has free exit from the other half of the cylinder. When the steam passes under the piston, it forces it upward; when the piston has reached the top of its course the position of the valve in K K changes, and the steam passes above the piston and forces it down again. The piston rod acts by means of the connecting rod P, on the crank Q of the flywheel X and sets this in motion. By means of the rod s, the motion of the rod regulates the opening and closing of the valve. But we need not here enter into those mechanical arrangements, however in-

Fig. 8

Fig. 9

geniously they have been devised. We are only interested in the manner in which heat produces elastic vapor, and how this vapor, in its endeavor to expand, is compelled to move the solid parts of the machine, and furnish work.

You all know how powerful and varied are the effects of which steam engines are capable; with them has really begun the great development of industry which has characterized our century before all others. Its most essential superiority over motive powers formerly known is that it is not restricted to a particular place. The store of coal and the small quantity of water which are the sources of its power can be brought everywhere, and steam engines can even be made movable, as is the case with steamships and locomotives. By means of these machines we can develop motive power to almost an indefinite extent at any place on the earth's surface, in deep mines and even on the middle of the ocean; while water and windmills are bound to special parts of the surface of the land. The locomotive transports travelers and goods over the land in numbers and with a speed which must have seemed an incredible fable to our forefathers, who looked upon the mailcoach with its six passengers in the inside, and its ten miles an hour, as an enormous progress. Steam engines traverse the ocean independently of the direction of the wind, and, successfully resisting storms which would drive sailing vessels far away, reach their goal at the appointed time. The advantages which the concourse of numerous and variously skilled workmen in all branches offers in large towns where wind and water power are wanting, can be utilized, for steam engines find place everywhere, and supply the necessary crude force; thus the more intelligent human force may be spared for better purposes; and, indeed, wherever the nature of the ground or the neighborhood of suitable lines of communication present a favorable opportunity for the development of industry, the motive power is also present in the form of steam engines.

We see, then, that heat can produce mechanical power; but in the cases which we have discussed we have seen that the quantity of force which can be produced by a given measure of a physical process is always accurately defined, and that the further capacity for work of the natural forces is either diminished or exhausted by the work which has been performed. How is it now with heat in this respect?

This question was of decisive importance in the endeavor to extend the law of the conservation of force to all natural processes. In the answer lay the chief difference between the older and newer views in

these respects. Hence it is that many physicists designate that view of nature corresponding to the law of the conservation of force with the name of *mechanical theory of heat.*

The older view of the nature of heat was that it is a substance, very fine and imponderable indeed, but indestructible, and unchangeable in quantity, which is an essential fundamental property of all matter. And, in fact, in a large number of natural processes, the quantity of heat which can be demonstrated by the thermometer is unchangeable.

By conduction and radiation, it can indeed pass from hotter to colder bodies; but the quantity of heat which the former lose can be shown by the thermometer to have reappeared in the latter. Many processes, too, were known, especially in the passage of bodies from the solid to the liquid and gaseous states, in which heat disappeared—at any rate, as regards the thermometer. But when the gaseous body was restored to the liquid, and the liquid to the solid state, exactly the same quantity of heat reappeared which formerly seemed to have been lost. Heat was said *to have become latent.* On this view, liquid water differed from solid ice in containing a certain quantity of heat bound, which, just because it was bound, could not pass to the thermometer, and therefore was not indicated by it. Aqueous vapor contains a far greater quantity of heat thus bound. But if the vapor be precipitated, and the liquid water restored to the state of ice, exactly the same amount of heat is liberated as had become latent in the melting of the ice and in the vaporization of the water.

Finally, heat is sometimes produced and sometimes disappears in chemical processes. But even here it might be assumed that the various chemical elements and chemical compounds contain certain constant quantities of latent heat, which, when they change their composition, are sometimes liberated and sometimes must be supplied from external sources. Accurate experiments have shown that the quantity of heat which is developed by a chemical process—for instance, in burning a pound of pure carbon into carbonic acid—is perfectly constant, whether the combustion is slow or rapid, whether it takes place all at once or by intermediate stages. This also agreed very well with the assumption, which was the basis of the theory of heat, that heat is a substance entirely unchangeable in quantity. The natural processes which have here been briefly mentioned, were the subject of extensive experimental and mathematical investigations, especially of the great French physicists in the last decade of the former, and the first decade of the present, century; and a rich and accurately worked chapter of physics had been developed, in which everything agreed excellently with the hypothe-

sis—that heat is a substance. On the other hand, the invariability in the quantity of heat in all these processes could at that time be explained in no other manner than that heat is a substance.

But one relation of heat—namely, that to mechanical work—had not been accurately investigated. A French engineer, Sadi Carnot, son of the celebrated War Minister of the Revolution, had indeed endeavored to deduce the work which heat performs, by assuming that the hypothetical caloric endeavored to expand like a gas; and from this assumption he deduced in fact a remarkable law as to the capacity of heat for work, which even now, though with an essential alteration introduced by Clausius, is among the bases of the modern mechanical theory of heat, and the practical conclusions from which, so far as they could at that time be compared with experiments, have held good.

But it was already known that whenever two bodies in motion rubbed against each other, heat was developed anew, and it could not be said whence it came.

The fact is universally recognized; the axle of a carriage which is badly greased and where the friction is great, becomes hot—so hot, indeed, that it may take fire; machine wheels with iron axles going at a great rate may become so hot that they weld to their sockets. A powerful degree of friction is not, indeed, necessary to disengage an appreciable degree of heat; thus, a lucifer match, which by rubbing is so heated that the phosphoric mass ignites, teaches this fact. Nay, it is enough to rub the dry hands together to feel the heat produced by friction, and which is far greater than the heating which takes place when the hands lie gently on each other. Uncivilized people use the friction of two pieces of wood to kindle a fire. With this view, a sharp spindle of hard wood is made to revolve rapidly on a base of soft wood in the manner represented in Fig. 10 [see p. 472].

So long as it was only a question of the friction of solids, in which particles from the surface become detached and compressed, it might be supposed that some changes in structure of the bodies rubbed might here liberate latent heat, which would thus appear as heat of friction.

But heat can also be produced by the friction of liquids, in which there could be no question of changes in structure, or of the liberation of latent heat. The first decisive experiment of this kind was made by Sir Humphry Davy in the commencement of the present century. In a cooled space he made two pieces of ice rub against each other, and thereby caused them to melt. The latent heat which the newly formed water must have here assimilated could not have been conducted to it

by the cold ice, or have been produced by a change of structure; it could have come from no other cause than from friction, and must have been created by friction.

Heat can also be produced by the impact of imperfectly elastic bodies as well as by friction. This is the case, for instance, when we produce fire by striking flint against steel, or when an iron bar is worked for some time by powerful blows of the hammer.

Fig. 10

If we inquire into the mechanical effects of friction and of inelastic impact, we find at once that these are the processes by which all terrestrial movements are brought to rest. A moving body whose motion was not retarded by any resisting force would continue to move to all eternity. The motions of the planets are an instance of this. This is apparently never the case with the motion of the terrestrial bodies, for they are always in contact with other bodies which are at rest, and rub against them. We can, indeed, very much diminish their friction, but never completely annul it. A wheel which turns about a well-worked axle, once set in motion, continues it for a long time; and the longer, the more truly and smoother the axle is made to turn, the better it is greased, and the less the pressure it has to support. Yet the *vis viva* of the motion which we have imparted to such a wheel when we started it, is gradually lost in consequence of friction. It disappears, and if we do not carefully consider the matter, it seems as if the *vis viva* which the wheel had possessed had been simply destroyed without any substitute.

A bullet which is rolled on a smooth horizontal surface continues to roll until its velocity is destroyed by friction on the path, caused by the very minute impacts on its little roughnesses.

A pendulum which has been put in vibration can continue to oscillate

for hours if the suspension is good, without being driven by a weight; but by the friction against the surrounding air, and by that at its place of suspension, it ultimately comes to rest.

A stone which has fallen from a height has acquired a certain velocity on reaching the earth; this we know is the equivalent of a mechanical work; so long as this velocity continues as such, we can direct it upwards by means of suitable arrangements, and thus utilize it to raise the stone again. Ultimately the stone strikes against the earth and comes to rest; the impact has destroyed its velocity, and therewith apparently also the mechanical work which this velocity could have affected.

If we review the results of all these instances, which each of you could easily add to from your own daily experience, we shall see that friction and inelastic impact are processes in which mechanical work is destroyed, and heat produced in its place.

The experiments of Joule, which have been already mentioned, lead us a step further. He has measured in foot-pounds the amount of work which is destroyed by the friction of solids and by the friction of liquids; and, on the other hand, he has determined the quantity of heat which is thereby produced, and has established a definite relation between the two. His experiments show that when heat is produced by the consumption of work, a definite quantity of work is required to produce that amount of heat which is known to physicists as the *unit of heat;* the heat, that is to say, which is necessary to raise one gram of water through one degree centigrade. The quantity of work necessary for this is, according to Joule's best experiments, equal to the work which a gram would perform in falling through a height of 425 meters.

In order to show how closely concordant are his numbers, I will adduce the results of a few series of experiments which he obtained after introducing the latest improvements in his methods.

1. A series of experiments in which water was heated by friction in a brass vessel. In the interior of this vessel a vertical axle provided with sixteen paddles was rotated, the eddies thus produced being broken by a series of projecting barriers, in which parts were cut out large enough for the paddles to pass through. The value of the equivalent was 424.9 meters.

2. Two similar experiments, in which mercury in an iron vessel was substituted for water in a brass one, gave 425 and 426.3 meters.

3. Two series of experiments, in which a conical ring rubbed against another, both surrounded by mercury, gave 426.7 and 425.6 meters.

Exactly the same relations between heat and work were also found in

the reverse process—that is, when work was produced by heat. In order to execute this process under physical conditions that could be controlled as perfectly as possible, permanent gases and not vapors were used, although the latter are, in practice, more convenient for producing large quantities of work, as in the case of the steam engine. A gas which is allowed to expand with moderate velocity becomes cooled. Joule was the first to show the reason of this cooling. For the gas has, in expanding, to overcome the resistance which the pressure of the atmosphere and the slowly yielding side of the vessel oppose to it: or, if it cannot of itself overcome this resistance, it supports the arm of the observer which does it. Gas thus performs work, and this work is produced at the cost of its heat. Hence the cooling. If, on the contrary, the gas is suddenly allowed to issue into a perfectly exhausted space where it finds no resistance, it does not become cool, as Joule has shown; or if individual parts of it become cool, others become warm; and, after the temperature has become equalized, this is exactly as much as before the sudden expansion of the gaseous mass.

How much heat the various gases disengage when they are compressed, and how much work is necessary for their compression; or, conversely, how much heat disappears when they expand under a pressure equal to their own counterpressure, was partly known from the older physical experiments, and has partly been determined by the recent experiments of Regnault by extremely perfect methods. Calculations with the best data of this kind give us the value of the thermal equivalent from experiments:

With atmospheric air	426.0	meters
" oxygen	425.7	"
" nitrogen	431.3	"
" hydrogen	425.3	"

Comparing these numbers with those which determine the equivalence of heat and mechanical work in friction, as close an agreement is seen as can at all be expected from numbers which have been obtained by such varied investigations of different observers.

Thus then: a certain quantity of heat may be changed into a definite quantity of work; this quantity of work can also be retransformed into heat, and, indeed, into exactly the same quantity of heat as that from which it originated; in a mechanical point of view, they are exactly equivalent. Heat is a new form in which a quantity of work may appear.

These facts no longer permit us to regard heat as a substance, for its

quantity is not unchangeable. It can be produced anew from the *vis viva* of motion destroyed; it can be destroyed, and then produces motion. We must rather conclude from this that heat itself is a motion, an internal invisible motion of the smallest elementary particles of bodies. If, therefore, motion seems lost in friction and impact, it is not actually lost, but only passes from the great visible masses to their smallest particles; while in steam engines the internal motion of the heated gaseous particles is transferred to the piston of the machine, accumulated in it, and combined in a resultant whole.

But what is the nature of this internal motion can only be asserted with any degree of probability in the case of gases. Their particles probably cross one another in rectilinear paths in all directions, until, striking another particle, or against the side of the vessel, they are reflected in another direction. A gas would thus be analogous to a swarm of gnats, consisting, however, of particles infinitely small and infinitely more closely packed. This hypothesis, which has been developed by Krönig, Clausius, and Maxwell, very well accounts for all the phenomena of gases.

What appeared to the earlier physicists to be the constant quantity of heat is nothing more than the whole motive power of the motion of heat, which remains constant so long as it is not transformed into other forms of work, or results afresh from them.

We turn now to another kind of natural forces which can produce work—I mean the chemical. We have today already come across them. They are the ultimate cause of the work which gunpowder and the steam engine produce; for the heat which is consumed in the latter, for example, originates in the combustion of carbon—that is to say, in a chemical process. The burning of coal is the chemical union of carbon with the oxygen of the air, taking place under the influence of the chemical affinity of the two substances.

We may regard this force as an attractive force between the two, which, however, only acts through them with extraordinary power, if the smallest particles of the two substances are in closest proximity to each other. In combustion this force acts; the carbon and oxygen atoms strike against each other and adhere firmly, inasmuch as they form a new compound—carbonic acid—a gas known to all of you as that which ascends from all fermenting and fermented liquids—from beer and champagne. Now this attraction between the atoms of carbon and of oxygen performs work just as much as that which the earth in the form of gravity exerts upon a raised weight. When the weight falls to the ground, it produces an agitation, which is partly transmitted to the vicin-

ity as sound waves, and partly remains as the motion of heat. The same result we must expect from chemical action. When carbon and oxygen atoms have rushed against each other, the newly formed particles of carbonic acid must be in the most violent molecular motion—that is, in the motion of heat. And this is so. A pound of carbon burned with oxygen to form carbonic acid, gives as much heat as is necessary to raise 80.9 pounds of water from the freezing to the boiling point; and just as the same amount of work is produced when a weight falls, whether it falls slowly or fast, so also the same quantity of heat is produced by the combustion of carbon, whether this is slow or rapid, whether it takes place all at once, or by successive stages.

When the carbon is burned, we obtain in its stead, and in that of the oxygen, the gaseous product of combustion—carbonic acid. Immediately after combustion it is incandescent. When it has afterwards imparted heat to the vicinity, we have in the carbonic acid the entire quantity of carbon and the entire quantity of oxygen, and also the force of affinity quite as strong as before. But the action of the latter is now limited to holding the atoms of carbon and oxygen firmly united; they can no longer produce either heat or work any more than a fallen weight can do work if it has not been again raised by some extraneous force. When the carbon has been burned we take no further trouble to retain the carbonic acid; it can do no more service, we endeavor to get it out of the chimneys of our houses as fast as we can.

Is it possible, then, to tear asunder the particles of carbonic acid, and give to them once more the capacity of work which they had before they were combined, just as we can restore the potentiality of a weight by raising it from the ground? It is indeed possible. We shall afterwards see how it occurs in the life of plants; it can also be effected by inorganic processes, though in roundabout ways, the explanation of which would lead us too far from our present course.

This can, however, be easily and directly shown for another element, hydrogen, which can be burned just like carbon. Hydrogen with carbon is a constituent of all combustible vegetable substances, among others, it is also an essential constituent of the gas which is used for lighting our streets and rooms; in the free state it is also a gas, the lightest of all, and burns when ignited with a feebly luminous blue flame. In this combustion—that is, in the chemical combination of hydrogen with oxygen, a very considerable quantity of heat is produced; for a given weight of hydrogen, four times as much heat as in the combustion of

the same weight of carbon. The product of combustion is water, which, therefore, is not of itself further combustible, for the hydrogen in it is completely saturated with oxygen. The force of affinity, therefore, of hydrogen for oxygen, like that of carbon for oxygen, performs work in combustion, which appears in the form of heat. In the water which has been formed during combustion, the force of affinity is exerted between the elements as before, but its capacity for work is lost. Hence the two elements must be again separated, their atoms torn apart, if new effects are to be produced from them.

Fig. 11

This we can do by the aid of currents of electricity. In the apparatus depicted in Fig. 11, we have two glass vessels filled with acidulated water a and a_1, which are separated in the middle by a porous plate moistened with water. In both sides are fitted platinum wires, k, which are attached to platinum plates, i and i_1. As soon as a galvanic current is transmitted through the water by the platinum wires, k, you see bubbles of gas ascend from the plates i and i_1. These bubbles are the two elements of water, hydrogen on the one hand, and oxygen on the other. The gases emerge through the tubes g and g_1. If we wait until the upper part of the vessels and the tubes have been filled with it, we can inflame hydrogen at one side; it burns with a blue flame. If I bring a glimmering spill near the mouth of the other tube, it bursts into flame, just as happens with oxygen gas, in which the processes of combustion are far more intense than in atmospheric air, where the oxygen mixed with nitrogen is only one-fifth of the whole volume.

If I hold a glass flask filled with water over the hydrogen flame, the water, newly formed in combustion, condenses upon it.

If a platinum wire be held in the almost non-luminous flame, you see how intensely it is ignited; in a plentiful current of a mixture of the gases, hydrogen and oxygen, which have been liberated in the above experiment, the almost infusible platinum might even be melted. The hydrogen which has here been liberated from the water by the electrical current has regained the capacity of producing large quantities of heat by a fresh combination with oxygen; its affinity for oxygen has regained for it its capacity for work.

We here become acquainted with a new source of work, the electric current which decomposes water. This current is itself produced by a galvanic battery, Fig. 12. Each of the four vessels contains nitric acid, in which there is a hollow cylinder of very compact carbon. In the middle

Fig. 12

of the carbon cylinder is a cylindrical porous vessel of white clay, which contains dilute sulfuric acid; in this dips a zinc cylinder. Each zinc cylinder is connected by a metal ring with the carbon cylinder of the next vessel, the last zinc cylinder, *n*, is connected with one platinum plate, and the first carbon cylinder, *p*, with the other platinum plate of the apparatus for the decomposition of water.

If now the conducting circuit of this galvanic apparatus is completed, and the decomposition of water begins, a chemical process takes place simultaneously in the cells of the voltaic battery. Zinc takes oxygen from the surrounding water and undergoes a slow combustion. The product of combustion thereby produced, oxide of zinc, unites further with sulfuric acid, for which it has a powerful affinity, and sulfate of zinc, a saline kind of substance, dissolves in the liquid. The oxygen, moreover, which is withdrawn from it is taken by the water from the nitric acid surrounding the cylinder of carbon, which is very rich in it, and readily gives it up. Thus, in the galvanic battery, zinc burns to sulfate of zinc at the cost of the oxygen of nitric acid.

Thus, while one product of combustion, water, is again separated, a new combustion is taking place—that of zinc. While we there reproduce chemical affinity which is capable of work, it is here lost. The electrical current is, as it were, only the carrier which transfers the chemical force of the zinc uniting with oxygen and acid to water in the decomposing cell, and uses it for overcoming the chemical force of hydrogen and oxygen.

In this case, we can restore work which has been lost, but only by using another force, that of oxidizing zinc.

Here we have overcome chemical forces by chemical forces, through the instrumentality of the electrical current. But we can attain the same object by mechanical forces, if we produce the electrical current by a magnetoelectrical machine, Fig. 13. If we turn the handle, the anker R R', on which is coiled copper wire, rotates in front of the poles of the horseshoe magnet, and in these coils electrical currents are produced, which can be led from the points a and b. If the ends of these wires are connected with the apparatus for decomposing water, we obtain hydrogen and oxygen, though in far smaller quantity than by the aid of the battery which we used before. But this process is interesting, for the mechanical force of the arm which turns the wheel produces the work which is required for separating the combined chemical elements. Just as the steam engine changes chemical into mechanical force the magneto-electrical machine transforms mechanical force into chemical.

The application of electrical currents opens out a large number of relations between the various natural forces. We have decomposed water into its elements by such currents, and should be able to decompose a large number of other chemical compounds. On the other hand, in ordinary galvanic batteries electrical currents are produced by chemical forces.

In all conductors through which electrical currents pass they produce heat; I stretch a thin platinum wire between the ends *n* and *p* of the galvanic battery, Fig. 12; it becomes ignited and melts. On the other hand, electrical currents are produced by heat in what are called thermo-electric elements.

Iron which is brought near a spiral of copper wire, traversed by an electrical current, becomes magnetic, and then attracts other pieces of

Fig. 13

iron, or a suitably placed steel magnet. We thus obtain mechanical actions which meet with extended applications in the electrical telegraph, for instance. Fig. 14 represents a Morse's telegraph in one-third of the natural size. The essential part is a horseshoe-shaped iron core, which

stands in the copper spirals $b\ b$. Just over the top of this is a small steel magnet $c\ c$, which is attracted the moment an electrical current, arriving by the telegraph wire, traverses the spirals $b\ b$. The magnet $c\ c$ is rigidly fixed in the lever $d\ d$, at the other end of which is a style; this makes a mark on a paper band, drawn by a clockwork, as often and as long as $c\ c$ is attracted by the magnetic action of the electrical current. Conversely, by reversing the magnetism in the iron core of the spirals $b\ b$, we should obtain in them an electrical current just as we have obtained such currents in the magnetoelectrical machine, Fig. 13; in the spirals of that machine there is an iron core which, by being approached to the poles of the large horseshoe magnet, is sometimes magnetized in one and sometimes in the other direction.

Fig. 14

I will not accumulate examples of such relations; in subsequent lectures we shall come across them. Let us review these examples once more, and recognize in them the law which is common to all.

A raised weight can produce work, but in doing so it must necessarily sink from its height, and, when it has fallen as deep as it can fall, its gravity remains as before, but it can no longer do work.

A stretched spring can do work, but in so doing it becomes loose. The velocity of a moving mass can do work, but in doing so it comes to rest. Heat can perform work; it is destroyed in the operation. Chemical forces can perform work, but they exhaust themselves in the effort.

Electrical currents can perform work, but to keep them up we must consume either chemical or mechanical forces, or heat.

We may express this generally. *It is a universal character of all known natural forces that their capacity for work is exhausted in the degree in which they actually perform work.*

We have seen, further, that when a weight fell without performing any work, it *either* acquired velocity or produced heat. We might also drive a magnetoelectrical machine by a falling weight; it would then furnish electrical currents.

We have seen that chemical forces, when they come into play, produce either heat or electrical currents or mechanical work.

We have seen that heat may be changed into work; there are apparatus (thermoelectric batteries) in which electrical currents are produced by it. Heat can directly separate chemical compounds; thus, when we burn limestone, it separates carbonic acid from lime.

Thus, whenever the capacity for work of one natural force is destroyed, it is transformed into another kind of activity. Even within the circuit of inorganic natural forces, we can transform each of them into an active condition by the aid of any other natural force which is capable of work. The connections between the various natural forces which modern physics has revealed, are so extraordinarily numerous that several entirely different methods may be discovered for each of these problems.

I have stated how we are accustomed to measure mechanical work, and how the equivalent in work of heat may be found. The equivalent in work of chemical processes is again measured by the heat which they produce. By similar relations, the equivalent in work of the other natural forces may be expressed in terms of mechanical work.

If, now, a certain quantity of mechanical work is lost, there is obtained, as experiments made with the object of determining this point show, an equivalent quantity of heat, or, instead of this, of chemical force; and, conversely, when heat is lost, we gain an equivalent quantity of chemical or mechanical force; and, again, when chemical force disappears, an equivalent of heat or work; so that in all these interchanges between various inorganic natural forces working force may indeed disappear in one form, but then it reappears in exactly equivalent quantity in some other form; it is thus neither increased nor diminished, but always remains in exactly the same quantity. We shall subsequently see that the same law holds good also for processes in organic nature, so far as the facts have been tested.

It follows thence *that the total quantity of all the forces* capable of work *in the whole universe remains eternal and unchanged throughout all their changes.* All change in nature amounts to this, that force can change its form and locality without its quantity being changed. The universe possesses, once for all, a store of force which is not altered by any change of phenomena, can neither be increased nor diminished, and which maintains any change which takes place on it.

You see how, starting from considerations based on the immediate practical interests of technical work, we have been led up to a universal natural law, which, as far as all previous experience extends, rules and embraces all natural processes; which is no longer restricted to the practical objects of human utility, but expresses a perfectly general and particularly characteristic property of all natural forces, and which, as regards generality, is to be placed by the side of the laws of the unalterability of mass, and the unalterability of the chemical elements.

At the same time, it also decides a great practical question which has been much discussed in the last two centuries, to the decision of which an infinity of experiments has been made and an infinity of apparatus constructed—that is, the question of the possibility of a perpetual motion. By this was understood a machine which was to work continuously without the aid of any external driving force. The solution of this problem promised enormous gains. Such a machine would have had all the advantages of steam without requiring the expenditure of fuel. Work is wealth. A machine which could produce work from nothing was as good as one which made gold. This problem had thus for a long time occupied the place of gold making, and had confused many a pondering brain. That a perpetual motion could not be produced by the aid of the then known mechanical forces could be demonstrated in the last century by the aid of the mathematical mechanics which had at that time been developed. But to show also that it is not possible even if heat, chemical forces, electricity, and magnetism were made to co-operate, could not be done without a knowledge of our law in all its generality. The possibility of a perpetual motion was first finally negatived by the law of the conservation of force, and this law might also be expressed in the practical form that no perpetual motion is possible, that force cannot be produced from nothing; something must be consumed.

You will only be ultimately able to estimate the importance and the scope of our law when you have before your eyes a series of its applications to individual processes in nature.

What I have today mentioned as to the origin of the moving forces which are at our disposal, directs us to something beyond the narrow confines of our laboratories and our manufactories, to the great operations at work in the life of the earth and of the universe. The force of falling water can only flow down from the hills when rain and snow bring it to them. To furnish these, we must have aqueous vapor in the atmosphere, which can only be effected by the aid of heat, and this heat comes from the sun. The steam engine needs the fuel which the vegetable life yields, whether it be the still active life of the surrounding vegetation, or the extinct life which has produced the immense coal deposits in the depths of the earth. The forces of man and animals must be restored by nourishment; all nourishment comes ultimately from the vegetable kingdom, and leads us back to the same source.

You see then that when we inquire into the origin of the moving forces which we take into our service, we are thrown back upon the meteorological processes in the earth's atmosphere, on the life of plants in general, and on the sun.

The foregoing consists of an introduction to a series of lectures delivered at Carlsruhe in the winter of 1862–1863, translated by Edmund Atkinson.

Albert Einstein

1879–1955

Leopold Infeld

(1898–)

Albert Einstein was born at Ulm, Germany, in 1879. In 1896 he entered the Swiss Federal Polytechnic School at Zürich; but bored by the teaching, he found time to read the works of the great physicists of the nineteenth century. Receiving his degree in 1900, he searched in vain for a teaching post. He finally took a job in the Berne patent office. Again he found himself with free time, which he used for further reading and thinking. In 1905, when he was twenty-six, he published four papers, each of which contained a great discovery in physics, and which had the effect of creating three new branches of physics: relativity, statistical mechanics, and the quantum theory of radiation.

In 1909 Einstein was made professor of physics at the University of Zürich, where he had received his Ph.D. in 1905. He continued to work on relativity, the special theory of which had constituted one of his papers of 1905; and in 1916 he published his famous paper on the general theory of relativity. He received the Nobel Prize in physics for 1921.

After 1920 Einstein to some extent parted company from the main development of modern physics. Its dependence on probability concerned him, for this seemed to indicate that its laws were only provisional. He asserted that an over-all reduction of all physical laws to geometry would be the test of a true theory. He believed that he had made such a reduction before his death, but most physicists do not as yet agree that his final formulation adequately explains the observed phenomena.

To escape the anti-Jewish persecutions of Hitler's Germany, and in order to continue his researches in freedom, Einstein left Europe for the United States in 1933. He joined the Institute for Advanced

Study, in Princeton, New Jersey, and remained there for the rest of his life. In 1939 it became known to him that two German physicists had brought about the fission of uranium. He was asked to inform the American government of the possible results of this achievement, and he did so, in a letter to President Roosevelt. As a consequence, the Manhattan Project was instituted, which built the atomic bomb. There was a profound irony in this, for Einstein was always a sincere pacifist and humanitarian. He died at Princeton in 1955.

Leopold Infeld was born at Crakow, Poland, in 1898. He studied at Lwów and Crakow, receiving his Ph.D. from the latter's university in 1921. He went to England and then to America, where he joined the Institute for Advanced Study, 1936–38. He was professor of applied mathematics at the University of Toronto from 1939–50, after which he returned to Poland. He is now associated with the University of Warsaw.

He made contributions to the theory of relativity and to quantum theory, and he wrote several books of a popular nature. It was at the Institute for Advanced Study that he and Einstein planned and wrote *The Evolution of Physics* (1938), from which the following selection is taken.

Scientific concepts often begin with those used in ordinary language for the affairs of everyday life," say the authors, "but they develop quite differently. They are transformed and lose the ambiguity associated with them in ordinary language, gaining in rigorousness so that they may be applied to scientific thought." They go on to explain that the special language of science is mathematics. "Mathematics as a tool of reasoning," they write, "is necessary if we wish to draw conclusions which may be compared with experiment." And they point out that "the price which must be paid for abandoning the language of mathematics is a loss in precision, and the neces-

Notes from the artist: "Einstein and his collaborator, Infeld, are presented in a double portrait, together with the famous formula expressing the relation of mass and energy. A sketch of Einstein as a boy is also included. The quotation is from The Evolution of Physics.*"*

$E = mc^2$

Science is not just a collection of laws, a catalogue of unrelated facts. It is a creation of the human mind, with its freely invented ideas and concepts. Physical theories try to form a picture of reality and to establish its connection with the wide world of sense impressions. Thus the only justification for our mental structures is whether and in what way our theories form such a link. (R.E.S. 1/33).

$ds^2 = dx^i dx^i, \quad x^i = (x_1^2 = y^2 + z^2)$ (R.E.S. 1/33)

$dS = g_{ik} dx^i dx^k$

$ds^2 = y_{ik} dx^i dx^k (dx^i)^2 = dx^i dx^i$ (R.E.-0.1/33)

E. I. H. 1938

E. I. 1939

Infeld

A. Einstein

sity of sometimes quoting results without showing how they were reached."

However, the authors are willing to pay the price. The reader will notice that in this long selection—indeed, in the entire book from which it is taken—there is not a single mathematical formula. This discussion of classical physical theory and its transformation into modern physics is written in a language other than the special language that made the transformation possible and necessary.

That revolutionary changes in scientific theory are necessary, and indeed inevitable, is a point emphasized by the authors. "Physical concepts are free creations of the human mind," they say, "and are not, however it may seem, uniquely determined by the external world." They compare the scientist to a man "trying to understand the mechanism of a closed watch." He can never open the watch; he can only form a picture of a mechanism that would explain what he sees happening on the face of the watch. "He will never be able to compare his picture with the real mechanism. . . . But he certainly believes that, as his knowledge increases, his picture of reality will become simpler and simpler and will explain a wider and wider range of his sensuous impressions."

This idea is an extremely important one for modern science. Successive theories only approximate the "objective truth," they can never reach it. Indeed, its existence may be denied. The criteria by which one theory is preferred to another would still remain the same. They are, as Einstein and Infeld point out, simplicity and comprehensibility.

The authors indicate why it is that "there are no eternal theories in science." They write: "It always happens that some of the facts predicted by a theory are disproved by experiment. Every theory has its period of gradual development and triumph, after which it may experience a rapid decline. . . . Nearly every great advance in science arises from a crisis in the old theory, through an endeavor to find a way out of the difficulties created. We must examine old ideas, old theories, although they belong to the past, for this is the only way to understand the importance of the new ones and the extent of their validity."

This, too, is an important point. And it applies not only in science. In philosophy, in history, in law, and in medicine, it is equally essential, for an adequate understanding of the present, to understand the past. It is often said that the unwillingness of modern

education to recognize this principle is one of its most striking failures.

The following selection from *The Evolution of Physics* is a remarkable piece of writing. It treats of difficult ideas with the utmost simplicity; it makes plain what would otherwise be dark. Its discussion, for example, of the change from the substance theory of heat to the mechanical theory of heat is a model of clarity. It is particularly useful for the reader of this volume, for it reviews the history of physics from Galileo and Newton to Einstein himself. That is a period in which most of the essays and lectures reprinted here were first published. Besides being illuminating in itself, it can thus serve as background reading for many of them.

The selection is most valuable of all, perhaps, for the questions it raises. Indeed, it suggests that asking questions is of primary importance. "The formulation of a problem," the authors say, "is often more essential than its solution, which may be merely a matter of mathematical or experimental skill."

The Rise and Decline of
Classical Physics
from *The Evolution of Physics*

THE RISE OF THE MECHANICAL VIEW

The Great Mystery Story

I n imagination there exists the perfect mystery story. Such a story presents all the essential clues, and compels us to form our own theory of the case. If we follow the plot carefully we arrive at the complete solution for ourselves just before the author's disclosure at the end of the book. The solution itself, contrary to those of inferior mysteries, does not disappoint us; moreover, it appears at the very moment we expect it.

Can we liken the reader of such a book to the scientists, who throughout successive generations continue to seek solutions of the mysteries in the book of nature? The comparison is false and will have to be abandoned later, but it has a modicum of justification which may be extended and modified to make it more appropriate to the endeavor of science to solve the mystery of the universe.

This great mystery story is still unsolved. We cannot even be sure that it has a final solution. The reading has already given us much; it has taught us the rudiments of the language of nature; it has enabled us to understand many of the clues, and has been a source of joy and excitement in the oftentimes painful advance of science. But we realize that in spite of all the volumes read and understood we are still far from a complete solution, if, indeed, such a thing exists at all. At every stage we try to find an explanation consistent with the clues already discovered. Tentatively accepted theories have explained many of the facts, but no general solution compatible with all known clues has yet been evolved. Very often a seemingly perfect theory has

proved inadequate in the light of further reading. New facts appear, contradicting the theory or unexplained by it. The more we read, the more fully do we appreciate the perfect construction of the book, even though a complete solution seems to recede as we advance.

In nearly every detective novel since the admirable stories of Conan Doyle there comes a time where the investigator has collected all the facts he needs for at least some phase of his problem. These facts often seem quite strange, incoherent, and wholly unrelated. The great detective, however, realizes that no further investigation is needed at the moment, and that only pure thinking will lead to a correlation of the facts collected. So he plays his violin, or lounges in his armchair enjoying a pipe, when suddenly, by Jove, he has it! Not only does he have an explanation for the clues at hand, but he knows that certain other events must have happened. Since he now knows exactly where to look for it, he may go out, if he likes, to collect further confirmation for his theory.

The scientist reading the book of nature, if we may be allowed to repeat the trite phrase, must find the solution for himself, for he cannot, as impatient readers of other stories often do, turn to the end of the book. In our case the reader is also the investigator, seeking to explain, at least in part, the relation of events to their rich context. To obtain even a partial solution the scientist must collect the unordered facts available and make them coherent and understandable by creative thought.

It is our aim, in the following pages, to describe in broad outline that work of physicists which corresponds to the pure thinking of the investigator. We shall be chiefly concerned with the role of thoughts and ideas in the adventurous search for knowledge of the physical world.

The First Clue. Attempts to read the great mystery story are as old as human thought itself. Only a little over three hundred years ago, however, did scientists begin to understand the language of the story. Since that time, the age of Galileo and Newton, the reading has proceeded rapidly. Techniques of investigation, systematic methods of finding and following clues, have been developed. Some of the riddles of nature have been solved although many of the solutions have proved temporary and superficial in the light of further research.

A most fundamental problem, for thousands of years wholly obscured by its complications, is that of motion. All those motions we observe in nature, that of a stone thrown into the air, a ship sailing the sea, a cart pushed along the street, are in reality very intricate. To understand

these phenomena it is wise to begin with the simplest possible cases, and proceed gradually to the more complicated ones. Consider a body at rest, where there is no motion at all. To change the position of such a body it is necessary to exert some influence upon it, to push it or lift it, or let other bodies, such as horses or steam engines, act upon it. Our intuitive idea is that motion is connected with the acts of pushing, lifting or pulling. Repeated experience would make us risk the further statement that we must push harder if we wish to move the body faster. It seems natural to conclude that the stronger the action exerted on a body, the greater will be its speed. A four-horse carriage goes faster than a carriage drawn by only two horses. Intuition thus tells us that speed is essentially connected with action.

It is a familiar fact to readers of detective fiction that a false clue muddles the story and postpones the solution. The method of reasoning dictated by intuition was wrong and led to false ideas of motion which were held for centuries. Aristotle's great authority throughout Europe was perhaps the chief reason for the long belief in this intuitive idea. We read in the *Mechanics*, for two thousand years attributed to him:

> The moving body comes to a standstill when the force which pushes it along can no longer so act as to push it.

The discovery and use of scientific reasoning by Galileo was one of the most important achievements in the history of human thought, and marks the real beginning of physics. This discovery taught us that intuitive conclusions based on immediate observation are not always to be trusted, for they sometimes lead to the wrong clues.

But where does intuition go wrong? Can it possibly be wrong to say that a carriage drawn by four horses must travel faster than one drawn by only two?

Let us examine the fundamental facts of motion more closely, starting with simple everyday experiences familiar to mankind since the beginning of civilization and gained in the hard struggle for existence.

Suppose that someone going along a level road with a pushcart suddenly stops pushing. The cart will go on moving for a short distance before coming to rest. We ask: how is it possible to increase this distance? There are various ways, such as oiling the wheels, and making the road very smooth. The more easily the wheels turn, and the smoother the road, the longer the cart will go on moving. And just what has been done by the oiling and smoothing? Only this: the external influences have been made smaller. The effect of what is called friction has been diminished, both in the wheels and between the wheels and the road.

This is already a theoretical interpretation of the observable evidence, an interpretation which is, in fact, arbitrary. One significant step further and we shall have the right clue. Imagine a road perfectly smooth, and wheels with no friction at all. Then there would be nothing to stop the cart, so that it would run forever. This conclusion is reached only by thinking of an idealized experiment, which can never be actually performed, since it is impossible to eliminate all external influences. The idealized experiment shows the clue which really formed the foundation of the mechanics of motion.

Comparing the two methods of approaching the problem we can say: the intuitive idea is—the greater the action the greater the velocity. Thus the velocity shows whether or not external forces are acting on a body. The new clue found by Galileo is: if a body is neither pushed, pulled, nor acted on in any other way, or, more briefly, if no external forces act on a body, it moves uniformly, that is, always with the same velocity along a straight line. Thus, the velocity does not show whether or not external forces are acting on a body. Galileo's conclusion, the correct one, was formulated a generation later by Newton as the *law of inertia*. It is usually the first thing about physics which we learn by heart in school, and some of us may remember it:

> Every body perseveres in its state of rest, or of uniform motion in a right line, unless it is compelled to change that state by forces impressed thereon.

We have seen that this law of inertia cannot be derived directly from experiment, but only by speculative thinking consistent with observation. The idealized experiment can never be actually performed, although it leads to a profound understanding of real experiments.

From the variety of complex motions in the world around us we choose as our first example uniform motion. This is the simplest, because there are no external forces acting. Uniform motion can, however, never be realized; a stone thrown from a tower, a cart pushed along a road can never move absolutely uniformly because we cannot eliminate the influence of external forces.

In a good mystery story the most obvious clues often lead to the wrong suspects. In our attempts to understand the laws of nature we find, similarly, that the most obvious intuitive explanation is often the wrong one.

Human thought creates an ever-changing picture of the universe. Galileo's contribution was to destroy the intuitive view and replace it by a new one. This is the significance of Galileo's discovery.

But a further question concerning motion arises immediately. If the velocity is no indication of the external forces acting on a body, what is? The answer to this fundamental question was found by Galileo and still more concisely by Newton, and forms a further clue in our investigation.

To find the correct answer we must think a little more deeply about the cart on a perfectly smooth road. In our idealized experiment the uniformity of the motion was due to the absence of all external forces. Let us now imagine that the uniformly moving cart is given a push in the direction of the motion. What happens now? Obviously its speed is increased. Just as obviously, a push in the direction opposite to that of the motion would decrease the speed. In the first case the cart is accelerated by the push, in the second case decelerated, or slowed down. A conclusion follows at once: the action of an external force changes the velocity. Thus not the velocity itself but its change is a consequence of pushing or pulling. Such a force either increases or decreases the velocity according to whether it acts in the direction of motion or in the opposite direction. Galileo saw this clearly and wrote in his *Two New Sciences:*

> . . . any velocity once imparted to a moving body will be rigidly maintained as long as the external causes of acceleration or retardation are removed, a condition which is found only on horizontal planes; for in the case of planes which slope downwards there is already present a cause of acceleration; while on planes sloping upward there is retardation; from this it follows that motion along a horizontal plane is perpetual; for, if the velocity be uniform, it cannot be diminished or slackened, much less destroyed.

By following the right clue we achieve a deeper understanding of the problem of motion. The connection between force and the change of velocity and not, as we should think according to our intuition, the connection between force and the velocity itself is the basis of classical mechanics as formulated by Newton.

We have been making use of two concepts which play principal roles in classical mechanics: force and change of velocity. In the further development of science both of these concepts are extended and generalized. They must, therefore, be examined more closely.

What is force? Intuitively, we feel what is meant by this term. The concept arose from the effort of pushing, throwing or pulling; from the muscular sensation accompanying each of these acts. But its gener-

alization goes far beyond these simple examples. We can think of force even without picturing a horse pulling a carriage! We speak of the force of attraction between the sun and the earth, the earth and the moon, and of those forces which cause the tides. We speak of the force by which the earth compels ourselves and all the objects about us to remain within its sphere of influence, and of the force with which the wind makes waves on the sea, or moves the leaves of trees. When and where we observe a change in velocity, an external force, in the general sense, must be held responsible. Newton wrote in his *Principia:*

> An impressed force is an action exerted upon a body, in order to change its state, either of rest, or of moving uniformly forward in a right line.
>
> This force consists in the action only; and remains no longer in the body, when the action is over. For a body maintains every new state it acquires, by its *vis inertiae* [force of inertia] only. Impressed forces are of different origins; as from percussion, from pressure, from centripetal force.

If a stone is dropped from the top of a tower its motion is by no means uniform; the velocity increases as the stone falls. We conclude: an external force is acting in the direction of the motion. Or, in other words: the earth attracts the stone. Let us take another example. What happens when a stone is thrown straight upward? The velocity decreases until the stone reaches its highest point and begins to fall. This decrease in velocity is caused by the same force as the acceleration of a falling body. In one case the force acts in the direction of the motion, in the other case in the opposite direction. The force is the same, but it causes acceleration or deceleration according to whether the stone is dropped or thrown upward.

Vectors. All motions we have been considering are *rectilinear,* that is, along a straight line. Now we must go one step further. We gain an understanding of the laws of nature by analyzing the simplest cases and by leaving out of our first attempts all intricate complications. A straight line is simpler than a curve. It is, however, impossible to be satisfied with an understanding of rectilinear motion alone. The motions of the moon, the earth and the planets, just those to which the principles of mechanics have been applied with such brilliant success, are motions along curved paths. Passing from rectilinear motion to motion along a curved path brings new difficulties. We must have the courage to overcome them if we wish to understand the principles of classical mechanics which gave us the first clues and so formed the starting point for the development of science.

Let us consider another idealized experiment, in which a perfect sphere rolls uniformly on a smooth table. We know that if the sphere is given a push, that is, if an external force is applied, the velocity will be changed. Now suppose that the direction of the blow is not, as in the example of the cart, in the line of motion, but in a quite different direction, say, perpendicular to that line. What happens to the sphere? Three stages of the motion can be distinguished: the initial motion, the action of the force, and the final motion after the force has ceased to act. According to the law of inertia the velocities before and after the action of the force are both perfectly uniform. But there is a difference between the uniform motion before and after the action of the force: the direction is changed. The initial path of the sphere and the direction of the force are perpendicular to each other. The final motion will be along neither of these two lines, but somewhere between them, nearer the direction of the force if the blow is a hard one and the initial velocity small, nearer the original line of motion if the blow is gentle and the initial velocity great. Our new conclusion, based on the law of inertia, is: in general the action of an external force changes not only the speed but also the direction of the motion. An understanding of this fact prepares us for the generalization introduced into physics by the concept of *vectors*.

We can continue to use our straightforward method of reasoning. The starting point is again Galileo's law of inertia. We are still far from exhausting the consequences of this valuable clue to the puzzle of motion.

Let us consider two spheres moving in different directions on a smooth table. So as to have a definite picture we may assume the two directions perpendicular to each other. Since there are no external forces acting, the motions are perfectly uniform. Suppose, further, that the speeds are equal, that is, both cover the same distance in the same interval of time. But is it correct to say that the two spheres have the same velocity? The answer can be yes or no! If the speedometers of two cars both show forty miles per hour it is usual to say that they have the same speed or velocity, no matter in which direction they are traveling. But science must create its own language, its own concepts, for its own use. Scientific concepts often begin with those used in ordinary language for the affairs of everyday life, but they develop quite differently. They are transformed and lose the ambiguity associated with them in ordinary language, gaining in rigorousness so that they may be applied to scientific thought.

From the physicist's point of view it is advantageous to say that the velocities of the two spheres moving in different directions are different. Although purely a matter of convention, it is more convenient to say that four cars traveling away from the same traffic circle on different roads do not have the same velocity even though the speeds, as registered on the speedometers, are all forty miles per hour. This differentiation between speed and velocity illustrates how physics, starting with a concept used in everyday life, changes it in a way which proves fruitful in the further development of science.

If a length is measured, the result is expressed as a number of units. The length of a stick may be 3 ft. 7 in.; the weight of some object 2 lb. 3 oz.; a measured time interval so many minutes or seconds. In each of these cases the result of the measurement is expressed by a number. A number alone is, however, insufficient for describing some physical concepts. The recognition of this fact marked a distinct advance in scientific investigation. A direction as well as a number is essential for the char- 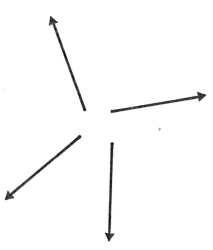 acterization of a velocity, for example. Such a quantity, possessing both magnitude and direction, is called a *vector*. A suitable symbol for it is an arrow. Velocity may be represented by an arrow or, briefly speaking, by a vector whose length in some chosen scale of units is a measure of the speed, and whose direction is that of the motion.

If four cars diverge with equal speed from a traffic circle, their velocities can be represented by four vectors of the same length, as seen from our last drawing. In the scale used one inch stands for 40 m.p.h. In this way any velocity may be denoted by a vector, and conversely, if the scale is known, one may ascertain the velocity from such a vector diagram.

 If two cars pass each other on the highway and their speedometers both show 40 m.p.h. we characterize their velocities by two different vectors with arrows pointing in opposite directions. So also the arrows indicating "uptown" and "downtown" subway trains must point in

opposite directions. But all trains moving uptown at different stations or on different avenues with the same speed have the same velocity, which may be represented by a single vector. There is nothing about a vector to

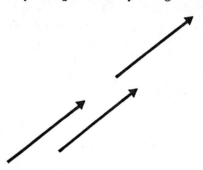

indicate which stations the train passes or on which of the many parallel tracks it is running. In other words, according to the accepted convention, all such vectors, as drawn [at left], may be regarded as equal; they lie along the same or parallel lines, are of equal length, and finally, have arrows pointing in the same direction. The next figure shows vectors all different, because they differ either in length or direction, or both. The same four vectors may be drawn in another way, in which they all diverge from

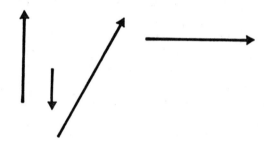

a common point. Since the starting point does not matter, these vectors can represent the velocities of four cars moving away from the same traffic circle, or the velocities of four cars in different parts of the country traveling with the indicated speeds in the indicated directions.

This vector representation may now be used to describe the facts previously discussed concerning rectilinear motion. We talked of a cart, moving uniformly in a straight line and receiving a push in the direction of its motion which increases its velocity. Graphically [p. 499] this may be represented by two vectors, a shorter one denoting the velocity before the push and a longer one in the

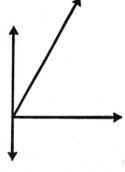

same direction denoting the velocity after the push. The meaning of the dotted [dashed] vector is clear; it represents the change in velocity for which, as we know, the push is responsible. For the case where the force

is directed against the motion, where the motion is slowed down, the diagram is somewhat different. Again the dotted vector corresponds to a change in velocity, but in this case its direction is different. It is clear that not only velocities themselves but also their changes are vectors. But every change in velocity is due to the action of an external force; thus the force

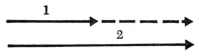

must also be represented by a vector. In order to characterize a force it is not sufficient to state how hard we push the cart; we must also say in which direction we push. The force, like the velocity or its change, must be represented by a vector and not by a number alone. Therefore: the external force is also a vector, and must have the same direction as the change

in velocity. In the last two drawings the dotted vectors show the direction of the force as truly as they indicate the change in velocity.

Here the skeptic may remark that he sees no advantage in the introduction of vectors. All that has been accomplished is the translation of previously recognized facts into an unfamiliar and complicated language. At this stage it would indeed be difficult to convince him that he is wrong. For the moment he is, in fact, right. But we shall see that just this strange language leads to an important generalization in which vectors appear to be essential.

The Riddle of Motion. So long as we deal only with motion along a straight line we are far from understanding the motions observed in nature. We must consider motions along curved paths, and our next step is to determine the laws governing such motions. This is no easy task. In the case of rectilinear motion our concepts of velocity, change of velocity, and force proved most useful. But we do not immediately see how we can apply them to motion along a curved path. It is indeed possible to imagine that the old concepts are unsuited to the description of general motion, and that new ones must be created. Should we try to follow our old path, or seek a new one?

The generalization of a concept is a process very often used in science. A method of generalization is not uniquely determined, for there are usually numerous ways of carrying it out. One requirement, however, must be rigorously satisfied: any generalized concept must reduce to the original one when the original conditions are fulfilled.

We can best explain this by the example with which we are now dealing. We can try to generalize the old concepts of velocity, change

of velocity and force for the case of motion along a curved path. Technically, when speaking of curves, we include straight lines. The straight line is a special and trivial example of a curve. If, therefore, velocity, change in velocity and force are introduced for motion along a curved line, then they are automatically introduced for motion along a straight line. But this result must not contradict those results previously obtained. If the curve becomes a straight line, all the generalized concepts must reduce to the familiar ones describing rectilinear motion. But this restriction is not sufficient to determine the generalization uniquely. It leaves open many possibilities. The history of science shows that the simplest generalizations sometimes prove successful and sometimes not. We must first make a guess. In our case it is a simple matter to guess the right method of generalization. The new concepts prove very successful and help us to understand the motion of a thrown stone as well as that of the planets.

And now just what do the words velocity, change in velocity, and force mean in the general case of motion along a curved line? Let us begin with velocity. Along the curve a very small body is moving from left to right. Such a small body is often called a *particle*. The dot on the curve in our drawing shows the position of the particle at some instant of time. What is the velocity corresponding to this time and position?

Again Galileo's clue hints at a way of introducing the velocity. We must, once more, use our imagination and think about an idealized experiment. The particle moves along the curve, from left to right, under the influence of external forces. Imagine that at a given time and at the point indicated by the dot, all these forces suddenly cease to act. Then, the motion must, according to the law of inertia, be uniform. In practice we can, of course, never completely free a body from all external influences. We can only surmise "what would happen if . . . ?" and judge the pertinence of our guess by the conclusions which can be drawn from it and by their agreement with experiment.

The vector in the next drawing indicates the guessed direction of the uniform motion if all external forces were to vanish. It is the direction of the so-called tangent. Looking at a moving particle through a microscope one sees a very small part of the curve, which appears as a small

segment. The tangent is its prolongation. Thus the vector drawn represents the velocity at a given instant. The velocity vector lies on the

tangent. Its length represents the magnitude of the velocity, or the speed as indicated, for instance, by the speedometer of a car.

Our idealized experiment about destroying the motion in order to find the velocity vector must not be taken too seriously. It only helps us to understand what we should call the velocity vector and enables us to determine it for a given instant at a given point.

In the next drawing, the velocity vectors for three different positions of a particle moving along a curve are shown. In this case not only the

direction but the magnitude of the velocity, as indicated by the length of the vector, varies during the motion.

Does this new concept of velocity satisfy the requirement formulated for all generalizations? That is: does it reduce to the familiar concept if the curve becomes a straight line? Obviously it does. The tangent to a straight line is the line itself. The velocity vector lies in the line of the motion, just as in the case of the moving cart or the rolling spheres.

The next step is the introduction of the change in velocity of a particle moving along a curve. This also may be done in various ways, from which we choose the simplest and most convenient. The last drawing showed several velocity vectors representing the motion at various

points along the path. The first two of these may be drawn again so that they have a common starting point, as we have seen is possible

with vectors. The dotted vector, we call the change in velocity. Its starting point is the end of the first vector and its end point the end of the second vector. This definition of the change in velocity may, at first sight, seem artificial and meaningless. It becomes much clearer in the special case in which vectors (1) and (2) have the same direction. This, of course, means going over to the case of straight-line motion. If both vectors have the same initial point the dotted vector again connects their end points. The drawing is now identical with that on page 499, and the previous concept is regained as a special case of the

new one. We may remark that we had to separate the two lines in our drawing since otherwise they would coincide and be indistinguishable.

We now have to take the last step in our process of generalization. It is the most important of all the guesses we have had to make so far. The connection between force and change in velocity has to be established so that we can formulate the clue which will enable us to understand the general problem of motion.

The clue to an explanation of motion along a straight line was simple: external force is responsible for change in velocity; the force vector has the same direction as the change. And now what is to be regarded as the clue to curvilinear motion? Exactly the same! The only difference is that change of velocity has now a broader meaning than before. A glance at the dotted vectors of the last two drawings shows this point clearly. If the velocity is known for all points along the curve, the direction of the force at any point can be deduced at once. One must draw the velocity vectors for two instants separated by a very short time-interval and therefore corresponding to positions very near each other. The vector from the end point of the first to that of the second indicates the direction of the acting force. But it is essential that the two velocity vectors should be separated only by a "very short" time-interval. The rigorous analysis of such words as "very near," "very short" is far from simple. Indeed it was this analysis which led Newton and Leibnitz to the discovery of differential calculus.

It is a tedious and elaborate path which leads to the generalization of Galileo's clue. We cannot show here how abundant and fruitful the consequences of this generalization have proved. Its application leads to simple and convincing explanations of many facts previously incoherent and misunderstood.

From the extremely rich variety of motions we shall take only the simplest and apply to their explanation the law just formulated.

A bullet shot from a gun, a stone thrown at an angle, a stream of water emerging from a hose, all describe familiar paths of the same type, the parabola. Imagine a speedometer attached to a stone, for example, so that its velocity vector may be drawn for any instant. The

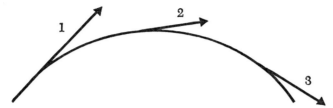

result may well be that represented in the last drawing. The direction of the force acting on the stone is just that of the change in velocity, and we have seen how it may be determined. The result, shown in the next drawing, indicates that the force is vertical, and directed down-

 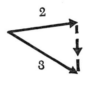

ward. It is exactly the same as when a stone is allowed to fall from the top of a tower. The paths are quite different, as also are the velocities, but the change in velocity has the same direction, that is, toward the center of the earth.

A stone attached to the end of a string and swung around in a horizontal plane moves in a circular path.

All the vectors in the diagram representing this motion have the same length if the speed is uniform. Nevertheless, the velocity is not uniform, for the path is not a straight line. Only in uniform, rectilinear motion are there no forces involved. Here, however, there are, and the velocity changes not in magnitude

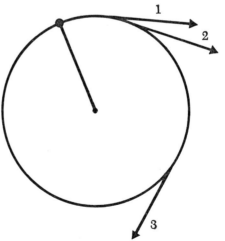

but in direction. According to the law of motion there must be some force responsible for this change, a force in this case between the stone and

the hand holding the string. A further question arises immediately: in what direction does the force act? Again a vector diagram shows the an-

swer. The velocity vectors for two very near points are drawn, and the change of velocity found. This last vector is seen to be directed along the string toward the center of the circle, and is always perpendicular to the velocity vector, or tangent. In other words the hand exerts a force on the stone by means of the string.

Very similar is the more important example of the revolution of the moon around the earth. This may be represented approximately as uniform circular motion. The force is directed toward the earth for the same reason that it was directed toward the hand in our former example. There is no string connecting the earth and the moon, but we can imagine a line between the centers of the two bodies; the force lies along this line and is directed toward the center of the earth, just as the force on a stone thrown in the air or dropped from a tower.

All that we have said concerning motion can be summed up in a single sentence. *Force and change of velocity are vectors having the same direction.* This is the initial clue to the problem of motion, but it certainly does not suffice for a thorough explanation of all motions observed. The transition from Aristotle's line of thought to that of Galileo formed a most important cornerstone in the foundation of science. Once this break was made, the line of further development was clear. Our interest here lies in the first stages of development, in following initial clues, in showing how new physical concepts are born in the painful struggle with old ideas. We are concerned only with pioneer work in science, which consists of finding new and unexpected paths of development; with the adventures in scientific thought which create an ever-changing picture of the universe. The initial and fundamental steps are always of a revolutionary character. Scientific imagination finds old concepts too confining, and replaces them by new ones. The continued development along any line already initiated is more in the nature of evolution, until the next turning point is reached when a still newer field must be conquered. In order to understand, however, what reasons and what difficulties force a change in important concepts, we must know not only the initial clues, but also the conclusions which can be drawn.

One of the most important characteristics of modern physics is that the conclusions drawn from initial clues are not only qualitative but

also quantitative. Let us again consider a stone dropped from a tower. We have seen that its velocity increases as it falls, but we should like to know much more. Just how great is this change? And what is the position and the velocity of the stone at any time after it begins to fall? We wish to be able to predict events and to determine by experiment whether observation confirms these predictions and thus the initial assumptions.

To draw quantitative conclusions we must use the language of mathematics. Most of the fundamental ideas of science are essentially simple, and may, as a rule, be expressed in a language comprehensible to everyone. To follow up these ideas demands the knowledge of a highly refined technique of investigation. Mathematics as a tool of reasoning is necessary if we wish to draw conclusions which may be compared with experiment. So long as we are concerned only with fundamental physical ideas we may avoid the language of mathematics. Since in these pages we do this consistently, we must occasionally restrict ourselves to quoting, without proof, some of the results necessary for an understanding of important clues arising in the further development. The price which must be paid for abandoning the language of mathematics is a loss in precision, and the necessity of sometimes quoting results without showing how they were reached.

A very important example of motion is that of the earth around the sun. It is known that the path is a closed curve, called the ellipse. The construction of a vector diagram of the change in velocity shows that the force on the earth is directed toward the sun. But this, after all, is scant information. We should like to be able to predict the position of the earth and the other planets for any arbitrary instant of time, we should like to predict the date and duration of the next solar eclipse and many other astronomical events. It is possible to do these things, but not on the basis of our initial clue alone,

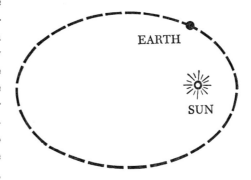

for it is now necessary to know not only the direction of the force but also its absolute value, its magnitude. It was Newton who made the inspired guess on this point. According to his law of gravitation the force of attraction between two bodies depends in a simple way on their distance

from each other. It becomes smaller when the distance increases. To be specific it becomes $2 \times 2 = 4$ times smaller if the distance is doubled, $3 \times 3 = 9$ times smaller if the distance is made three times as great.

Thus we see that in the case of gravitational force we have succeeded in expressing, in a simple way, the dependence of the force on the distance between the moving bodies. We proceed similarly in all other cases where forces of different kinds, for instance, electric, magnetic, and the like, are acting. We try to use a simple expression for the force. Such an expression is justified only when the conclusions drawn from it are confirmed by experiment.

But this knowledge of the gravitational force alone is not sufficient for a description of the motion of the planets. We have seen that vectors representing force and change in velocity for any short interval of time have the same direction, but we must follow Newton one step further and assume a simple relation between their lengths. Given all other conditions the same, that is, the same moving body and changes considered over equal time intervals, then, according to Newton, the change of velocity is proportional to the force.

Thus just two complementary guesses are needed for quantitative conclusions concerning the motion of the planets. One is of a general character, stating the connection between force and change in velocity. The other is special, and states the exact dependence of the particular kind of force involved on the distance between the bodies. The first is Newton's general law of motion, the second his law of gravitation. Together they determine the motion. This can be made clear by the following somewhat clumsy-sounding reasoning. Suppose that at a given time the position and velocity of a planet can be determined, and that the force is known. Then, according to Newton's laws we know the change in velocity during a short time interval. Knowing the initial velocity and its change, we can find the velocity and position of the planet at the end of the time interval. By a continued repetition of this process the whole path of the motion may be traced without further recourse to observational data. This is, in principle, the way mechanics predicts the course of a body in motion, but the method used here is hardly practical. In practice such a step-by-step procedure would be extremely tedious as well as inaccurate. Fortunately, it is quite unnecessary; mathematics furnishes a short cut, and makes possible precise description of the motion in much less ink than we use for a single sentence. The conclusions reached in this way can be proved or disproved by observation.

The same kind of external force is recognized in the motion of a stone falling through the air and in the revolution of the moon in its orbit, namely, that of the earth's attraction for material bodies. Newton recognized that the motions of falling stones, of the moon, and of planets are only very special manifestations of a universal gravitational force acting between any two bodies. In simple cases the motion may be described and predicted by the aid of mathematics. In remote and extremely complicated cases, involving the action of many bodies on each other, a mathematical description is not so simple, but the fundamental principles are the same.

We find the conclusions, at which we arrived by following our initial clues, realized in the motion of a thrown stone, in the motion of the moon, the earth, and the planets.

It is really our whole system of guesses which is to be either proved or disproved by experiment. No one of the assumptions can be isolated for separate testing. In the case of the planets moving around the sun it is found that the system of mechanics works splendidly. Nevertheless we can well imagine that another system, based on different assumptions, might work just as well.

Physical concepts are free creations of the human mind, and are not, however it may seem, uniquely determined by the external world. In our endeavor to understand reality we are somewhat like a man trying to understand the mechanism of a closed watch. He sees the face and the moving hands, even hears its ticking, but he has no way of opening the case. If he is ingenious he may form some picture of a mechanism which could be responsible for all the things he observes, but he may never be quite sure his picture is the only one which could explain his observations. He will never be able to compare his picture with the real mechanism and he cannot even imagine the possibility or the meaning of such a comparison. But he certainly believes that, as his knowledge increases, his picture of reality will become simpler and simpler and will explain a wider and wider range of his sensuous impressions. He may also believe in the existence of the ideal limit of knowledge and that it is approached by the human mind. He may call this ideal limit the objective truth.

One Clue Remains. When first studying mechanics one has the impression that everything in this branch of science is simple, fundamental and settled for all time. One would hardly suspect the existence of an important clue which no one noticed for three hundred years. The neglected clue is connected with one of the fundamental concepts of mechanics, that of *mass.*

Again we return to the simple idealized experiment of the cart on a perfectly smooth road. If the cart is initially at rest and then given a push, it afterwards moves uniformly with a certain velocity. Suppose that the action of the force can be repeated as many times as desired, the mechanism of pushing acting in the same way and exerting the same force on the same cart. However many times the experiment is repeated the final velocity is always the same. But what happens if the experiment is changed, if previously the cart was empty and now it is loaded? The loaded cart will have a smaller final velocity than the empty one. The conclusion is: if the same force acts on two different bodies, both initially at rest, the resulting velocities will not be the same. We say that the velocity depends on the mass of the body, being smaller if the mass is greater.

We know, therefore, at least in theory, how to determine the mass of a body or, more exactly, how many times greater one mass is than another. We have identical forces acting on two resting masses. Finding that the velocity of the first mass is three times greater than that of the second we conclude that the first mass is three times smaller than the second. This is certainly not a very practical way of determining the ratio of two masses. We can, nevertheless, well imagine having done it in this, or in some similar way, based upon the application of the law of inertia.

How do we really determine mass in practice? Not, of course, in the way just described. Everyone knows the correct answer. We do it by weighing on a scale.

Let us discuss in more detail the two different ways of determining mass.

The first experiment had nothing whatever to do with gravity, the attraction of the earth. The cart moves along a perfectly smooth and horizontal plane after the push. Gravitational force, which causes the cart to stay on the plane, does not change, and plays no role in the determination of the mass. It is quite different with weighing. We could never use a scale if the earth did not attract bodies, if gravity did not exist. The difference between the two determinations of mass is that the first has nothing to do with the force of gravity while the second is based essentially on its existence.

We ask: if we determine the ratio of two masses in both ways described above do we obtain the same result? The answer given by experiment is quite clear. The results are exactly the same! This conclu-

sion could not have been foreseen, and is based on observation, not reason. Let us, for the sake of simplicity, call the mass determined in the first way the *inertial mass* and that determined in the second way the *gravitational mass*. In our world it happens that they are equal but we can well imagine that this should not have been the case at all. Another question arises immediately: is this identity of the two kinds of mass purely accidental, or does it have a deeper significance? The answer, from the point of view of classical physics, is: the identity of the two masses is accidental and no deeper significance should be attached to it. The answer of modern physics is just the opposite: the identity of the two masses is fundamental and forms a new and essential clue leading to a more profound understanding. This was, in fact, one of the most important clues from which the so-called general theory of relativity was developed.

A mystery story seems inferior if it explains strange events as accidents. It is certainly more satisfying to have the story follow a rational pattern. In exactly the same way a theory which offers an explanation for the identity of gravitational and inertial mass is superior to one which interprets their identity as accidental, provided, of course, that the two theories are equally consistent with observed facts.

Since this identity of inertial and gravitational mass was fundamental for the formulation of the theory of relativity we are justified in examining it a little more closely here. What experiments prove convincingly that the two masses are the same? The answer lies in Galileo's old experiment in which he dropped different masses from a tower. He noticed that the time required for the fall was always the same, that the motion of a falling body does not depend on the mass. To link this simple but highly important experimental result with the identity of the two masses needs some rather intricate reasoning.

A body at rest gives way before the action of an external force, moving and attaining a certain velocity. It yields more or less easily, according to its inertial mass, resisting the motion more strongly if the mass is large than if it is small. We may say, without pretending to be rigorous: the readiness with which a body responds to the call of an external force depends on its inertial mass. If it were true that the earth attracts all bodies with the same force, that of greatest inertial mass would move more slowly in falling than any other. But this is not the case: all bodies fall in the same way. This means that the force by which the earth attracts different masses must be different. Now the

earth attracts a stone with the force of gravity and knows nothing about its inertial mass. The "calling" force of the earth depends on the gravitational mass. The "answering" motion of the stone depends on the inertial mass. Since the "answering" motion is always the same—all bodies dropped from the same height fall in the same way—it must be deduced that gravitational mass and inertial mass are equal.

More pedantically a physicist formulates the same conclusion: the acceleration of a falling body increases in proportion to its gravitational mass and decreases in proportion to its inertial mass. Since all falling bodies have the same constant acceleration, the two masses must be equal.

In our great mystery story there are no problems wholly solved and settled for all time. After three hundred years we had to return to the initial problem of motion, to revise the procedure of investigation, to find clues which had been overlooked, thereby reaching a different picture of the surrounding universe.

Is Heat a Substance? Here we begin to follow a new clue, one originating in the realm of heat phenomena. It is impossible, however, to divide science into separate and unrelated sections. Indeed, we shall soon find that the new concepts introduced here are interwoven with those already familiar, and with those we shall still meet. A line of thought developed in one branch of science can very often be applied to the description of events apparently quite different in character. In this process the original concepts are often modified so as to advance the understanding both of those phenomena from which they sprang and of those to which they are newly applied.

The most fundamental concepts in the description of heat phenomena are *temperature* and *heat*. It took an unbelievably long time in the history of science for these two to be distinguished, but once this distinction was made rapid progress resulted. Although these concepts are now familiar to everyone we shall examine them closely, emphasizing the differences between them.

Our sense of touch tells us quite definitely that one body is hot and another cold. But this is a purely qualitative criterion, not sufficient for a quantitative description and sometimes even ambiguous. This is shown by a well-known experiment: we have three vessels containing, respectively, cold, warm and hot water. If we dip one hand into the cold water and the other into the hot, we receive a message from the first that it is cold and from the second that it is hot. If we then dip both hands into the same warm water we receive two contradictory mes-

sages, one from each hand. For the same reason an Eskimo and a native of some equatorial country meeting in New York on a spring day would hold different opinions as to whether the climate was hot or cold. We settle all such questions by the use of a thermometer, an instrument designed in a primitive form by Galileo. Here again that familiar name! The use of a thermometer is based on some obvious physical assumptions. We shall recall them by quoting a few lines from lectures given about a hundred and fifty years ago by Black, who contributed a great deal toward clearing up the difficulties connected with the two concepts, heat and temperature:

> By the use of this instrument we have learned, that if we take 1000, or more, different kinds of matter, such as metals, stones, salts, woods, feathers, wool, water and a variety of other fluids, although they be all at first of different *heats*, let them be placed together in the same room without a fire, and into which the sun does not shine, the heat will be communicated from the hotter of these bodies to the colder, during some hours perhaps, or the course of a day, at the end of which time, if we apply a thermometer to them all in succession, it will point precisely to the same degree.

The italicized word *heats* should, according to present-day nomenclature, be replaced by the word *temperatures*.

A physician taking the thermometer from a sick man's mouth might reason like this: "The thermometer indicates its own temperature by the length of its column of mercury. We assume that the length of the mercury column increases in proportion to the increase in temperature. But the thermometer was for a few minutes in contact with my patient, so that both patient and thermometer have the same temperature. I conclude, therefore, that my patient's temperature is that registered on the thermometer." The doctor probably acts mechanically, but he applies physical principles without thinking about it.

But does the thermometer contain the same amount of heat as the body of the man? Of course not. To assume that two bodies contain equal quantities of heat just because their temperatures are equal would, as Black remarked, be

> taking a very hasty view of the subject. It is confounding the quantity of heat in different bodies with its general strength or intensity, though it is plain that these are two different things, and should always be distinguished, when we are thinking of the distribution of heat.

An understanding of this distinction can be gained by considering a very simple experiment. A pound of water placed over a gas flame takes some time to change from room temperature to the boiling point. A much longer time is required for heating twelve pounds, say, of water in the same vessel by means of the same flame. We interpret this fact as indicating that now more of "something" is needed and we call this "something"—*heat*.

A further important concept, *specific heat,* is gained by the following experiment: let one vessel contain a pound of water and another a pound of mercury, both to be heated in the same way. The mercury gets hot much more quickly than the water, showing that less "heat" is needed to raise the temperature by one degree. In general, different amounts of "heat" are required to change by one degree, say from 40 to 41 degrees Fahrenheit, the temperatures of different substances such as water, mercury, iron, copper, wood, etc., all of the same mass. We say that each substance has its individual *heat capacity,* or *specific heat.*

Once having gained the concept of heat we can investigate its nature more closely. We have two bodies, one hot, the other cold, or more precisely, one of a higher temperature than the other. We bring them into contact and free them from all other external influences. Eventually they will, we know, reach the same temperature. But how does this take place? What happens between the instant they are brought into contact and the achievement of equal temperatures? The picture of heat "flowing" from one body to another suggests itself, like water flowing from a higher level to a lower. This picture, though primitive, seems to fit many of the facts, so that the analogy runs:

Water — Heat
Higher level — Higher temperature
Lower level — Lower temperature

The flow proceeds until both levels, that is, both temperatures, are equal. This naïve view can be made more useful by quantitative considerations. If definite masses of water and alcohol, each at a definite temperature, are mixed together, a knowledge of the specific heats will lead to a prediction of the final temperature of the mixture. Conversely, an observation of the final temperature, together with a little algebra, would enable us to find the ratio of the two specific heats.

We recognize in the concept of heat which appears here a similarity to other physical concepts. Heat is, according to our view, a substance, such as mass in mechanics. Its quantity may change or not, like money put aside in a safe or spent. The amount of money in a safe will remain

unchanged so long as the safe remains locked, and so will the amounts of mass and heat in an isolated body. The ideal Thermos bottle is analogous to such a safe. Furthermore, just as the mass of an isolated system is unchanged even if a chemical transformation takes place, so heat is conserved even though it flows from one body to another. Even if heat is not used for raising the temperature of a body but for melting ice, say, or changing water into steam, we can still think of it as a substance and regain it entirely by freezing the water or liquefying the steam. The old names, latent heat of melting or vaporization, show that these concepts are drawn from the picture of heat as a substance. Latent heat is temporarily hidden, like money put away in a safe, but available for use if one knows the lock combination.

But heat is certainly not a substance in the same sense as mass. Mass can be detected by means of scales, but what of heat? Does a piece of iron weigh more when red-hot than when ice-cold? Experiment shows that it does not. If heat is a substance at all, it is a weightless one. The "heat-substance" was usually called *caloric* and is our first acquaintance among a whole family of weightless substances. Later we shall have occasion to follow the history of the family, its rise and fall. It is sufficient now to note the birth of this particular member.

The purpose of any physical theory is to explain as wide a range of phenomena as possible. It is justified in so far as it does make events understandable. We have seen that the substance theory explains many of the heat phenomena. It will soon become apparent, however, that this again is a false clue, that heat cannot be regarded as a substance, even weightless. This is clear if we think about some simple experiments which marked the beginning of civilization.

We think of a substance as something which can be neither created nor destroyed. Yet primitive man created by friction sufficient heat to ignite wood. Examples of heating by friction are, as a matter of fact, much too numerous and familiar to need recounting. In all these cases some quantity of heat is created, a fact difficult to account for by the substance theory. It is true that a supporter of this theory could invent arguments to account for it. His reasoning would run something like this: "The substance theory can explain the apparent creation of heat. Take the simplest example of two pieces of wood rubbed one against the other. Now rubbing is something which influences the wood and changes its properties. It is very likely that the properties are so modified that an unchanged quantity of heat comes to produce a higher temperature than before. After all, the only thing we notice is

the rise in temperature. It is possible that the friction changes the specific heat of the wood and not the total amount of heat."

At this stage of the discussion it would be useless to argue with a supporter of the substance theory, for this is a matter which can be settled only by experiment. Imagine two identical pieces of wood and suppose equal changes of temperature are induced by different methods; in one case by friction and in the other by contact with a radiator, for example. If the two pieces have the same specific heat at the new temperature the whole substance theory must break down. There are very simple methods for determining specific heats, and the fate of the theory depends on the result of just such measurements. Tests which are capable of pronouncing a verdict of life or death on a theory occur frequently in the history of physics, and are called *crucial* experiments. The crucial value of an experiment is revealed only by the way the question is formulated, and only one theory of the phenomena can be put on trial by it. The determination of the specific heats of two bodies of the same kind, at equal temperatures attained by friction and heat flow respectively, is a typical example of a crucial experiment. This experiment was performed about a hundred and fifty years ago by Rumford, and dealt a death blow to the substance theory of heat. An extract from Rumford's own account tells the story:

> It frequently happens, that in the ordinary affairs and occupations of life, opportunities present themselves of contemplating some of the most curious operations of Nature; and very interesting philosophical experiments might often be made, almost without trouble or expense, by means of machinery contrived for the mere mechanical purposes of the arts and manufactures.
>
> I have frequently had occasion to make this observation; and am persuaded that a habit of keeping the eyes open to every thing that is going on in the ordinary course of the business of life has oftener led, as it were by accident, or in the playful excursions of the imagination, put into action by contemplating the most common appearances, to useful doubts, and sensible schemes for investigation and improvement, than all the more intense meditations of philosophers, in the hours expressly set apart for study. . . .
>
> Being engaged, lately, in superintending the boring of cannon, in the workshops of the military arsenal at Munich, I was struck with the very considerable degree of Heat which a brass gun acquires, in a short time, in being bored; and with the still more intense Heat (much greater than that of boiling water, as I found by experiment) of the metallic chips separated from it by the borer. . . .

From whence comes the Heat actually produced in the mechanical operation above mentioned?

Is it furnished by the metallic chips which are separated by the borer from the solid mass of metal?

If this were the case, then, according to the modern doctrines of latent Heat, and of caloric, the capacity ought not only to be changed, but the change undergone by them should be sufficiently great to account for all the Heat produced.

But no such change had taken place; for I found, upon taking equal quantities, by weight, of these chips, and of thin slips of the same block of metal separated by means of a fine saw and putting them, at the same temperature (that of boiling water), into equal quantities of cold water (that is to say, at the temperature of 59½° F.) the portion of water into which the chips were put was not, to all appearance, heated either less or more than the other portion, in which the slips of metal were put.

Finally we reach his conclusion:

And, in reasoning on this subject, we must not forget to consider that most remarkable circumstance, that the source of the Heat generated by friction, in these Experiments, appeared evidently to be *inexhaustible*.

It is hardly necessary to add, that anything which any *insulated* body, or system of bodies, can continue to furnish *without limitation*, cannot possibly be a *material substance;* and it appears to me to be extremely difficult, if not quite impossible, to form any distinct idea of anything, capable of being excited and communicated, in the manner the Heat was excited and communicated in these Experiments, except it be MOTION.

Thus we see the breakdown of the old theory, or to be more exact, we see that the substance theory is limited to problems of heat flow. Again, as Rumford has intimated, we must seek a new clue. To do this, let us leave for the moment the problem of heat and return to mechanics.

The Roller Coaster. Let us trace the motion of that popular thrill-giver, the roller coaster. A small car is lifted or driven to the highest point of the track. When set free it starts rolling down under the force of gravity, and then goes up and down along a fantastically curved line, giving the occupants a thrill by the sudden changes in velocity. Every roller coaster has its highest point, that from which it starts. Never again, throughout the whole course of the motion will it reach the same height. A complete description of the motion would be very complicated. On the one hand is the mechanical side of the problem, the changes of velocity and position in time. On the other there is friction

and therefore the creation of heat, on the rail and in the wheels. The only significant reason for dividing the physical process into these two aspects is to make possible the use of the concepts previously discussed. The division leads to an idealized experiment, for a physical process in which only the mechanical aspect appears can be only imagined but never realized.

For the idealized experiment we may imagine that someone has learned to eliminate entirely the friction which always accompanies motion. He decides to apply his discovery to the construction of a roller coaster, and must find out for himself how to build one. The car is to run up and down, with its starting point, say, at one hundred feet above ground level. He soon discovers by trial and error that

he must follow a very simple rule: he may build his track in whatever path he pleases so long as no point is higher than the starting point. If the car is to proceed freely to the end of the course its height may attain a hundred feet as many times as he likes, but never exceed it. The initial height can never be reached by a car on an actual track because of friction, but our hypothetical engineer need not consider that.

Let us follow the motion of the idealized car on the idealized roller coaster as it begins to roll downward from the starting point. As it moves its distance from the ground diminishes, but its speed increases. This sentence at first sight may remind us of one from a language lesson: "I have no pencil, but you have six oranges." It is not so stupid, however. There is no connection between my having no pencil and your having six oranges, but there is a very real correlation between the distance of the car from the ground and its speed. We can calculate the speed of the car at any moment if we know how high it happens to be above the ground, but we omit this point here because of its quantitative character which can best be expressed by mathematical formulae.

At its highest point the car has zero velocity and is one hundred feet from the ground. At the lowest possible point it is no distance from the ground, and has its greatest velocity. These facts may be expressed in other terms. At its highest point the car has *potential energy* but no *kinetic energy* or energy of motion. At its lowest point it has the greatest kinetic energy and no potential energy whatever. At all intermediate positions, where there is some velocity and some elevation, it has both kinetic and potential energy. The potential energy increases with the elevation, while the kinetic energy becomes greater as the velocity increases. The principles of mechanics suffice to explain the motion. Two expressions for energy occur in the mathematical description, each of which changes, although the sum does not vary. It is thus possible to introduce mathematically and rigorously the concepts of potential energy, depending on position, and kinetic energy, depending on velocity. The introduction of the two names is, of course, arbitrary and justified only by convenience. The sum of the two quantities remains unchanged, and is called a constant of the motion. The total energy, kinetic plus potential, is like a substance, for example, money kept intact as to amount but changed continually from one currency to another, say from dollars to pounds and back again, according to a well-defined rate of exchange.

In the real roller coaster, where friction prevents the car from again reaching as high a point as that from which it started, there is still a continuous change between kinetic and potential energy. Here, however, the sum does not remain constant, but grows smaller. Now one important and courageous step more is needed to relate the mechanical and heat aspects of motion. The wealth of consequences and generalizations from this step will be seen later.

Something more than kinetic and potential energies is now in-

volved, namely, the heat created by friction. Does this heat correspond to the diminution in mechanical energy, that is kinetic and potential energy? A new guess is imminent. If heat may be regarded as a form of energy, perhaps the sum of all three, heat, kinetic and potential energies, remains constant. Not heat alone, but heat and other forms of energy taken together are, like a substance, indestructible. It is as if a man must pay himself a commission in francs for changing dollars to pounds, the commission money also being saved so that the sum of dollars, pounds, and francs is a fixed amount according to some definite exchange rate.

The progress of science has destroyed the older concept of heat as a substance. We try to create a new substance, energy, with heat as one of its forms.

The Rate of Exchange. Less than a hundred years ago the new clue which led to the concept of heat as a form of energy was guessed by Mayer and confirmed experimentally by Joule. It is a strange coincidence that nearly all the fundamental work concerned with the nature of heat was done by nonprofessional physicists who regarded physics merely as their great hobby. There was the versatile Scotsman Black, the German physician Mayer, and the great American adventurer Count Rumford, who afterward lived in Europe, and among other activities, became Minister of War for Bavaria. There was also the English brewer Joule who, in his spare time, performed some most important experiments concerning the conservation of energy.

Joule verified by experiment the guess that heat is a form of energy, and determined the rate of exchange. It is worth our while to see just what his results were.

The kinetic and potential energy of a system together constitute its *mechanical* energy. In the case of the roller coaster we made a guess that some of the mechanical energy was converted into heat. If this is right there must be here and in all other similar physical processes a definite *rate of exchange* between the two. This is rigorously a quantitative question, but the fact that a given quantity of mechanical energy can be changed into a definite amount of heat is highly important. We should like to know what number expresses the rate of exchange, *i.e.*, how much heat we obtain from a given amount of mechanical energy.

The determination of this number was the object of Joule's researches. The mechanism of one of his experiments is very much like that of a weight clock. The winding of such a clock consists of elevating two weights, thereby adding potential energy to the system. If the clock is

not further interfered with it may be regarded as a closed system. Gradually the weights fall and the clock runs. At the end of a certain time the weights will have reached their lowest position and the clock will have stopped. What has happened to the energy? The potential energy of the weights has changed into kinetic energy of the mechanism, and has then gradually been dissipated as heat.

A clever alteration in this sort of mechanism enabled Joule to measure the heat lost and thus the rate of exchange. In his apparatus two weights caused a paddle wheel to turn while immersed in water. The potential energy of the weights was changed into kinetic energy of the movable parts, and thence into heat which raised the temperature of

the water. Joule measured this change of temperature and, making use of the known specific heat of water, calculated the amount of heat absorbed. He summarized the results of many trials as follows:

> 1st. That the quantity of heat produced by the friction of bodies, whether solid or liquid, is always proportional to the quantity of force [by force Joule means energy] expended. And
>
> 2nd. That the quantity of heat capable of increasing the temperature of a pound of water (weighed in vacuo and taken at between 55° and 60°) by 1° Fahr. requires for its evolution the expenditure of a mechanical force [energy] represented by the fall of 772 lb. through the space of one foot.

In other words the potential energy of 772 pounds elevated one foot above the ground is equivalent to the quantity of heat necessary to raise the temperature of one pound of water from 55° F. to 56° F. Later experimenters were capable of somewhat greater accuracy, but the mechanical equivalent of heat is essentially what Joule found in his pioneer work.

Once this important work was done, further progress was rapid. It was soon recognized that these kinds of energy, mechanical and heat, are only two of its many forms. Everything which can be converted into either of them is also a form of energy. The radiation given off by the sun is energy, for part of it is transformed into heat on the earth. An electric current possesses energy, for it heats a wire or turns the wheels of a motor. Coal represents chemical energy, liberated as heat when the coal burns. In every event in nature one form of energy is being converted into another, always at some well-defined rate of exchange. In a closed system, one isolated from external influences, the energy is conserved and thus behaves like a substance. The sum of all possible forms of energy in such a system is constant, although the amount of any one kind may be changing. If we regard the whole universe as a closed system we can proudly announce with the physicists of the nineteenth century that the energy of the universe is invariant, that no part of it can ever be created or destroyed.

Our two concepts of substance are, then, *matter* and *energy*. Both obey conservation laws: An isolated system cannot change either in mass or in total energy. Matter has weight but energy is weightless. We have therefore two different concepts and two conservation laws. Are these ideas still to be taken seriously? Or has this apparently well-founded picture been changed in the light of newer developments? It has! Further changes in the two concepts are connected with the theory of relativity. We shall return to this point later.

The Philosophical Background. The results of scientific research very often force a change in the philosophical view of problems which extend far beyond the restricted domain of science itself. What is the aim of science? What is demanded of a theory which attempts to describe nature? These questions, although exceeding the bounds of physics, are intimately related to it, since science forms the material from which they arise. Philosophical generalizations must be founded on scientific results. Once formed and widely accepted, however, they very often influence the further development of scientific thought by indicating one of the many possible lines of procedure. Successful revolt

against the accepted view results in unexpected and completely different developments, becoming a source of new philosophical aspects. These remarks necessarily sound vague and pointless until illustrated by examples quoted from the history of physics.

We shall here try to describe the first philosophical ideas on the aim of science. These ideas greatly influenced the development of physics until nearly a hundred years ago, when their discarding was forced by new evidence, new facts and theories, which in their turn formed a new background for science.

In the whole history of science from Greek philosophy to modern physics there have been constant attempts to reduce the apparent complexity of natural phenomena to some simple fundamental ideas and relations. This is the underlying principle of all natural philosophy. It is expressed even in the work of the Atomists. Twenty-three centuries ago Democritus wrote:

> By convention sweet is sweet, by convention bitter is bitter, by convention hot is hot, by convention cold is cold, by convention color is color. But in reality there are atoms and the void. That is, the objects of sense are supposed to be real and it is customary to regard them as such, but in truth they are not. Only the atoms and the void are real.

This idea remains in ancient philosophy nothing more than an ingenious figment of the imagination. Laws of nature relating subsequent events were unknown to the Greeks. Science connecting theory and experiment really began with the work of Galileo. We have followed the initial clues leading to the laws of motion. Throughout two hundred years of scientific research force and matter were the underlying concepts in all endeavors to understand nature. It is impossible to imagine one without the other because matter demonstrates its existence as a source of force by its action on other matter.

Let us consider the simplest example: two particles with forces acting between them. The easiest forces to imagine are those of attraction and repulsion. In both cases the force vectors lie on a line connecting the material points. The demand for simplicity leads to the picture of particles attracting or repelling each other; any other assumption about the direction of the acting forces would give a much more complicated picture. Can we make an equally simple assumption about

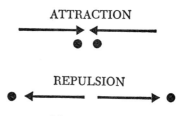

ATTRACTION

REPULSION

the length of the force vectors? Even if we want to avoid too special assumptions we can still say one thing: The force between any two given particles depends only on the distance between them, like gravitational forces. This seems simple enough. Much more complicated forces could be imagined, such as those which might depend not only on the distance but also on the velocities of the two particles. With matter and force as our fundamental concepts we can hardly imagine simpler assumptions than that forces act along the line connecting the particles and depend only on the distance. But is it possible to describe all physical phenomena by forces of this kind alone?

The great achievements of mechanics in all its branches, its striking success in the development of astronomy, the application of its ideas to problems apparently different and non-mechanical in character, all these things contributed to the belief that it *is* possible to describe all natural phenomena in terms of simple forces between unalterable objects. Throughout the two centuries following Galileo's time such an endeavor, conscious or unconscious, is apparent in nearly all scientific creation. This was clearly formulated by Helmholtz about the middle of the nineteenth century:

> Finally, therefore, we discover the problem of physical material science to be to refer natural phenomena back to unchangeable attractive and repulsive forces whose intensity depends wholly upon distance. The solubility of this problem is the condition of the complete comprehensibility of nature.

Thus, according to Helmholtz, the line of development of science is determined and follows strictly a fixed course:

> And its vocation will be ended as soon as the reduction of natural phenomena to simple forces is complete and the proof given that this is the only reduction of which the phenomena are capable.

This view appears dull and naïve to a twentieth-century physicist. It would frighten him to think that the great adventure of research could be so soon finished, and an unexciting if infallible picture of the universe established for all time.

Although these tenets would reduce the description of all events to simple forces, they do leave open the question of just how the forces should depend on distance. It is possible that for different phenomena this dependence is different. The necessity of introducing many different kinds of force for different events is certainly unsatisfactory from a philosophical point of view. Nevertheless this so-called *me-*

chanical view, most clearly formulated by Helmholtz, played an important role in its time. The development of the kinetic theory of matter is one of the greatest achievements directly influenced by the mechanical view.

Before witnessing its decline, let us provisionally accept the point of view held by the physicists of the past century and see what conclusions we can draw from their picture of the external world.

The Kinetic Theory of Matter. Is it possible to explain the phenomena of heat in terms of the motions of particles interacting through simple forces? A closed vessel contains a certain mass of gas, air, for example, at a certain temperature. By heating we raise the temperature, and thus increase the energy. But how is this heat connected with motion? The possibility of such a connection is suggested both by our tentatively accepted philosophical point of view and by the way in which heat is generated by motion. Heat must be mechanical energy if every problem is a mechanical one. The object of the *kinetic theory* is to present the concept of matter just in this way. According to this theory a gas is a congregation of an enormous number of particles, or *molecules,* moving in all directions, colliding with each other and changing in direction of motion with each collision. There must exist an average speed of molecules, just as in a large human community there exists an average age, or an average wealth. There will therefore be an average kinetic energy per particle. More heat in the vessel means a greater average kinetic energy. Thus heat, according to this picture, is not a special form of energy different from the mechanical one but is just the kinetic energy of molecular motion. To any definite temperature there corresponds a definite average kinetic energy per molecule. This is, in fact, not an arbitrary assumption. We are forced to regard the kinetic energy of a molecule as a measure of the temperature of the gas if we wish to form a consistent mechanical picture of matter.

This theory is more than a play of the imagination. It can be shown that the kinetic theory of gases is not only in agreement with experiment, but actually leads to a more profound understanding of the facts. This may be illustrated by a few examples.

We have a vessel closed by a piston which can move freely. The vessel contains a certain amount of gas to be kept at a constant temperature. If the piston is initially at rest in some position it can be moved upward by removing and downward by adding weight. To push the piston down force must be used acting against the inner pressure of the gas. What is the mechanism of this inner pressure according to

the kinetic theory? A tremendous number of particles constituting the gas are moving in all directions. They bombard the walls and the piston, bouncing back like balls thrown against a wall. This continual bombardment by a great number of particles keeps the piston at a certain height by opposing the force of gravity acting downward on the piston and the weights. In one direction there is a constant gravitational force, in the other very many irregular blows from the molecules. The net effect on the piston of all these small irregular forces must be equal to that of the force of gravity if there is to be equilibrium.

GRAVITATIONAL FORCE

INNER PRESSURE

Suppose the piston were pushed down so as to compress the gas to a fraction of its former volume, say one-half, its temperature being kept unchanged. What, according to the kinetic theory, can we expect to happen? Will the force due to the bombardment be more or less effective than before? The particles are now packed more closely. Although the average kinetic energy is still the same, the collisions of the particles with the piston will now occur more frequently and thus the total force will be greater. It is clear from this picture presented by the kinetic theory that to keep the piston in this lower position more weight is required. This simple experimental fact is well known, but its prediction follows logically from the kinetic view of matter.

Consider another experimental arrangement. Take two vessels containing equal volumes of different gases, say hydrogen and nitrogen, both at the same temperature. Assume the two vessels are closed with identical pistons, on which are equal weights. This means, briefly, that both gases have the same volume, temperature, and pressure. Since the temperature is the same, so, according to the theory, is the average kinetic energy per particle. Since the pressures are equal, the two pistons are bombarded with the same total force. On the average every particle carries the same energy and both vessels have the same volume. Therefore, *the number of molecules in each must be the same*, although the gases are chemically different. This result is very important for the understanding of many chemical phenomena. It means that the number of molecules in a given volume, at a certain tem-

perature and pressure, is something which is characteristic, not of a particular gas, but of all gases. It is most astonishing that the kinetic theory not only predicts the existence of such a universal number, but enables us to determine it. To this point we shall return very soon.

The kinetic theory of matter explains quantitatively as well as qualitatively the laws of gases as determined by experiment. Furthermore, the theory is not restricted to gases, although its greatest successes have been in this domain.

A gas can be liquefied by means of a decrease of temperature. A fall in the temperature of matter means a decrease in the average kinetic energy of its particles. It is therefore clear that the average kinetic energy of a liquid particle is smaller than that of a corresponding gas particle.

A striking manifestation of the motion of particles in liquids was given for the first time by the so-called Brownian movement, a remarkable phenomenon which would remain quite mysterious and incomprehensible without the kinetic theory of matter. It was first observed by the botanist Brown, and was explained eighty years later, at the beginning of this century. The only apparatus necessary for observing Brownian motion is a microscope, which need not even be a particularly good one.

Brown was working with grains of pollen of certain plants, that is:

> particles or granules of unusually large size varying from one four-thousandth to about five-thousandth of an inch in length.

He reports further:

> While examining the form of these particles immersed in water, I observed many of them evidently in motion. . . . These motions were such as to satisfy me, after frequently repeated observation, that they arose neither from current in the fluid nor from its gradual evaporation, but belonged to the particle itself.

What Brown observed was the unceasing agitation of the granules when suspended in water and visible through the microscope. It is an impressive sight!

Is the choice of particular plants essential for the phenomenon? Brown answered this question by repeating the experiment with many different plants, and found that all the granules, if sufficiently small, showed such motion when suspended in water. Furthermore, he found the same kind of restless, irregular motion in very small particles of in-

organic as well as organic substances. Even with a pulverized fragment of a sphinx he observed the same phenomenon!

How is this motion to be explained? It seems contradictory to all previous experience. Examination of the position of one suspended particle, say every thirty seconds, reveals the fantastic form of its path. The amazing thing is the apparently eternal character of the motion. A swinging pendulum placed in water soon comes to rest if not impelled by some external force. The existence of a never diminishing motion seems contrary to all experience. This difficulty was splendidly clarified by the kinetic theory of matter.

Looking at water through even our most powerful microscopes we cannot see molecules and their motion as pictured by the kinetic theory of matter. It must be concluded that if the theory of water as a congregation of particles is correct, the size of the particles must be beyond the limit of visibility of the best microscopes. Let us nevertheless stick to the theory and assume that it represents a consistent picture of reality. The Brownian particles visible through a microscope are bombarded by the smaller ones composing the water itself. The Brownian movement exists if the bombarded particles are sufficiently small. It exists because this bombardment is not uniform from all sides and cannot be averaged out, owing to its irregular and haphazard character. The observed motion is thus the result of the unobservable one. The behavior of the big particles reflects in some way that of the molecules, constituting, so to speak, a magnification so high that it becomes visible through the microscope. The irregular and haphazard character of the path of the Brownian particles reflects a similar irregularity in the path of the smaller particles which constitute matter. We can understand, therefore, that a quantitative study of Brownian movement can give us deeper insight into the kinetic theory of matter. It is apparent that the visible Brownian motion depends on the size of the invisible bombarding molecules. There would be no Brownian motion at all if the bombarding molecules did not possess a certain amount of energy or, in other words, if they did not have mass and velocity. That the study of Brownian motion can lead to a determination of the mass of a molecule is therefore not astonishing.

Through laborious research, both theoretical and experimental, the quantitative features of the kinetic theory were formed. The clue originating in the phenomenon of Brownian movement was one of those which led to the quantitative data. The same data can be obtained in

different ways, starting from quite different clues. The fact that all
these methods support the same view is most important, for it demon-
strates the internal consistency of the kinetic theory of matter.

Consecutive positions
observed
through a microscope
for one
Brownian particle.

The path averaged
from these
consecutive positions.

Only one of the many quantitative results reached by experiment
and theory will be mentioned here. Suppose we have a gram of the
lightest of all elements, hydrogen, and ask: how many particles are
there in this one gram? The answer will characterize not only hydro-
gen but also all other gases, for we already know under what condi-
tions two gases have the same number of particles.

The theory enables us to answer this question from certain meas-
urements of the Brownian motion of a suspended particle. The answer
is an astonishingly great number: a three followed by twenty-three other
digits! The number of molecules in one gram of hydrogen is

$$303,000,000,000,000,000,000,000.$$

Imagine the molecules of a gram of hydrogen so increased in size
that they are visible through a microscope, say that the diameter be-
comes one five-thousandth of an inch, such as that of a Brownian par-
ticle. Then, to pack them closely, we should have to use a box each
side of which is about one-quarter of a mile long!

We can easily calculate the mass of one such hydrogen molecule by
dividing 1 by the number quoted above. The answer is a fantastically
small number: 0.000 000 000 000 000 000 000 0033 grams, represent-
ing the mass of one molecule of hydrogen.

The experiments on Brownian motion are only some of the many independent experiments leading to the determination of this number which plays such an important part in physics.

In the kinetic theory of matter and in all its important achievements we see the realization of the general philosophical program: to reduce the explanation of all phenomena to the interaction between particles of matter.

We summarize:

In mechanics the future path of a moving body can be predicted and its past disclosed if its present condition and the forces acting upon it are known. Thus, for example, the future paths of all planets can be foreseen. The active forces are Newton's gravitational forces depending on the distance alone. The great results of classical mechanics suggest that the mechanical view can be consistently applied to all branches of physics, that all phenomena can be explained by the action of forces representing either attraction or repulsion, depending only upon distance and acting between unchangeable particles.

In the kinetic theory of matter we see how this view, arising from mechanical problems, embraces the phenomena of heat and how it leads to a successful picture of the structure of matter.

THE DECLINE OF THE MECHANICAL VIEW

The Two Electric Fluids. The following pages contain a dull report of some very simple experiments. The account will be boring not only because the description of experiments is uninteresting in comparison with their actual performance, but also because the meaning of the experiments does not become apparent until theory makes it so. Our purpose is to furnish a striking example of the role of theory in physics.

1. A metal bar is supported on a glass base, and each end of the bar is connected by means of a wire to an electroscope. What is an electroscope? It is a simple apparatus consisting essentially of two leaves of gold foil hanging from the end of a short piece of metal. This is enclosed in a glass jar or flask and the metal is in contact only with nonmetallic bodies, called insulators. In addition to the electroscope and metal bar we are equipped with a hard rubber rod and a piece of flannel.

The experiment is performed as follows: we look to see whether the leaves hang close together, for this is their normal position. If by

chance they do not, a touch of the finger on the metal rod will bring them together. These preliminary steps being taken, the rubber rod is rubbed vigorously with the flannel and brought into contact with the

metal. The leaves separate at once! They remain apart even after the rod is removed.

2. We perform another experiment, using the same apparatus as before, again starting with the gold leaves hanging close together. This time we do not bring the rubbed rod into actual contact with the metal, but only near it. Again the leaves separate. But there is a difference! When the rod is taken away without having touched the metal, the leaves immediately fall back to their normal position instead of remaining separated.

3. Let us change the apparatus slightly for a third experiment. Suppose that the metal bar consists of two pieces, joined together. We rub the rubber rod with flannel and again bring it near the metal. The same phenomenon occurs, the leaves separate. But now let us divide the metal rod into its two separate parts and then take away the rubber rod. We notice that in this case the leaves remain apart, instead of falling back to their normal position as in the second experiment.

It is difficult to evince enthusiastic interest in these simple and naïve experiments. In the Middle Ages their performer would probably have been condemned; to us they seem both dull and illogical. It would be very difficult to repeat them, after reading the account only once, without becoming confused. Some notion of the theory makes them understandable. We could say more: it is hardly possible to imagine such experiments performed as accidental play, without the pre-existence of more or less definite ideas about their meaning.

We shall now point out the underlying ideas of a very simple and naïve theory which explains all the facts described.

There exist two *electric fluids,* one called *positive* (+) and the other *negative* (−). They are somewhat like substance in the sense already explained, in that the amount can be enlarged or diminished, but the total in any isolated system is preserved. There is, however, an essential difference between this case and that of heat, matter or energy. We have two electrical substances. It is impossible here to use the previous analogy of money unless it is somehow generalized. A body is electrically neutral if the positive and negative electric fluids exactly cancel each other. A man has nothing, either because he really has nothing, or because the amount of money put aside in his safe is exactly equal to the sum of his debts. We can compare the debit and credit entries in his ledger to the two kinds of electric fluids.

The next assumption of the theory is that two electric fluids of the same kind repel each other, while two of the opposite kind attract. This can be represented graphically in the following way:

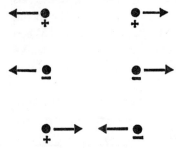

A final theoretical assumption is necessary: There are two kinds of bodies, those in which the fluids can move freely, called *conductors,* and those in which they cannot, called *insulators.* As is always true in such cases, this division is not to be taken too seriously. The ideal conductor or insulator is a fiction which can never be realized. Metals, the earth, the human body, are all examples of conductors, although not equally good. Glass, rubber, china, and the like are insulators. Air is only partially an insulator as everyone who has seen the described experiments knows. It is always a good excuse to ascribe the bad results of electrostatic experiments to the humidity of the air, which increases its conductivity.

These theoretical assumptions are sufficient to explain the three experiments described. We shall discuss them once more, in the same order as before, but in the light of the theory of electric fluids.

1. The rubber rod, like all other bodies under normal conditions, is electrically neutral. It contains the two fluids, positive and negative, in equal amounts. By rubbing with flannel we separate them. This statement is pure convention, for it is the application of the terminology created by the theory to the description of the process of rub-

bing. The kind of electricity that the rod has in excess afterwards is called negative, a name which is certainly only a matter of convention. If the experiments had been performed with a glass rod rubbed with cat's fur we should have had to call the excess positive, to conform with the accepted convention. To proceed with the experiment, we bring electric fluid to the metal conductor by touching it with the rubber. Here it moves freely, spreading over the whole metal including the gold leaves. Since the action of negative on negative is repulsion, the two leaves try to get as far from each other as possible and the result is the observed separation. The metal rests on glass or some other insulator so that the fluid remains on the conductor, as long as the conductivity of the air permits. We understand now why we have to touch the metal before beginning the experiment. In this case the metal, the human body, and the earth form one vast conductor, with the electric fluid so diluted that practically nothing remains on the electroscope.

2. This experiment begins just in the same way as the previous one. But instead of being allowed to touch the metal the rubber is now only brought near it. The two fluids in the conductor, being free to move, are separated, one attracted and the other repelled. They mix again when the rubber rod is removed, as fluids of opposite kinds attract each other.

3. Now we separate the metal into two parts and afterwards remove the rod. In this case the two fluids cannot mix, so that the gold leaves retain an excess of one electric fluid and remain apart.

In the light of this simple theory all the facts mentioned here seem comprehensible. The same theory does more, enabling us to understand not only these, but many other facts in the realm of "electrostatics." The aim of every theory is to guide us to new facts, suggest new experiments, and lead to the discovery of new phenomena and new laws. An example will make this clear. Imagine a change in the second experiment. Suppose I keep the rubber rod near the metal and at the same time touch the conductor with my finger. What will happen now? Theory answers: the repelled fluid (−) can now make its escape through my body, with the result that only

one fluid remains, the positive. Only the leaves of the electroscope near the rubber rod will remain apart. An actual experiment confirms this prediction.

The theory with which we are dealing is certainly naïve and inadequate from the point of view of modern physics. Nevertheless it is a good example showing the characteristic features of every physical theory.

There are no eternal theories in science. It always happens that some of the facts predicted by a theory are disproved by experiment. Every theory has its period of gradual development and triumph, after which it may experience a rapid decline. The rise and fall of the substance theory of heat, already discussed here, is one of many possible examples. Others, more profound and important, will be discussed later. Nearly every great advance in science arises from a crisis in the old theory, through an endeavor to find a way out of the difficulties created. We must examine old ideas, old theories, although they belong to the past, for this is the only way to understand the importance of the new ones and the extent of their validity.

In the first pages of our book we compared the role of an investigator to that of a detective who, after gathering the requisite facts, finds the right solution by pure thinking. In one essential this comparison must be regarded as highly superficial. Both in life and in detective novels the crime is given. The detective must look for letters, fingerprints, bullets, guns, but at least he knows that a murder has been committed. This is not so for a scientist. It should not be difficult to imagine someone who knows absolutely nothing about electricity, since all the ancients lived happily enough without any knowledge of it. Let this man be given metal, gold foil, bottles, hard-rubber rod, flannel, in short, all the material required for performing our three experiments. He may be a very cultured person, but he will probably put wine into the bottles, use the flannel for cleaning, and never once entertain the idea of doing the things we have described. For the detective the crime is given, the problem formulated: who killed Cock Robin? The scientist must, at least in part, commit his own crime, as well as carry out the investigation. Moreover, his task is not to explain just one case, but all phenomena which have happened or may still happen.

In the introduction of the concept of fluids we see the influence of those mechanical ideas which attempt to explain everything by substances and simple forces acting between them. To see whether the mechanical point of view can be applied to the description of elec-

trical phenomena, we must consider the following problem. Two small spheres are given, both with an electric charge, that is, both carrying an excess of one electric fluid. We know that the spheres will either attract or repel each other. But does the force depend only on the distance, and if so, how? The simplest guess seems to be that this force depends on the distance in the same way as gravitational force, which diminishes, say, to one-ninth of its former strength if the distance is made three times as great. The experiments performed by Coulomb showed that this law is really valid. A hundred years after Newton discovered the law of gravitation, Coulomb found a similar dependence of electrical force on distance. The two major differences between Newton's law and Coulomb's law are: gravitational attraction is always present, while electric forces exist only if the bodies possess electric charges. In the gravitational case there is only attraction, but electric forces may either attract or repel.

There arises here the same question which we considered in connection with heat. Are the electrical fluids weightless substances or not? In other words, is the weight of a piece of metal the same whether neutral or charged? Our scales show no difference. We conclude that the electric fluids are also members of the family of weightless substances.

Further progress in the theory of electricity requires the introduction of two new concepts. Again we shall avoid rigorous definitions, using instead analogies with concepts already familiar. We remember how essential it was for an understanding of the phenomena of heat to distinguish between heat itself and temperature. It is equally important here to distinguish between electric potential and electric charge. The difference between the two concepts is made clear by the analogy:

Electric potential — Temperature
Electric charge — Heat

Two conductors, for example two spheres of different size, may have the same electric charge, that is the same excess of one electric fluid, but the potential will be different in the two cases, being higher for the smaller and lower for the larger sphere. The electric fluid will have greater density and thus be more compressed on the small conductor. Since the repulsive forces must increase with the density, the tendency of the charge to escape will be greater in the case of the smaller sphere than in that of the larger. This tendency of charge to

escape from a conductor is a direct measure of its potential. In order to show clearly the difference between charge and potential we shall formulate a few sentences describing the behavior of heated bodies, and the corresponding sentences concerning charged conductors.

Heat	*Electricity*
Two bodies, initially at different temperatures, reach the same temperature after some time if brought into contact.	Two insulated conductors, initially at different electric potentials, very quickly reach the same potential if brought into contact.
Equal quantities of heat produce different changes of temperature in two bodies if their heat capacities are different.	Equal amounts of electric charge produce different changes of electric potential in two bodies if their electrical capacities are different.
A thermometer in contact with a body indicates—by the length of its mercury column—its own temperature and therefore the temperature of the body.	An electroscope in contact with a conductor indicates—by the separation of the gold leaves—its own electric potential and therefore the electric potential of the conductor.

But this analogy must not be pushed too far. An example shows the differences as well as the similarities. If a hot body is brought into contact with a cold one, the heat flows from the hotter to the colder. On the other hand suppose that we have two insulated conductors having equal but opposite charges, one positive and the other negative. The two are at different potentials. By convention we regard the potential corresponding to a negative charge as lower than that corresponding to a positive charge. If the two conductors are brought together or connected by a wire, it follows from the theory of electric fluids that they will show no charge and thus no difference of electric potential at all. We must imagine a "flow" of electric charge from one conductor to the other during the short time in which the potential difference is equalized. But how? Does the positive fluid flow to the negative body, or the negative fluid to the positive body?

In the material presented here we have no basis for deciding between these two alternatives. We can assume either of the two possibilities, or that the flow is simultaneous in both directions. It is only a matter of adopting a convention, and no significance can be attached to the choice, for we know no method of deciding the question experimentally. Further development leading to a much more profound theory of electricity gave an answer to this problem, which is quite meaningless when formulated in terms of the simple and primitive theory of electric

fluids. Here we shall simply adopt the following mode of expression. The electric fluid flows from the conductor having the higher potential to that having the lower. In the case of our two conductors the electricity thus flows from positive to negative. This expression is only a matter of

convention and is at this point quite arbitrary. The whole difficulty indicates that the analogy between heat and electricity is by no means complete.

We have seen the possibility of adapting the mechanical view to a description of the elementary facts of electrostatics. The same is possible in the case of magnetic phenomena.

The Magnetic Fluids. We shall proceed here in the same manner as before, starting with very simple facts and then seeking their theoretical explanation.

1. We have two long bar magnets, one suspended freely at its center, the other held in the hand. The ends of the two magnets are brought together in such a way that a strong attraction is noticed between them. This can always be done. If no attraction results we must turn the magnet and try the other end. Something will happen if the bars are magnetized at all. The ends of the magnets are called their *poles*. To continue with the experiment we move the pole of the magnet held in the hand along the other magnet. A decrease in the attrac-

tion is noticed and when the pole reaches the middle of the suspended magnet there is no evidence of any force at all. If the pole is moved further in the same direction a repulsion is observed, attaining its greatest strength at the second pole of the hanging magnet.

2. The above experiment suggests another. Each magnet has two poles. Can we not isolate one of them? The idea is very simple: just break a magnet into two equal parts. We have seen that there is no force between the pole of one magnet and the middle of the other. But the result of actually breaking a magnet is surprising and unexpected. If we repeat the experiment described under (1), with only half a magnet suspended, the results are exactly the same as before!

Where there was no trace of magnetic force previously, there is now a strong pole.

How are these facts to be explained? We can attempt to pattern a theory of magnetism after the theory of electric fluids. This is suggested by the fact that here, as in electrostatic phenomena, we have attraction and repulsion. Imagine two spherical conductors possessing equal charges, one positive and the other negative. Here "equal" means having the same absolute value; +5 and −5, for example, have the same absolute value. Let us assume that these spheres are connected by means of an insulator such as a glass rod. Schematically this ar-

rangement can be represented by an arrow directed from the negatively charged conductor to the positive one. We shall call the whole thing an electric *di-pole*. It is clear that two such dipoles would behave exactly like the bar magnets in experiment (1). If we think of our invention as a model for a real magnet, we may say, assuming the existence of magnetic fluids, that a magnet is nothing but a *magnetic dipole,* having at its ends two fluids of different kinds. This simple theory, imitating the theory of electricity, is adequate for an explanation of the first experiment. There would be attraction at one end, repulsion at the other, and a balancing of equal and opposite forces in the middle. But what of the second experiment? By breaking the glass rod in the case of the electric dipole we get two isolated poles. The same ought to hold good for the iron bar of the magnetic dipole, contrary to the results of the second experiment. Thus this contradiction forces us to introduce a somewhat more subtle theory. In-

stead of our previous model we may imagine that the magnet consists of very small *elementary* magnetic dipoles which cannot be broken into separate poles. Order reigns in the magnet as a whole, for all the ele-

mentary dipoles are directed in the same way. We see immediately why cutting a magnet causes two new poles to appear on the new ends, and why this more refined theory explains the facts of experiment (1) as well as (2).

For many facts, the simpler theory gives an explanation and the refinement seems unnecessary. Let us take an example: We know that a magnet attracts pieces of iron. Why? In a piece of ordinary iron the two

magnetic fluids are mixed, so that no net effect results. Bringing a positive pole near acts as a "command of division" to the fluids, attracting the negative fluid of the iron and repelling the positive. The attraction between iron and magnet follows. If the magnet is removed, the fluids go back to more or less their original state, depending on the extent to which they remember the commanding voice of the external force.

Little need be said about the quantitative side of the problem. With two very long magnetized rods we could investigate the attraction (or repulsion) of their poles when brought near one another. The effect of the other ends of the rods is negligible if the rods are long enough. How does the attraction or repulsion depend on the distance between the poles? The answer given by Coulomb's experiment is that this dependence on distance is the same as in Newton's law of gravitation and Coulomb's law of electrostatics.

We see again in this theory the application of a general point of view: the tendency to describe all phenomena by means of attractive and repulsive forces depending only on distance and acting between unchangeable particles.

One well-known fact should be mentioned, for later we shall make use of it. The earth is a great magnetic dipole. There is not the slightest trace of an explanation as to why this is true. The North Pole is approximately the minus ($-$) and the South Pole the plus ($+$) magnetic pole of the earth. The names plus and minus are only a matter of convention, but when once fixed, enable us to designate poles in any other case. A magnetic needle supported on a vertical axis obeys the command of the magnetic force of the earth. It directs its ($+$) pole toward the North Pole, that is, toward the ($-$) magnetic pole of the earth.

Although we can consistently carry out the mechanical view in the domain of electric and magnetic phenomena introduced here, there is no reason to be particularly proud or pleased about it. Some features of the theory are certainly unsatisfactory if not discouraging. New kinds of substances had to be invented: two electric fluids and the elementary magnetic dipoles. The wealth of substances begins to be overwhelming!

The forces are simple. They are expressible in a similar way for gravitational, electric, and magnetic forces. But the price paid for this simplicity is high: the introduction of new weightless substances. These are rather artificial concepts, and quite unrelated to the fundamental substance, mass.

The First Serious Difficulty. We are now ready to note the first grave difficulty in the application of our general philosophical point of view. It will be shown later that this difficulty, together with another even more serious, caused a complete breakdown of the belief that all phenomena can be explained mechanically.

The tremendous development of electricity as a branch of science and technique began with the discovery of the electric current. Here we find in the history of science one of the very few instances in which accident seemed to play an essential role. The story of the convulsion of a frog's leg is told in many different ways. Regardless of the truth concerning details, there is no doubt that Galvani's accidental discovery led Volta at the end of the eighteenth century to the construction of what is known as a *voltaic battery*. This is no longer of any practical use, but it still furnishes a very simple example of a source of current in school demonstrations and in textbook descriptions.

The principle of its construction is simple. There are several glass tumblers, each containing water with a little sulphuric acid. In each glass two metal plates, one copper and the other zinc, are immersed in the solution. The copper plate of one glass is connected to the zinc of the next, so that only the zinc plate of the first and the copper plate of the last glass remain unconnected. We can detect a difference in electric potential between the copper in the first glass and the zinc in the last by means of a fairly sensitive electroscope if the number of the "elements," that is, glasses with plates, constituting the battery, is sufficiently large.

It was only for the purpose of obtaining something easily measurable with apparatus already described that we introduced a battery consisting of several elements. For further discussion, a single element will serve just as well. The potential of the copper turns out to be higher than that of the zinc. "Higher" is used here in the sense in which $+2$ is greater than -2. If one conductor is connected to the free copper plate and another to the zinc, both will become charged, the first positively and the other negatively. Up to this point nothing particularly new or striking has appeared, and we may try to apply our previous ideas about potential differences. We have seen that a potential difference between two conductors can be quickly nullified by connecting them with a wire, so that there is a flow of electric fluid from one conductor to the other. This process was similar to the equalization of temperatures by heat flow. But does this work in the case of a voltaic battery? Volta wrote in his report that the plates behave like conductors:

. . . feebly charged, which act unceasingly or so that their charge after each discharge re-establishes itself; which, in a word, provides an unlimited charge or imposes a perpetual action or impulsion of the electric fluid.

The astonishing result of his experiment is that the potential difference between the copper and zinc plates does not vanish as in the case of two charged conductors connected by a wire. The difference persists, and according to the fluids theory it must cause a constant flow of electric fluid from the higher potential level (copper plate) to the lower (zinc plate). In an attempt to save the fluid theory, we may assume that some constant force acts to regenerate the potential difference and cause a flow of electric fluid. But the whole phenomenon is astonishing from the standpoint of energy. A noticeable quantity of heat is generated in the wire carrying the current, even enough to melt the wire if it is a thin one. Therefore, heat-energy is created in the wire. But the whole voltaic battery forms an isolated system, since no external energy is being supplied. If we want to save the law of conservation of energy we must find where the transformations take place, and at what expense the heat is created. It is not difficult to realize that complicated chemical processes are taking place in the battery, processes in which the immersed copper and zinc, as well as the liquid itself, take active parts. From the standpoint of energy this is the chain of transformations which are taking place: chemical energy → energy of the flowing electric fluid, i.e., the current → heat. A voltaic battery does not last forever; the chemical changes associated with the flow of electricity make the battery useless after a time.

The experiment which actually revealed the great difficulties in applying the mechanical ideas must sound strange to anyone hearing about it for the first time. It was performed by Oersted about a hundred and twenty years ago. He reports:

> By these experiments it seems to be shown that the magnetic needle was moved from its position by help of a galvanic apparatus, and that, when the galvanic circuit was closed, but not when open, as certain very celebrated physicists in vain attempted several years ago.

Suppose we have a voltaic battery and a conducting wire. If the wire is connected to the copper plate but not to the zinc, there will exist a potential difference but no current can flow. Let us assume that the wire is bent to form a circle, in the center of which a magnetic needle is placed, both wire and needle lying in the same plane. Nothing hap-

pens as long as the wire does not touch the zinc plate. There are no forces acting, the existing potential difference having no influence what-

ever on the position of the needle. It seems difficult to understand why the "very celebrated physicists," as Oersted called them, expected such an influence.

But now let us join the wire to the zinc plate. Immediately a strange thing happens. The magnetic needle turns from its previous position. One of its poles now points to the reader if the page of this book represents the plane of the circle. The effect is that of a force, *perpendicular* to the plane, acting on the magnetic pole. Faced with the facts of the experiment, we can hardly avoid drawing such a conclusion about the direction of the force acting.

This experiment is interesting, in the first place, because it shows a relation between two apparently quite different phenomena, magnetism and electric current. There is another aspect even more important. The force between the magnetic pole and the small portions of the wire through which the current flows cannot lie along lines connecting the wire and needle, or the particles of flowing electric fluid and the elementary magnetic dipoles. The force is perpendicular to these lines! For the first time there appears a force quite different from that to which, according to our mechanical point of view, we intended to reduce all actions in the external world. We remember that the forces of gravitation, electrostatics, and magnetism, obeying the laws of Newton and Coulomb, act along the line joining the two attracting or repelling bodies.

This difficulty was stressed even more by an experiment performed with great skill by Rowland nearly sixty years ago. Leaving out technical details, this experiment could be described as follows. Imagine a small charged sphere. Imagine further that this sphere moves very fast in a circle at the center of which is a magnetic needle. This is, in principle, the same experiment as Oersted's, the only difference being that instead of an ordinary current we have a mechanically effected motion of the electric charge. Rowland found that the result is indeed

similar to that observed when a current flows in a circular wire. The magnet is deflected by a perpendicular force.

Let us now move the charge faster. The force acting on the magnetic pole is, as a result, increased; the deflection from its initial position becomes more distinct. This observation presents another grave complication. Not only does the force fail to lie on the line connecting charge and magnet, but the intensity of the force depends on the velocity of the charge. The whole mechanical point of view was based on the belief that all phenomena can be explained in terms of forces depending only on the distance and not on the velocity. The result of Rowland's experiment certainly shakes this belief. Yet we may choose to be conservative and seek a solution within the frame of old ideas.

Difficulties of this kind, sudden and unexpected obstacles in the triumphant development of a theory, arise frequently in science. Sometimes a simple generalization of the old ideas seems, at least temporarily, to be a good way out. It would seem sufficient, in the present case, for example, to broaden the previous point of view and introduce more general forces between the elementary particles. Very often, however, it is impossible to patch up an old theory, and the difficulties result in its downfall and the rise of a new one. Here it was not only the behavior of a tiny magnetic needle which broke the apparently well-founded and successful mechanical theories. Another attack, even more vigorous, came from an entirely different angle. But this is another story, and we shall tell it later.

The Velocity of Light. In Galileo's *Two New Sciences*, we listen to a conversation of the master and his pupils about the velocity of light:

SAGREDO: But of what kind and how great must we consider this speed of light to be? Is it instantaneous or momentary or does it, like other motion, require time? Can we not decide this by experiment?

SIMPLICIO: Everyday experience shows that the propagation of light is instantaneous; for when we see a piece of artillery fired, at great distance, the flash reaches our eyes without lapse of time; but the sound reaches the ear only after a noticeable interval.

SAGREDO: Well, Simplicio, the only thing I am able to infer from this familiar bit of experience is that sound, in reaching our ears, travels more

slowly than light; it does not inform me whether the coming of the light is instantaneous or whether, although extremely rapid, it still occupies time. . . .

SALVIATI: The small conclusiveness of these and other similar observations once led me to devise a method by which one might accurately ascertain whether illumination, *i.e.*, propagation of light, is really instantaneous. . . .

Salviati goes on to explain the method of his experiment. In order to understand his idea let us imagine that the velocity of light is not only finite, but also small, that the motion of light is slowed down, like that in a slow-motion film. Two men, A and B, have covered lanterns and stand, say, at a distance of one mile from each other. The first man, A, opens his lantern. The two have made an agreement that B will open his the moment he sees A's light. Let us assume that in our "slow motion" the light travels one mile in a second. A sends a signal by uncovering his lantern. B sees it after one second and sends an answering signal. This is received by A two seconds after he had sent his own. That is to say, if light travels with a speed of one mile per second, then two seconds will elapse between A's sending and receiving a signal, assuming that B is a mile away. Conversely, if A does not know the velocity of light but assumes that his companion kept the agreement, and he notices the opening of B's lantern two seconds after he opened his, he can conclude that the speed of light is one mile per second.

With the experimental technique available at that time Galileo had little chance of determining the velocity of light in this way. If the distance were a mile, he would have had to detect time intervals of the order of one hundred-thousandth of a second!

Galileo formulated the problem of determining the velocity of light, but did not solve it. The formulation of a problem is often more essential than its solution, which may be merely a matter of mathematical or experimental skill. To raise new questions, new possibilities, to regard old problems from a new angle, requires creative imagination and marks real advance in science. The principle of inertia, the law of conservation of energy were gained only by new and original thoughts about already well-known experiments and phenomena. Many instances of this kind will be found in the following pages of this book, where the importance of seeing known facts in a new light will be stressed and new theories described.

Returning to the comparatively simple question of determining the velocity of light, we may remark that it is surprising that Galileo did not

realize that his experiment could be performed much more simply and accurately by one man. Instead of stationing his companion at a distance he could have mounted there a mirror, which would automatically send back the signal immediately after receiving it.

About two hundred and fifty years later this very principle was used by Fizeau, who was the first to determine the velocity of light by terrestrial experiments. It had been determined by Roemer much earlier, though less accurately, by astronomical observation.

It is quite clear that in view of its enormous magnitude, the velocity of light could be measured only by taking distances comparable to that between the earth and another planet of the solar system or by a great refinement of experimental technique. The first method was that of Roemer, the second that of Fizeau. Since the days of these first experiments the very important number representing the velocity of light has been determined many times, with increasing accuracy. In our own century a highly refined technique was devised for this purpose by Michelson. The result of these experiments can be expressed simply: The velocity of light *in vacuo* is approximately 186,000 miles per second, or 300,000 kilometers per second.

Light as Substance. Again we start with a few experimental facts. The number just quoted concerns the velocity of light *in vacuo*. Undisturbed, light travels with this speed through empty space. We can see through an empty glass vessel if we extract the air from it. We see planets, stars, nebulae, although the light travels from them to our eyes through empty space. The simple fact that we can see through a vessel whether or not there is air inside shows us that the presence of air matters very little. For this reason we can perform optical experiments in an ordinary room with the same effect as if there were no air.

One of the simplest optical facts is that the propagation of light is rectilinear. We shall describe a primitive and naïve experiment showing this. In front of a point source is placed a screen with a hole in it. A point source is a very small source of light, say, a small opening in a closed lantern. On a distant wall the hole in the screen will be represented as light on a dark background. The next drawing [p. 544] shows how this phenomenon is connected with the rectilinear propagation of light. All such phenomena, even the more complicated cases in which light, shadow, and half-shadows appear, can be explained by the assumption that light, *in vacuo* or in air, travels along straight lines.

Let us take another example, a case in which light passes through matter. We have a light beam traveling through a vacuum and falling on a

glass plate. What happens? If the law of rectilinear motion were still valid, the path would be that shown by the dotted line. But actually it

is not. There is a break in the path, such as is shown in the drawing [below]. What we observe here is the phenomenon known as *refraction*. The familiar appearance of a stick which seems to be bent in the middle if half-immersed in water is one of the many manifestations of refraction.

These facts are sufficient to indicate how a simple mechanical theory of light could be devised. Our aim here is to show how the ideas of substances, particles, and forces penetrated the field of optics, and how finally the old philosophical point of view broke down.

The theory here suggests itself in its simplest and most primitive form. Let us assume that all lighted bodies emit particles of light, or *corpuscles*, which, falling on our eyes, create the sensation of light. We are already so accustomed to introduce new substances, if necessary

for a mechanical explanation, that we can do it once more without any great hesitation. These corpuscles must travel along straight lines through empty space with a known speed, bringing to our eyes messages from the bodies emitting light. All phenomena exhibiting the rectilinear propagation of light support the corpuscular theory, for just this kind of motion was prescribed for the corpuscles. The theory also explains very simply the reflection of light by mirrors as the same kind of reflection as that shown in the mechanical experiment of elastic balls thrown against a wall, as the next drawing indicates.

The explanation of refraction is a little more difficult. Without going into details we can see the possibility of a mechanical explanation. If corpuscles fall on the surface of glass, for example, it may be that a force is exerted on them by the particles of the matter, a force which strangely enough acts only in the immediate neighborhood of matter. Any force acting on a moving particle changes the velocity, as we

already know. If the net force on the light-corpuscles is an attraction perpendicular to the surface of the glass, the new motion will lie somewhere between the line of the original path and the perpendicular.

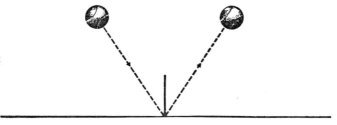

This simple explanation seems to promise success for the corpuscular theory of light. To determine the usefulness and range of validity of the theory, however, we must investigate new and more complicated facts.

The Riddle of Color. It was again Newton's genius which explained for the first time the wealth of color in the world. Here is a description of one of Newton's experiments in his own words:

> In the year 1666 (at which time I applied myself to the grinding of optick glasses of other figures than spherical) I procured me a triangular glass prism, to try therewith the celebrated phenomena of colours. And in order thereto, having darkened my chamber, and made a small hole in my window-shuts, to let in a convenient quantity of the sun's light, I placed my prism at its entrance, that it might thereby be refracted to the opposite wall. It was at first a very pleasing divertisement, to view the vivid and intense colours produced thereby.

The light from the sun is "white." After passing through a prism it shows all the colors which exist in the visible world. Nature herself reproduces the same result in the beautiful color scheme of the rainbow. Attempts to explain this phenomenon are very old. The Biblical story that a rainbow is God's signature to a covenant with man is, in a sense, a "theory." But it does not satisfactorily explain why the rainbow is repeated from time to time, and why always in connection with rain. The whole puzzle of color was first scientifically attacked and the solution pointed out in the great work of Newton.

One edge of the rainbow is always red and the other violet. Between them all other colors are arranged. Here is Newton's explanation of this phenomenon: every color is already present in white light. They all traverse interplanetary space and the atmosphere in unison and give the effect of white light. White light is, so to speak, a mixture of

corpuscles of different kinds, belonging to different colors. In the case of Newton's experiment the prism separates them in space. According to the mechanical theory, refraction is due to forces acting on the particles of light and originating from the particles of glass. These forces are different for corpuscles belonging to different colors, being strongest for the violet and weakest for the red. Each of the colors will therefore be refracted along a different path and be separated from the others when the light leaves the prism. In the case of a rainbow, drops of water play the role of the prism.

The substance theory of light is now more complicated than before. We have not one light substance but many, each belonging to a different color. If, however, there is some truth in the theory, its consequences must agree with observation.

The series of colors in the white light of the sun, as revealed by Newton's experiment, is called the *spectrum* of the sun, or more precisely, its *visible spectrum*. The decomposition of white light into its components, as described here, is called the *dispersion* of light. The separated colors of the spectrum could be mixed together again by a second prism properly adjusted, unless the explanation given is wrong. The process should be just the reverse of the previous one. We should obtain white light from the previously separated colors. Newton showed by experiment that it is indeed possible to obtain white light from its spectrum and the spectrum from white light in this simple way as many times as one pleases. These experiments formed a strong support for the theory in which corpuscles belonging to each color behave as unchangeable substances. Newton wrote thus:

> . . . which colours are not new generated, but only made apparent by being parted; for if they be again entirely mixt and blended together, they will again compose that colour, which they did before separation. And for the same reason, transmutations made by the convening of divers colours are not real; for when the difform rays are again severed, they will exhibit the very same colours which they did before they entered the composition; as you see blue and yellow powders, when finely mixed, appear to the naked eye, green, and yet the colours of the component corpuscles are not thereby really transmuted, but only blended. For when viewed with a good microscope they still appear blue and yellow interspersedly.

Suppose that we have isolated a very narrow strip of the spectrum. This means that of all the many colors we allow only one to pass through the slit, the others being stopped by a screen. The beam which

comes through will consist of *homogeneous* light, that is, light which cannot be split into further components. This is a consequence of the theory and can be easily confirmed by experiment. In no way can such a beam of single color be divided further. There are simple means of obtaining sources of homogeneous light. For example, sodium, when incandescent, emits homogeneous yellow light. It is very often convenient to perform certain optical experiments with homogeneous light, since, as we can well understand, the result will be much simpler.

Let us imagine that suddenly a very strange thing happens: our sun begins to emit only homogeneous light of some definite color, say yellow. The great variety of colors on the earth would immediately vanish. Everything would be either yellow or black! This prediction is a consequence of the substance theory of light, for new colors cannot be created. Its validity can be confirmed by experiment: in a room where the only source of light is incandescent sodium everything is either yellow or black. The wealth of color in the world reflects the variety of color of which white light is composed.

The substance theory of light seems to work splendidly in all these cases, although the necessity for introducing as many substances as colors may make us somewhat uneasy. The assumption that all the corpuscles of light have exactly the same velocity in empty space also seems very artificial.

It is imaginable that another set of suppositions, a theory of entirely different character, would work just as well and give all the required explanations. Indeed, we shall soon witness the rise of another theory, based on entirely different concepts, yet explaining the same domain of optical phenomena. Before formulating the underlying assumptions of this new theory, however, we must answer a question in no way connected with these optical considerations. We must go back to mechanics and ask:

What Is a Wave? A bit of gossip starting in Washington reaches New York very quickly, even though not a single individual who takes part in spreading it travels between these two cities. There are two quite different motions involved, that of the rumor, Washington to New York, and that of the persons who spread the rumor. The wind, passing over a field of grain, sets up a wave which spreads out across the whole field. Here again we must distinguish between the motion of the wave and the motion of the separate plants, which undergo only small oscillations. We have all seen the waves that spread in wider and wider

circles when a stone is thrown into a pool of water. The motion of the wave is very different from that of the particles of water. The particles merely go up and down. The observed motion of the wave is that of a state of matter and not of matter itself. A cork floating on the wave shows this clearly, for it moves up and down in imitation of the actual motion of the water, instead of being carried along by the wave.

In order to understand better the mechanism of the wave let us again consider an idealized experiment. Suppose that a large space is filled quite uniformly with water, or air, or some other "medium." Somewhere in the center there is a sphere. At the beginning of the experiment there is no motion at all. Suddenly the sphere begins to "breathe" rhythmically, expanding and contracting in volume, although retaining its spherical shape. What will happen in the medium? Let us begin our examination at the moment the sphere begins to expand. The particles of the medium in the immediate vicinity of the sphere are pushed out, so that the density of a spherical shell of water, or air, as the case may be, is increased above its normal value. Similarly, when the sphere contracts, the density of that part of the medium immediately surrounding it will be decreased. These changes of density are propagated throughout the entire medium. The particles constituting the medium perform only small vibrations, but the whole motion is that of a progressive wave. The essentially new thing here is that for the first time we consider the motion of something which is not matter, but energy propagated through matter.

Using the example of the pulsating sphere, we may introduce two general physical concepts, important for the characterization of waves. The first is the velocity with which the wave spreads. This will depend on the medium, being different for water and air, for example. The second concept is that of *wave length*. In the case of waves on a sea or river it is the distance from the trough of one wave to that of the next, or from the crest of one wave to that of the next. Thus sea waves have greater wave length than river waves. In the case of our waves set up by a pulsating sphere the wave length is the distance, at some definite time, between two neighboring spherical shells showing maxima or minima of density. It is evident that this distance will not depend on the medium alone. The rate of pulsation of the sphere will certainly have a great effect, making the wave length shorter if the pulsation becomes more rapid, longer if the pulsation becomes slower.

This concept of a wave proved very successful in physics. It is

definitely a mechanical concept. The phenomenon is reduced to the motion of particles which, according to the kinetic theory, are constituents of matter. Thus every theory which uses the concept of wave can, in general, be regarded as a mechanical theory. For example, the explanation of acoustical phenomena is based essentially on this concept. Vibrating bodies, such as vocal cords and violin strings, are sources of sound waves which are propagated through the air in the manner explained for the pulsating sphere. It is thus possible to reduce all acoustical phenomena to mechanics by means of the wave concept.

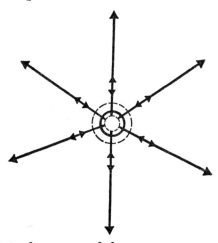

It has been emphasized that we must distinguish between the motion of the particles and that of the wave itself, which is a state of the medium. The two are very different but it is apparent that in our example of the pulsating sphere both motions take place in the same straight line. The particles of the medium oscillate along short line segments, and the density increases and decreases periodically in accordance with this motion. The direction in which the wave spreads and the line on which the oscillations lie are the same. This type of wave is called *longitudinal*. But is this the only kind of wave? It is important for our further considerations to realize the possibility of a different kind of wave, called *transverse*.

Let us change our previous example. We still have the sphere, but it is immersed in a medium of a different kind, a sort of jelly instead of air or water. Furthermore, the sphere no longer pulsates but rotates in one direction through a small angle and then back again, always in the same rhythmical way and about a definite axis. The jelly adheres to the sphere and thus the adhering portions are forced to imitate the motion. These portions force those situated a little further away to imitate the same motion, and so on, so that a wave is set up in the medium. If we keep in mind the distinction between the motion of the medium and the motion of the wave we see that here they do not lie on the same line. The wave is propagated in the direction of the radius of the sphere, while the parts of the medium move perpendicularly to this direction. We have thus created a transverse wave [see p. 550].

Waves spreading on the surface of water are transverse. A floating cork only bobs up and down, but the wave spreads along a horizontal plane.

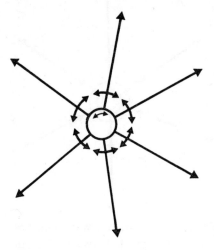

Sound waves, on the other hand, furnish the most familiar example of longitudinal waves.

One more remark: the wave produced by a pulsating or oscillating sphere in a homogeneous medium is a *spherical* wave. It is called so because at any given moment all points on any sphere surrounding the source behave in the same way. Let us consider a portion of such a sphere at a great distance from the source. The farther away the portion is, and the smaller we take it, the more it resembles a plane. We can say, without trying to be too rigorous, that there is no essential difference between a part of a plane and a part of a sphere whose radius is sufficiently large. We very often speak of small portions of a spherical wave far removed from the source as *plane waves*. The farther we place the shaded portion of our drawing from the center of the spheres and the smaller the angle between the two radii, the better our representation of a plane wave. The concept of a plane wave, like

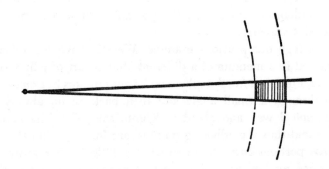

many other physical concepts, is no more than a fiction which can be realized with only a certain degree of accuracy. It is, however, a useful concept which we shall need later.

The Wave Theory of Light. Let us recall why we broke off the description of optical phenomena. Our aim was to introduce another

theory of light, different from the corpuscular one, but also attempting to explain the same domain of facts. To do this we had to interrupt our story and introduce the concept of waves. Now we can return to our subject.

It was Huygens, a contemporary of Newton, who put forward a quite new theory. In his treatise on light he wrote:

> If, in addition, light takes time for its passage—which we are now going to examine—it will follow that this movement, impressed on the intervening matter, is successive; and consequently it spreads, as sound does, by spherical surfaces and waves, for I call them waves from their resemblance to those which are seen to be formed in water when a stone is thrown into it, and which present a successive spreading as circles, though these arise from another cause, and are only in a flat surface.

According to Huygens, light is a wave, a transference of energy and not of substance. We have seen that the corpuscular theory explains many of the observed facts. Is the wave theory also able to do this? We must again ask the questions which have already been answered by the corpuscular theory, to see whether the wave theory can do the answering just as well. We shall do this here in the form of a dialogue between N and H, where N is a believer in Newton's corpuscular theory, and H in Huygen's theory. Neither is allowed to use arguments developed after the work of the two great masters was finished.

N: In the corpuscular theory the velocity of light has a very definite meaning. It is the velocity at which the corpuscles travel through empty space. What does it mean in the wave theory?

H: It means the velocity of the light wave, of course. Every known wave spreads with some definite velocity, and so should a wave of light.

N: That is not as simple as it seems. Sound waves spread in air, ocean waves in water. Every wave must have a material medium in which it travels. But light passes through a vacuum, whereas sound does not. To assume a wave in empty space really means not to assume any wave at all.

H: Yes, that is a difficulty, although not a new one to me. My master thought about it very carefully, and decided that the only way out is to assume the existence of a hypothetical substance, the *ether*, a transparent medium permeating the entire universe. The universe is, so to speak, immersed in ether. Once we have the courage to introduce this concept, everything else becomes clear and convincing.

N: But I object to such an assumption. In the first place it introduces a new hypothetical substance, and we already have too many substances in physics. There is also another reason against it. You no doubt believe that we must explain everything in terms of mechanics. But what about the ether? Are you able to answer the simple question as to how the ether is constructed from its elementary particles and how it reveals itself in other phenomena?

H: Your first objection is certainly justified. But by introducing the somewhat artificial weightless ether we at once get rid of the much more artificial light corpuscles. We have only one "mysterious" substance instead of an infinite number of them corresponding to the great number of colors in the spectrum. Do you not think that this is real progress? At least all the difficulties are concentrated on one point. We no longer need the factitious assumption that particles belonging to different colors travel with the same speed through empty space. Your second argument is also true. We cannot give a mechanical explanation of ether. But there is no doubt that the future study of optical and perhaps other phenomena will reveal its structure. At present we must wait for new experiments and conclusions, but finally, I hope, we shall be able to clear up the problem of the mechanical structure of the ether.

N: Let us leave the question for the moment, since it cannot be settled now. I should like to see how your theory, even if we waive the difficulties, explains those phenomena which are so clear and understandable in the light of the corpuscular theory. Take, for example, the fact that light rays travel *in vacuo* or in air along straight lines. A piece of paper placed in front of a candle produces a distinct and sharply outlined shadow on the wall. Sharp shadows would not be possible if the wave theory of light were correct, for waves would bend around the edges of the paper and thus blur the shadow. A small ship is not an obstacle for waves on the sea, you know; they simply bend around it without casting a shadow.

H: That is not a convincing argument. Take short waves on a river impinging on the side of a large ship. Waves originating on one side of the ship will not be seen on the other. If the waves are small enough and the ship large enough a very distinct shadow appears. It is very probable that light seems to travel in straight lines only because its wave length is very small in comparison with the size of ordinary obstacles and of apertures used in experiments. Possibly, if we could create a sufficiently small obstruction, no shadow would occur. We might meet

with great experimental difficulties in constructing apparatus which would show whether light is capable of bending. Nevertheless, if such an experiment could be devised it would be crucial in deciding between the wave theory and the corpuscular theory of light.

N: The wave theory may lead to new facts in the future, but I do not know of any experimental data confirming it convincingly. Until it is definitely proved by experiment that light may be bent I do not see any reason for not believing in the corpuscular theory, which seems to me to be simpler, and therefore better, than the wave theory.

At this point we may interrupt the dialogue, though the subject is by no means exhausted.

It still remains to be shown how the wave theory explains the refraction of light and the variety of colors. The corpuscular theory is capable of this, as we know. We shall begin with refraction, but it will be useful to consider first an example having nothing to do with optics.

There is a large open space in which there are walking two men holding between them a rigid pole. At the beginning they are walking straight ahead, both with the same velocity. As long as their velocities remain the same, whether great or small, the stick will be undergoing parallel displacement; that is, it does not turn or change its direction. All consecutive positions of the pole are parallel to each other. But now imagine that for a time which may be as short as a fraction of a second the motions of the two men are not the same. What will happen? It is clear that during this moment the stick will turn, so that it will no longer be displaced parallel to its original position. When the equal velocities are resumed it is in a direction different from the previous one. This is shown clearly in the drawing. The change in direction took place during the time interval in which the velocities of the two walkers were different.

This example will enable us to understand the refraction of a wave. A plane wave traveling through the ether strikes a plate of glass. In the next drawing we see a wave which presents a comparatively wide front as it marches along. The wave front is a plane on which at any given moment all parts of the ether behave in precisely the same way. Since the velocity depends on the medium through which the light is passing it will be different in glass from the velocity in empty space. During the very short time in which the wave front enters the glass, dif-

ferent parts of the wave front will have different velocities. It is clear that the part which has reached the glass will travel with the velocity

of light in glass, while the other still moves with the velocity of light in ether. Because of this difference in velocity along the wave front during the time of "immersion" in the glass, the direction of the wave itself will be changed.

Thus we see that not only the corpuscular theory, but also the wave theory, leads to an explanation of refraction. Further consideration, together with a little mathematics, shows that the wave theory explanation is simpler and better, and that the consequences are in perfect agreement with observation. Indeed, quantitative methods of reasoning enable us to deduce the velocity of light in a refractive medium if we know how the beam refracts when passing into it. Direct measurements splendidly confirm these predictions, and thus also the wave theory of light.

There still remains the question of color.

It must be remembered that a wave is characterized by two numbers, its velocity and its wave length. The essential assumption of the wave theory of light is that *different wave lengths correspond to different colors*. The wave length of homogeneous yellow light differs from that of red or violet. Instead of the artificial segregation of corpuscles belonging to various colors we have the natural difference in wave length.

It follows that Newton's experiments on the dispersion of light can be described in two different languages, that of the corpuscular theory and that of the wave theory. For example:

Corpuscular Language	*Wave Language*
The corpuscles belonging to different colors have the same velocity *in vacuo*, but different velocities in glass.	The rays of different wave length belonging to different colors have the same velocity in the ether, but different velocities in glass.
White light is a composition of corpuscles belonging to different colors, whereas in the spectrum they are separated.	White light is a composition of waves of all wave lengths, whereas in the spectrum they are separated.

It would seem wise to avoid the ambiguity resulting from the exist-
ence of two distinct theories of the same phenomena, by deciding in fa-
vor of one of them after a careful consideration of the faults and merits
of each. The dialogue between N and H shows that this is no easy task.
The decision at this point would be more a matter of taste than of scien-
tific conviction. In Newton's time, and for more than a hundred years
after, most physicists favored the corpuscular theory.

History brought in its verdict, in favor of the wave theory of light and
against the corpuscular theory, at a much later date, the middle of
the nineteenth century. In his conversation with H, N stated that a de-
cision between the two theories was, in principle, experimentally
possible. The corpuscular theory does not allow light to bend, and de-
mands the existence of sharp shadows. According to the wave theory,
on the other hand, a sufficiently small obstacle will cast no shadow. In
the work of Young and Fresnel this result was experimentally realized
and theoretical conclusions were drawn.

An extremely simple experiment has already been discussed, in which
a screen with a hole was placed in front of a point source of light and
a light appeared on the wall. We shall simplify the experiment fur-
ther by assuming that the source emits homogeneous light. For
the best results the source should be a strong one. Let us imagine that
the hole in the screen is made smaller and smaller. If we use a strong
source and succeed in making the hole small enough, a new and surpris-
ing phenomenon appears, something quite incomprehensible from
the point of view of the corpuscular theory. There is no longer a
sharp distinction between light and dark. Light gradually fades into
the dark background in a series of light and dark rings. The appear-
ance of rings is very characteristic of a wave theory. The explanation
for alternating light and dark areas will be clear in the case of a some-
what different experimental arrangement. Suppose we have a sheet of
dark paper with two pinholes through which light may pass. If the
holes are close together and very small, and if the source of homo-
geneous light is strong enough, many light and dark bands will ap-
pear on the wall, gradually fading off at the sides into the dark back-
ground. The explanation is simple. A dark band is where a trough of
a wave from one pinhole meets the crest of a wave from the other
pinhole, so that the two cancel. A band of light is where two troughs or
two crests from waves of the different pinholes meet and reinforce
each other. The explanation is more complicated in the case of the
dark and light rings of our previous example in which we used a screen

with one hole, but the principle is the same. . . . The experiments described here show the *diffraction* of light, the deviation from the rectilinear propagation when small holes or obstacles are placed in the way of the light wave.

With the aid of a little mathematics we are able to go much further. It is possible to find out how great or, rather, how small the wave length must be to produce a particular pattern. Thus the experiments described enable us to measure the wave length of the homogeneous light used as a source. To give an idea of how small the numbers are we shall cite two wave lengths, those representing the extremes of the solar spectrum, that is, the red and the violet.

The wave length of red light is 0.00008 cm.
The wave length of violet light is 0.00004 cm.

We should not be astonished that the numbers are so small. The phenomenon of distinct shadow, that is, the phenomenon of rectilinear propagation of light, is observed in nature only because all apertures and obstacles ordinarily met with are extremely large in comparison with the wave lengths of light. It is only when very small obstacles and apertures are used that light reveals its wave-like nature.

But the story of the search for a theory of light is by no means finished. The verdict of the nineteenth century was not final and ultimate. For the modern physicist the entire problem of deciding between corpuscles and waves again exists, this time in a much more profound and intricate form. Let us accept the defeat of the corpuscular theory of light until we recognize the problematic nature of the victory of the wave theory.

Longitudinal or Transverse Light Waves? All the optical phenomena we have considered speak for the wave theory. The bending of light around small obstacles and the explanation of refraction are the strongest arguments in its favor. Guided by the mechanical point of view we realize that there is still one question to be answered: the determination of the mechanical properties of the ether. It is essential for the solution of this problem to know whether light waves in the ether are longitudinal or transverse. In other words: is light propagated like sound? Is the wave due to changes in the density of the medium, so that the oscillations of the particles are in the direction of the propagation? Or does the ether resemble an elastic jelly, a medium in which only transverse waves can be set up and whose particles move in a direction perpendicular to that in which the wave itself travels?

Before solving this problem let us try to decide which answer should be preferred. Obviously, we should be fortunate if light waves were longitudinal. The difficulties in designing a mechanical ether would be much simpler in this case. Our picture of ether might very probably be something like the mechanical picture of a gas that explains the propagation of sound waves. It would be much more difficult to form a picture of ether carrying transverse waves. To imagine a jelly as a medium made up of particles in such a way that transverse waves are propagated by means of it is no easy task. Huygens believed that the ether would turn out to be "air-like" rather than "jelly-like." But nature cares very little for our limitations. Was nature, in this case, merciful to the physicists attempting to understand all events from a mechanical point of view? In order to answer this question we must discuss some new experiments.

We shall consider in detail only one of many experiments which are able to supply us with an answer. Suppose we have a very thin plate of tourmaline crystal, cut in a particular way which we need not describe here. The crystal plate must be thin so that we are able to see a source of light through it. But now let us take two such plates and place both of them between our eyes and the light. What do we ex-

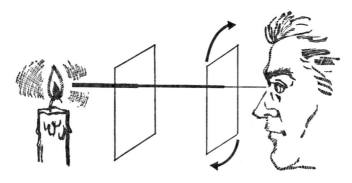

pect to see? Again a point of light, if the plates are sufficiently thin. The chances are very good that the experiment will confirm our expectation. Without worrying about the statement that it may be chance, let us assume we do see the light point through the two crystals. Now let us gradually change the position of one of the crystals by rotating it. This statement makes sense only if the position of the axis about which the rotation takes place is fixed. We shall take as an axis the line determined by the incoming ray. This means that we displace all the points of the one crystal except those on the axis. A

strange thing happens! The light gets weaker and weaker until it vanishes completely. It reappears as the rotation continues and we regain the initial view when the initial position is reached.

Without going into the details of this and similar experiments we can ask the following question: can these phenomena be explained if the light waves are longitudinal? In the case of longitudinal waves the particles of the ether would move along the axis, as the beam does. If the crystal rotates, nothing along the axis changes. The points on the axis do not move, and only a very small displacement takes place nearby. No such distinct change as the vanishing and appearance of a new picture could possibly occur for a longitudinal wave. This and many other similar phenomena can be explained only by the assumption that light waves are transverse and not longitudinal! Or, in other words, the "jelly-like" character of the ether must be assumed.

This is very sad! We must be prepared to face tremendous difficulties in the attempt to describe the ether mechanically.

Ether and the Mechanical View. The discussion of all the various attempts to understand the mechanical nature of the ether as a medium for transmitting light, would make a long story. A mechanical construction means, as we know, that the substance is built up of particles with forces acting along lines connecting them and depending only on the distance. In order to construct the ether as a jelly-like mechanical substance physicists had to make some highly artificial and unnatural assumptions. We shall not quote them here; they belong to the almost forgotten past. But the result was significant and important. The artificial character of all these assumptions, the necessity for introducing so many of them all quite independent of each other, was enough to shatter the belief in the mechanical point of view.

But there are other and simpler objections to ether than the difficulty of constructing it. Ether must be assumed to exist everywhere, if we wish to explain optical phenomena mechanically. There can be no empty space if light travels only in a medium.

Yet we know from mechanics that interstellar space does not resist the motion of material bodies. The planets, for example, travel through the ether-jelly without encountering any resistance such as a material medium would offer to their motion. If ether does not disturb matter in its motion, there can be no interaction between particles of ether and particles of matter. Light passes through ether and also through glass and

water, but its velocity is changed in the latter substances. How can this fact be explained mechanically? Apparently only by assuming some interaction between ether particles and matter particles. We have just seen that in the case of freely moving bodies such interactions must be assumed not to exist. In other words, there is interaction between ether and matter in optical phenomena, but none in mechanical phenomena! This is certainly a very paradoxical conclusion!

There seems to be only one way out of all these difficulties. In the attempt to understand the phenomena of nature from the mechanical point of view, throughout the whole development of science up to the twentieth century, it was necessary to introduce artificial substances like electric and magnetic fluids, light corpuscles, or ether. The result was merely the concentration of all the difficulties in a few essential points, such as ether in the case of optical phenomena. Here all the fruitless attempts to construct an ether in some simple way, as well as the other objections, seem to indicate that the fault lies in the fundamental assumption that it is possible to explain all events in nature from a mechanical point of view. Science did not succeed in carrying out the mechanical program convincingly, and today no physicist believes in the possibility of its fulfillment.

In our short review of the principal physical ideas we have met some unsolved problems, have come upon difficulties and obstacles which discouraged the attempts to formulate a uniform and consistent view of all the phenomena of the external world. There was the unnoticed clue in classical mechanics of the equality of gravitational and inertial mass. There was the artificial character of the electric and magnetic fluids. There was, in the interaction between electric current and magnetic needle, an unsolved difficulty. It will be remembered that this force did not act in the line connecting the wire and the magnetic pole, and depended on the velocity of the moving charge. The law expressing its direction and magnitude was extremely complicated. And finally, there was the great difficulty with the ether.

Modern physics has attacked all these problems and solved them. But in the struggle for these solutions new and deeper problems have been created. Our knowledge is now wider and more profound than that of the physicist of the nineteenth century, but so are our doubts and difficulties.

We summarize:

In the old theories of electric fluids, in the corpuscular and wave theories of light, we witness the further attempts to apply the mechanical view. But in the realm of electric and optical phenomena we meet grave difficulties in this application.

A moving charge acts upon a magnetic needle. But the force, instead of depending only upon distance, depends also upon the velocity of the charge. The force neither repels nor attracts but acts perpendicular to the line connecting the needle and the charge.

In optics we have to decide in favor of the wave theory against the corpuscular theory of light. Waves spreading in a medium consisting of particles, with mechanical forces acting between them, are certainly a mechanical concept. But what is the medium through which light spreads and what are its mechanical properties? There is no hope of reducing the optical phenomena to the mechanical ones before this question is answered. But the difficulties in solving this problem are so great that we have to give it up and thus give up the mechanical view as well.

The foregoing consists of Chapters I and II
from Einstein and Infeld's
THE EVOLUTION OF PHYSICS.

Sir Arthur Eddington

1882–1944

Arthur Stanley Eddington was born in England in 1882. He was educated at Trinity College, Cambridge, where he was senior wrangler in 1904. (For a discussion of the intellectual eminence implied by this position, see the selection from Galton's *Hereditary Genius*.) [1] He was elected a fellow of Trinity and, in 1913, at the age of thirty-one, made the Plumian Professor of Astronomy and Experimental Philosophy at Cambridge. He succeeded a long line of distinguished scientists in this position; his immediate predecessor was Sir George Darwin, son of Charles.

Eddington made contributions to the theory of star clusters and, more important, to the theory of the evolution of stars; the latter are contained in his book, *The Internal Constitution of the Stars* (1926). He was deeply interested in Einstein's theory of relativity, and besides doing research which helped to validate its predictions, he wrote several popular books explaining the theory to laymen. Among them is *Space, Time and Gravitation* (1920). His interest in the new theory had a broad base. He believed that many observed facts could be predicted by means of pure mathematical reasoning; that is, he felt that most of the fundamental constants of nature could be calculated without recourse to experiment, and he performed astounding feats of calculation to prove his point.

Relativity was grist for his mill; by means of it and other theories he even claimed to be able to calculate definitely the number of electrons in the universe. His claim has been considered by many later physicists to be overambitious. Eddington himself appeared to believe that in this and similar contentions he was merely carrying

[1] Vol. 8, pp. 227–261, in this set.

to their inevitable conclusions the fundamental assumptions of modern physics.

The Nature of the Physical World, a work of popular exposition that exerted wide intellectual influence, appeared in 1928. The following selection is a chapter from that work. Eddington died on November 22, 1944.

The second law of thermodynamics, as Eddington explains it, is simplicity itself: "Entropy always increases"—that is all there is to it. Entropy is "the practical measure of the random element which can increase in the universe but can never decrease." The law holds, Eddington says, "the supreme position among the laws of nature." As such, it is of great importance. But it is also fraught with grave consequences.

Entropy is "time's arrow"; it points in one direction—to the future—and in one direction only. It is the law of nature which puts "some sense into the world." That is, it is the bridge between the apparently cold, inhuman, mathematical world of the primary laws of physics, and the—perhaps again apparently—warm, disorderly and familiar world which we sense and in which we live.

Furthermore, Eddington points out, it must follow from the law that the farther back we go in time the more organized, the less shuffled (to use his metaphor), the world must have been. Such a process—whether we consider it backward or forward—cannot, he says, be conceived as going on infinitely. The universe must have had a beginning, then, and must be expected to have an end. The law demands both.

This conclusion does not mean that Eddington is here disputing the claim that science can tell us nothing about the end and the beginning—"the first and the last catastrophe." Whether the world was created in the first place, and whether it will rejuvenate itself in the last, are, Eddington says, from the strictly scientific point of view questions susceptible only to "pure speculation."

Notes from the artist: "Behind the seated portrait of Eddington is an abstract interpretation of Eddington's prediction of the eventual gradual disintegration of the entire universe. The quotation is from The Nature of the Physical World.*"*

Verily, it is easier for a camel to pass through the eye of a needle than for a scientific man to pass through a door

Arthur Stanley Eddington

On the question whether the universe is running down once and for all, "science is silent," Eddington says, "and all that one can say is prejudice." He is willing, in his last paragraph, to be prejudiced—but toward a view which many people would call pessimistic. He is opposed to the assumption of "a never-ending cycle of rebirth of matter and worlds." "I am an Evolutionist," he says, "not a Multiplicationist."

The Running–Down
of the Universe

The modern outlook on the physical world is not composed exclusively of conceptions which have arisen in the last twenty-five years; and we have now to deal with a group of ideas dating far back in the last century which have not essentially altered since the time of Boltzmann. These ideas display great activity and development at the present time. The subject is relevant at this stage because it has a bearing on the deeper aspects of the problem of time; but it is so fundamental in physical theory that we should be bound to deal with it sooner or later in any comprehensive survey.

If you take a pack of cards as it comes from the maker and shuffle it for a few minutes, all trace of the original systematic order disappears. The order will never come back however long you shuffle. Something has been done which cannot be undone, namely, the introduction of a random element in place of arrangement.

Illustrations may be useful even when imperfect, and therefore I have slurred over two points which affect the illustration rather than the application which we are about to make. It was scarcely true to say that the shuffling cannot be undone. *You* can sort out the cards into their original order if you like. But in considering the shuffling which occurs in the physical world we are not troubled by a *deus ex machina* like you. I am not prepared to say how far the human mind is bound by the conclusions we shall reach. So I exclude you—at least I exclude that activity of your mind which you employ in sorting the cards. I allow you to shuffle them because you can do that *absent-mindedly*.

Secondly, it is not quite true that the original order never comes back. There is a ghost of a chance that some day a thoroughly shuffled pack will be found to have come back to the original order. That is because of the comparatively small number of cards in the pack. In our applica-

tions the units are so numerous that this kind of contingency can be disregarded.

We shall put forward the contention that—

Whenever anything happens which cannot be undone, it is always reducible to the introduction of a random element analogous to that introduced by shuffling.

Shuffling is the only thing which nature cannot undo.

When Humpty Dumpty had a great fall—

All the king's horses and all the king's men
Cannot put Humpty Dumpty together again.

Something had happened which could not be undone. The fall could have been undone. It is not necessary to invoke the king's horses and the king's men; if there had been a perfectly elastic mat underneath, that would have sufficed. At the end of his fall Humpty Dumpty had kinetic energy which, properly directed, was just sufficient to bounce him back on to the wall again. But, the elastic mat being absent, an irrevocable event happened at the end of the fall—namely, the introduction of a *random element* into Humpty Dumpty.

But why should we suppose that shuffling is the *only* process that cannot be undone?

The Moving Finger writes; and, having writ,
Moves on: nor all thy Piety and Wit
Shall lure it back to cancel half a Line.

When there is no shuffling, is the Moving Finger stayed? The answer of physics is unhesitatingly Yes. To judge of this we must examine those operations of nature in which no increase of the random element can possibly occur. These fall into two groups. Firstly, we can study those laws of nature which control the behaviour of a single unit. Clearly no shuffling can occur in these problems; you cannot take the King of Spades away from the pack and shuffle him. Secondly, we can study the processes of nature in a crowd which is already so completely shuffled that there is no room for any further increase of the random element. If our contention is right, everything that occurs in these conditions is capable of being undone. We shall consider the first condition immediately; the second must be deferred until p. 575.

Any change occurring to a body which can be treated as a single unit can be undone. The laws of nature admit of the undoing as easily as of the doing. The earth describing its orbit is controlled by laws of motion

and of gravitation; these admit of the earth's actual motion, but they also admit of the precisely opposite motion. In the same field of force the earth could retrace its steps; it merely depends on how it was started off. It may be objected that we have no right to dismiss the starting-off as an inessential part of the problem; it may be as much a part of the coherent scheme of nature as the laws controlling the subsequent motion. Indeed, astronomers have theories explaining why the eight planets all started to move the same way round the sun. But that is a problem of eight planets, not of a single individual—a problem of the pack, not of the isolated card. So long as the earth's motion is treated as an isolated problem, no one would dream of putting into the laws of nature a clause requiring that it must go *this* way round and not the opposite.

There is a similar reversibility of motion in fields of electric and magnetic force. Another illustration can be given from atomic physics. The quantum laws admit of the emission of certain kinds and quantities of light from an atom; these laws also admit of absorption of the same kinds and quantities, *i.e.*, the undoing of the emission. I apologize for an apparent poverty of illustration; it must be remembered that many properties of a body, *e.g.*, temperature, refer to its constitution as a large number of separate atoms, and therefore the laws controlling temperature cannot be regarded as controlling the behaviour of a single individual.

The common property possessed by laws governing the individual can be stated more clearly by a reference to time. A certain sequence of states running from past to future is the *doing* of an event; the same sequence running from future to past is the *undoing* of it—because in the latter case we turn round the sequence so as to view it in the accustomed manner from past to future. So if the laws of nature are indifferent as to the doing and undoing of an event, they must be indifferent as to a direction of time from past to future. That is their common feature, and it is seen at once when (as usual) the laws are formulated mathematically. There is no more distinction between past and future than between right and left. In algebraic symbolism, left is $-x$, right is $+x$; past is $-t$, future is $+t$. This holds for all laws of nature governing the behaviour of non-composite individuals—the "primary laws," as we shall call them. There is only one law of nature—the second law of thermodynamics—which recognizes a distinction between past and future more profound than the difference of plus and minus. It stands aloof from all the rest. But this law has no application to the behaviour

of a single individual, and as we shall see later its subject matter is the random element in a crowd.

Whatever the primary laws of physics may say, it is obvious to ordinary experience that there is a distinction between past and future of a different kind from the distinction of left and right. In *The Plattner Story* H. G. Wells relates how a man strayed into the fourth dimension and returned with left and right interchanged. But we notice that this interchange is not the theme of the story; it is merely a corroborative detail to give an air of verisimilitude to the adventure. In itself the change is so trivial that even Mr. Wells cannot weave a romance out of it. But if the man had come back with past and future interchanged, then indeed the situation would have been lively. Mr. Wells in *The Time-Machine* and Lewis Carroll in *Sylvie and Bruno* give us a glimpse of the absurdities which occur when time runs backwards. If space is "looking-glassed" the world continues to make sense; but looking-glassed time has an inherent absurdity which turns the world drama into the most nonsensical farce.

Now the primary laws of physics taken one by one all declare that they are entirely indifferent as to which way you consider time to be progressing, just as they are indifferent as to whether you view the world from the right or the left. This is true of the classical laws, the relativity laws, and even of the quantum laws. It is not an accidental property; the reversibility is inherent in the whole conceptual scheme in which these laws find a place. Thus the question whether the world does or does not "make sense" is outside the range of these laws. We have to appeal to the one outstanding law—the second law of thermodynamics—to put some sense into the world. It opens up a new province of knowledge, namely, the study of organization; and it is in connection with organization that a direction of time-flow and a distinction between doing and undoing appears for the first time.

Time's Arrow. The great thing about time is that it goes on. But this is an aspect of it which the physicist sometimes seems inclined to neglect. In the four-dimensional world considered [previously] the events past and future lie spread out before us as in a map. The events are there in their proper spatial and temporal relation; but there is no indication that they undergo what has been described as "the formality of taking place," and the question of their doing or undoing does not arise. We see in the map the path from past to future or from future to past; but there is no signboard to indicate that it is a one-way street. Something must be added to the geometrical conceptions comprised in Minkowski's world before it becomes a complete picture of the world as we know it. We

may appeal to consciousness to suffuse the whole—to turn *existence* into *happening, being* into *becoming*. But first let us note that the picture as it stands is entirely adequate to represent those primary laws of nature which, as we have seen, are indifferent to a direction of time. Objection has sometimes been felt to the relativity theory because its four-dimensional picture of the world seems to overlook the directed character of time. The objection is scarcely logical, for the theory is in this respect no better and no worse than its predecessors. The classical physicist has been using without misgiving a system of laws which do not recognize a directed time; he is shocked that the new picture should expose this so glaringly.

Without any mystic appeal to consciousness it is possible to find a direction of time on the four-dimensional map by a study of organization. Let us draw an arrow arbitrarily. If as we follow the arrow we find more and more of the random element in the state of the world, then the arrow is pointing towards the future; if the random element decreases the arrow points towards the past. That is the only distinction known to physics. This follows at once if our fundamental contention is admitted that the introduction of randomness is the only thing which cannot be undone.

I shall use the phrase "time's arrow" to express this one-way property of time which has no analogue in space. It is a singularly interesting property from a philosophical standpoint. We must note that—

(1) It is vividly recognized by consciousness.

(2) It is equally insisted on by our reasoning faculty, which tells us that a reversal of the arrow would render the external world nonsensical.

(3) It makes no appearance in physical science except in the study of organization of a number of individuals. Here the arrow indicates the direction of progressive increase of the random element.

Let us now consider in detail how a random element brings the irrevocable into the world. When a stone falls it acquires kinetic energy, and the amount of the energy is just that which would be required to lift the stone back to its original height. By suitable arrangements the kinetic energy can be made to perform this task; for example, if the stone is tied to a string it can alternately fall and reascend like a pendulum. But if the stone hits an obstacle its kinetic energy is converted into heat energy. There is still the same quantity of energy, but even if we could scrape it together and put it through an engine we could not lift the stone back with it. What has happened to make the energy no longer serviceable?

Looking microscopically at the falling stone we see an enormous multi-

tude of molecules moving downwards with equal and parallel velocities —an organized motion like the march of a regiment. We have to notice two things, the *energy* and the *organization of the energy.* To return to its original height the stone must preserve both of them.

When the stone falls on a sufficiently elastic surface the motion may be reversed without destroying the organization. Each molecule is turned backwards and the whole array retires in good order to the starting-point—

> The famous Duke of York
> With twenty thousand men,
> He marched them up to the top of the hill
> And marched them down again.

History is not made that way. But what usually happens at the impact is that the molecules suffer more or less random collisions and rebound in all directions. They no longer conspire to make progress in any one direction; they have lost their organization. Afterwards they continue to collide with one another and keep changing their directions of motion, but they never again find a common purpose. Organization cannot be brought about by continued shuffling. And so, although the energy remains quantitatively sufficient (apart from unavoidable leakage which we suppose made good), it cannot lift the stone back. To restore the stone we must supply extraneous energy which has the required amount of organization.

Here a point arises which unfortunately has no analogy in the shuffling of a pack of cards. No one (except a conjurer) can throw two half-shuffled packs into a hat and draw out one pack in its original order and one pack fully shuffled. But we can and do put partly disorganized energy into a steam-engine, and draw it out again partly as fully organized energy of motion of massive bodies and partly as heat-energy in a state of still worse disorganization. Organization of energy is negotiable, and so is the disorganization or random element; disorganization does not for ever remain attached to the particular store of energy which first suffered it, but may be passed on elsewhere. We cannot here enter into the question why there should be a difference between the shuffling of energy and the shuffling of material objects; but it is necessary to use some caution in applying the analogy on account of this difference. As regards heat energy the temperature is the measure of its degree of organization; the lower the temperature, the greater the disorganization.

Coincidences. There are such things as chance coincidences; that is to

say, chance can deceive us by bringing about conditions which look very unlike chance. In particular chance might imitate organization, whereas we have taken organization to be the antithesis of chance or, as we have called it, the "random element." This threat to our conclusions is, however, not very serious. *There is safety in numbers.*

Suppose that you have a vessel divided by a partition into two halves, one compartment containing air and the other empty. You withdraw the partition. For the moment all the molecules of air are in one half of the vessel; a fraction of a second later they are spread over the whole vessel and remain so ever afterwards. The molecules will not return to one half of the vessel; the spreading cannot be undone—unless other material is introduced into the problem to serve as a scapegoat for the disorganization and carry off the random element elsewhere. This occurrence can serve as a criterion to distinguish past and future time. If you observe first the molecules spread through the vessel and (as it seems to you) an instant later the molecules all in one half of it—then your consciousness is going backwards, and you had better consult a doctor.

Now each molecule is wandering round the vessel with no preference for one part rather than the other. On the average it spends half its time in one compartment and half in the other. There is a faint possibility that at one moment all the molecules might in this way happen to be visiting the one half of the vessel. You will easily calculate that if n is the number of molecules (roughly a quadrillion) the chance of this happening is $(\frac{1}{2})^n$. The reason why we ignore this chance may be seen by a rather classical illustration. If I let my fingers wander idly over the keys of a typewriter it *might* happen that my screed made an intelligible sentence. If an army of monkeys were strumming on typewriters they *might* write all the books in the British Museum. The chance of their doing so is decidedly more favourable than the chance of the molecules returning to one half of the vessel.

When numbers are large, chance is the best warrant for certainty. Happily in the study of molecules and energy and radiation in bulk we have to deal with a vast population, and we reach a certainty which does not always reward the expectations of those who court the fickle goddess.

In one sense the chance of the molecules returning to one half of the vessel is too absurdly small to think about. Yet in science we think about it a great deal, because it gives a measure of the irrevocable mischief we did when we casually removed the partition. Even if we had good reasons for wanting the gas to fill the vessel there was no need to waste

the organization; as we have mentioned, it is negotiable and might have been passed on somewhere where it was useful.[1] When the gas was released and began to spread across the vessel, say from left to right, there was no immediate increase of the random element. In order to spread from left to right, left-to-right velocities of the molecules must have preponderated, that is to say the motion was partly organized. Organization of position was replaced by organization of motion. A moment later the molecules struck the farther wall of the vessel and the random element began to increase. But, before it was destroyed, the left-to-right organization of molecular velocities was the exact numerical equivalent of the lost organization in space. By that we mean that the chance against the left-to-right preponderance of velocity occurring by accident is the same as the chance against segregation in one half of the vessel occurring by accident.

The adverse chance here mentioned is a preposterous number which (written in the usual decimal notation) would fill all the books in the world many times over. We are not interested in it as a practical contingency; but we are interested in the fact that it is definite. It raises "organization" from a vague descriptive epithet to one of the measurable quantities of exact science. We are confronted with many kinds of organization. The uniform march of a regiment is not the only form of organized motion; the organized evolutions of a stage chorus have their natural analogue in sound waves. A common measure can now be applied to all forms of organization. Any loss of organization is equitably measured by the chance against its recovery by an accidental coincidence. The chance is absurd regarded as a contingency, but it is precise as a measure.

The practical measure of the random element which can increase in the universe but can never decrease is called *entropy*. Measuring by entropy is the same as measuring by the chance explained in the last paragraph, only the unmanageably large numbers are transformed (by a simple formula) into a more convenient scale of reckoning. Entropy continually increases. We can, by isolating parts of the world and postulating rather idealized conditions in our problems, arrest the increase, but we cannot turn it into a decrease. That would involve something much worse than a violation of an ordinary law of nature, namely, an improbable coincidence. The law that entropy always increases—the second law of thermodynamics—holds, I think, the supreme position among

1. If the gas in expanding had been made to move a piston, the organization would have passed into the motion of the piston.

the laws of nature. If someone points out to you that your pet theory of the universe is in disagreement with Maxwell's equations—then so much the worse for Maxwell's equations. If it is found to be contradicted by observation—well, these experimentalists do bungle things sometimes. But if your theory is found to be against the second law of thermodynamics I can give you no hope; there is nothing for it but to collapse in deepest humiliation. This exaltation of the second law is not unreasonable. There are other laws which we have strong reason to believe in, and we feel that a hypothesis which violates them is highly improbable; but the improbability is vague and does not confront us as a paralysing array of figures, whereas the chance against a breach of the second law (*i.e.*, against a decrease of the random element) can be stated in figures which are overwhelming.

I wish I could convey to you the amazing power of this conception of entropy in scientific research. From the property that entropy must always increase, practical methods of measuring it have been found. The chain of deductions from this simple law have been almost illimitable; and it has been equally successful in connection with the most recondite problems of theoretical physics and the practical tasks of the engineer. Its special feature is that the conclusions are independent of the nature of the microscopical processes that are going on. It is not concerned with the nature of the individual; it is interested in him only as a component of a crowd. Therefore the method is applicable in fields of research where our ignorance has scarcely begun to lift, and we have no hesitation in applying it to problems of the quantum theory, although the mechanism of the individual quantum process is unknown and at present unimaginable.

Primary and Secondary Law. I have called the laws controlling the behaviour of single individuals "primary laws," implying that the second law of thermodynamics, although a recognized law of nature, is in some sense a secondary law. This distinction can now be placed on a regular footing. Some things never happen in the physical world because they are *impossible*; others because they are *too improbable*. The laws which forbid the first are the primary laws; the laws which forbid the second are the secondary laws. It has been the conviction of nearly all physicists [2] that at the root of everything there is a complete scheme of primary law governing the career of every particle or constituent of the world with an iron determinism. This primary scheme is all-sufficing, for,

2. There are, however, others beside myself who have recently begun to question it.

since it fixes the history of every constituent of the world, it fixes the whole world history.

But for all its completeness primary law does not answer every question about nature which we might reasonably wish to put. Can a universe evolve backwards, *i.e.*, develop in the opposite way to our own system? Primary law, being indifferent to a time direction, replies, "Yes, it is not impossible." Secondary law replies, "No, it is too improbable." The answers are not really in conflict; but the first, though true, rather misses the point. This is typical of some much more commonplace queries. If I put *this* saucepan of water on *this* fire, will the water boil? Primary law can answer definitely if it is given the chance; but it must be understood that "this" translated into mathematics means a specification of the positions, motions, etc., of some quadrillions of particles and elements of energy. So in practice the question answered is not quite the one that is asked: If I put *a* saucepan resembling this one in a few major respects on *a* fire, will the water boil? Primary law replies, "It may boil; it may freeze; it may do pretty well anything. The details given are insufficient to exclude any result as impossible." Secondary law replies plainly, "It will boil because it is too improbable that it should do anything else." Secondary law is not in conflict with primary law, nor can we regard it as essential to complete a scheme of law already complete in itself. It results from a different (and rather more practical) conception of the aim of our traffic with the secrets of nature.

The question whether the second law of thermodynamics and other statistical laws are mathematical deductions from the primary laws, presenting their results in a conveniently usable form, is difficult to answer; but I think it is generally considered that there is an unbridgeable hiatus. At the bottom of all the questions settled by secondary law there is an elusive conception of "*a priori* probability of states of the world" which involves an essentially different attitude to knowledge from that presupposed in the construction of the scheme of primary law.

Thermodynamical Equilibrium. Progress of time introduces more and more of the random element into the constitution of the world. There is less of chance about the physical universe to-day than there will be tomorrow. It is curious that in this very matter-of-fact branch of physics, developed primarily because of its importance for engineers, we can scarcely avoid expressing ourselves in teleological language. We admit that the world contains both chance and design, or at any rate chance and the antithesis of chance. This antithesis is emphasized by our method of measurement of entropy; we assign to the organization or non-

chance element a measure which is, so to speak, proportional to the strength of our disbelief in a chance origin for it. "A fortuitous concourse of atoms"—that bugbear of the theologian—has a very harmless place in orthodox physics. The physicist is acquainted with it *as a much-prized rarity*. Its properties are very distinctive, and unlike those of the physical world in general. The scientific name for a fortuitous concourse of atoms is "thermodynamical equilibrium."

Thermodynamical equilibrium is the other case which we promised to consider in which no increase in the random element can occur, namely, that in which the shuffling is already as thorough as possible. We must isolate a region of the universe, arranging that no energy can enter or leave it, or at least that any boundary effects are precisely compensated. The conditions are ideal, but they can be reproduced with sufficient approximation to make the ideal problem relevant to practical experiment. A region in the deep interior of a star is an almost perfect example of thermodynamical equilibrium. Under these isolated conditions the energy will be shuffled as it is bandied from matter to ether and back again, and very soon the shuffling will be complete.

The possibility of the shuffling becoming complete is significant. If after shuffling the pack you tear each card in two, a further shuffling of the half-cards becomes possible. Tear the cards again and again; each time there is further scope for the random element to increase. With infinite divisibility there can be no end to the shuffling. The experimental fact that a definite state of equilibrium is rapidly reached indicates that energy is not infinitely divisible, or at least that it is not infinitely divided in the natural processes of shuffling. Historically this is the result from which the quantum theory first arose. . . .

In such a region we lose time's arrow. You remember that the arrow points in the direction of increase of the random element. When the random element has reached its limit and become steady the arrow does not know which way to point. It would not be true to say that such a region is timeless; the atoms vibrate as usual like little clocks; by them we can measure speeds and durations. Time is still there and retains its ordinary properties, but it has lost its arrow; like space it extends, but it does not "go on."

This raises the important question, Is the random element (measured by the criterion of probability already discussed) the only feature of the physical world which can furnish time with an arrow? Up to the present we have concluded that no arrow can be found from the behaviour of isolated individuals, but there is scope for further search among the

properties of crowds beyond the property represented by entropy. To give an illustration which is perhaps not quite so fantastic as it sounds, Might not the assemblage become more and more *beautiful* (according to some agreed aesthetic standard) as time proceeds? [3] The question is answered by another important law of nature which runs—

> Nothing in the statistics of an assemblage can distinguish a direction of time when entropy fails to distinguish one.

I think that although this law was only discovered in the last few years there is no serious doubt as to its truth. It is accepted as fundamental in all modern studies of atoms and radiation and has proved to be one of the most powerful weapons of progress in such researches. It is, of course, one of the secondary laws. It does not seem to be rigorously deducible from the second law of thermodynamics, and presumably must be regarded as an additional secondary law.[4]

The conclusion is that whereas other statistical characters besides entropy might perhaps be used to discriminate time's arrow, they can only succeed when it succeeds and they fail when it fails. Therefore they cannot be regarded as independent tests. So far as physics is concerned time's arrow is a property of entropy alone.

Are Space and Time Infinite? I suppose that everyone has at some time plagued his imagination with the question, Is there an end to space? If space comes to an end, what is beyond the end? On the other hand the idea that there is no end, but space beyond space for ever, is inconceivable. And so the imagination is tossed to and fro in a dilemma. Prior to the relativity theory the orthodox view was that space is infinite. No one can conceive infinite space; we had to be content to admit in the physical world an inconceivable conception—disquieting but not necessarily illogical. Einstein's theory now offers a way out of the dilemma. Is space infinite, or does it come to an end? Neither. Space is finite but it has no end; "finite but unbounded" is the usual phrase.

3. In a kaleidoscope the shuffling is soon complete and all the patterns are equal as regards random element, but they differ greatly in elegance.
4. The law is so much disguised in the above enunciation that I must explain to the advanced reader that I am referring to "the Principle of Detailed Balancing." This principle asserts that to every type of process (however minutely particularized) there is a converse process, and in thermodynamical equilibrium direct and converse processes occur with equal frequency. Thus every statistical enumeration of the processes is unaltered by reversing the time direction, *i.e.*, interchanging direct and converse processes. Hence there can be no statistical criterion for a direction of time when there is thermodynamical equilibrium, *i.e.* when entropy is steady and ceases to indicate time's arrow.

Infinite space cannot be conceived by anybody; finite but unbounded space is difficult to conceive but not impossible. I shall not expect you to conceive it; but you can try. Think first of a circle; or, rather, not the circle, but the line forming its circumference. This is a finite but endless line. Next think of a sphere—the surface of a sphere—that also is a region which is finite but unbounded. The surface of this earth never comes to a boundary; there is always some country beyond the point you have reached; all the same there is not an infinite amount of room on the earth. Now go one dimension more; circle, sphere—the next thing. Got that? Now for the real difficulty. Keep a tight hold of the skin of this hypersphere and imagine that the inside is not there at all—that the skin exists without the inside. That is finite but unbounded space.

No; I don't think you have quite kept hold of the conception. You overbalanced just at the end. It was not the adding of one more dimension that was the real difficulty; it was the final taking away of a dimension that did it. I will tell you what is stopping you. You are using a conception of space which must have originated many million years ago and has become rather firmly embedded in human thought. But the space of physics ought not to be dominated by this creation of the dawning mind of an enterprising ape. Space is not necessarily like this conception; it is like—whatever we find from experiment it is like. Now the features of space which we discover by experiment are extensions, *i.e.*, lengths and distances. So space is *like* a network of distances. Distances are linkages whose intrinsic nature is inscrutable; we do not deny the inscrutability when we apply measure numbers to them—2 yards, 5 miles, etc.—as a kind of code distinction. We cannot predict out of our inner consciousness the laws by which code numbers are distributed among the different linkages of the network, any more than we can predict how the code numbers for electromagnetic force are distributed. Both are a matter for experiment.

If we go a very long way to a point A in one direction through the universe and a very long way to a point B in the opposite direction, it is believed that between A and B there exists a linkage of the kind indicated by a very small code number; in other words these points reached by travelling vast distances in opposite directions would be found experimentally to be close together. Why not? This happens when we travel east and west on the earth. It is true that our traditional inflexible conception of space refuses to admit it; but there was once a traditional conception of the earth which refused to admit circumnavigation. In our approach to the conception of spherical space the difficult part was

to destroy the inside of the hypersphere leaving only its three-dimensional surface existing. I do not think that is so difficult when we conceive space as a network of distances. The network over the surface constitutes a self-supporting system of linkage which can be contemplated without reference to extraneous linkages. We can knock away the constructional scaffolding which helped us to approach the conception of this kind of network of distances without endangering the conception.

We must realize that a scheme of distribution of inscrutable relations linking points to one another is not bound to follow any particular preconceived plan, so that there can be no obstacle to the acceptance of any scheme indicated by experiment.

We do not yet know what is the radius of spherical space; it must, of course, be exceedingly great compared with ordinary standards. On rather insecure evidence it has been estimated to be not many times greater than the distance of the furthest known nebulae. But the boundlessness has nothing to do with the bigness. Space is boundless by re-entrant form not by great extension. *That which is* is a shell floating in the infinitude of *that which is not.* We say with Hamlet, "I could be bounded in a nutshell and count myself a king of infinite space."

But the nightmare of infinity still arises in regard to time. The world is closed in its space dimensions like a sphere, but it is open at both ends in the time dimension. There is a bending round by which East ultimately becomes West, but no bending by which Before ultimately becomes After.

I am not sure that I am logical but I cannot feel the difficulty of an infinite future time very seriously. The difficulty about A.D. ∞ will not happen until we reach A.D. ∞, and presumably in order to reach A.D. ∞ the difficulty must first have been surmounted. It should also be noted that according to the second law of thermodynamics the whole universe will reach thermodynamical equilibrium at a not infinitely remote date in the future. Time's arrow will then be lost altogether and the whole conception of progress towards a future fades away.

But the difficulty of an infinite past is appalling. It is inconceivable that we are the heirs of an infinite time of preparation; it is not less inconceivable that there was once a moment with no moment preceding it.

This dilemma of the beginning of time would worry us more were it not shut out by another overwhelming difficulty lying between us and the infinite past. We have been studying the running-down of the universe; if our views are right, somewhere between the beginning of time and the present day we must place the winding up of the universe.

Travelling backwards into the past we find a world with more and more organization. If there is no barrier to stop us earlier we must reach a moment when the energy of the world was wholly organized with none of the random element in it. It is impossible to go back any further under the present system of natural law. I do not think the phrase "wholly organized" begs the question. The organization we are concerned with is exactly definable, and there is a limit at which it becomes perfect. There is not an infinite series of states of higher and still higher organization; nor, I think, is the limit one which is ultimately approached more and more slowly. Complete organization does not tend to be more immune from loss than incomplete organization.

There is no doubt that the scheme of physics as it has stood for the last three-quarters of a century postulates a date at which either the entities of the universe were created in a state of high organization, or pre-existing entities were endowed with that organization which they have been squandering ever since. Moreover, this organization is admittedly the antithesis of chance. It is something which could not occur fortuitously.

This has long been used as an argument against a too aggressive materialism. It has been quoted as scientific proof of the intervention of the Creator at a time not infinitely remote from to-day. But I am not advocating that we draw any hasty conclusions from it. Scientists and theologians alike must regard as somewhat crude the naïve theological doctrine which (suitably disguised) is at present to be found in every textbook of thermodynamics, namely that some billions of years ago God wound up the material universe and has left it to chance ever since. This should be regarded as the working hypothesis of thermodynamics rather than its declaration of faith. It is one of those conclusions from which we can see no logical escape—only it suffers from the drawback that it is incredible. As a scientist I simply do not believe that the present order of things started off with a bang; unscientifically I feel equally unwilling to accept the implied discontinuity in the divine nature. But I can make no suggestion to evade the deadlock.

Turning again to the other end of time, there is one school of thought which finds very repugnant the idea of a wearing out of the world. This school is attracted by various theories of rejuvenescence. Its mascot is the Phoenix. Stars grow cold and die out. May not two dead stars collide, and be turned by the energy of the shock into fiery vapour from which a new sun—with planets and with life—is born? This theory, very prevalent in the last century, is no longer contemplated

seriously by astronomers. There is evidence that the present stars at any rate are products of one evolutionary process which swept across primordial matter and caused it to aggregate; they were not formed individually by haphazard collisions having no particular time connection with one another. But the Phoenix complex is still active. Matter, we believe, is gradually destroyed and its energy set free in radiation. Is there no counter-process by which radiation collects in space, evolves into electrons and protons, and begins star-building all over again? This is pure speculation and there is not much to be said on one side or the other as to its truth. But I would mildly criticize the mental outlook which *wishes* it to be true. However much we eliminate the minor extravagances of nature, we do not by these theories stop the inexorable running-down of the world by loss of organization and increase of the random element. Whoever wishes for a universe which can continue indefinitely in activity must lead a crusade against the second law of thermodynamics; the possibility of re-formation of matter from radiation is not crucial and we can await conclusions with some indifference.

At present we can see no way in which an attack on the second law of thermodynamics could possibly succeed, and I confess that personally I have no great desire that it should succeed in averting the final running-down of the universe. I am no Phoenix worshipper. This is a topic on which science is silent, and all that one can say is prejudice. But since prejudice in favour of a never-ending cycle of rebirth of matter and worlds is often vocal, I may perhaps give voice to the opposite prejudice. I would feel more content that the universe should accomplish some great scheme of evolution and, having achieved whatever may be achieved, lapse back into chaotic changelessness, than that its purpose should be banalised by continual repetition. I am an Evolutionist, not a Multiplicationist. It seems rather stupid to keep doing the same thing over and over again.

The foregoing consists of Chapter IV
from Eddington's THE NATURE OF THE PHYSICAL WORLD.

Sir James Jeans

1877–1946

James Hopwood Jeans was born in London on September 11, 1877. He studied at Cambridge; he was second wrangler in 1898. The reader of Galton's *Hereditary Genius* [1] will realize that the last fact not only meant that Jeans had extraordinary intellectual gifts but that his career in the academic world was practically assured. Jeans became a lecturer in applied mathematics at Cambridge, was later a professor of the same subject at Princeton University, in New Jersey, and still later a professor of astronomy at the Royal Institution. His early studies were in the area of energy and radiation, but he made elegant contributions to astronomical theory, and it is as an astronomer that he is best known. He constructed mathematical models of the actions and interactions of astronomical bodies; in the course of this work he proved that Laplace's theory of the origin of the solar system was impossible.

Jeans conceived several original cosmogonies—theories, that is, of how the universe came into existence. And he wrote a number of widely read books for the laymen on this and other aspects of science and astronomy. Among these the best known is perhaps *The Universe Around Us*, which appeared in 1929, and from which the following selection is taken. We reprint here the last chapter of the book. Jeans was knighted in 1928 and was awarded the Order of Merit in 1939. He died on September 17, 1946.

The reader who compares the foregoing biographical note with that of A. S. Eddington [2] will not fail to see the very many similarities

[1] See Vol. 8, pp. 227–261, in this set.
[2] See Vol. 8, pp. 561–564, in this set.

between the two men. Jeans was five years older; he was second rather than senior wrangler; and he died two years later. But both men won the Smith Prize at Cambridge, a great honor; both were Cambridge teachers; both were astronomers; both were knighted; both were O.M.'s; and both were successful scientific popularizers. More significantly for our purposes, perhaps, is that both, in the selections which appear in these volumes, concern themselves with the beginning and end of the universe. And it is notable that in some respects they have the same things to say.

For example, in such a discussion it is now customary to mention entropy and the second law of thermodynamics, and both men do so. As to the question whether the universe will rejuvenate itself after its inevitable running down, both seem to agree that rebirth is not desirable, even if it is possible. And both emphasize the vastness of the time, space and radiation scales by which astronomers measure the world in which we live. But at this point an important difference may seem to appear between them.

Where Eddington refuses to speculate, or does so unwillingly, Jeans leaps in. His qualifications for doing so should not be questioned. He was a great mathematical astronomer, and he probably knew as much about the fate of the universe as anybody. But he is in the following selection not speaking of that fate from a strictly mathematical point of view. What strikes him about the immense amount of time that stretches before the earth is the opportunities it affords for the amelioration of man's condition. "Looked at in terms of time," he writes, "the message of astronomy . . . becomes one of almost endless possibility and hope." Eddington had apparently seen no such thing, in a book written only a year before. There is about Eddington's statements a kind of stoic resignation. Jeans is not resigned at all. "We have come into being in the fresh glory of the dawn," he says, "and a day of almost unthinkable length stretches before us with unimaginable opportunities for accomplish-

Notes from the artist: "*A modern technique, resembling that of the painter Miro, was used for the portrait of Jeans because of the very contemporary style of Jeans's own writings, which combined profundity with a colorful, popular style. The quotation is from* The Mysterious Universe."

if the universe is a universe of thought, then its creation must
have been an act of thought......Time and space must have come
into being as part of this act........ modern scientific
theory compels us to think of the Creator as working
outside time and space, which are part of his
creation, just as the artist is outside his canvas.

ment." All the problems of living will be possible of solution in this vast time, he seems to be implying, and life will have a meaning and, one supposes, a beauty that are practically inconceivable to the "dim heroic figures" of today.

It should be noted that Jeans, though he is by comparison with Eddington of a highly optimistic temperament, is not entirely optimistic. "We may perhaps be glad," he writes, "that our lives have fallen in the beginning, rather than at the end, of this great stretch of time. We may well imagine that if man survives to the end of it, he will have infinitely more knowledge than now, but one thing he will no longer know—the thrill of pleasure of the pioneer who opens up new realms of knowledge." For him, the thrill is in the pursuit of knowledge, not in its possession.

Beginnings and Endings

We have seen how the solid substance of the material universe is continually dissolving away into intangible radiation. Yesterday the sun weighed 360,000 million tons more than it does to-day, the difference being the weight of 24-hours' emission of radiation which is now travelling through space, and, so far as direct observation goes, is destined to journey on through space until the end of time. Less than a gramme of this radiation contains enough energy to take a liner across the Atlantic, while a pound of it would suffice to keep the whole British nation going for a fortnight—domestic fires, power stations, factories, trains, ships and all. The same transformation of material substance into radiation is in progress in all the stars, and to a lesser degree on earth, while the cosmic radiation may be found to provide evidence that the transformation takes place on a far grander scale throughout the depths of interstellar space.

Cyclic Processes. It is natural to ask whether a study of the universe as a whole reveals these processes as part only of a closed cycle, so that the wastage which we see in progress in the sun and stars and on the earth is made good elsewhere. When we stand on the banks of a river and watch its current ever carrying water out to sea, we know that this water is in due course transformed into clouds and rain which replenish the river. Is the physical universe a similar cyclic system, or ought it rather to be compared to a stream which, having no source of replenishment, must cease flowing after it has spent itself?

THERMODYNAMICS

To this question, the wide scientific principle known as the second law of thermodynamics provides an answer in very general terms. If we ask what is the underlying cause of all the varied animation we see around us in the world, the answer is, in every case, energy—the chemical

energy of the fuel which drives our ships, trains and cars, or of the food which keeps our bodies alive and is used in muscular effort, the mechanical energy of the earth's motion which is responsible for the alternations of day and night, of summer and winter, of high tide and low tide, the heat energy of the sun which makes our crops grow and provides us with wind and rain.

The science of thermodynamics deals primarily with energy and the various changes which it can undergo. It is based fundamentally on two laws which are generally known as the first and second laws of thermodynamics. These deal respectively with the quantity and quality of energy.

First Law of Thermodynamics. The first law of thermodynamics, which embodies the principle of "conservation of energy," teaches that energy is indestructible; it may change about from one form to another, but its total amount remains unaltered through all these changes, so that the total energy of the universe remains always the same. As the energy which is the cause of all the life of the universe is indestructible, it might be thought that this life would go on for ever undiminished in amount.

Availability of Energy. The second law of thermodynamics shows that this is not so. Energy is indestructible as regards its amount, but it continually changes in form, and generally speaking we may compare the two directions of change to journeys uphill and downhill. And it is the usual story. The descent is easy; but to retrace the steps—this is so difficult that we rightly treat it as impossible and think of energy as passing only in the one direction.

Actually it is not impossible, for the second law does not deal in certainties, but only in probabilities—and these of a somewhat unusual kind. It is perfectly in accordance with the laws of mechanics that energy should change its quality in the direction just described as upwards. But the odds against such a change in the energy either of the universe as a whole, or of any considerable part of it, are immense. The number of particles in the universe is perhaps of the order of 10^{79}, and the odds against such an occurrence as we have just mentioned are found to involve very high powers of 10^{79}. When the odds are of this kind, we need not trouble to differentiate too closely between long odds and certainties.

For instance, both light and heat are forms of energy, and a million ergs of light-energy can be transformed into a million ergs of heat with the utmost ease; let the light fall on any cool, black surface, and the thing is done. But the odds against the reverse transformation are of the kind we have just described, so that we generally say that it is impossible;

a million ergs which have once assumed the form of heat can never again assume the form of a million ergs of light. This is a special example of the general principle that radiative energy tends always to change into a form of longer, not shorter, wave-length. In general, for instance, fluorescence increases the wave-length of the light; it changes blue light into green, yellow or red, but not red light into yellow, green or blue. Exceptions to the general principle are known, but they are of special type, admitting of special explanations, and do not affect the general principle.

It may be objected that the everyday act of lighting a fire disproves all this. Has not the sun's heat been stored up in the coal we burn, and cannot we produce light by burning coal? The answer is that the sun's radiation is a mixture of both light and heat, and indeed of radiation of all wave-lengths. What is stored up in the coal is primarily the sun's light and other radiation of still shorter wave-length. When we burn coal we get some light, but not as much as the sun originally put into the coal; we also get some heat, and this is more than the amount of heat which was originally put in. On balance, the net result of the whole transaction is that a certain amount of light has been transformed into a certain amount of heat.

All this shows that we must learn to think of energy, not only in terms of quantity, but also in terms of quality. Its total quantity remains always the same; this is the first law of thermodynamics. But its quality changes, and tends to change always in the same direction; this is the second law of thermodynamics. Turnstiles are set up between the different qualities of energy; the passage is easy in one direction, impossible in the other. A human crowd may contrive to find a way round without jumping over turnstiles, but in nature there is no way round; energy flows always in the same direction, as surely as water flows downhill.

Part of the downward path consists, as we have seen, of the transition from radiation of short wave-length into radiation of longer wave-length. In terms of quanta the transition is from a few quanta of high energy to a large number of quanta of low energy, the total amount of energy of course remaining unaltered. The downfall of the energy accordingly consists in the breaking of its quanta into smaller units. And when once the fall and breakage have taken place, it is as impossible to reconstitute the original large quanta as it was to put Humpty-Dumpty back on his wall.

Although this is the main part of the downward path, it is not the whole of it. Thermodynamics teaches that all the different forms of

energy have different degrees of "availability," and that the downward path is always from higher to lower availability.

And now we may return to the question with which we started the present chapter: "What is it that keeps the varied life of the universe going?" Our original answer "energy" is seen to be incomplete. Energy is no doubt essential, but the really complete answer is that it is the transformation of energy from a more available to a less available form; it is the running downhill of energy. To argue that the total energy of the universe cannot diminish, and therefore the universe must go on for ever, is like arguing that as a clock weight cannot diminish, the clock-hand must go round and round for ever.

THE FINAL END OF THE UNIVERSE

Energy cannot run downhill for ever, and, like the clock weight, it must touch bottom at last. And so the universe cannot go on for ever; sooner or later the time must come when its last erg of energy has reached the lowest rung on the ladder of descending availability, and at this moment the active life of the universe must cease. The energy is still there, but it has lost all capacity for change; it is as little able to work the universe as the water in a flat pond is able to turn a water-wheel. We are left with a dead, although possibly a warm, universe—a "heat-death."

Such is the teaching of modern thermodynamics. There is no reason for doubting or challenging it, and indeed it is so fully confirmed by the whole of our terrestrial experience, that it would be difficult to find any point at which it could be open to attack. It disposes at once of any possibility of a cyclic universe in which the events we see are as the pouring of river water into the sea, while events we do not see restore this water back to the river. The water of a river can go round and round in this way, just because it is not the whole of the universe; something extraneous to the river cycle keeps it continually in motion—namely, the heat of the sun. But the universe as a whole cannot so go round and round. Short of postulating some sort of action from outside the universe, whatever this may mean, the energy of the universe must continually lose availability; a universe in which the energy had no further availability to lose would be dead already. Change can occur only in the one direction, which leads to the heat-death. With universes as with mortals, the only possible life is progress to the grave.

Even the flow of the river to the sea, which we selected as an obvious instance of true cyclic motion, is seen to illustrate this, as soon as all the

relevant factors are taken into account. As the river pours seaward over its falls and cascades, the tumbling of its waters generates heat, which ultimately passes off into space in the form of heat radiation. But the energy which keeps the river pouring along comes ultimately from the sun in the form mainly of light; shut off the sun's radiation and the river will soon stop flowing. The river flows only by continually transforming light-energy into heat-energy, and as soon as the cooling sun ceases to supply energy of sufficiently high availability the flow must cease.

The same general principles may be applied to the astronomical universe. There is no question as to the way in which energy runs down here. It is first liberated in the hot interior of a star in the form of quanta of extremely short wave-length and excessively high energy. As this radiant energy struggles out to the star's surface, it continually adjusts itself, through repeated absorption and re-emission, to the temperature of that part of the star through which it is passing. As longer wave-lengths are associated with lower temperatures, the wave-length of the radiation is continually lengthened; a few energetic quanta are being transformed into numerous feeble quanta. Once these are free in space, they travel onward unchanged until they meet dust particles, stray atoms, free electrons, or some other form of interstellar matter. Except in the highly improbable event of this matter being at a higher temperature than the surfaces of the stars, these encounters still further increase the wave-length of the radiation, and the final result of innumerable encounters is radiation of very great wave-length; the quanta have increased enormously in numbers, but have paid for their increase by a corresponding decrease in individual strength. Thus the main physical process of the universe consists in the energy of exceedingly high availability which is bottled up in atomic and nuclear structures being transformed into heat-energy at the lowest level of availability.

Many, giving rein to their fancy, have speculated that this low-level heat-energy may in due course re-form itself into new electrons and protons. As the existing universe dissolves away into radiation, their imagination sees new heavens and a new earth coming into being out of the ashes of the old. Science can give no support to such fancies. She cannot, it is true, prove that the fanciful will not happen—she can only calculate the odds against it happening. And these prove to be so enormous that we may disregard altogether the possibility of its occurrence. Perhaps it is as well; it is hard to see what advantage could accrue from an eternal reiteration of the same theme, or even from endless variations of it.

The final state of the universe will be attained when all the material

mass which is capable of being transformed into radiation has been so transformed.

We have seen that matter is distributed in space at an average rate of something like 10^{-28} gramme per cubic centimetre. The transformation of a gramme of matter into radiation liberates 9×10^{20} ergs of energy, so that the transformation of 10^{-28} gramme of matter liberates 9×10^{-8} erg of energy. It follows that the complete transformation of all the substance of the existing universe would only fill space with energy at the rate of 9×10^{-8} erg per cubic centimetre. This would only raise the temperature of space from absolute zero to a temperature which is still well below that of liquid air; it would only raise the temperature of the earth's surface by about a tenth part of a degree Centigrade. The reason why the effect of annihilating a whole universe is so extraordinarily slight is of course that space is so extraordinarily empty of matter; trying to warm space by annihilating all the matter in it is like trying to warm Waterloo Station by burning a few specks of dust here and there inside it.

Such would be the final result of transforming the whole substance of the universe into radiation, but it is improbable that more than a small fraction of it can ever be transformed, so that the maximum result ever to be expected must be far below that just mentioned. As compared with any amount of radiation that is ever likely to be poured into it, the capacity of space is that of a bottomless pit.

Such is the final end of things to which, so far as present-day science can see, the material universe must inevitably come in some far-off age, unless the course of nature is changed in the meantime. It is a state of things in which life, as we know it on earth, could not possibly survive.

LIFE AND THE UNIVERSE

Let us now glance for a moment at the relation of life to this dying universe.

The old view that every point of light in the sky represented a possible home for life is quite foreign to modern astronomy. The stars have surface temperatures of anything from 1,650 degrees to 60,000 degrees or more and, as we have seen, are at far higher temperatures inside. A large part of the matter of the universe consists of stellar matter at a temperature of millions of degrees, its molecules being broken up into atoms, and the atoms broken up, partially or wholly, into their constituent parts. The rest consists, for the most part, of nebular gas or dust. Now the very con-

cept of life implies duration in time; there can be no life—or at least no life at all similar to that we know on earth—where atoms change their make-up millions of times a second and no pair of atoms can ever stay joined together. It also implies a certain mobility in space, and these two implications restrict life to the small range of physical conditions in which the liquid state is possible. Our survey of the universe has shown how small this range is in comparison with that exhibited by the universe as a whole. It is not to be found in the stars, nor in the nebulae out of which the stars are born. Indeed, probably only an infinitesimal fraction of the matter of the universe is in the liquid state.

Actually we know of no type of astronomical body in which the conditions can be favourable to life except planets like our own revolving round a sun. Even these may be too hot or too cold for life to obtain a footing. In the solar system, for instance, it is hard to imagine life existing on Mercury or Neptune since liquids boil on the former and freeze hard on the latter.

Even when all the requisite conditions are satisfied, will life come or will it not? We must probably discard the at one time widely accepted view that if once life had come into the universe in any way whatsoever, it would rapidly spread from planet to planet and from one planetary system to another until the whole universe teemed with life; space now seems too cold, and planetary systems too far apart. Our terrestrial life must in all probability have originated on the earth itself. What we should like to know is whether it originated as the result of some amazing accident or succession of coincidences, or whether it is the normal event for inanimate matter to produce life in due course, when the physical environment is suitable. We look to the biologist for the answer, which so far he has not been able to produce.

The astronomer might be able to give a partial answer if he could find evidence of life on some other planet, for we should then at least know that life had occurred more than once in the history of the universe, but so far no convincing evidence has been forthcoming. There is no definite evidence of life anywhere in the universe, except on our own planet.

Apart from the certain knowledge that life exists on earth, our only definite knowledge is that, at the best, life must be limited to a tiny fraction of the universe. Millions of millions of stars exist which support no life, which have never done so and never will do so. Of the planetary systems in the sky, many must be entirely lifeless, and in others life, if it exists at all, is probably limited to a few of the planets. The three

centuries and more which have elapsed since Giordano Bruno expressed his belief in an infinite number of worlds have changed our conception of the universe almost beyond description, but they have not brought us appreciably nearer to understanding the relation of life to the universe. We can still only guess as to the meaning of this life which, to all appearances, is so rare. Is it the final climax towards which the whole creation moves, for which the thousands of millions of years of transformation of matter in uninhabited stars and nebulae, and of waste of radiation in desert space, have been only an incredibly extravagant preparation? Or is it a mere accidental and possibly quite unimportant by-product of natural processes, which have some other and more stupendous end in view? Or, to glance at a still more modest line of thought, must we regard it as something of the nature of a disease, which affects matter when it has lost the high temperature with which most of the matter in the universe would at once destroy life? Or, throwing humility aside, shall we venture to imagine that it is the only reality, which creates, instead of being created by, the colossal masses of the stars and nebulae and the almost inconceivably long vistas of astronomical time?

Again it is not for the astronomer to select between these alternative guesses; his task is done when he has delivered the message of astronomy. Perhaps it is over rash for him even to formulate the questions this message suggests.

THE EARTH AND ITS FUTURE PROSPECTS

Let us leave these rather abstract speculations and come down to earth. We feel the solid earth under our feet, and the rays of the sun overhead. Somehow, but we know not how or why, life also is here; we ourselves are part of it. And it is natural to enquire what astronomy has to say as to its future prospects.

The earth, which started life as a hot mass of gas, has gradually cooled, until it has now about touched bottom, and has almost no heat beyond that which it receives from the sun. This just about balances the amount it radiates away into space, so that it would stay at its present temperature for ever if external conditions did not change, and any changes in its condition will be forced on it by changes occurring outside. These changes may be either gradual or catastrophic.

Of the gradual changes which are possible, the most obvious is a diminution in the light and heat received from the sun. We have seen that if the sun consisted of pure hydrogen, it could lose one part in 150 of its

whole mass through the transformation of hydrogen into helium. The energy thus set free would provide for radiation at the present rate through a period of 100,000 million years.

The sun does not consist of pure hydrogen, and has never done so, but a fair proportion of its present substance is probably hydrogen, and this ought to provide radiation for at least several thousands of millions of years, at the present rate. After all the available supplies of hydrogen are used up, the sun will, so far as we can guess, proceed to contract to the white dwarf state, probably to a condition resembling that of the faint companion of Sirius. The shrinkage of the sun to this state would transform our oceans into ice and our atmosphere into liquid air; it seems impossible that terrestrial life could survive. The vast museum of the sky must almost certainly contain examples of shrunken suns of this type, and some will have planets like our earth revolving round them. Whether these planets carry on them the frozen remains of a life which was once as active as our present life on earth we can hardly even surmise.

Such at least would be the normal course of events, the tragedy we have described happening after a time of the order of perhaps 10,000 millions of years. But a variety of accidents may intervene to bring the human race to an end long before any such interval has elapsed. To mention only possible astronomical occurrences, the sun may run into another star, any asteroid may hit any other asteroid and, as a result, be so deflected from its path as to strike the earth, any of the stars in space may wander into the solar system and, in so doing, upset all the planetary orbits to such an extent that the earth becomes impossible as an abode of life. It is difficult to estimate the likelihood of any of these events happening, but rough calculations suggest that none of them is at all likely to happen within the next 10,000 million years or so.

A more serious possibility is that the sun's light and heat may increase so much as to shrivel up all terrestrial life. We have seen how "novae" occasionally appear in the sky, temporarily emitting anything up to 25,000 times the radiation of the sun. It seems fairly certain that if our sun were suddenly to become a nova, its emission of light and heat would so increase as to scorch all life off the earth, but we are completely in the dark as to whether our sun runs any risk of entering the nova stage. If it does, this is probably the greatest of all the risks to which life on earth is exposed.

Many a nova has been proved to be an ordinary star which was visible as a very faint star long before it appeared as a nova, flashed into brilliance for a brief span of life, and then lapsed back into commonplace-

ness, and it seems reasonable to suppose that all novae are of this kind, although the star may often escape detection until it assumes its brilliant nova state. These apparitions are by no means rare; something like six are noticed every year in the galactic system alone. Let us suppose that a further six occur unnoticed. Then, if the galactic system contains about 300,000 million stars, it follows that the average star becomes a nova once every 24,000 million years. This purely statistical consideration suggests that there is a substantial danger that our sun may do the same before 10,000 million years have elapsed.

What we should like to know is whether our sun is in danger of becoming a nova—so far as can be told from the geological record, it does not seem to have done so for the last 1000 million years or so. So far there is no agreement among astronomers either as to the physical causes which turn an ordinary star into a nova, or as to the physical conditions which prevail in novae. Various suggestions are in the field, but none of them wins general acceptance. But it seems quite possible that the nova stage is merely what happens when an ordinary main-sequence star first begins to contract into a white dwarf—if so, we need not count our dangers twice over.

Apart from improbable accidents, it seems that if the solar system is left to the natural course of evolution, the earth is likely to remain a possible abode of life for thousands of millions of years to come.

If so, we may perhaps be glad that our lives have fallen in the beginning, rather than at the end, of this great stretch of time. We may well imagine that if man survives to the end of it, he will have infinitely more knowledge than now, but one thing he will no longer know—the thrill of pleasure of the pioneer who opens up new realms of knowledge. Disease, perhaps even death, will have been conquered, and life will doubtless be safer and incomparably better-ordered than now. It will seem incredible that a time could have existed when men risked, and lost, their lives in traversing unexplored country, in climbing hitherto unclimbed peaks, in fighting wild beasts for the fun of it. Life will be more of a routine and less of an adventure than now; it will also be more purposeless when the human race knows that within a measurable space of time it must face extinction and the eternal destruction of all its hopes, endeavours, and achievements.

The 10,000 million years which seems a possible future for the existence of life on earth is more than three times the past age of the earth, and more than 10,000 times the period through which humanity has so far existed on earth. Let us try to set these times in their proper proportion

by the help of yet another simple model. Take a postage stamp, and stick it on to a penny. Now climb Cleopatra's needle and lay the penny flat, postage stamp uppermost, on top of the obelisk. The height of the whole structure may be taken to represent the time that has elapsed since the earth was born. On this scale, the thickness of the penny and postage stamp together represents the time that man has lived on earth. The thickness of the postage stamp represents the time he has been civilized, the thickness of the penny representing the time he lived in an uncivilized state. Now stick another postage stamp on top of the first to represent the next 10,000 years of civilization, and keep sticking on postage stamps until you have a pile as high as the towers of Westminster Abbey. Such a pile still provides an inadequate representation of the length of the future which, so far as astronomy can see, probably stretches before civilized humanity, unless an accident cuts it short. The first postage stamp was the past of civilization; a column higher than the abbey is its future. Or, to look at it another way, the first postage stamp represents what man has already achieved; a pile which out-tops Westminster Abbey represents what he may achieve, if his achievement is proportional simply to his time on earth.

Up to now, we know that his achievement has not been simply proportional to his time. In some respects at least—the mechanical arts, for instance—we advance at an ever increasing tempo. The contributions of successive generations are not equal, but continually increase in geometrical progression, so that material civilization advances more in a generation now than it did in a millennium when it was at its commencement. If this continual speeding-up were to persist throughout the whole astronomical future of the earth, it is impossible to imagine what the rate of advance would become before life disappeared from earth. But we can think of only too many factors which are likely to compel a slowing-down before long.

We must remember too that we cannot count on such a length of future with any certainty. Accidents may happen to the race as to the individual. Celestial collisions may occur; shrinking into a white dwarf, the sun may freeze terrestrial life out of existence; bursting out as a nova it may scorch our race to death. Accident may replace our tower of postage stamps by a truncated column of only a fraction of the height of which we have spoken. Even so, our race has an "expectation of life" which must be measured in terms of thousands of millions of years. It is a period which the human mind, as apart from the mind of the mathematician, can hardly conceive with any clearness. For all practical pur-

poses the only statement that conveys any real meaning is that our race may look forward to occupying the earth for a time longer than any we can think of, and achieving incomparably more than anything we can possibly imagine.

Looked at in terms of space, the message of astronomy is at best one of melancholy grandeur and oppressive vastness. Looked at in terms of time, it becomes one of almost endless possibility and hope. As inhabitants of a civilized earth, we are living at the very beginning of time. We have come into being in the fresh glory of the dawn, and a day of almost unthinkable length stretches before us with unimaginable opportunities for accomplishment. Our descendants of far-off ages, looking down this long vista of time from the other end, will see our present age as the misty morning of the world's history; they will see our contemporaries of to-day as dim heroic figures who fought their way through jungles of ignorance, error and superstition to discover truth, to learn how to harness the forces of nature, and to make a world worthy for mankind to live in. We are still too much engulfed in the greyness of the morning mists to be able to imagine, even vaguely, how this world of ours will appear to those who will come after us and see it in the full light of day. But by what light we have, we seem to discern that the main message of astronomy is one of hope to the race and of responsibility to the individual—of responsibility because we are drawing plans and laying foundations for a longer future than we can well imagine.

The foregoing is Chapter VII from Jeans's THE UNIVERSE AROUND US.

Kees Boeke

1884–

Kees Boeke was born in Holland in 1884. He was trained as a civil engineer and later became a teacher. He founded the internationally famous Werkplaats Children's Community at Bilthoven, Holland. *Werkplaats* means "workshop." In its organization, methods, and curriculum this is a typical progressive school. But Boeke is far from being a typical educator. He is greatly interested in the possibilities of international education, and pupils in the Children's Community come from many lands. He founded the Dutch section of the New Education Fellowship. And he wrote *Cosmic View*.

Cosmic View is unique. It is the only selection in this set—indeed, it may be the only book in the world—that can be read backward as easily and as naturally as it can be read forward.

That sounds impossible. But if you will take a quick look at it, you will immediately see what is meant. It would take much longer to explain how and why the statement is true than for the reader to see that it is true. A glance at the author's introduction will also be helpful to an understanding of just what it is that Boeke is trying to do and, in particular, of the method of organization he makes use of to present his cosmic view.

Once this organization is understood, it becomes clear that the book, though it has a first and last page, has no real starting place. It is arranged according to the powers of ten, but it could have been arranged according to the powers of a thousand, or a million, or a billion. To put it another way, picture number 1, which corresponds in this arrangement to the first power of ten, could as easily have

been picture number 3, or 8, or 15. The basis of the arrangement is arbitrary. The book could begin and end anywhere.

It is arbitrary, however, only from one point of view—from a point of view which could be called abstract, or mathematical. From another point of view, the beginning of the book is not arbitrary at all. The author starts with the familiar. The first picture is of a little girl, with a cat in her arms. They are quite recognizable. Toward the middle of the book, this picture is repeated. That is not surprising. We expect to find something of human size at the center of the scale.

It is a traditional idea that man is at the center of things. Plato has Protagoras say that "man is the measure of all things." Pope sees man "in this isthmus of a middle state." And the astronomer Harlow Shapley suggests that man is really about halfway in size between our galaxy as a whole—that is, the largest thing we know anything about—and an atomic particle—the smallest thing. Whether this is strictly true is not the question. Man is the reference point for man. Science, like everything else, starts with our seeing the world around us. And we see the world in relation to ourselves. What is small is small relative to us; what is large is large relative to us, too.

It should be noted that on Boeke's scale there is a great deal more "space" in the direction of the vast than in the direction of the minute. Using powers of ten, he journeys "upward" to ten to the twenty-sixth power, and "downward" only to ten to the minus thirteenth power. Thus he has gone farther "up" and "out" than he has gone "down" and "in." And anyone who is acquainted with power series will realize that, though twenty-six is twice thirteen, he has gone much more than twice as far "out" as he has gone "in." Indeed, he has gone millions and billions of times farther in the one direction on his scale than in the other, because he stops at the relative magnitude of the atomic nucleus on his "inward" journey. An atomic particle would be much smaller—how much, we do not really know.

Not only is the reading direction of this book arbitrary—its length is arbitrary, too. Why does Boeke stop in the "outward" direction at ten to the twenty-sixth power? The reason is that beyond that order of magnitude we know almost nothing, if anything at all. Perhaps, as he suggests, the "curvature of space" would begin, at this point, to come into play. Perhaps we will know more about that in a few years or generations. And why does he stop on his "inward" journey at ten to the minus thirteenth power? Again it is a question of the limits of our knowledge. The universe is bounded, Boeke seems to be

saying, only by our ignorance. Nature itself does not stop in either direction. It is man, at the center of things, who can see only so far. But he sees farther all the time.

That is an exciting thought. Another exciting idea is the one that Boeke suggests at the end of the book. "Looking back on the whole series of 40 pictures," he says, "we find that in only 10 of them (3 to −6) is life known to exist. In other scales there may, however, be forms of life we do not yet know."

He does not speculate, as some science fiction writers have done, on what these forms of life might be. He realizes that his guess would be no better than anyone else's. But he does remind us, in a few wise, final sentences, what our responsibilities are when we are faced with a cosmic view. "Man, if he is to become really human," he writes, "must combine in his being the greatest humility with the most careful and considerate use of the cosmic powers that are at his disposal." Man, he is asking us to remember, is both very large and very small.

Cosmic View

We all, children and grownups alike, are inclined to live in our own little world, in our immediate surroundings, or at any rate with our attention concentrated on those things with which we are directly in touch. We tend to forget how vast are the ranges of existing reality which our eyes cannot directly see, and our attitudes may become narrow and provincial. We need to develop a wider outlook, to see ourselves in our relative position in the great and mysterious universe in which we have been born and live.

At school we are introduced to many different spheres of existence, but they are often not connected with each other, so that we are in danger of collecting a large number of images without realizing that they all join together in one great whole. It is therefore important in our education to find the means of developing a wider and more connected view of our world and a truly cosmic view of the universe and our place in it.

This book presents a series of forty pictures composed so that they may help to develop this wider view. They really give a series of views as seen during an imaginary and fantastic journey through space—a journey in one direction, straight upward from the place where it begins. Although these views are as true to reality as they can be made with our present knowledge, they portray a wonderland as full of marvels as that which Alice saw in her dreams.

The pictures originated in a school in the Netherlands, the Werkplaats Children's Community at Bilthoven, where a group of children under my guidance drew the first versions of them. I began the project because of the importance of developing a *sense of scale*, and I therefore proposed to draw the same objects in different scales. In doing this I took advantage of the metric system, which logically corresponds with our numerical system, and made each successive scale one-tenth of the one before. When we do this we seem to go right up into the sky, so that we see objects from

ever-increasing heights, and at the same time see a constantly increasing field around them. We also notice that each imaginary jump we make to move from one scale to another one ten times smaller must be ten times greater than the previous jump. That is, if we start at, say, five meters from an object and we first move to a distance of 50 meters in order to see it at one-tenth scale, we have moved 45 meters; if we then move again, to a distance of 500 meters, to reduce the scale again to one-tenth the previous scale, we will have moved 450 meters, or ten times the length of our first jump. The next jump would be 4,500 meters, to a distance of 5,000 meters, etc. We soon find that we have started on a tremendous journey of exploration, and we begin to wonder what we shall discover if we continue in the same way.

The first 26 pictures of this book are the record of such an imaginary journey.

When we undertook our plan, we saw that we must first decide on the date and the time of day of the journey, for we must know where the sun would be at that moment. So we assumed that the moment of observation in each case would be and would remain December 21st at noon. We knew that the sun would then be at the winter solstice and that it would stand in the south. As an "object" to start with, we chose a child sitting in a deck chair in the courtyard of the school building, facing toward the south.

As we raised our point of observation we saw first the school itself, then our village: Bilthoven near the town of Utrecht in the center of the Netherlands. Next our view included the whole central part of that country. Going still higher, we saw the western part of Europe, and then the whole earth. Soon the moon came into view, then the nearer planets and the sun. The size of the whole solar system diminished with an astonishing rapidity as the height of our viewpoint increased, tenfold each time.

As we continue in this way, our nearest neighbor stars are drawn into the picture, and before we know it we have passed right out of the Milky Way, our galaxy, and see it from the outside. As we go on in ever more stupendous jumps our whole galaxy in turn shrinks and shrinks, until finally it becomes a small spot, and we gaze through the numberless universes which are beyond and which look like a cloud of tiny specks of light.

The question then arises: What should we see if, instead of decreasing the scale, we should increase it tenfold each time? To find this out, we first go back to the original picture of the little girl sitting in front of the school, and then we begin a second journey of exploration, which proves to be as full of marvels as the first, and which will be shown in the second half of this picture story.

1. The first picture, from which we start, is as we said already one of a child sitting in front of the school, with a cat on her lap. It is drawn on a scale of 1 to 10. This means that a centimeter on the drawing is in reality 10 centimeters. A centimeter (abbreviated "cm.") is the hundredth part of a meter, which corresponds to the yard as a unit of length. To be precise, a meter is 3.37 inches longer than 1 yard. One centimeter is therefore nearly 0.4 inch. In both length and height, the picture measures 15 centimeters, or nearly 6 inches. An arrow shows the direction of north.

1 cm. in picture = 10 cm. in actuality. Scale of picture therefore = 1:10

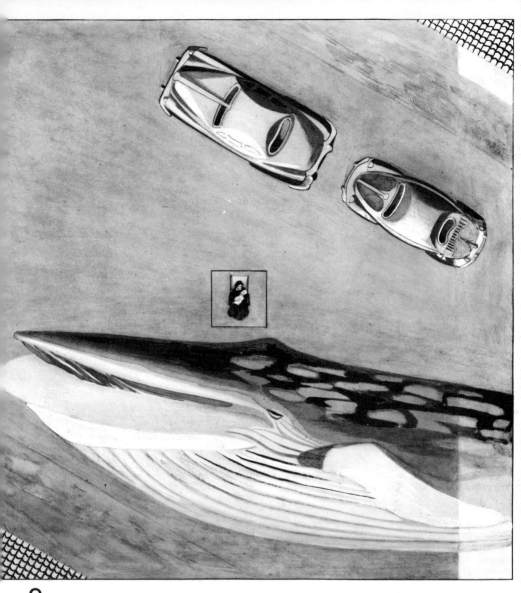

2. In the center of this second illustration we see a square 1.5 centimeters on each side and in it the picture of the opposite page to one-tenth size, for the sake of comparison. Shown to the same scale are two automobiles, a smaller and a larger type, and also a strange object which at first we hardly recognize as the front part of a whale. A long and unlikely story would certainly be needed to make the presence of a whale at this place and time plausible or even possible. For our present purpose, however, we shall not be held back by such considerations; our aim in putting the poor dead whale there lying on its side is only to enable us to compare the size of the young human being with one of the largest living creatures, also a mammal. Later this will enable us to observe in how many of the domains of scale living creatures occur.

1 cm. in picture = 100 cm. = 1 meter in actuality. Scale = 1:100 = $1:10^2$

3. In the center we now see a tiny square, the sides of which are only 1.5 millimeters in width (abbreviated 1.5 mm.). It clearly represents the illustration two pages before: #1. The child (1) in it is barely visible, but the cars (2) can easily be distinguished and the whale (3) shows up nicely in its full length of some 30 meters, which is about the record length these fellow mammals reach. The U-shaped building (4) tells a story of the war years, when the German military built it during the occupation of the Netherlands. After the liberation it was rebuilt and enlarged to become the central building for the Werkplaats Children's Community. The long building (5), typical of Holland, is a bicycle shed. *Note* that the number of each picture corresponds with the exponent of the power of 10 in the statement of the boldface line below each caption giving the scale.

1 cm. in picture = 1,000 cm. = 10 m. Scale = 1:1000 = $1:10^3$

4. It is surprising that already in this fourth illustration the child, who filled the greater part of the first picture, has completely disappeared. The reason, as we said in the introduction, is that each time we jumped upward, we had to go ten times higher than we were, in order to produce an image at a scale one-tenth that of the one before. If we viewed the little girl from a height of, say, 5 meters in picture 1, we had of necessity risen to 50 meters to see #2, to 500 meters for #3, and now we look down from a height of 5,000 meters. That is higher than Mont Blanc, Europe's highest mountain! No wonder that the huge whale can now hardly be distinguished. We notice a strange wavy line reaching the school building. We wonder what that is. The next drawing will show.

1 cm. in picture = 10,000 cm. = 10^4 cm. = 100 m. Scale = 1:10,000 = 1:10^4 605

5. We have now jumped to a height of 50,000 meters or 50 kilometers, that is more than 30 miles, and we notice a second effect of our jumps: not only are all lengths we see reduced tenfold each time, but the area which comes into our field of vision increases a hundredfold. So the above illustration covers a square 15 kilometers on a side, and we see Bilthoven (1) as a suburb of Utrecht (2). A dotted wavy line symbolizes a radio wave of 298 meters wave length reaching Bilthoven from the transmitter southwest of Utrecht, called "Hilversum" after the town (3) where its studios are. The 1.5-centimeter square in the middle gives again, as it has done each time, a reduced representation of the preceding illustration. As this illustration contains a photograph of a detailed plan of Bilthoven, it just shows the houses, though very minutely.

1 cm. in picture $= 10^5$ cm. $= 1,000$ m. $= 1$ km. Scale $= 1:100,000 = 1:10^5$

6. Here we see the central part of the Netherlands. The small square in the middle of course shows the town of Utrecht, and the tiny square inside is the twice-reduced picture of illustration 4. There is Bilthoven, and . . . there is the little girl: we know she must be there, but we cannot see her! The drawing has now become like a geographical map of central Holland. We see the largest towns: Amsterdam (1), The Hague (2), Rotterdam (3), also the rivers Rhine (4) and Meuse (5). The bay in the North used to be the Zuyder Zee. It now has become a lake, the "Yssel Lake," named thus after the Yssel (6), the arm of the Rhine which flows into it. In the Yssel Lake new land (7) is being reclaimed by making dikes (8) and removing the water by pumping. In the lower right center the town of Arnheim (9) is shown.

7. Whereas picture 5 gave us the *villages* of a *local district,* and #6 the *towns* of a *country,* this 7th drawing covers part of a *continent*—western Europe—and shows a number of its *countries.* Actually 15 different countries are wholly or partly visible, as well as 10 of their capitals and a number of rivers, too many to mention by name. The map further shows three seas—the North Sea, the Baltic, and the Adriatic—and a portion of one of the oceans, the Atlantic. As a square 1,500 kilometers on a side is covered, the spherical shape of the earth becomes visible; one of the parallels of latitude is drawn to demonstrate this, but the curvature is still so slight that the map can still be thought of as flat. It will need one more jump to reveal it as part of the surface of a sphere.

1 cm. in picture = 10⁷ cm. = 100 km. Scale = 1:10,000,000 = 1:10⁷

8.

Until now we have been getting each time a wider view of our "world." We now see the whole of it as a limited dwelling place in the surrounding blackness of space. Whereas in the last picture we could see countries, we now can see five of the six continents: only Australia does not come into the picture. We notice that the northern part of the globe is in shadow; as the picture was taken on December 21st at noon, the sun was in the south, and daylight did not reach farther north than the Arctic Circle. This shaded part of the earth in reality would have been much darker. It has, however, been left a dark gray, in order to show the visible portions of North America and northeast Asia. The North Pole (1) and the Equator (2), as well as the meridians and the parallels of latitude for every 15 degrees, are shown as dotted lines.

1 cm. in picture $= 10^8$ cm. $= 1,000$ km. Scale $= 1:100,000,000 = 1:10^8$ 609

9. The earth, which reached nearly to the large square on the previous page, now fits into the small square. The distance we have had to travel straight up, to get its size thus reduced, is tremendous: according to our reckoning in drawings 4 and 5, we should be now 500,000 kilometers up, or about 312,500 miles —more than the distance to the moon. From here we see the earth as a planet spinning counterclockwise in the empty, dark, surrounding space. The sun, in the south, makes it shed its shadow toward the north. Two faint dotted lines mark the limits of this "umbra" (1). Another dotted line (2) gives the path along which the earth moves, from right to left. Many faraway stars would be visible, but these are left out in this drawing and others that follow, to concentrate attention on our "immediate surroundings."

1 cm. in picture = 10^9 cm. = 10,000 km. Scale = 1.1,000,000,000 = 1.10^9

10. It must have struck the reader that in the last two illustrations the shaded part of the earth was not of even darkness, but was clearly lighter on the left hand side. The cause of this becomes clear in this picture. In it we not only see the earth (1), its umbra (2) and the path (3) along which it moves, but we notice around the earth what looks like a circle. This line (4) is the path or orbit of the moon as it moves around the earth. The actual position of the moon (5) on that December 21st when we were supposed to make our celestial jump of exploration is shown. It now is clear that as the moon was there on the left, the night on earth was lit up on that side. As light travels 300,000 kilometers per second (that is, 3 centimeters on this scale), we see that it would need 1.3 seconds to cover the distance from the moon to the earth.

1 cm. in picture = 10^{10} cm. = 100,000 km. Scale = 1:10,000,000,000 = 1:10^{10}

11. In the preceding drawing, the actual shape of the moon's orbit appears to be practically a circle. As a matter of fact, it is not exactly a circle, but the difference is so slight that it is only visible in the position of the earth, which is in one focus of the ellipse, and therefore not in the center. There actually would be a slight flattening of the circle, because we are perpendicular above the earth, and therefore not straight above the plane of the moon's orbit, which itself makes a small angle with the earth's. These factors have been taken into account in composing the curve (6), *i.e.*, the orbit as it would really appear to us from above; but they are small even in #10 and in this drawing they are not noticeable. It shows the earth (1), the moon (5), and its orbit (4); the earth's umbra (2), and its orbit (3), which now can be seen to be very slightly curved.

1 cm. in picture $= 10^{11}$ cm. $= 1,000,000$ km. Scale $= 1:10^{11}$

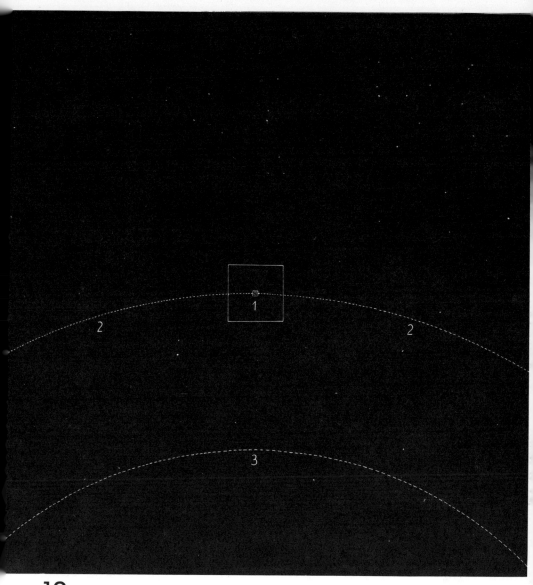

12. The tiny circle (1) in the center of the smallest square is now the moon's orbit. The earth's position is marked by a dot, although the dot is much too large and actually the earth would be invisible on this scale. Its orbit (2) is now clearly curved. Under the earth's orbit another curve (3) is drawn. That is the orbit of the planet Venus, which moves around the sun as the earth does and in the same direction: in this drawing, from right to left. The size of the sun, if it were drawn at this scale, would be 1.4 millimeters. We will repeat here that the black area of the above square would in reality be studded with a multitude of stars. We leave them out in this drawing and in the following drawings for the reason stated earlier.

1 cm. in picture = 10^{12} cm. = 10,000,000 km.

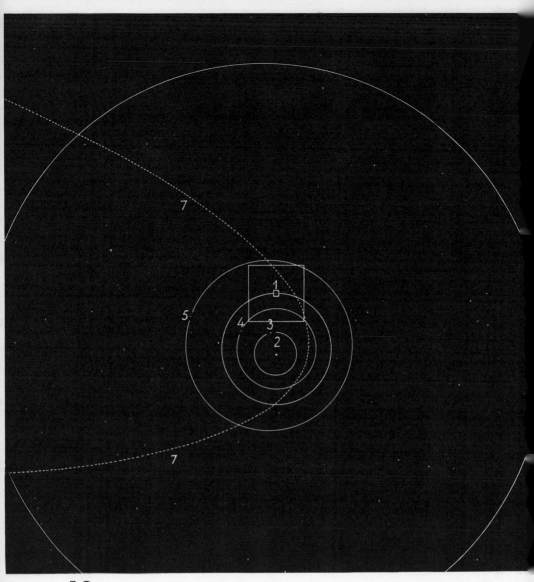

13. The sun (2) has now come into the picture. It is 1.5 centimeters away from the earth (1). The size of the earth has shrunk to 1.3 micron and even the sun's size should be only 140 microns. The dots denoting them are therefore much too big, for a micron is only a thousandth of a millimeter! Inside the earth's orbit we see the planets Mercury (3) and Venus (4). Outside it are Mars (5) and Jupiter (6) with their orbits. The positions of the planets (just as that of the moon in #10) in this and following drawings are those which they occupied when we undertook our miraculous and timeless journey through space. We will now state more precisely when this was: It was December 21st of the year 1951. In addition to the sun and the planets we see part of the orbit of Halley's Comet (7), which comes into our "neighborhood" once every 77 years.

1 cm. in picture = 10^{13} cm. = 100 million km. Scale = 1:10^{13}

14. The whole solar system is now in view. The sun and the planets nearest it—Mercury, Venus, earth, Mars—have together been reduced to a tiny circle (1), but the other planets and their wider orbits are clearly seen: Jupiter (2), Saturn (3), Uranus (4), Neptune (5), and Pluto (6). The latter's orbit at one place comes inside Neptune's. The whole orbit of Halley's Comet is here; also its position in 1951 (7). It will be near the earth again in 1986. The elliptic nature of the planets' orbits has been taken into account. In most cases, however, this again means only that the sun is not in the center of an orbit, for the difference of its shape from the circle cannot be seen in any of them except Pluto's. The inclination of the orbits to the plane of the horizon of Bilthoven has been neglected. Light would on this scale travel about 1 centimeter per hour.

1 cm. in picture = 10^{14} cm. = 1,000,000,000 km. Scale = $1:10^{14}$ 615

15. In this drawing the whole solar system, that is, the sun with all the smaller bodies which move around it, has been reduced to the space of a circle a little over 1 centimeter in diameter. Apart from the planets and Halley's Comet, which were shown in #13 and #14, there are a number of very small bodies, which we leave out because they are too small to be seen from such distances. These pictures really give a wrong impression of what the solar system would look like, for all the orbits are shown. What would be seen would be only the sun as a small star (it would at this distance seem only about 100 times as bright as Venus looks from the earth) and near it the planets, which themselves give no light but are merely lit up by the sun on the sides turned toward it. Light takes nearly 11 hours to travel across the solar system.

616 1 cm. in picture $= 10^{15}$ cm. $= 10,000,000,000$ km. Scale $= 1:10^{15}$

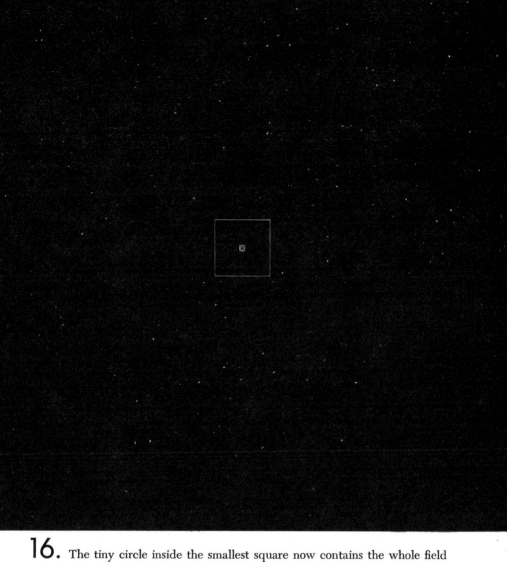

16. The tiny circle inside the smallest square now contains the whole field in which the vicissitudes of the solar system take place. If we continue the reckoning we used in drawings 4, 5, and 9, we should be now at a height of 5 million million kilometers above the horizon of that village in Holland from where we started. As we have imagined all along that we are making our trip without spending time, this means that it would have taken the light rays which we now see more than six months to cover the enormous distance from the earth, even though they travel at the rate of 299,800 kilometers per second! It also means that if we had a marvelously good telescope and could see details of events on earth, the events we watched would be those that happened more than six months ago!

1 cm. in picture = 10^{16} cm. = 100,000,000,000 km. Scale = 1:10^{16}

17. This seems a very uninteresting picture: it contains no more than one tiny white spot in the center of a black square! That spot, however, stands for the whole solar system, which on this scale would be only little more than 0.1 millimeter in diameter. In reality this illustration therefore is a very interesting one, because we now know and understand that that little speck of light contains not only the sun, but with it, all the planets, comets, asteroids, and meteorites which move around it . . . and their orbits! And we now realize that it is quite possible that numberless other stars that we see at night may have such satellites moving around them. All other stars that could be seen besides our sun are still left out, as our aim is primarily to show our own "immediate surroundings." Light, on this scale, would travel 9.46 centimeters, or about 4 inches, in a year.

618 1 cm. in picture = 10^{17} cm. 1 light-year = 9.46 cm. Scale = $1:10^{17}$

18. For the first time we now show just one star besides the sun; there is no longer fear of confusion, as the whole solar system has been reduced to a point (1). The star marked (2) is the double star called Alpha in the constellation Centaurus. This star, Alpha Centauri, is the star nearest to the earth, if we do not reckon the very faint Proxima Centauri, which may be slightly nearer. Its distance from the earth is about 4 light-years, which means that light needs about 4 years to cover that distance. On the scale of this drawing, 1 light-year would be 0.946 centimeters, that is, about 1 centimeter. Alpha Centauri is therefore at a distance of about 4 centimeters from the sun. In the drawing it seems nearer. The explanation of this seeming discrepancy is that Alpha Centauri is farther away than the sun from our faraway point of observation.

1 cm. in picture = 10^{18} cm. = about 1 light-year. Scale = $1:10^{18}$

19. Every time, the jump we make to our next point of observation gets more inconceivably large. From the present one we could no longer see the sun with the naked eye, for without the help of a telescope a star such as the sun is barely visible at a distance of 55 light-years, and our point of observation would now be at a distance of 500 light-years. It is not surprising that the sun could no longer be seen with the naked eye from that distance, as its size at the scale of this drawing would only be 0.00014 micron, or about the size of an atom! Apart from the sun and Alpha Centauri, 36 stars are shown all of which are known to be at less than 50 light-years distance from the sun. They are all where they would seem to be if we looked down on them on December 21, 1951, at noon. A circle marks the distance of 50 light-years from the sun.

1 cm. in picture = 10^{19} cm. = about 10 light-years. Scale = $1:10^{19}$

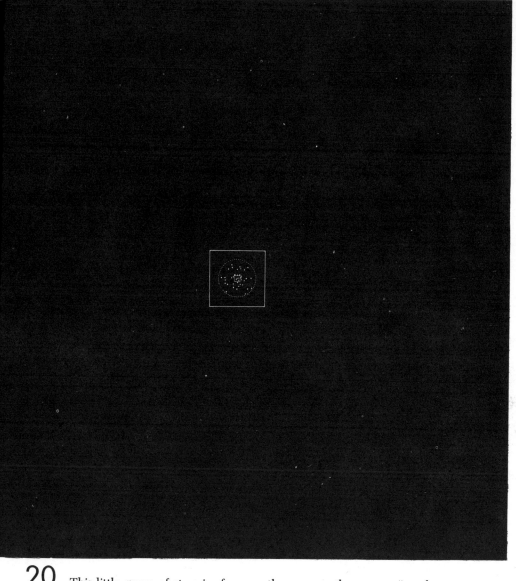

20. This little group of stars is of course the same as the one on #19, but seen from ten times farther away. We could give for all of them the names by which the astronomers know them, but we mention only 12 of the best known, putting numbers under the corresponding stars in #19, as there is room for them there. First the sun (1); then Alpha Centauri (2), Beta Hydri (3), Delta Pavloni (4), Castor (5), Pollux (6), Capella (7), Procyon (8), Sirius (9), Arcturus (10), Altair (11) and Vega (12). No attempt has been made to indicate the relative brightness of the stars shown, for it would be very different as seen from our present faraway point of observation from what it appears to be from the earth.

1 cm. in picture $= 10^{20}$ cm. $=$ about 100 light-years. Scale $= 1{:}10^{20}$ 621

21. We have now jumped so high that we have come out of the complex of stars to which our solar system belongs, and which we can see on a clear starlit night as a faintly lighted strip right across the sky: the Milky Way. It is usually called the galactic system and contains many thousand millions of stars. The sun is only a very unimportant one of these, and it is situated not in the center but in the outskirts, which we see in the above drawing. In the tiny square we notice that the sun and its 37 neighbor stars, which in #20 filled the small square, have now become but one dot. The other stars are huddled together in irregularly formed groupings, in which we can hardly discover any clear shape or line. We shall need to make another jump to discover the general form of the galaxy and of the formation of stars nearest to the sun.

1 cm. in picture $= 10^{21}$ cm. $=$ about 1,000 light-years. Scale $= 1:10^{21}$

22. Here we have the entire galactic system or galaxy, of which on the previous page we saw only what is now in the small square. Our galaxy is a spiral; it has the shape of a disk from which a number of spiral arms protrude. At the center the disk is much thicker than at the edges, where it is quite thin; the bright shining center bulges out. We see this circular disk partly tilted from the side, so that it looks like an ellipse. In the small square we now recognize in the streak of light a rather irregular spiral arm near which our solar system is situated. Apart from this one, other spiral arms can be seen. Below on the right there is a strange nebulous body. It is the Great Magellanic Cloud, a much smaller galaxy, far behind our own Milky Way. The white spots around the galaxy are the hundred and more globular clusters of stars which surround it.

1 cm. in picture = 10^{22} cm. = about 10,000 light-years. Scale = $1:10^{22}$

23. However large the object is, the next jump reduces it to one-tenth its size. So here we find our galaxy again, but as an ellipse (1) barely 8 millimeters in length, and inside the small square. The Great Magellanic Cloud (2) is again partly visible, but it lies far behind it. The Small Magellanic Cloud (3) can now be seen, and also two more of the galaxies which are relatively near our Milky Way. They are the Sculptor (4) and the Fornax (5) systems. No other galaxies are drawn, although many further away would be visible, for again we want to concentrate attention on "our own world" and its "nearest neighbors." We must think of our galaxy whirling around, clockwise, only once in 200 million years. And yet this movement gives to our solar system, because it is so close to the edge of the disk, the terrific speed of 216 kilometers per second!

1 cm. in picture = 10^{23} cm. = about 100,000 light-years. Scale = 1:10^{23}

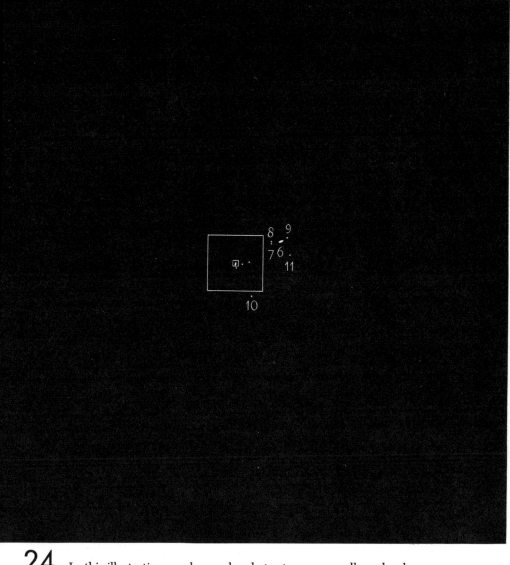

24. In this illustration we show only what astronomers call our local group of galaxies, leaving out all others. There is a general tendency of galaxies to gather in groups, some not numerous, others several hundred or even a thousand strong. How many must be reckoned to belong to our local group it is not possible to say; at these stupendous distances, it is no longer possible to obtain very precise data. It is certain that our local group includes the galaxies numbered 1, 2, and 3 in the previous drawing, and also, in the above illustration, the great spiral in Andromeda called Messier 31 (6) with its companions NGC 147 (7) and NGC 185 (8) and the spiral system Messier 33 in the constellation Triangulum (9). Other galaxies which are usually considered to belong are those numbered 4 and 5 on the previous page and the systems NGC 6822 (10) and IC 1613 (11).

1 cm. in picture = 10²⁴ cm. = about 1 million light-years. Scale = 1:10²⁴

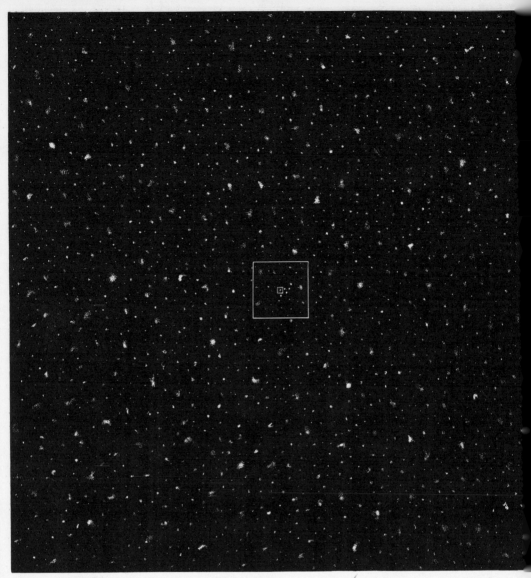

25. Now that our whole local group of galaxies has shrunk to the size of less than 2 millimeters in the center of the small square, we have in the above drawing indicated some of the countless other galaxies and clusters of galaxies which are spread out in all directions. Their distribution is known to be fairly uniform. Naturally the above drawing does not try to be an exact representation. In the two previous ones the galaxies shown were actually placed in the positions they would be in, with reference to our galaxy, if we could look at them from our imaginary point of observation above that place on earth and on that moment when we undertook our fantastic flight. Now, however, all we can do is to sketch a large number of galaxies and groups of galaxies of different sizes and to make their average distance the kind of dimension it is known to be.

1 cm. in picture = 10^{25} cm = about 10 million light-years. Scale = 1:10^{25}

26. In this last picture of the series at reduced scales, we naturally find that all galaxies and groups of galaxies, even the largest of them, are reduced to dots of various sizes. It goes without saying that the placing of them has been of necessity quite arbitrary. The object is merely to give a very faint idea of the inconceivably large number of galaxies in the midst of which our Milky Way is placed. The number of galaxies which are visible with our present telescopes is of the nature of a thousand million. The farthest of these would be at a distance from the earth of 2,000 million light-years, that is, something like the length of a diagonal of the large square above. What is drawn here is therefore certainly less than what exists. For the galaxies would be much nearer to each other than the picture shows, and they would continue far beyond its confines. . . .

1 cm. in picture = 10^{26} cm. = about 100 million light-years. Scale = 1:10^{26}

O n this page there might have been put a drawing 27 to continue the series, representing what would be seen if we could take up a point of observation 10 times farther away and thus reduce the lengths of #26 to one-tenth. But we have not attempted it for more reasons than one. To begin with, it would be quite impossible to draw the galaxies and clusters of galaxies small enough and near enough to each other. But also, the limits of what is supposed to be the curved space of our universe would be within that 27th square, and there would be no possibility at all of portraying or even visualizing the "curvature of space," which would be the determining factor there.

How far the countless millions of universes would continue in this picture 27, if we attempted to draw it, is not known. All these worlds seem to be rushing away from a center somewhere, and therefore from each other, and their speeds seem to increase the farther they have proceeded on their ways.

As all this is still so vague and uncertain, we end our imaginary journey into these infinite expanses of space and turn back, to go through all the stages we passed on our flight upward. We would advise you, reader, to concentrate your thought on this return journey. Try to picture how what you see in front of you would extend and extend as you came down . . . , how the small central square would grow, until it was the size of the large square on the previous page; how the small square on that page would in its turn extend as you dropped down and down. . . . It is clear that on this return journey the height from which we view the panorama each time *decreases* tenfold from station to station. When we have returned to the original picture of the little girl in her chair, which we reproduce again on the right, the height of our point of observation has once more become only 5 meters, and when we go on in the same way to the next picture, it will be one tenth of this, that is, only 50 centimeters.

We shall find, when we continue our exploration in the same way, that on this leg of our journey we can go through only half the number of stages that we passed on the first: we shall reach the unknown already after 13 of them, whereas in the journey up we counted just twice that number, 26. But who will say what wonders are hidden beyond the limits of man's investigations of today?

1. We said before that the reason why we took as the initial picture this little girl with her cat was that we wanted to find out in how many of the total number of domains of scale living creatures are known to occur. We have found them so far only in pictures 1, 2, and 3. Now we shall continue to look for representatives of the living world in all succeeding scales. Rather strange coincidences will occur in the following pictures: unexpected things coming together on the hand of this child! We feel justified, however, in bringing them together, as this helps us to compare their sizes. In this and all the remaining pictures, of course, the small square in the center encloses what is to be found in the *next* picture, rather than in the preceding one as in the first series; and the tiny square (beginning with #0) shows the area of the second following picture.

1 cm. in picture = 10 cm. in actuality. Scale = 1:10 629

O. The living creature portrayed in this drawing is a mosquito, to be exact an anopheles, or malaria mosquito. We can see this from the way it sticks up its hind legs. This is the first strange coincidence, for from the first series of pictures we know that it was in December that the scene occurred, and this insect is rather rare in Holland in winter. We notice that there is a little cut in the girl's finger. Right in the center of the tiny square in the middle is a minute white spot. It is a grain of salt which stuck to the girl's hand, having been left there, we may assume, after she ate her lunch. As it is not exactly the thing we would most expect to find there, it will be evident that there is a special reason for choosing it. That reason will appear later.

1 cm. in picture = 1 cm. in actuality. Scale: "life size" = 1:1 = 1:10°

—1. We have now come down to 5 centimeters above the girl's hand, and with a magnifying glass we can distinguish the grooves in its skin. On it we notice some small organisms (1): water mites and bacteria. They got there, probably, when the girl put her hand in the water of a ditch nearby. In the right-hand bottom corner inside the quarter circle there is a bacterium, which however is so small that we can't see it. In the cut we see a section of the epidermis. In a real cut in a finger not all the detail shown here could be distinguished, but it is interesting to include it. The malaria mosquito is clearly visible: its large compound eyes (2), feelers (3), and jaws (4); also its proboscis (5), with which it is busy stinging the poor child. We see the flexible sheath (6) bent in a curve as it touches the skin.

1 cm. in picture = 0.1 cm. = 10^{-1} cm. = 1 mm. Scale = 10:1 (Enlarged 10 times) 631

—2. To see this picture, taken from a height of only 5 millimeters, we should need a microscope. Again there is a member of the animal kingdom visible: one of the water mites we saw on the previous drawing, a cyclops (1). This is again not the most likely thing to happen, that it would lie thus comfortably with its feelers over the edge of the cut in the girl's finger, but it could happen! In the section of the skin we notice the horny keratin layer (2) on top. Under it is the Malpighian layer (3) with its numerous cells and the orifice of a sweat duct (4). Under that lies the corium (5) with its nerve papillae (6), small blood vessels (7), and fat cells (8). We see how the mosquito's proboscis (9) sticks into the skin. In the smaller of the two quarter circles in the right-hand bottom corner we can now just see the bacterium (10).

1 cm. in picture = 0.01 cm. = 10^{-2} cm. Scale = 100:1 = 10^{2}

—3. The height from where we are supposed to be looking has now been reduced to 0.5 millimeters or 500 microns. This is the last domain of scale in which an impression of color can be gotten by the human eye. The living creatures here are bacteria. We see some on the girl's hand: colon bacilli (1) and diphtheria bacteria (2), tubercle bacilli (3), and pneumonia bacteria (4). The bacterium in the inset in the lower right corner can now be recognized as a typhoid bacillus (5), such as humans may "carry" unknowingly for a long time. Its flagella (by which it moves) are clearly shown. We shall magnify it separately in an inset at the same place in the following pictures. This means that what is shown in the small quarter circle will each time be magnified 10 times, so that it will fit into the large quarter circle in the next picture.

1 cm. in picture $= 10^{-3}$ cm. Scale $= 1,000:1 = 10^3$

—4. The electron microscope helps us to get an idea of the shapes of some of the living creatures. We see a diphtheria bacillus (1) and a colon bacillus (2), which itself is being attacked by bacteriophages (3), as well as a smallpox virus (4). We see how keratin of the skin is curling up (5) before falling off. Some gold leaf (6) left on the girl's hand, possibly from book binding, demonstrates its extreme thinness; in fact this gold leaf is so thin that you could use it to cut a bacterium, such as is depicted near it, in two, if only you could hit it. The visible rays from the sun are symbolically represented by two sinusoids (waves) with the wave lengths of red (7) and violet (8) light. The inset shows the typhoid bacillus (9) with its flagella (10). The salt crystal's height on this scale would be 5 meters.

1 cm. in picture $= 10^{-4}$ cm. $= 1$ micron Scale $= 10,000{:}1 = 10^4$

—5. On the upper layer of keratin (1) a number of viruses are crowded to-
gether, as they often actually are on the skin. One of the larger ones is small-
pox (2). A bacteriophage (3) of medium size as we saw in the previous draw-
ing is shown here very distinctly from an electron-microscopic observation—
just to give its size and shape, for it would not be likely to lie here by itself!
Many molecules could be shown on this scale. Some starch molecules (4) are
drawn. The inset shows the helical structure of the flagellum (5) as seen in
the electron microscope. The flagellum clearly is composed of three strands
wound into what looks like a cord. Magnification is here 100,000 times, about
the maximum that can be reached with the electron microscope. The height of
the salt crystal on this scale would be 50 meters.

1 cm. in picture $= 10^{-5}$ cm. $= 0.1$ micron Scale $= 100,000{:}1 = 10^{5}$

—6. This scale has a magnification of a million. The electron microscope therefore can no longer give us clear images, for at most it can magnify 100,000 times. A more schematic image is therefore unavoidable, that is, a diagram rather than a photographic enlargement. Yet we know that there would still be living creatures. We show the infantile paralysis virus (1), already visible in —5, and one of hoof and mouth disease (2). The latter is about the smallest now known. Apart from the viruses shown there exist several with shapes sharply different from these wholly or nearly spherical forms. The sinusoid (3) shown is of an ultraviolet ray. The dots in the upper left quadrant indicate molecules of the air. The inset has the flagellum composed of three strands as already shown in —5. The height of the salt crystal on this scale would be 500 meters.

1 cm. in picture = 10^{-6} cm. = 0.01 micron Scale = 1,000,000:1 = 10^6

—**7**. Magnification here is ten million times, and the structure of the salt crystal can be shown. Distances between the successive layers of sodium (1) and chlorine (2) atoms in the lattice of the crystal are known, though its height would be 5 kilometers on this scale. To the left oxygen (3) and nitrogen (4) molecules are moving about as air at average distances indicated. Nitrogen molecules are more than 3 times as numerous as oxygen. In the inset a schematic sketch is given of just one strand of the flagellum, and even so only the hydrogen atoms on the near side are indicated. Otherwise the representation would become unintelligible, as the other atoms behind them are not placed in regular rows as they are in the salt crystal. Total width of the protein molecule including the amino acids which are bound to the strand is indicated (5).

1 cm. in picture $= 10^{-7}$ cm. $= 0.001$ micron Scale $= 10,000,000:1 = 10^7$

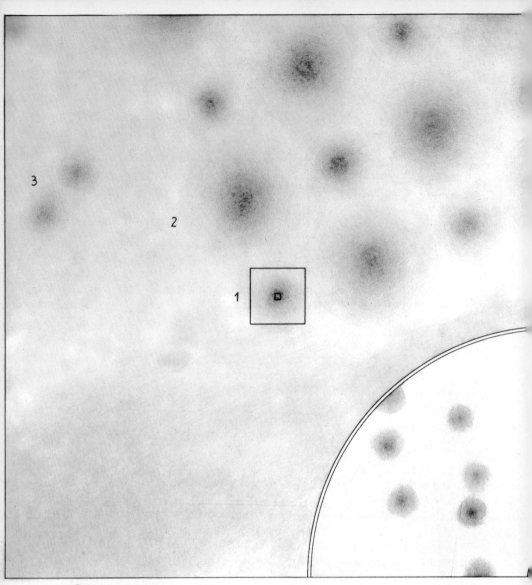

—8. The sodium (1) and chlorine (2) atoms of the salt crystal are clearly indicated. The shading here and in later pictures has only a symbolic value: a darker gray only means that the probability is greater that an electron will be found there than in a place that is more lightly shaded. As to the oxygen molecules (3) moving in the air, their average speed at a temperature of 10° Centigrade (= 50° Fahrenheit) would be 470 meters per second (= 1,000 miles per hour) in reality. *In the image* that speed would be 10^8 times greater, that is, more than 100 times the speed of light! In the inset the helical structure of the flagellum which could be recognized in —7 can no longer be seen, as again only hydrogen atoms are indicated, and all other atoms behind them (oxygen, carbon, and nitrogen) are left out. In the corner is one-quarter of a hydrogen atom.

1 cm. in picture $= 10^{-8}$ cm. $=$ 1A (angstrom unit) Scale $= 100,000,000{:}1 = 10^8$

—9. Again in this picture darkness of tone denotes the probability that an electron will be found in a certain place. As the sodium atom is here drawn at a 10 times larger scale, the area depicted in it is only 1/100th that of #—8. The probability that an electron will be found there will be that much smaller and the shading in consequence is made lighter. The same holds for the hydrogen atom in the inset. The nucleus of the sodium atom is in the center. Its size on this scale is only 7 microns. Twelve electrons are whirling around this nucleus at speeds of about 1,000 kilometers per second in reality, or a thousand million times more on this imagined magnified image. The sinusoid drawn shows the wave length of the finest X rays on this scale. In the inset a quarter of a hydrogen atom is visible.

1 cm. in picture = 10^{-9} cm. = 0.1 A Scale = 1,000,000,000:1 = 10^9

—10. It will be noticed that the tone that symbolizes the probable presence of an electron is again a lighter gray than that of the previous drawing, because the actual area depicted in the square is here again reduced to 1/100th. The sinusoid coming from the left shows the wave length of a typical gamma ray (wave length here 5 millimeters) such as is emitted from a radium-dial watch. The girl of picture 1 would on this scale have a length of about 15 million kilometers! The salt crystal would now be more than 3,000 kilometers high. The sodium nucleus would be 0.0333 millimeter, the hydrogen nucleus (a proton) 0.01 millimeter.

1 cm. in picture $= 10^{-10}$ cm. $= 0.01$ A Scale $= 10,000,000,000{:}1 = 10^{10}$

—11. This is already the third jump we have made since we saw the atom from the outside in —8 and we are still in the seemingly endless emptiness of the inside. The chance of our meeting an electron has again become a hundred times smaller. The color in consequence is again a lighter gray. The wave length of the gamma ray has increased to 5 centimeters. The grain of salt which was only half a millimeter when we saw it in actual size on the girl's hand has now become an unthinkably huge cube with sides of more than 50,000 kilometers. The nucleus of the sodium atom is 0.7 millimeters and of hydrogen 0.2 millimeters.

1 cm. in picture $= 10^{-11}$ cm. $= 0.001$ A Scale $= 100,000,000,000:1 = 10^{11}$

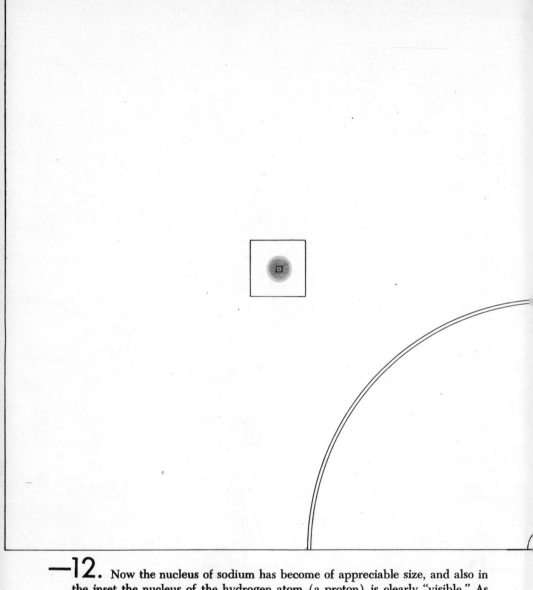

−12. Now the nucleus of sodium has become of appreciable size, and also in the inset the nucleus of the hydrogen atom (a proton) is clearly "visible." As was pointed out in −4, there is no question of the objects themselves being "visible," as we are dealing here with dimensions which are a hundred million times smaller than the wave lengths of light. Light functioned only up to that drawing. So did color, which could play an appreciable role in only 14 domains of scale (#10 to −3); 11 to 26 could give no more than white spots on a black background.

1 cm. in picture = 10^{-12} cm. = 0.0001 A Scale = 1 million million:1 = 10^{12}

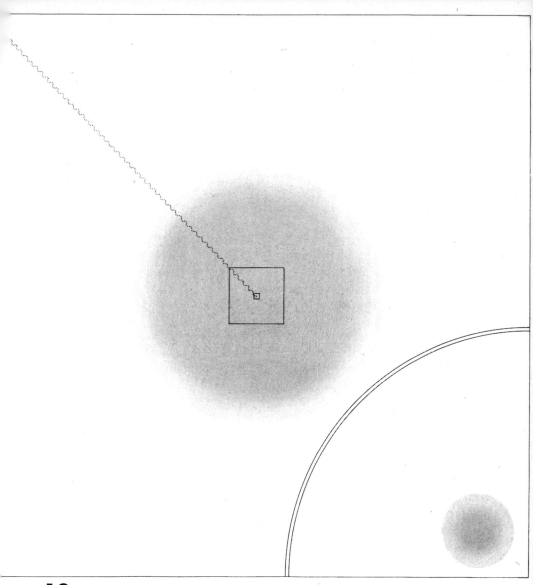

—13. In this final picture we see the nucleus of the sodium atom. We cannot even guess how the 12 protons and 11 neutrons in it are placed. This nucleus is not painted an even gray; its edge is of a somewhat lighter tone which gradually merges into the darker hue in the center. The meaning of this difference of tone is again different from that in drawings —7 to —11. Here a darker gray denotes greater density of electric charge. As a new element there is a gamma ray, full of astonishingly penetrating power, coming in from the left. Its wave length is only a millionth of an angstrom unit, which itself is a hundred millionth of a centimeter! Looking back on the whole series of 40 pictures we find that in only 10 of them (3 to —6) is life known to exist. In other scales there may, however, be forms of life we do not yet know.

1 cm. in picture $= 10^{-13}$ cm. $= 0.00001$ A Scale $= 10$ million million:$1 = 10^{13}$

And so our journey ends at the nucleus of the atom, that mysterious, utterly small, and incredibly powerful center of energy which only recently has unveiled some of its mighty secrets to mankind. Whereas at the end of our first journey we stood in awe before the imposing greatness of the dimensions of the universe, and felt as nothing in comparison to their immensity, the conditions are now completely different. True, we feel as much awe and reverence when we attempt to think of the miracles of dynamic power that are hidden in these domains of the smallest existing entities, but our own dimensions are now indescribably colossal compared with what we see.

Thus on the scale of the last drawing, the height of the little girl would be about 15,000 million kilometers, that is, more than the diameter of the solar system! If we add the thought that man is beginning to control and use these limitless nuclear powers, it is clear that unthinkable possibilities are within his reach. When we thus think in cosmic terms, we realize that man, if he is to become really human, must combine in his being the greatest humility with the most careful and considerate use of the cosmic powers that are at his disposal.

The problem, however, is that primitive man at first tends to use the power put in his hands for himself, instead of spending his energy and life for the good of the whole growing human family, which has to live together in the limited space of our planet. It therefore is a matter of life and death for the whole of mankind that we learn to live together, caring for each other regardless of birth or upbringing. No difference of nationality, of race, creed, or conviction, age or sex may weaken our effort as human beings to live and work for the good of all.

It is therefore an urgent need that we all, children and grown ups alike, be educated in this spirit and toward this goal. Learning to live together in mutual respect and with the definite aim to further the happiness of all, without privilege for any, is a clear duty for mankind, and it is imperative that education shall be brought onto this plane.

In this education the development of a cosmic view is an important and necessary element; and to develop such a wide, all-embracing view, the expedition we have made in these "forty jumps through the universe" may

help just a little. If so, let us hope that many will make it!

GATEWAY TO THE GREAT BOOKS

VOLUME 7	VOLUME 8
BACON	BACON
SWIFT	TYNDALL
HUME	EVE CURIE
PLUTARCH	DARWIN
STEVENSON	FABRE
RUSKIN	EISELEY
WILLIAM JAMES	RACHEL CARSON
SCHOPENHAUER	HALDANE
FARADAY	HUXLEY
BURKE	GALTON
CALHOUN	BERNARD
MACAULAY	PAVLOV
VOLTAIRE	WÖHLER
DANTE	LYELL
ROUSSEAU	GALILEO
KANT	CAMPANELLA
CLAUSEWITZ	FARADAY
MALTHUS	MENDELEEV
❧	HELMHOLTZ